ELEMENTS OF BIOLOGY

The ALLYN AND BACON
12-year Science Program

THE THURBER SCIENCE SERIES 1 to 6

Exploring Science

THE OUR ENVIRONMENT SERIES 7 to 9

Our Environment — Its Relation to Us
Our Environment — How We Adapt Ourselves to It
Our Environment — How We Use and Control It

HIGH SCHOOL TEXTS

Health and Fitness for Modern Living
Elements of Biology
Chemistry — Man's Servant
Elements of Chemistry
Elements of Physics

ELEMENTS OF
BIOLOGY

Revised by

RUTH A. DODGE

1966 **ALLYN AND BACON, INC.**

BOSTON   ROCKLEIGH, N. J.   ATLANTA   DALLAS   BELMONT, CALIF.

ORIGINAL AUTHORS

William M. Smallwood
Ida L. Reveley
Guy A. Bailey

ARTISTS

Isabel B. Carleton
Philip B. Parsons
Hugh Spencer
Austin N. Stevens

TITLE PAGE

Mary S. Shakespeare

Preface

Elements of Biology is a basic text for a high school course in general biology. Its style is simple, direct, and narrative—well within the range of the beginning student of biology. Its content is comprehensive enough to meet the needs of both the general course and the college preparatory course. It is organized into major Parts, arranged in Units and Chapters within the Parts, and includes extensive study aids at the end of every chapter.

This edition of *Elements of Biology* has been carefully revised and brought up to date while retaining the successful format and organization of the previous edition. The well-chosen illustrations are exceptional for a book in this field. The colorful kodachromes, the functional use of color, and the wide array of text-integrated line drawings and photographs invite even the casual student to read and learn. Equally helpful is the typography, which emphasizes key terms and sets off study aids in an effective arrangement.

Even a quick scanning of the book shows that it is particularly suited to the vital needs of the teenager. Good physical health, constructive attitudes toward good mental health, and sound adjustment to changes in physical development and mental growth are main objectives for the student.

Basic biological principles—the study of the cell and its importance, a brief survey of a wide variety of plant and animal life, and an introduction to ecology—are presented in Part One. In Parts Two, Three, and Four the systematic method of organization is used to present the groups of animals and plants in an orderly progression from simple to complex. A typical organism is studied in each group to illustrate the basic structure and function.

Part Five personalizes the offerings of the course, giving special attention to conservation of natural resources, the place of science in human progress, and the vocational offerings in the field of biology. Part Five also includes the intensive study of the life processes, principles of heredity, classification, and developmental studies. Each Unit is complete within itself, so that it may be studied in series as arranged in the textbook or studied independently according to seasonal availability of materials.

Among the topics which have been revised and updated are the structure and functions of cells, mitotic cell division, and the importance of DNA and RNA. The classification of plants has been revised in the light of modern taxonomic thinking, and the processes of water absorption by plant roots and of photosynthesis in green plants have been brought up to date.

Aids designed to improve independent study are the phonetic pronunciation key; *Words to Remember*—a vocabulary-building device; *Facts to Remember*—a summary of principles and ideas; *Questions and Completion Tests*—for stimulation of careful reading and recall of content; *Projects*—with suggestions for performing experiments and following individual interests; and *References*—at many different reading levels.

Deep appreciation is expressed to all who assisted in the preparation of the manuscript, especially to Miss Alice Comstock, Teacher of English, Guilderland Central High School, Guilderland Center, New York, for her careful reading, suggestions, and checking of references.

R. A. D.

Contents

Part Three   BIOLOGY OF MAN

Part Four BIOLOGY OF PLANT LIFE

Part Five BIOLOGY PAST AND FUTURE

BIOGRAPHIES

Part One

Principles of Biology

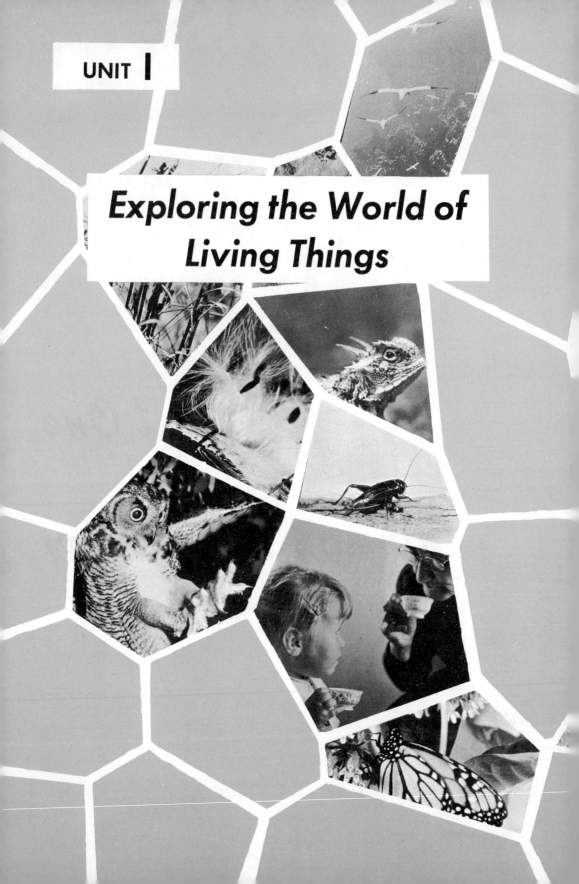

UNIT 1

Exploring the World of
Living Things

To explore this world of living things is to observe that enormous numbers of plants and animals live in the ocean, in the soil, on the ground, and in the air. Have you ever tried to count the animal life in a very small pond? Do you think you could count the plants that grow on a square yard of soil? Can you name a dozen plants and animals that spend much time in the air?

To investigate this world of living things is to search for more knowledge of life as it exists today and as it has existed in the past. Men have flown airplanes to great heights and sent rockets and satellites still farther to find how far into outer space life can exist. Explorers have gone very deep into the ocean to search for living things, and have traveled from the North Pole to the South Pole seeking facts pertaining to our environment. Scientists have not only pried into the secrets of tiny living things with microscopes but they have also hunted whales and elephants with motion picture cameras to learn more about their lives. You can begin your search by investigating the world of living things around you.

To experiment is to establish theories and confirm laws about nature. Scientists are constantly experimenting to find out new things about ourselves, the plant and animal life around us, and our physical environment. They experiment and observe in their attempt to learn more about our world and to make it a better place in which to live, work, and play.

In Unit I and the following units of this book you will have the opportunity to begin your exploration of the world of living things by: (1) observing more about the plants and animals you see every day and those in the classroom and laboratory; (2) investigating more carefully the life processes of many common plants and animals; (3) experimenting to prove facts for yourself and discover new ones; (4) reading the topics in these units and solving the problems; and (5) doing projects, taking trips, or undertaking some research of your own.

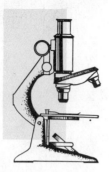

CHAPTER 1

Our Biological Environment

1.1 Biology—A Fascinating Study

Have you ever watched small birds learning to fly? Have you seen the mother bird trying to make the young leave the nest? Have you noticed how a bird takes off and lands?

For years man has been watching birds and dreaming of being able to fly. It took a long time for him to invent an airplane which could take off, fly forward or in circles, and land. But man still was not satisfied. He dreamed of the days when he could invent a machine that would really fly like a hummingbird. He dreamed of a plane that could rise vertically, fly forward and backward, and hover over one place as a hummingbird poises over a flower while it drinks nectar through its long beak. Finally man invented the helicopter, sometimes called the whirlybird. This is useful in helping farmers spray their land, in carrying lumber and fuel to remote places, and in rescue work where landing space is limited. With his knowledge of biology, man has learned many useful things from plants and animals.

Biology is the study of living things. It not only includes the study of people, pets, plants, and animals, but also is the study of many things which were once alive, like meat, lumber, and flour.

FIGURE 1-1. *HUMMINGBIRD AND WHIRLYBIRD*

Man imitates nature in his never-ending quest for better and better ways of doing things. Both these birds can hover in space, one to obtain food, the other to perform a multitude of useful tasks.

Courtesy General Biological Supply House

Courtesy Texaco

We all learn much about biology in carrying out our daily activities. We are learning biology when we select food and clothing. Looking about the room, we see many articles made from living things like furniture, books and paper.

Many people learn about biology as they do their work or have fun. Fishermen learn about water plants and animals; gardeners learn about flowers and vegetables; fruit growers learn about different kinds of fruit; and dairymen learn about cattle. Hikers and campers learn to distinguish food plants from poisonous plants, and helpful animals from harmful ones. Ball players learn how to keep their bodies healthy. Animal breeders know how to select the best stock. All are increasing their knowledge of living things and learning biology too.

Some people go on exploring expeditions and make special studies of biology. Men succeeded in climbing Mt. Everest, the world's highest mountain, but could only do so after they had gained enough knowledge of the body so they could provide for its need for oxygen and food. Men are exploring the ocean depths by descending in huge metal spheres. Others are searching coral reefs and spying on sea creatures by using the aqualung, an underwater breathing apparatus.

David Falconer

FIGURE 1-2. *MOUNTAINEER*

A knowledge of human biology is useful in the selection of clothing and equipment for a strenuous climb.

Exploring the world of living things does not need to be done at a distance. Medical men with their microscopes are finding the causes of diseases. Boys and girls with field glasses are watching birds and small animals build their homes and search for food. Advanced students are banding birds and tagging fish to learn about their breeding habits. Naturalists

FIGURE 1-3. *TRAPPING WILD DUCKS*

Naturalists study the migratory routes of ducks and other birds by banding and releasing them. They are caught at various points during flight in traps like this one, so that their habits can be recorded and studied.

Courtesy General Biological
Supply House

5

FIGURE 1-4. *CHANGE OF COSTUME*

All living things must adapt to their environment. The weasel, shown here in summer and winter outfits, not only turns white but also grows a thicker coat for cold weather. Thus nature helps him to keep warm, and—just as important—to escape his enemies.

are using radioactive substances to trace the movements of underground animals. Doctors are using tagged atoms to locate diseased tissues. In the study of biology you will have an opportunity to explore the world of living things that exists very near to you.

1.2 Seasonal Biology

Some people study living things at the time of year when their most interesting habits can be observed in their natural environment. This is **seasonal biology**. It emphasizes the dependence of living things on the physical world about them, how living things have adapted themselves to the world, and what man has done to control them.

In the spring the sun's rays become stronger, and the hours of daylight lengthen. Plants grow faster, and pets which have been kept indoors during the winter seek the warmth and the light of the sun. We can watch birds moving north from the south, some of them changing colors, like the goldfinches, which turn from green to yellow.

In summer we watch flowers blossom and young animals grow up. In the soil we may study various insects, earthworms, or small animals, like the mole. Bacteria are more abundant in summer and spoil our food unless we care for it.

In autumn the sun's rays begin to lessen and the days become shorter. The flowers turn to seeds and fruits, the fruits ripen, the grain is harvested, and squirrels and chipmunks lay in their winter supply of nuts and seeds.

And finally, in the winter we may learn how all living things adjust themselves to the cold season. Many trees shed their leaves, bears and groundhogs go to their shelters to sleep, certain birds fly south to a warmer climate.

1.3 The Main Divisions of Biology

There are two main divisions or groups of biology, plants and animals. The study of plants is known as **botany** and

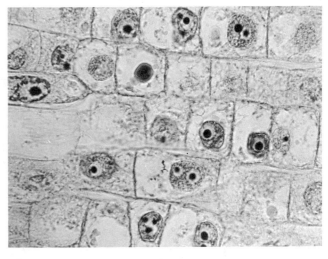

FIGURE 1-5. *BUILDING BLOCKS OF LIFE*

All living matter is composed of cells. In this picture of the cells of a pond lily, magnified 1000 times under a microscope, can you identify the protoplasm? the cell wall?

the study of animals is called **zoölogy** (zoh-*ol-uh*-jee). Biologists call all living things, both plants and animals, **organisms**.

There are many specialized branches of biology such as *bacteriology* (bak-tihr-ee-*ol*-uh-jee), the study of bacteria; *forestry,* the study and care of forests; *anatomy* (uh-*nat*-uh-mee), the study of the structure of living things; and *physiology* (fiz-ee-*ol*-uh-jee), the study of the life processes of organisms.

1.4 The Characteristics of Living Things

There are certain characteristics of living things which distinguish them from nonliving things. (*a*) Living things have a *definite form* and *size*. Nonliving things—a rock, for instance—may be of any size. (*b*) Living things also have a *definite length of life* (except for accidents and disease). This period of time, known as the **life span,** is the time between the beginning of life and death. For example, the life span of the cat is much shorter than that of the elephant. (*c*) Living things are in a state of constant activity. They depend upon a continual supply of *vital energy* to carry on their activities. (*d*) Living things reproduce. (*e*) Living things grow.

1.5 What Are Living Things Made Of?

All living things are made of one or more cells. A **cell** is the unit of structure of a living thing, just as a brick may be the unit of material of which a house is made. The outer covering of the cell helps to give support and to protect the living material within, much as a brick gives support to a house and protects the inside of the house.

The living material in a cell is called **protoplasm** (*proh*-tuh-plazm). It is able to carry on such activities as growth and repair, respiration and reproduction. Protoplasm is the active, functioning part of the cell. For this reason, the cell is also called the *unit of function* of an organism. Later we shall study more about the structure and function of cells.

1.6 Life Processes of Plants and Animals

There are certain activities which both plants and animals must carry on in order to exist. These common activities of plants and animals are called **life processes.** The life processes are *irritability, movement, food-getting, digestion, absorption, circulation, assimilation and growth, respiration, excretion,* and *reproduction.*

FIGURE 1-6. *PLANT AND ANIMAL SENSATION*

The dandelion turning its face to the sunlight is responding to a stimulus just as the snowshoe hare (*right*) is responding to the stimulus of his enemy, the weasel. A quick response may mean the difference between life and death. What stimulated the weasel to seek out the hare?

Plants and animals appear so different that we find it hard to believe that they really do much the same kind of things. Plants respire (breathe) without taking a breath. Frogs get their air in winter without using their mouths or nostrils. Cats and dogs drink by lapping; horses and cows, by sipping. Plants "drink" water through their roots. A study of the life processes will show us some of the ways in which plants and animals are alike.

1.7   Irritability

Animals and plants react to heat, light, and other outside factors which we call *stimuli*. They are also affected by internal stimuli and respond to them. This reaction is called **irritability**; it enables plants and animals to exist in their surroundings. The leaves of the geranium plant turn toward the stimulus of light in order that the plant may make more food. Most animals move in response to the stimulus of touch or fear. Man, like many other animals, responds to the stimuli of taste, sight, hearing, smell, and touch.

1.8   Motion

In biology **motion** is defined as the ability of living things to change their position without using an outside force, like the wind or gravity. A living thing supplies from its own body the energy required for motion; all by itself it can change the direction and speed of its movements. Animals can move from place to place. This is locomotion. Many plants move their leaves toward the sunlight; the trunks of trees expand each year by growth. Most movements in plants, however, result from differences in the rate of growth of various parts.

W. L. Miller
from National Audubon Society

FIGURE 1-7. *HUNTER AND HUNTED*

The cottontail rabbit has lost to the red fox in the eternal struggle for survival. Some animals of each species die in order to provide food for others.

1.9 Food-Getting

If we live normal lives, we eat regularly, in the morning, at noon, and again at night. We feed our pets regularly, if we have any. The farmer has to feed his cattle, horses, and sheep when they are confined in the stables. In summer, when they are turned out to pasture, they secure their own food. All this shows the life process of *food-getting.*

There are a few plants, like the Venus's-flytrap, that can capture insects and use their bodies as food. But this is not usual with plants. Most green plants manufacture their own food, chiefly in their leaves.

1.10 Digestion and Absorption

The preparation of food so that the animal or plant cells may have it in a usable form is called *digestion.* The food is broken up into very small particles. It is then acted upon by body chemicals until the small particles are hydrolyzed. The small hydrolyzed particles can pass through the cell membrane in a form useful to the protoplasm of the organism. The life process of taking the digested food through the membranes of cells or into fluids as blood or lymph is called *absorption* (ab-*sorp*-sh'n).

1.11 Circulation, Assimilation, and Growth

The soluble food materials are then carried through the conducting tubes of the plants and the blood vessels of animals to the cells in all parts of the body. This life process is *circulation.* The materials are distributed within the cells by *diffusion* (dif-*yoo*-zh'n) which is the spreading-out of molecules within a cer-

FIGURE 1-8. *SPROUTING PINE*

All growing plants change food, taken from sap, into living protoplasm.

Grace Thompson
from National Audubon Society

9

tain area until they are distributed equally in that area.

Each part of the animal or plant must then take from the blood or sap the food that it needs and change it into the living material of the cell, protoplasm. This life process is **assimilation** (uh-sim-uh-*lay*-shun). It results in the repair of worn cells and the **growth** of new ones. This quality is a distinguishing characteristic of all living things.

1.12   Respiration

All animals and plants require energy in order to live. When oxygen enters a body, it burns the food by a process called oxidation, setting energy free. Two waste products result, a gas called *carbon dioxide,* and *water.* **Respiration** is the exchange of oxygen and carbon dioxide in the cells of the body with the release of energy. The process of respiration must not be confused with *breathing,* which is merely the bringing of oxygen in the air into contact with the part of the body which can use it, such as the blood vessels of the lungs. Plants and animals without lungs respire by other structures. Some use gills, which admit oxygen dissolved in water; others exchange gases directly through their cell membranes by diffusion (equal distribution) of the gas molecules.

1.13.   Excretion

During respiration, the gas carbon dioxide is formed as a waste product. It passes into the fluid surrounding the cells. It is removed from the bodies of higher animals through the lungs. The carbon dioxide may pass directly into the air from the leaf of a plant or through the skin of an earthworm. The chemical processes of living things produce other waste products. These are removed by the kidneys and intestines. To an animal or plant, a waste product is one that does not yield any energy to the living organism. **Excretion** is the elimination of waste products from inside animals and plants.

1.14   Reproduction

All kinds of animals and plants either produce young or become extinct. It is common knowledge that all living things grow old and eventually die, and if there were no provision for producing young, there would be no such thing as continuing life. While the bodies of animals and plants are mature, nature gives them the means and the instinct to produce more animals and plants like themselves. This has been the story since the beginning of life so far as science can determine, and it is the only means by which there can be an increase in the total

FIGURE 1-9. *MOTHER OPOSSUM AND YOUNG*

With nature's gift of reproduction, this mother can have as many as 16 in one litter. She cares for the helpless babies until they can fend for themselves.

Lynwood M. Chace

10

numbers of living things. **Reproduction,** then, is the process by which life continues from generation to generation.

1.15 Differences Between Plants and Animals

Plants differ from animals in the structure of their cells. Plant cells have **cell walls** made of *cellulose* (*sel*-yuh-lohs), a substance which man uses in making paper but which plants need for support. This cellulose is in addition to the **cell membrane,** which surrounds the liquid part of the cell. The cell wall lies just outside the cell membrane. Animal cells on the other hand have only the cell membrane for covering.

Most plants remain rooted in one place and for this reason must be equipped to withstand changes in temperature and to obtain their food. Those plants which are green make their own food.

Most animals move about in search of food, shelter, and protection from their enemies. Many, like woodchucks and beavers can build homes; some, like squirrels and chipmunks, can store food; others, like birds and reindeer, can migrate.

1.16 Uses of Plants

Nearly every part of most plants is of use to man. Many plants are used for

Courtesy Michigan Dept. of Conservation

FIGURE 1-10. *HOLD TIGHT!*

Both living organisms, the tree and the bear cub differ. Can you tell how?

food. Fruits, vegetables, grains, and cereals make up the greatest part of our diet. In fact, man is absolutely dependent on plants for his very existence.

Some plants furnish us *clothing.* Thus linen comes from the stem of flax; cotton from the blossom (fruit) of the cotton plant; rubber from the sap of a tree; and rayon from wood pulp.

Our houses, furniture, and many implements are often made of wood. We

FIGURE 1-11. *PLANT CONTRIBUTION*

Few plants are as useful to man as cotton. Three people out of every four in the world wear cotton clothing. Cottonseed oil is also useful.

Keystone View Co.

11

constantly make use of paper from wood pulp, and rope from the fiber of many plants. Cork is taken from the bark of certain oak trees.

Plants also provide other useful products. *Perfumes* are extracted from the flowers of gardenias, roses, and violets; *medicines,* such as digitalis, from the foxglove; *drugs,* like quinine, from the cinchona bark; and *narcotics,* such as opium, from poppy seeds. *Oils* from cotton, flax, and coconut are useful in various ways, from lubricating motors to polishing furniture.

Blue *dyes* are made from indigo, yellow from gamboge, and brown from the logwood trees of tropical America.

Most of our *flavoring* and *spices* are taken from plants. Cloves from flower buds, cinnamon from bark, mints from leaves, and mustard from seed, all find wide use in the preparation of our food. *Beverages* are made from tea leaves, coffee beans, and cacao nuts.

Many countries furnish us with our food supply. Wheat, rye, rice, barley, sorghum, oats, buckwheat, and other grains have been brought over to this country where they were not native. Potatoes originated in South America and have been taken to other countries. Some plants, such as cabbage, beets, carrots, spinach, and sugar cane, were carried from their native land in Western Asia to Europe and then brought to America.

From America we have native pineapples, chocolate, sweet potatoes, tomatoes, corn, and tobacco. Some plants thought to be native to the United States are grapes, strawberries, raspberries, cranberries, and blackberries.

1.17   Uses of Animals

Animals help us in countless ways. Much of our *food* comes from them. Unless we are vegetarians, we eat the meat of cattle, poultry, and fish. Animal products, such as eggs, milk, butter, and cheese, are also useful as food.

Much of our *clothing* comes from animals. Our warm woolens and fine silks are from sheep and silkworms. Our shoes, gloves, fur coats, and belts are

FIGURE 1-12. *ONE OF OUR MOST IMPORTANT MAMMALS*

Sheep are one of our most highly prized animals. The principal products obtained are leather, meat, and wool from the processed fleece.

Courtesy General Biological Supply House

FIGURE 1-13. *THE BUSY, BUSY BEE*

Bees perform an invaluable service when they carry pollen on their bodies from flower to flower, thus helping to perpetuate plant life.

made of the skins of various animals ranging all the way from horses to snakes. Our soft pillows are contributed by birds. Horns, shells, and ivory tusks are used for buttons or ornaments.

Skeletons of animals give us sponges, coral from the reefs of the oceans, and chalk from the cliffs of Dover, England. Earthworms help to cultivate and fertilize the soil, bees carry pollen from flower to flower, birds eat harmful insects, and fish furnish fertilizer, glue, and oil.

Animals are also *beasts of burden.* We know how horses, mules, and donkeys serve this purpose. Dogs are used for sledding in the Arctic, elephants work hard in India and Africa, camels trudge over the sands of the desert, and in Peru the llama serves as a beast of burden.

Most of the world's domestic animals were first tamed in Asia. Reindeer native to the Eurasia tundra have been introduced into Alaska. The turkey, however, is native to America.

We must not forget the part played by animals as *pets.* Homes are happier when they have a dog, cat, parrot, parakeet, or canary. Who has not wanted to keep rabbits or have an aquarium with goldfish, guppies, or a turtle?

1.18 Importance of Biology

Because living things are of use to us for food and clothing, a necessity to us for healthful living, and of interest to us for their beauty, the government has set aside large sums of money to be used for experimental purposes and research. National and state departments of agriculture, bureaus of plant and animal industry, and experiment stations have been established, and biological surveys have been made to make the work practical. However, not all plants and animals are useful. Clothes moths destroy our clothes, grasshoppers eat our crops, and many bacteria cause disease. Our government, as well as our universities, industries, and other interested individuals try to combat harmful plants and animals through research. Thus man is continually trying to make use of the plants and animals which can help him and to destroy those which do him harm.

1.19 Biology as a Science

The study of biology as a science is based on (*1*) accurate observation, (*2*) controlled experimentation, (*3*) careful recording of notes, (*4*) drawing conclusions, (*5*) testing conclusions, and (*6*) finding a practical use for the conclusions, or stating a basic theory, principle, or fact.

A biologist chooses his particular method of study according to the nature of his *problem*. The migration of birds is studied by banding the birds when young or when living in certain places. These bands have numbers which identify the birds when found in other places. You may be able to make a small mark on the shell of a turtle with your teacher's

FIGURE 1-14. *BIOLOGY IS A SCIENCE*

Careful observation is the cornerstone of science. These girls learn to use the microscope, a valuable aid to understanding the mysteries of living things.

Gorodess

help and later find the same turtle. In this way you may study its habits. This is *observation* and *recording of notes*.

A biologist may test foods for the vitamins they contain and then experiment with some animals to find out the effects these vitamins have. The knowledge which he gains may later help you in knowing which foods to choose. This is *experimentation* and *finding a practical use*.

When undertaking the study of an interesting topic, a biologist keeps in mind the following steps (**the scientific method**) that scientists use in solving problems:

(*1*) State the problem or the purpose.

(*2*) List the facts and the materials needed for the study or experiment.

(*3*) Set up the experiment.

(*4*) Try the experiment.

(*5*) Record the facts or observation.

(*6*) Study the findings and draw a conclusion.

(*7*) Test the conclusion and find out whether it solves the problem.

In doing an experiment biologists and other scientists use a *control*. This means that some of the plants or animals used for testing are kept under *normal* or *controlled conditions*. The others being tested are kept under *experimental conditions*. For example, if you wish to find out whether moisture is necessary for seeds to grow, you could place some seeds in a dish without moisture and some in a dish with moisture. The seeds without moisture would be the control. The seeds with moisture would be under the experimental condition.

1.20 Biology Is Fun

Many people study biology for a vocation or a profession. Doctors, farmers, food experts, animal trainers, and explorers make it their life interest. But there are many thousands of boys and girls and men and women who make of biology a hobby.

Perhaps you yourself may wish to make biology a hobby. To do so would certainly help you in this course. You might start by making an aquarium for water life or a terrarium for land animals and plants, or by teaching your pet to do tricks. Perhaps you would like to take photographs of living things or to collect leaves, seeds, or flowers. Or you may enjoy making a biology scrapbook. Taming a pet is also fun.

Perhaps a group activity would be more interesting. Talk over the following projects with your classmates and suggest others. Carry out at least one project during the year.

1. Study and identify some shade trees.

2. Make a collection of pressed wild flowers and weeds.

3. Make a collection of insects or shells and mount them.

4. Collect different kinds of wood, bark, and buds for an exhibit.

5. Try to raise some guppies or other tropical fish.

6. Raise some rabbits, guinea pigs, white rats, or other animals.

Cushing

FIGURE 1-15. *BIOLOGY CLASS*

A fishing trip can be a short course in biology, as well as a hobby. Why?

7. Raise and tame a pigeon or a chipmunk.

8. Become a member of a bird club or Junior Audubon Society.

9. If you like fishing, be an authority on the different kinds of fish.

10. Construct a rock garden.

11. Make a scrapbook of plant and animal pictures.

Wide World

FIGURE 1-16. *HIS HOBBY IS SNAKES*

Though you may prefer butterflies or tropical fish, this avid fifteen-year-old collector is enjoying his hobby while learning.

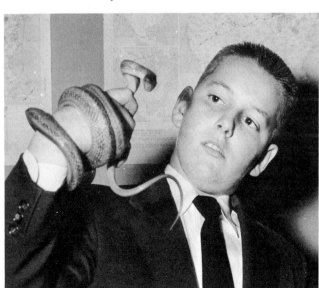

FACTS TO REMEMBER

Biology is the study of living things, plants and animals. Living things have a definite form and size, a definite life span, and are in a state of constant activity.

The *cell* is the unit of structure and function of all living things. *Protoplasm* is the living material found in the cells.

The *life processes* common to all living organisms are irritability, movement, food-getting, digestion, absorption, circulation, assimilation and growth, respiration, excretion, and reproduction.

Plants differ from animals in that plants have cell walls, they are unable to move from place to place, and the green plants can make their own food. Both plants and animals are useful to man and afford many opportunities for careers and hobbies.

The *scientific method* is a step-wise procedure used by all biologists and other scientists whenever they have a problem to solve. The steps are (1) stating the problem, (2) collecting all relevant data, (3) formulating a hypothesis, (4) experimenting to test the hypothesis, (5) recording all facts and observations from the experiment, (6) drawing a conclusion, and (7) applying the conclusion to the problem.

WORDS TO REMEMBER

absorption	excretion	physiology
assimilation	experimental	protoplasm
bacteriology	conditions	reproduction
biology	food-getting	respiration
botany	forestry	scientific method
cell	irritability	seasonal biology
circulation	life process	stimuli
controlled conditions	life span	vital energy
diffusion	movement	zoölogy
digestion	organism	

QUESTIONS

1. What is biology? Name the two main divisions. Define each.
2. Who studies biology? List ten occupations, like carpentry, printing, and so on, that are dependent on it. Tell how they depend on biology.
3. State some' differences between plants and animals.
4. List five ways in which animals are useful to man. Give at least three examples of each.
5. Name five uses of plants to man. Give two examples of each.
6. List the kinds of material of which your clothing is made. Name the plants and animals represented.
7. What is meant by a life process?
8. List the life processes and define each.
9. What are stimuli? Give some examples.

10. If you have a pet, describe it briefly.

11. Name the steps of the scientific method in solving a problem.

12. Choose one problem of your own and explain how you would try to solve it by using the scientific method.

13. What is meant by a control in an experiment?

COMPLETION TEST

As your teacher or a classmate reads the following incomplete statements, with your book closed, write on a clean sheet of paper the word or phrase which correctly completes the statement.

1. Biology is the study of _____ things.
2. Most green plants _____ their food.
3. Most animals have to _____ their food.
4. Many household sponges are the _____ of animals.
5. Earthworms help to _____ and _____ the soil.
6. _____ aid in cross-pollination of flowers.
7. Fish furnish us with _____, _____, and _____.
8. The bark of the _____ tree is used as a spice.
9. Blue dye is made from _____.
10. Many bacteria cause _____.
11. The _____ destroy our clothing.
12. The _____ eats our crops.
13. An aquarium is built for _____ forms.
14. A _____ is used for plants and animals which live on land.
15. _____ give money for research.
16. The elimination of waste products from the bodies of animals and plants is called _____.

PROJECTS

I. *Caring for an Aquarium.*—If your school has a large inactive aquarium, start it and make it balanced. If an active aquarium is already available, start observations, records, and class care at once.

II. *Making an Aquarium.*—If you wish an aquarium of your own, a large fruit or battery jar will serve the purpose. Place it in a room where the sunlight may reach it part of each day. Too much sun is as bad as too little.

1. Now put in a thin layer of soil, about one inch deep, from the bottom of a pond. Plant your water plants in this soil.

2. Next place pebbles and gravel here and there and, if you wish color, add some bright shells.

3. Fill the jar full of water, pouring it from a teakettle or similar container down the side so as not to disturb the soil.

4. Let the jar stand for a few days before putting in the animal life. The easiest animals to get are goldfish, small snails, or tadpoles. Some stores specialize in aquaria supplies, but it is more fun to secure your own. You will soon learn what may be safely added, and what not so safely.

III. *Field Trips.*—Go into the woods or fields; or search a near-by pond, and bring back interesting things to watch in the laboratory. There are more living things around you than you have ever guessed could exist. Keep careful records of your observations, and you will have a scientific record of many important natural happenings.

IV. *Museum Specimens.*—Bring in different kinds of plants and animals at any time during the year, and preserve them for the school museum.

V. *Photographs.*—If you have a camera, begin to take pictures of plants and animals in different seasons and locations.

VI. *Life Processes.*—Choose one plant and one animal with which you are familiar and make a comparison of their life processes.

REFERENCES

Beebe, *Half Mile Down.* Harcourt, Brace.
Carrigher, *One Day at Teton Marsh.* Knopf.
Carson, *The Sea Around Us.* Oxford University Press.
Cleveland, *The Complete Book of Helicopters.* World Book.
Comstock, *Handbook of Nature Study.* Comstock.
Curtis and Urban, *Biology in Daily Life.* Ginn.
Dodge and Zim, *Southwest: Golden Nature Guide.* Simon and Schuster.
Douglas, *Of Men and Mountains.* Harper.
Disney, *Living Desert.* Simon and Schuster.
Disney, *Vanishing Prairie.* Simon and Schuster.
Gooch, *The Strange World of Nature.* Crowell.
Hillcourt, *Field Book of Nature Activities.* Putnam's.
Houston, K_2 *The Savage Mountain.* McGraw-Hill.
Peterson, *Wildlife in Color.* Houghton Mifflin.
Sanderson, *Animal Treasure.* Viking.
Singer, *A History of Biology.* Henry Schuman.
Teale, *Circle of the Seasons.* Dodd, Mead.
Teale, *North with the Spring.* Dodd, Mead.
Ward and Whipple, *Fresh-Water Biology.* Wiley.
Webberley, *The Epics of Everest.* Farrar, Straus and Cudahy.
Wise's *American Wild Life.* William Wise.

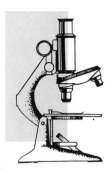

CHAPTER 2

Habitats and Life Zones

2.1 Environment of Living Things

Every plant and animal needs a place to live, food to live on, and some means of protection from its enemies. The study of the relationship between living things and their environment is called **ecology** (eh-*kol*-uh-jee). Physical, climatic, and biological conditions are some of the factors which make life possible in any plant or animal community. Whenever and wherever plants and animals find suitable conditions for living, they establish themselves and form communities. In this chapter we shall study such physical factors as light and soil and such climatic factors as air, temperature, and moisture, which enable plants and animals to exist where we find them.

2.2 Habitats of Living Things

A **habitat** is the place where any group of plants or animals lives. Fishes

FIGURE 2-1. *LAND DWELLERS*

The deer is a widely distributed big game animal, ranging the forests of America from Canada to Peru. It thrives in woodland surroundings, like these on the Olympic Peninsula of Washington.

Courtesy Northern Pacific Railway

FIGURE 2-2. *HABITATS: WHERE PLANTS AND ANIMALS LIVE*
The three kinds of habitats—water, land, and air—are natural dwelling

places for certain kinds of living things. The water habitat may be salt
(lower right) or fresh (lower left). What are some land habitats?

live in a water habitat, cacti grow in a desert habitat, lions hunt in the jungle, and prairie dogs build homes underground. Each one thrives best in a place where temperature, moisture, and sunlight are best suited to its way of life. Alligators need a warm habitat and polar bears a cold one. Corn will not grow well on wet land, and rice will not grow where it is dry. Thus every living thing is associated with a region where it can grow best and bear offspring. This region is its habitat.

There are three main kinds of habitats: water, land, and air. Plants and animals which live in swamps, ponds, along streams, or in the ocean live in a *water habitat*. Others, like trees, grass, rabbits, and bears, thrive in a *land habitat*. Birds, bats, butterflies, and all flying forms may be considered as living in an *air habitat,* since they spend much of their lives off the ground.

2.3   Water Habitat

Both plants and animals must meet a variety of conditions in order to live in water. They must adjust themselves to sunlight, temperature, pressure, and mineral content, all of which vary widely in different bodies of water.

Near the surface *sunlight* penetrates the water and enables green plants to make their own food. But at a depth of 300 feet it is absolutely dark and no plants can grow. Few of them live more than 50 or 60 feet from the surface. Yet

FIGURE 2-3. *TO EACH HIS OWN*

Most gulls make their home near the ocean, from which they take their food. The cow is adapted to life on land, using grasses as its food, while the lobster is equipped to find its meals beneath the surface of the sea.

Rovere Scott
Ewing Galloway
Courtesy New York Zoological Society

22

FIGURE 2-4. *WATER WORLD*

Showing no indication of the great variety of life that lives beneath it, the surface of the ocean appears desolate. What features of the ocean control the variety and distribution of life it supports?

Photo by Jan Hahn

some animals can live at great depths, since they have enormous eyes or phosphorescent light to help them in the darkness.

During the day the sun heats the water, though not so much as it does the land. This causes a noticeable variation of *temperature*. The heat, however, does not penetrate very deep; the farther one goes below the surface, the colder the water becomes. In deep lakes as well as in the ocean, the temperature at great depths drops to just above freezing, thus limiting the extent of the plant and animal life found there.

Pressure varies directly with the depth. Deep-sea fish are usually smaller than the surface forms since food is scarcer. Some have special air bladders to resist the pressure.

Water habitats also vary with *mineral* content. Sea lettuce and sharks thrive in the salt water of the ocean. Eelgrass and mangrove trees live in salt-water swamps. In contrast to these, water cress, moss, and frogs are found only in fresh-water swamps which are relatively free from minerals. Acid bogs contain pitcher plants, cotton grass, and cranberries.

Water exerts some *inertia,* that is, it offers resistance to objects which try to move through it. Thus, by resisting the thrust of propellers, the sweep of arms, and the flap of tail and fins, water makes it possible for steamboats to travel and for people and fish to swim.

Water contains *air,* and plants and animals need air to breathe. Watch a goldfish in an aquarium and notice how it breathes. Its mouth is continually opening to draw in water, which supplies the dissolved air.

Water is almost always in *motion*. There may be only tiny waves blown up by a summer breeze or huge ocean waves, which rise many feet high. Currents are set up by changes in temperature or by entering streams. Even small animals cause slight motion. Plants must be able to withstand this. Some of them, like the duckweed, are very tiny and float on the surface. Others, like water lilies, have their roots in the soil, but their leaves float on the surface. Their stems are flexible and this prevents the wave motion of the water from breaking them, as it might do otherwise.

In spite of the fact that plants and animals have to meet so many different conditions, life in the water is abundant. The plants make their own food and provide food for the animal life. Some animals also eat each other; larger fish often kill and eat smaller ones.

2.4 Land Habitat

On land living things are surrounded by *air* and need some means of breathing it. Animals such as turtles, birds, and rabbits have lungs; plants have tiny openings on the leaves and stems for letting in air.

Air offers very little *support*. To live on land, therefore, plants need sturdy stems, and animals need a bony framework.

Most plants remain fixed, and so are dependent on the soil for *water* and *minerals* with which to make food. Goosefoot and pigweed grow where there is salt in the soil. Clover and corn need lime in order to grow well. Only a few kinds of plants live where there is much acid in the soil.

On the other hand, animals can move about in search of a meal. They can exist, however, only where plants are able to supply them or their prey with food.

The *temperature* varies greatly, since land heats and cools more rapidly than water. Changes in temperature set up air currents, which cause winds and storms, making life harder for land forms.

Because of these conditions, most large animals have become *ground dwellers*. Bears live in the woods, elephants in the jungle, and zebras on the plains. Camels and lizards can exist in very dry land areas. Frogs live in swamps or near streams or ponds, where they have both land and water.

FIGURE 2-5. *SKYHIGH*

The birds in flight (*left*) are creatures of the air, mobile in the search for food and shelter. Their yearly migrations sometimes cover thousands of miles. Some wild ducks and other birds dive into the sea in search of fish. The tree on its lofty pinnacle (*right*) is, on the other hand, earthbound, and dependent on the land around it for its food supply.

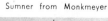

Some animals prefer to live *underground* for added protection from their enemies. Earthworms sometimes penetrate as deep as 20 feet. Woodchucks and prairie dogs make their homes in burrows. A few blind crickets and salamanders live in caves, but owing to the scarcity of food they are usually small.

Trees afford shelter for some land forms; monkeys sleep in trees and squirrels hide nuts in the hollow spaces. Birds and bees build their nests in trees; wood borers and other harmful insects also live there.

2.5 Air Habitat

For living things to spend much time in the air, special structures are required. Organisms must be light enough to float around on the air currents, as do bacteria and yeast. Otherwise they must possess some kind of support for gliding, or structure for flying. Air offers still *less support* than water or land; so birds must have a large wing spread, hollow, long bones with air spaces, and use considerable force to be able to stay in the air.

At high altitudes *atmospheric pressure* decreases and there is very little oxygen. The air is cold and variations of *temperature* cause air currents which sometimes make flying hazardous. There is little life at high altitudes.

2.6 Life Zones

A **life zone** is any area that includes the habitats of living things which can exist under the same general climatic conditions. Fish in a water habitat, maple trees and deer in a land habitat, and bats and birds in the air may all live in the same life zone, since they need a moderate degree of temperature. The extent of life in a zone, however, may be affected by elevation or may be limited by ocean, canyon, and desert barriers.

All the plant life in a zone is known as the **flora** (*flor*-uh) of that zone. The animal life is called the **fauna** (*fawn*-uh).

2.7 Zones and Altitudes

The type of life which can exist at sea level in a given region cannot necessarily survive at a great height. On plateaus and mountains there are other conditions to be met. The air becomes colder the higher we go, and while the days may be warm, the nights are always cold. Winds are stronger. Whether or not they are dry or moisture-laden depends upon their origin. Thus the winds from the Pacific are damp, and when they strike the cold air of the high mountains, they lose their moisture on the western slopes, making these fertile, but leaving the eastern slopes barren.

Increases in altitude present conditions similar to those we meet in traveling northward. For each thousand feet in altitude the conditions are similar to those found in traveling two hundred to three hundred miles northward, or about three degrees in latitude. For example, the trees near the foot of a mountain may be hardwood, while higher up there may be only pine and spruce or a few oaks, gnarled and twisted by the wind. Still higher up near the timber line, in what we call the arctic-alpine zone, may be found tiny willow trees, hardy blueberry bushes, grasses, lichens, mosses, and alpine roses. The summits of high mountains are bare of vegetation.

Animal life varies in the same way. Porcupines, squirrels, and wild cats may roam the lower regions. Mountain goats, jack rabbits, and thrushes live in the evergreen forests, while only a few birds and insects can exist in the upper areas.

Not only do mountains show zones of altitude, but canyons and valleys also show variation in plant life. The Grand

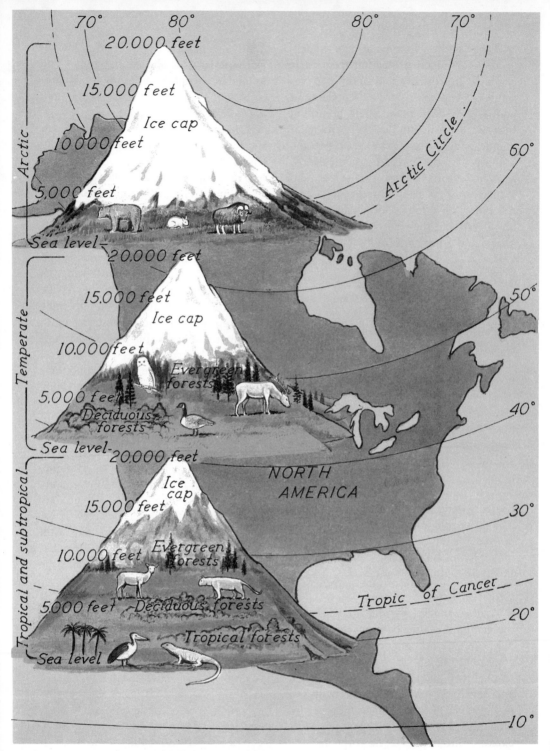

FIGURE 2-6. *ALTITUDE ZONES*

Plant and animal life varies greatly with changes in altitude, just as it does from latitude to latitude. Some of these changes are indicated here. Latitudes are marked at the right, and altitudes at the left. Notice the differences in plant and animal life at 10,000 ft. in the arctic, temperate, and tropical zones.

FIGURE 2-7. *DESERT OASIS*

Few plants and animals can survive in the desert because of the heat and lack of water. Thus the desert is a natural barrier to the range of life. Camels, however, have become adapted to the desert; they drink great quantities of water but do not perspire.

Arabian-American Oil Co., from Cushing

Canyon of the Colorado River has cut so deep that forms which can live near the river find it too cold on the rim several thousand feet above. In Death Valley National Park, a portion of which is below sea level, very little life can exist because of the extreme heat.

2.8 Range of Living Things

Each plant and animal is limited to a definite area of distribution known as a *range*. Such factors as water, food, mountains, deserts, temperature, and climate determine the extent to which a plant or animal may extend its habitat. A frog may live on the edge of a shallow pond. If the pond should completely dry up during the summer, this frog and the other forms of life which are dependent on water would die. Thus frogs could not continue to live in this place. But frogs, in general, might continue to live in other ponds over a large area or range.

The range of a cactus in a desert may be limited by salt or other chemicals in the soil. But the area over which the cactus does grow is its range.

Some plants and animals have very small ranges. Others, like rats and mice, range nearly all over the world. Birds, like wild geese or robins, have summer ranges and winter ranges.

FIGURE 2-8. *GRAND CANYON*

This famous canyon in Arizona, 217½ miles long and four to eighteen miles wide, is a natural barrier to plants and animals. Over ninety kinds of animals are found here, but because crossing is difficult, their habitats are limited.

Josef Muench

27

2.9 Barriers

There are many blockades or hindrances to the advance of plant and animal life. Deserts, canyons, mountains, rivers, and frozen wastes are barriers to the spread of living forms. At the Grand Canyon fauna and flora on the north and on the south sides differ slightly because many animals and plants find it difficult to cross the canyon.

Oceans are the greatest barriers. The kangaroo is found only in Australia while its near relative, the opossum, lives only in the Americas. There are no elephants now native to the Western Hemisphere, no llamas in the Eastern. Climatic and ocean barriers prevent each form from leaving its habitat.

Vast areas are desert wastes with few plants. Animal life is less abundant.

The same barriers prevented widespread travel. It was not until men had invented the steamship and airplane that barriers were greatly lessened. Now man's chief barrier is *climatic conditions*.

2.10 Climatic Regions

Since the climate varies with elevation, mountain ranges, and nearness to the ocean, there may be several life zones on one continent or in one country. These may be grouped into regions because of the wide temperature changes from the Poles to the Equator. The whole world has been divided into three main **climatic regions:** *tropic, temperate,* and *arctic.*

2.11 The Tropic Region

The tropic region extends as a belt around the earth on both sides of the Equator. The climate is very *hot* and is favorable for bananas, date palms, and bamboo. Orchids, ferns, and evergreen forests with hanging vines grow there, where moisture and heat are plentiful.

Lions and tigers hunt in the jungle; antelopes and zebras roam the plains; elephants and giraffes seek the water holes. Chimpanzees climb about the trees amid the tropical birdlife.

FIGURE 2-9. *LIFE AT THE EXTREMES*

The lush jungle growth of the tropics (*left*) stands out in sharp contrast to the sparse vegetation of the Arctic tundra (*right*). Are there any animals which can adjust to either of these extremes? Are plants more or less likely to be able to adjust to such differences?

Philip Gendreau, N. Y.

James Sawders—Cushing

2.12 The Temperate Regions

On each side of the tropic region are temperate regions, called the north and south temperate regions. They are characterized by a *mild* climate, although there is wide variation from the snow and ice of winter in some sections to almost constant sunshine in others. These regions are the best suited to the life and progress of mankind. Much land is under cultivation, and many plants and animals are domesticated. Wild animals, such as bears and deer in the woods, snakes and lizards in the desert, salamanders and frogs in the swamps, are found in these regions, although they live in different habitats and even different life zones. Plant life also varies from cactus and sagebrush in the desert to oak trees and sunflowers in regions of moderate rainfall. Evergreens, fruit trees, cereals, beans, peas, and grapes are numerous.

But in spite of the fact that the climate in the north and south temperate regions is similar, some of the fauna and flora are quite different. This is due to other factors, such as elevation and barriers.

2.13 The Arctic Regions

These are the *cold* regions around the North and South Poles, where the seas contain many icebergs and the land is mostly a frozen waste. During the six months of daylight each year, however, the sun's rays usually melt the snow and expose some land surface, even though it is only for a short time. Dwarf willow trees and bright flowers appear, masses of lichens, sedges, moss, and grass cover the vast *tundra,* as the treeless plains of the Arctic are called. These furnish food for the reindeer. Near and in the water are found seals, walruses, and polar bears. In the south polar region of Antarctica very few large animals are found, but seals and penguins are numerous.

2.14 Geographic Realms

A *realm* is a large area made up of a group of neighboring regions separated by barriers. Most of them are comprised of continents separated by ocean barriers, such as the North American, South American, and Australian realms. The Eurasian and Oriental realms in Europe and Asia are separated by mountain barriers. The desert barrier separates part of the continent of Africa into the African realm and the Eurasian realm.

The *North American realm,* which takes in the continent of North America and Central America, has a wide variety of plant and animal life from the semitropical palms of Florida to the tundra of the Arctic. It includes the sunflowers of the plains, the balsam of the evergreen forests, and the giant redwoods of the Pacific coast. Lizards, alligators, and opossums in the south; coyotes, rabbits, and deer in the temperate regions; and bear, moose, and seal in the north indicate the large extent of a realm.

The *South American realm* includes the huge continent of South America, where potatoes originated and where sugar cane and cereal grains are grown. Alpacas and goats climb about the mountains and brightly colored parrots flit about the jungle.

The *Eurasian realm* includes all of Europe, the part of Asia north of the Himalaya Mountains, and northern Africa. Lemons, olives, rice, and tea grow in various sections. Chamois, wild boars, and the dormouse are found there.

The *Oriental realm* consists of the Malay Peninsula, Indo-China, Siam, and India. It is separated from the rest of Asia by the Himalaya Mountain barrier. Wild elephants, Bengal tigers, and

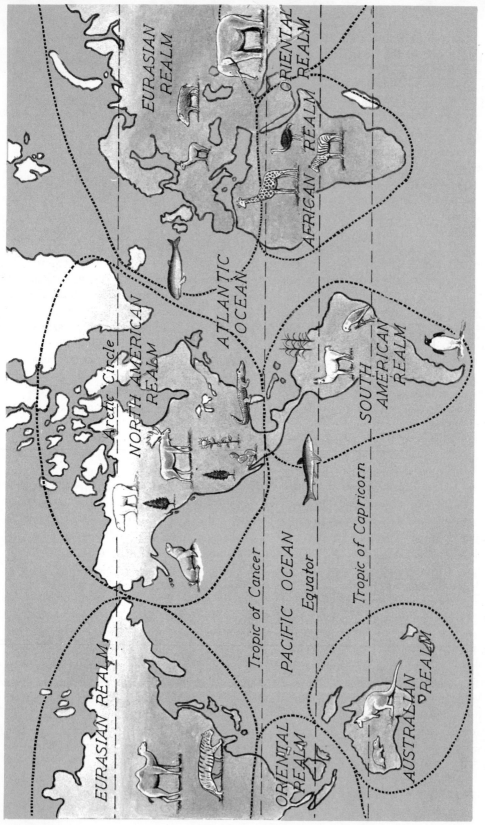

FIGURE 2-10. *GEOGRAPHIC REALMS*

The world may be divided into six realms or life zones, separated from each other by natural barriers such as oceans, mountains, or deserts. Each realm has its own characteristic plant and animal life because the barriers prevent easy movement.

FIGURE 2-11. *SWAMP RECLAMATION*

A system of canals, one of which is being dredged here, are slowly changing this swamp into valuable agricultural land. As the area changes character, the plant and animal communities will also change.

Sawders from Cushing

snakes abound there. Teakwood, valuable for lumber because termites will not destroy it, and many tropical fruits are plentiful.

The *African realm* includes all of Africa except the northern part. It is known for its native brown mahogany, its wild fig and yew trees. Zebras, elephants, lions, and giraffes roam the big game country along the Nile.

The *Australian realm* includes the islands of Australia, Tasmania, New Zealand, and New Guinea. The fauna and flora of this realm differ widely from those of other realms. Kangaroos, bandicoots, and pouched moles which carry their young in pouches are the most numerous mammals. The duckbilled platypus, an egg-laying mammal that nourishes its young with milk, is native to this region.

2.15 Ecology and Conservation

A change in the physical or biological character of an environment will affect the plants and animals. Man has caused many such changes. Draining swamps, cutting forests, destroying animal life, or killing weeds make a change in the balance of plants and animals. This disturbs the plant and animal communities with the result that some become scarce and some too numerous. In order to maintain a proper balance in which plant and animal life can flourish, **conservation** of biological resources is very important.

FACTS TO REMEMBER

Ecology is the study of the relationship between living things and their environment. A *habitat* is a place where any group of plants or animals lives, such as air, land, and water.

A *life zone* includes the habitats of all living things which can exist under the same general climatic conditions. The plant life in a zone is called *flora,* the animal life is the *fauna.* A *range* is the definite area of distribution of a plant or an animal.

The advance of plant and animal life into other areas is limited by certain natural *barriers*. *Climatic regions,* such as the tropic, temperate, and arctic, are based on temperatures, and also limit the areas in which different types of plant and animal life can survive.

A *realm* is a large area of neighboring life zones separated from other regions of the world. These include the North American, South American, Eurasian, Oriental, African, and Australian realms.

WORDS TO REMEMBER

climatic regions	fauna	range
conservation	flora	realm
ecology	habitat	tundra
environment	life zone	

QUESTIONS

1. What is a habitat? A life zone? A range? A region? A realm? Give an example of each.
2. State four characteristics of a water habitat.
3. Why are more living things found near the surface of the ocean or near the shore than in the deep sea?
4. How do conditions for life on land differ from those in the water?
5. Name some animals which live in each of the following habitats:

    a. Underground   *c.* On the ground
    b. In trees   *d.* On both land and water

6. What conditions must be met in air travel? Explain. How can birds maintain themselves in the air?
7. Describe the fauna and flora which are typical of the tropic region.
8. Explain how increases in altitude such as one experiences in climbing a mountain present conditions similar to traveling northward.
9. What is a barrier? List six types of barriers and locate one of each.
10. At present what is man's chief barrier?
11. Briefly describe the vegetation found in the arctic region.
12. Distinguish between life zones and climatic regions.
13. Name six realms and describe one of them.
14. Define ecology. Name several factors that limit the spread of plants and animals.

COMPLETION TEST

As your teacher or classmate reads the following incomplete statements, with your book closed, write on a clean sheet of paper the word or phrase which correctly completes the statement.

1. My home is in the _____ region.
2. Water plants cannot live more than _____ feet below the surface of the water.
3. All of the plant life of a zone is called its _____.
4. Polar bears are found in the _____ region.

5. Trees found near the tops of mountains are often gnarled and twisted because of the _____.

6. The tundra is characteristic of the _____ region.

7. _____ live in salt-water swamps.

8. I live in a _____ habitat.

9. The range of man is _____.

10. My home is in the _____ realm.

PROJECTS

I. *Making a Terrarium.*—If your school already has a large terrarium, start collecting material to put in it, and try to make it balanced. If this has already been done or someone else has started work on the school terrarium, you may make one of your own.

1. *Materials.*—Choose material suitable for a base. This may be a large agate dripping pan 12 × 15 inches or larger, purchased at a store or discarded at home, or it may be a wooden base covered with zinc or tin.

You will need 4 rectangular pieces of glass at least 12 inches wide to form the sides. These can be cut from ordinary window glass to fit the base.

Glass may also be used for the top, if you wish, to help hold the moisture. If there is a quantity of animal life, you may use a wire screen cut to the right size. Cover the edges of glass or wire with adhesive tape or bicycle tape to protect your hands when you wish to take off the cover.

2. *Construction.*—Fasten the pieces of glass together with strips of 1-inch-wide adhesive tape.

Attach the glass sides to the bottom of the dripping pan with putty or aquarium cement. If a wooden base is used, dig a ½-inch furrow along the edges of this base and sink the glass into it. Use putty or cement to make it secure. Place adhesive tape around the top to make the edges smooth.

3. *How to Start Your Terrarium.*

(a) Select a water container. This may be a small dish made of glass 4 × 6 inches or an agate pan of a size suitable for the animals.

(b) Place this dish in one end of your terrarium.

(c) Put a 1-inch layer of small stones and gravel on the bottom of the terrarium and pack it around the dish.

(d) Cover the gravel with rich soil from the woods, if you live where you can do so. If not, cover it with sand.

(e) Collect some moss, ferns, or partridge berries. Plant them in the soil. Other small wood plants may be used. If you live in a dry region, plant some cactus in the sand.

(f) Salamanders, frogs, and toads, or a small snake or lizard may be put in. A few land snails will also live in your terrarium.

(g) Put some stones or pebbles into the water container nearest the soil to form a ramp from the bottom to the soil surface. This will help a salamander to crawl out when he wants to.

4. If you live in a dry region near a desert, make a desert terrarium, using more sand and keeping it very dry. Make your sand deep enough for

some small animals to burrow under it if they wish. Find out the food habits of the animals and be sure you provide enough for them.

II. Explain how your terrarium fulfills the conditions of a land habitat.

III. If you helped make an aquarium for a project, try to answer the following questions:

1. How is food provided for the animal life?
2. Why are tadpoles or snails desirable in an aquarium?
3. What enables the fish to swim?
4. How do water plants differ from land plants?
5. Have you made a balanced aquarium? How can you tell that it is balanced?

IV. *Study of Habitats.*—1. Name and locate as many habitats near your home as you can.

2. List as many of the plants and animals of each as you can.

3. Look for the homes of termites, birds, beavers, spiders, bees, and ants. You will find that in constructing their homes these small creatures have developed a good knowledge of stresses and strains used by our present-day engineers in construction work. The use of these methods by animals is instinctive.

V. With a group of friends climb a mountain, if there is one near, and observe whether there is any change of zone. If you climb very high, you will probably note a difference in the plant life. Make a report of your trip.

VI. Go on a hike to a typical habitat and make a list of all the things you recognize there.

REFERENCES

Barnett, Lincoln and Editorial Staff of Life, *The World We Live In.* Life Magazine.

Carpenter, Neurath, *Iceberg and Jungles.* Hanover House.

Carrigher, *Icebound Summer: Arctic.* Knopf.

Carrigher, *One Day at Teton Marsh.* Knopf.

Carrigher, *One Day on Beetle Rock.* Knopf.

Disney, *Living Desert.* Simon and Schuster.

Disney, *Vanishing Prairie.* Simon and Schuster.

Dodge and Zim, *Southwest: Golden Nature Guide.* Simon and Schuster.

Ivah, *Animals Under Your Feet.* Grosset and Dunlap.

Jordan, *Hammond's Nature Atlas of America.* Hammond.

Mellen, *Fishes in the Home.* Dodd, Mead.

Milne and Milne, *A Multitude of Living Things.* Dodd, Mead.

Morton, *Boy's Guide to Fishing.* Greenberg.

Palmer, *The Mammal Guide.* Doubleday.

Peattie, *Flowering Earth.* Putnam's.

Teale, *Circle of the Seasons.* Dodd, Mead.

Teale, *North with the Spring.* Dodd, Mead.

Zim, Smith, *Reptiles: Golden Nature Guide.* Simon and Schuster.

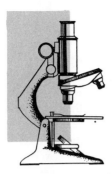

CHAPTER 3

Adaptation to Environment

3.1 What Is an Adaptation?

Any specialized part of a plant or an animal which fits the plant or animal to live in its environment is called an **adaptation**. When you use a fountain pen, notice in what ways your hand shows adaptations for handling it. As you take it from your pocket, your thumb and finger are able to grasp it. When you begin to write, the muscles, bones, and nerves make it possible for you to form definite letters. Your hand has adaptations which especially fit it for many different kinds of work.

3.2 Kinds of Adaptations

The main adaptations of living things are those which enable them to adjust themselves to their surroundings. These include adaptations for life in the water, on land, in the air, in dry regions, and in cold places. Most animals must have special adaptations for (1) *food-getting,* (2) *locomotion,* (3) *breathing,* and (4) *self-protection.* They must also be able to adjust themselves to the changing seasons, as from summer to winter and from rainy weather to dry.

3.3 Adaptations for Life in the Water

Water animals and plants need structures which will enable them to live in water. Fish have teeth and strong jaws for seizing and holding the smaller animals which they eat. Water plants have green coloring matter, *chlorophyll* (*klor-uh-fil*), to help in *food-making.*

To *move* in the water, fish have fins; walruses and seals have flippers; alligators have strong tails. For swimming, penguins use webbed feet and wings too.

FIGURE 3-1. *WATER ADAPTATIONS*

The loon, a water bird with webbed feet, feeds chiefly on fish, for which it can dive deep under water. The seal is also successfully adapted to the water, with flippers and a thick layer of blubber to seal in body heat.

Lynwood M. Chace

Breathing in the water also presents a problem. Most water animals, such as fish, have gills to take oxygen from the air in the water. Frogs take in some oxygen through their thin skins. Sea turtles and whales are air-breathers and so have to come to the surface for air. Water plants have thin coverings through which they take in oxygen from the air dissolved in the water.

For *protection* against enemies and changes in temperature, fish and water snakes are covered with scales. Clams and snails have hard shells; lobsters and crabs have tough outer coverings known as *exoskeletons*. Water plants have flexible stems to prevent breaking by wave motion. Some have air bladders to help their leaves to keep afloat.

3.4 Adaptations for Life on Land

Food is less abundant on land, and living things have to search farther for it. Frogs have long tongues for catching insects; tigers have prominent teeth and sharp claws for capturing live animals. Beavers and rabbits have long gnawing teeth to eat bark from trees. Elephants have trunks to help in food-taking.

Green plants living on land also have green coloring matter, chlorophyll, for food-making. A few have leaves fitted to catch insects for additional food supplies.

Since land is firm and offers resistance to objects, animals have developed many different means of *locomotion*. Horses, deer, and ostriches have slender legs for swift running. Kangaroos have long

FIGURE 3-2. *GETTING AROUND ON LAND*

The kangaroo uses its hind legs and powerful tail to move in a series of leaps. The red fox is a fast, cunning animal with great endurance. How does the legless earthworm move about?

Australian Official Photo
Lynwood M. Chace, from National Audubon Society
L. W. Brownell

hind legs for jumping, and rabbits, long hind legs for hopping. Snakes have supple muscular bodies for crawling. Squirrels have toes provided with sharp, curved nails that make it easy for them to hold fast to the rough bark of the trees, which they are able to climb. Their tails act as rudders when they jump from branch to branch. Monkeys and opossums have long, strong tails which grasp the branches of trees and help them in climbing.

Plants do not need special means of locomotion since they usually remain fixed and make their own food. But they do need to have their seeds scattered by wind, animals, insects, birds, or water. This prevents overcrowding and allows the plants to spread over a larger area until they reach the limit of their zone. By means of runners, which are projections from the stem, plants like strawberries can spread quite rapidly.

Land animals *breathe* air. Man, dogs, birds, and snakes have lungs. Insects have breathing tubes known as *tracheae* (*tray*-kee-ee) to carry air to all parts of their bodies.

Plants also obtain oxygen from the air that enters through openings in the bark and leaves. Cypress trees which live in swamps have special adaptations on their roots, known as *knees,* which extend above the water and afford extra surface for getting air to the roots.

Many animals have special adaptations for *protection*. Tigers fight with their sharp claws and teeth; horses strike with their hoofs; cattle hook with their horns. Some snakes inject poison through their fangs, and skunks emit a pungent odor from special scent glands. Many animals grow thicker fur in winter for protection against the cold.

Plants, likewise, have means of protection. Some of these are the thorns of

FIGURE 3-3. *CYPRESS SWAMP*
The roots of these water-surrounded cypress trees have special adaptations to take in air called "cypress knees." Note the Spanish moss.

Black Star

the rose, spines of the cactus, and prickles of the thistle. Some plants, such as poison oak, poison hemlock, and poison sumac, are harmful to man.

3.5 Adaptations for Life in the Air

Animals which spend much of their time in the air are dependent on other living things for their *food*. Insect-eating bats, swallows, chimney swifts, and flycatchers capture much of their food as they fly through the air. Plants found in the air are mostly bacteria, yeasts, and tiny spores, some of which grow to form molds. These plants cannot make their own food and sooner or later come to rest on some other plant or animal or some form of organic matter from which they can obtain the nourishment that they need.

Since air offers little support, animals must have a great deal of energy to be able to *move* rapidly. Birds are especially fitted to do this, because of their light bony structure and special air sacs which extend into their long, hollow bones. Birds also have overlapping feathers, stream-lined bodies, and heavy breast muscles which help move their curved wings. Their enormous appetite for food and high body temperature afford the necessary energy. Bats' wings are formed by a web between their long fingers (Fig. 3-4). This affords more surface and offers greater resistance to the air when flying.

Plants found in the air are tiny forms which are blown about by the wind and have no means of locomotion of their own. Some, however, have very fine projections which help to catch the air currents.

Some birds fly at great height and thus need *protection* from cold. Their thick layers of overlapping feathers help to keep them warm. Birds also have a body temperature even higher than that of people. Bats are covered with fine, soft hair for protection, but do not usually spend as much time in the air as birds do. Airborne plants have thick outer coverings which keep them from drying and enable them to withstand changes in temperature.

FIGURE 3-4. *FLYING ANIMALS*

The bird's wing (*left*) is a modified forelimb adapted for flying. In the bat, the only flying mammal, the forelimbs have long fingers with the wing membrane stretched between. The butterfly wing is a thin membrane.

WINGS

Bird   Bat   Butterfly

Alan Stebbins, from Black Star   Gita Packer, from Black Star

FIGURE 3-5. *DESERT DWELLERS*

The barrel cactus (*left*) and the horned lizard (*right*) are well adapted to the extreme heat and dryness of the desert. The cactus stores several quarts of sticky juice within it; the lizard is protected by a thick, scaly skin.

Neither animals nor plants are deeply concerned with the problem of *obtaining oxygen* from the air, since they are surrounded by it. Birds have lungs and special air sacs to insure an adequate supply. Bats breathe by lungs, but do not need an extra amount of oxygen, since they take relatively short flights. Plants take oxygen directly through their outer coverings. They need very little, for they do not expend much energy.

3.6 Organisms That Live in Dry Places

Where rainfall is scarce, plants and animals usually develop some means of water storage. The barrel cactus absorbs water during the rainy spells and thus provides itself with a steady supply. The camel has pouches in the lining of its stomach adapted for storing water.

To withstand the heat of the sun and prevent excessive loss of water, desert plants have a thick covering and reduced leaves. Often their long roots reach the water table many feet below the surface. Such plants bloom very quickly, their brilliant flowers promptly attracting in-sects for pollination, since they must wither and die in the heat of the sun.

Desert animals like snakes and lizards have thick scaly skins for protection. Many small animals live underground to protect themselves and to avoid the heat. They usually come out at night to hunt for food. Others, like the kangaroo rat, store their food.

3.7 Organisms That Live in Cold Regions

Life in cold regions is more abundant in the water than on land, because there is more food there. Such animals as whales, seals, and polar bears have thick skins and heavy layers of fat for protection in the icy water. There are few plants, and these must be able to endure long periods of freezing temperatures. Many are covered with hairlike structures and have heavy seed coats.

In the Arctic, ferns, mosses, lichens, and flowering plants take advantage of the short summer. A few dwarf willows and birches manage to survive. In the Antarctic, no trees are found, only the mosses, lichens, fungi, and algae.

ADAPTATION TO ENVIRONMENT   **39**

Black Star

Courtesy of the Davey Tree Expert Co.

FIGURE 3-6. *SPECIAL ADAPTATIONS*
The winged seeds of the maple tree (*right*) are carried away by the wind. They are said to resemble airplane propellers. The elephant's trunk is another kind of adaptation. Its great length compensates for his short neck.

3.8 Special Adaptations

The various shapes of our teeth permit us to eat a great variety of food. In front are the chisel-shaped teeth for cutting. On each side, are the teeth that tear and the broad-crowned teeth that crush and grind the food. Most fishes, frogs, and alligators have conical teeth to hold the captured prey or to tear the flesh. The teeth of such animals do not show as much adaptation as those of man.

The elephant is a very good example of adaptation. His two tusks, often several feet long, are overgrown teeth and are used for defense. The trunk is formed from the nose and upper lip, greatly drawn out. The trunk is used in browsing and drinking, because an elephant's huge bulk and short neck prevent him from reaching down to graze or to drink.

Many seeds have adaptations for traveling. The seeds of the maple tree grow large winglike vanes which help the wind carry them away from the parent tree and thus give them a better chance to grow. Milkweed seeds have downy tufts, and dandelion seeds have tiny plumes that may carry them miles away from the place where the parent plants grow.

The coconut has a buoyant husk that allows it to float down rivers and in the currents of the ocean for a great many miles, until the waves carry it up on the shore, where it may grow into a coconut tree. The wild geranium holds its seeds by a spring that throws them several feet when released. All these are adaptations that plants use in scattering their seeds. Many plants have special adaptations: the tendrils of the common pea and grapevine help them to climb; the prickles of the thistle keep some animals from eating the leaves. We know that the seeds of some plants travel long distances; so can some animals. Most birds go south in the winter and make very long flights. Reindeer wander over the tundra in search of moss, which they can find under the snow in winter. Animals also hunt for water holes or small ponds where they can drink. In dry seasons they often wander far for food and water.

We have learned that plants and animals are not so different as they seem. Both plants and animals live in habitats to which they have become adapted.

3.9 Adaptations for Community Living

Plants and animals living in the same life zone and extending over nearly the same range often find themselves in competition with other plants and animals for space to live, food to eat, and protection from climatic conditions. They also struggle against their enemies. In this *struggle for existence,* some are eaten by others while some move away. Many plants and animals depend upon each other. Some of their relationships are (1) *independent living,* (2) *parasitism,* (3) *saprophytism,* (4) *symbiosis,* and (5) *commensalism.* These are biotic factors of the environment.

3.10 Interrelationships of Plants and Animals

Some plants and animals are able to carry on **independent living.** An oak tree can make its own food from materials taken in through the air and soil,

and withstand many changes in the weather. A rabbit may live on the ground near the tree, hunt for its own food, escape its enemies, and take care of itself. However, all of the independent plants near-by and all of the animals in the vicinity are in reality depending upon each other. The air the rabbit breathes out contains carbon dioxide gas which may be used by the tree in making its food. The tree gives off some oxygen which the rabbit and other animals need to breathe. Although plants and animals may seem to live independently as individuals, they depend upon each other for materials necessary to their existence. When they supply each other's needs, a *balance of nature* is established and the community relationship is good.

FIGURE 3-7. *COMMUNITY LIVING*

Forest trees live so close to their neighbors that they must adapt by growing branches at the top.

Sawders from Cushing

FIGURE 3-8. *SAPROPHYTE*

The mushroom, a fungus, cannot make its own food and lives on other plants. Here, its food supply is a dead tree. These mushrooms are *saprophytes*.

Parasitism (*pair*-uh-sit-izm) is a relationship where one living form gains its existence from another and harms it, without giving anything in return. A tapeworm takes its food from a cat or dog and saps the strength of the **host,** the animal on which it lives. A mistletoe lives on the oak tree and takes the sap, thus depriving the tree of its strength. This parasite is disturbing the balance of nature when it causes destruction of oak trees.

Saprophytism (*sap*-roh-fit-izm) is the relationship where a living organism grows on a dead or decaying substance. Bread mold grows on bread made from flour which was once a part of a green plant. If a mushroom grows on the dead branch of an oak tree, the mushroom is a *saprophyte* (*sap*-roh-fyte).

Symbiosis (sim-bee-*oh* sis) is the relationship where two different kinds of living things help each other. Each one is called a *symbiont* (*sim*-bee-ont). Aphids, small sucking insects, take sap from plants. Some aphids live in a *symbiotic* relationship with ants. The aphids give sap to the ants in return for shelter and protection. The ants watch over the aphids so well that the aphids are sometimes called the ants' "cows."

Another illustration is the sea anemone and the hermit crab. The soft crab crawls inside the sea anemone and as the crab crawls from place to place the anemone move through the water to a better food supply. In return the crab is protected and camouflaged.

Commensalism (kuh-*menss*-uh-lizm) is a relationship in which one organism receives more benefit than the other. The remora fish, with a sucker-like structure on its head, attaches itself to a shark, receives a free ride and such food as escapes the shark's mouth. The shark may be guided toward a food supply but receives much less benefit. This is *commensalism.*

FIGURE 3-9. *SAND SHARK AND FRIENDS*

The remora fish attaches itself to the shark and eats any food the shark may leave behind. He doesn't do anything for his host but neither does he harm him.

Courtesy New York Zoological Society

3.11 Plant Communities

Many plants requiring the same environmental conditions live together and form a plant community. The cypress tree in the swamp is often covered with Spanish moss and may be closely associated with many other plants that live in the same swamp. Other plant communities are forests, tundras, grasslands, deserts, and sagebrush regions.

Since plant communities are constantly changing and passing through natural stages of growth, called *succession,* scientists can study these factors and learn how to practice wise conservation.

3.12 Animal Communities

Some animals are *solitary.* The bear, after the young are able to take care of themselves, wander around alone. It is its nature to do so. Some animals, such as the moles, live in *companies.* Wolves live in *packs* where there is an instinctive struggle for power. Deer live in *herds* which recognize a leader. Monkeys and apes travel in *troops* and *bands* but each individual looks out for himself. You may be able to think of the names of many other animal communities.

Bees are more highly organized and form a society in which each is quite dependent on the others in the *colony.* Ants and termites are also highly organized. The relationships are determined by the nature of the animals living in the group.

3.13 Man and His Community

Man is *gregarious,* wishing to be with others and not solitary or living alone. Man is dependent on plants and animals for food and clothes. He has to struggle for his existence against the insects that try to destroy his crops, the molds that

FIGURE 3-10. *A LIVING CLOUD*
   Wild ducks such as this flock, caught by the camera as they stopped in a game preserve during migration, commonly live together in communities. Some animals lead solitary lives while others live in groups.

Courtesy Asahel Curtis

destroy his food, the bacteria that cause disease, and the many other harmful organisms.

Man is continually disturbing the balance of nature by introducing or by destroying organisms in a community and by methods which impoverish the soil. For example, the building of docks and roadways near the ocean causes changes in the shoreline. Where marine life once lived may now be dry land, inhabited by a very different kind of animal and plant life. Construction of modern superhighways upsets communities of living things when swamps are drained, hills are lowered, and trees are destroyed.

Man is also trying to solve his problems in a world community of other people. He needs to bring his social relationships into balance, to adapt himself to his physical environment, and to adjust to his world community.

FACTS TO REMEMBER

An *adaptation* is any specialized part of a plant or animal which fits it to live in an environment of water, land, air, or in dry or cold regions. Most organisms have special adaptations for food-getting, locomotion, breathing, and protection.

Plants and animals *struggle for existence* in their competition for food and space to live. In doing so they live in such relationships as independent organisms and as parasites, saprophytes, symbionts, and commensals.

Living things form plant communities and animal communities when it is to their advantage to do so. Animals develop a social life from solitary forms to highly complex societies. Man is struggling to maintain the balance of nature in his environment and to adjust to a rapidly changing world community.

WORDS TO REMEMBER

adaptation	communities	saprophytism
chlorophyll	host	symbiosis
commensalism	independent living	tracheae
	parasitism	

QUESTIONS

1. What is an adaptation? What is environment?

2. Study your own hand and name as many adaptations as you can. Explain the purpose of each.

3. Name five animals that live in a water habitat and give at least one adaptation of each.

4. Name three adaptations of plants for protection.

5. State four ways in which birds have been adapted by nature for life in the air.

6. Name five animals (not previously mentioned) with which you are familiar, and state at least one adaptation of each.

7. What special adaptations do the following possess?

      a. skunk   *c.* coconut   *e.* whale
      b. cactus   *d.* elephant

8. How are animals adapted for locomotion? Mention several examples to show these adaptations.

9. Name five kinds of interrelationships of plants and animals. Give as many examples not mentioned in this chapter as you can to show these interrelationships.

10. Describe in detail one plant or animal community which you have observed.

COMPLETION TEST

As your teacher or classmate reads the following incomplete statements, with your book closed, write on a clean sheet of paper the word or phrase which correctly completes the statement.

1. Plants and animals must be able to _____ themselves to changing seasons.

2. Plants breathe air through openings in the bark as well as through _____.

3. The wings of bats are formed by a web of skin between their long _____.

4. The camel stores water in its _____.

5. A desert animal which stores its food is the _____.

6. The _____ of the grapevine enable it to climb.

7. The tusks of the elephant are really overgrown _____.

8. The reason plants do not need very much oxygen is that they expend little _____.

9. One plant community is _____.

10. One social insect you have observed is the _____.

PROJECTS

I. *Collecting Insects.*

1. *What to Collect.* You may collect different kinds of insects, or specialize on certain ones, such as beetles or butterflies.

2. *Materials.*

    (a) Small bottle of denatured alcohol for beetles.

    (b) Insect net for butterflies and other flying insects.

       To make the net, you will need:

         (1) a broomstick for a handle.

         (2) heavy piece of wire 3 feet long (or wire clothes hanger).

         (3) 1 yard of mosquito netting.

       Directions. Bend the wire into a circle, leaving 6 inches over at each end. Bend these ends so that they are parallel to the handle. Make a bag from the mosquito netting and fasten the top to the wire. Then attach the wire to the handle.

    (c) Poison bottles for killing insects.

        To prepare the bottle, you will need:
- (1) a small wide-mouthed bottle or jar with tight-fitting top.
- (2) absorbent cotton.
- (3) carbon tetrachloride (cleaning fluid).
- (4) blotting paper.

    Directions. Place absorbent cotton an inch thick in the jar. Put several thicknesses of blotting paper on this. When collecting, pour a spoonful of carbon tetrachloride into the bottle. This soon evaporates and smothers the insect. The jar must be kept tightly closed and the liquid frequently replaced. Do not inhale the fumes. Place a *POISON* label on the jar.

3. *How to Mount and Dry.*

    (a) *Materials. For butterflies* you will need (at once):
- (1) either a spreading board or else small blocks of wood which have grooves in them.
- (2) insect pins.

    (b) *Directions.* Push an insect pin through the thorax of the dead insect and fit its body into the groove. Spread its wings in a natural position and then keep them in place with strips of thick paper pinned at the ends. The antennae (feelers) should be straightened. Allow the preparation to dry for several days.

4. *How to Preserve a Collection.*

    (a) *Materials.*
- (1) Cigar boxes or other boxes at least 2 inches deep.
- (2) Corrugated pasteboard or thin sheets of cork.
- (3) Labels cut from white paper 1 $\times$ ¼ inch.
- (4) Mothballs or insect-killing fluid.

    (b) *Directions.* Cover the bottom of the boxes with corrugated pasteboard or cork and tack it or glue it down. Print the common name of the insect on a small card. Place the label on the pin under the specimen, which is put near the top of the pin, leaving just room enough to handle. If you can find out the name of the order to which it belongs, add this to your label. Put mothballs or insect-killing fluid placed on cotton in the box and keep it there all the time to prevent other insects from destroying your specimens.

II. Choose one of your pets, such as a dog, cat, or canary, and watch it closely. List as many adaptations as you can observe, and tell what each of these is for.

III. Locate, examine, and list the kinds of plants that are found in a typical association.

IV. Observe an animal living among others of its kind. What characteristics do you observe?

REFERENCES

Bishop, *Handbook of Salamanders*. Comstock.

Campbell, *Outline of Plant Geography*. Macmillan.

Carson, *Under the Sea-Wind*. Oxford University Press.

Colbert, *The Dinosaur Book*. The American Museum of Natural History, New York City.

Disney, *Living Desert*. Simon and Schuster.

Disney, *Vanishing Prairie*. Simon and Schuster.

Dodge and Zim, *Southwest: Golden Nature Guide*. Simon and Schuster.

Ivah, *Animals Under Your Feet*. Grosset and Dunlap.

Jaeger, *Denizens of the Desert*. Houghton Mifflin.

Sears, *Deserts on the March*. University of Oklahoma Press.

UNIT II

The Nature of Life

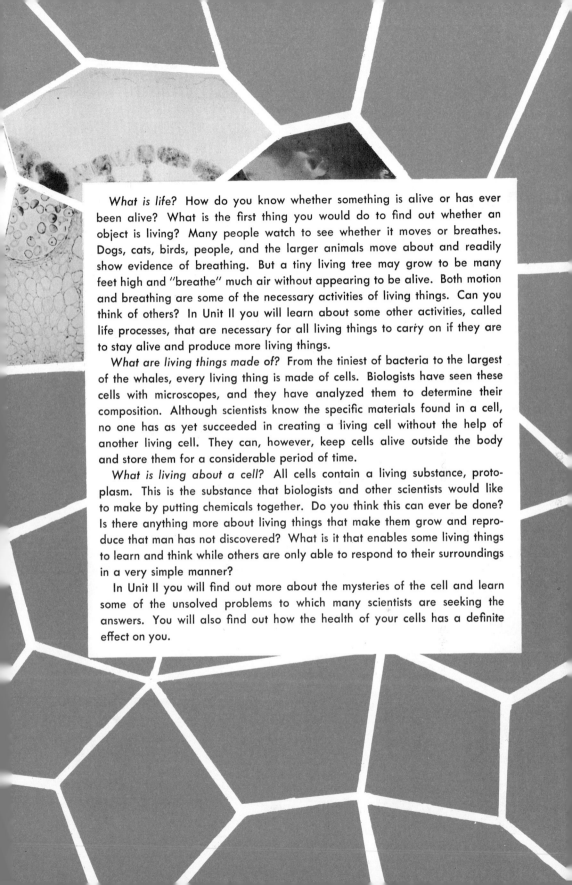

What is life? How do you know whether something is alive or has ever been alive? What is the first thing you would do to find out whether an object is living? Many people watch to see whether it moves or breathes. Dogs, cats, birds, people, and the larger animals move about and readily show evidence of breathing. But a tiny living tree may grow to be many feet high and "breathe" much air without appearing to be alive. Both motion and breathing are some of the necessary activities of living things. Can you think of others? In Unit II you will learn about some other activities, called life processes, that are necessary for all living things to carry on if they are to stay alive and produce more living things.

What are living things made of? From the tiniest of bacteria to the largest of the whales, every living thing is made of cells. Biologists have seen these cells with microscopes, and they have analyzed them to determine their composition. Although scientists know the specific materials found in a cell, no one has as yet succeeded in creating a living cell without the help of another living cell. They can, however, keep cells alive outside the body and store them for a considerable period of time.

What is living about a cell? All cells contain a living substance, protoplasm. This is the substance that biologists and other scientists would like to make by putting chemicals together. Do you think this can ever be done? Is there anything more about living things that make them grow and reproduce that man has not discovered? What is it that enables some living things to learn and think while others are only able to respond to their surroundings in a very simple manner?

In Unit II you will find out more about the mysteries of the cell and learn some of the unsolved problems to which many scientists are seeking the answers. You will also find out how the health of your cells has a definite effect on you.

CHAPTER 4

The Cell

4.1   Discovery of the Cell

For a long time man had known that living things carried on the life processes such as respiration and digestion, but it was difficult to explain just where these activities took place. It was not until a very simple microscope was invented that tiny structures called *cells* (Sec. 1.5) were discovered. A Dutch lens grinder, Anton van Leeuwenhoek (*lay-ven-hook*) (page 682), made many microscopes and described what he saw through them.

In 1665, Robert Hooke (page 680),

in England, was examining with a simple microscope some pieces of cork which he had sliced very thin, when he noticed that there were some tiny structures arranged in hundreds of rows. They resembled the rows of rooms in a monastery so much that he named them "cells."

Attention was again centered on these same structures nearly a hundred years later when, in 1833, Robert Brown described a large spherical structure well inside of each cell. This was the **nucleus** (*noo*-klee-us), which is the center of ac-

FIGURE 4-1.   *WINDOW ON THE WORLD*

From the primitive microscope of Leeuwenhoek (*left*) has come the modern compound microscope (*right*), used for general laboratory work.

Courtesy Bausch & Lomb

Courtesy Bausch & Lomb

FIGURE 4-2. *DESERT TALE*

By the process of assimilation, the desert iguana converts food materials into the substance of his own protoplasm, thus regenerating his lost tail.

tivity of the cell. In 1838, two German scientists, Matthias Schleiden (*shlyden*), a botanist, and Theodor Schwann (*shvon*), a zoologist, began to study a great many different plants and animals (page 685). They found that *every living thing is made of cells.*

4.2 Discovery of Protoplasm

As better microscopes were made, more scientists began to study the material inside of the cell to find out what makes it alive. This living material was discovered by Dujardin in 1835. It was called *protoplasm* (Sec. 1.5) by Purkinje. Von Mohl brought the term into general use. Max Schultze found that protoplasm, the living substance of cells, carried on the life processes of the cell. Protoplasm is a semi-transparent, jellylike substance, containing granules and some material in the form of globules or fibers which are suspended in it. Protoplasm is a growing, streaming, dividing substance that responds to touch, to

heat, and to other stimuli. It has been called the physical basis of life, since only living things possess it.

4.3 Differences in Protoplasm

The protoplasm of which cells are made is composed of many chemical elements, such as oxygen, carbon, nitrogen, and iron, combined in various ways to form compounds. Each group of living things differs from every other group in the special structure of its compounds. The protoplasm in the cells of a cat is more nearly like that in the cells of a lion than that of a turtle. The protoplasm in the cells of man differs in its chemical structure from any of the other animals. It also differs in its chemical, physical, and biological properties in the different parts and organs of any one animal.

Only living protoplasm can take in the chemical materials it needs in the form of foreign compounds and, by rearranging the parts, can change them into its own substance. This is the process of *assimilation* (Sec. 1.11), and it results in growth and repair. When you have eaten your lunch, the protoplasm in the body cells sorts out the calcium from the milk, the iron from the minerals in the salad, and the various amino acids from the meat. It builds them into your own kind of protoplasm. Some of the protoplasm oxidizes the foods, which releases energy to keep you warm and gives you strength to move about.

4.4   The Cell Theory

The conclusion reached by Schleiden and Schwann that plants and animals are made of cells is known as the **cell theory**. Since then many other scientists have studied all living things and have formed the present cell theory by adding conclusions drawn from new discoveries. The cell theory states that (a) *all living things are made of cells,* (b) *all living things are formed from other living things by cell division* (Chap. 5), and

(c) *the cell is the unit of structure and function of all living things* (Sec. 1.5).

The phase contrast microscope has enabled many more structures to be observed in living material. The electron microscope shows details in dead cells.

Cells are limited in size by at least four factors: (1) the exchange of materials must take place at a rate high enough to supply the needs of the cell; (2) the nucleus must control the chemical agents which diffuse into the cytoplasm; (3) the surface area must be kept small to keep the cell operating at a high rate; and (4) the cellular structure must be somewhat elastic and rigid.

4.5   Structure of Cells

The protoplasm which forms the cell has three main parts: (1) the **nucleus,** usually a spherical oval body near the center or end of a cell; (2) the **cytoplasm** (*sy*-toh-plazm), which is the part of the protoplasm outside the nucleus; and (3) the **cell (plasma) membrane.**

FIGURE 4-3.   *STRUCTURE OF THE CELL*

All cells are similar in structure, although plant cells differ in some ways from animal cells. Can you see these differences?

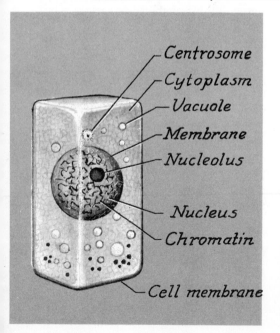

Centrosome
Cytoplasm
Vacuole
Membrane
Nucleolus
Nucleus
Chromatin
Cell membrane

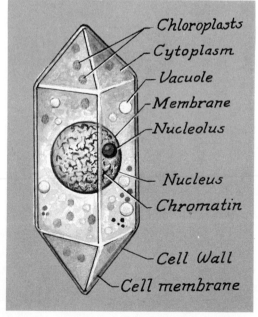

Chloroplasts
Cytoplasm
Vacuole
Membrane
Nucleolus
Nucleus
Chromatin
Cell Wall
Cell membrane

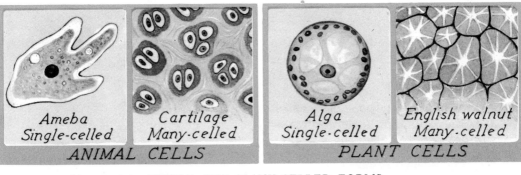

FIGURE 4-4. *SINGLE AND MANY-CELLED FORMS*
Some forms exist as one cell; others are many-celled and highly organized.

The *cytoplasm* forms the greater part of the cell. It includes all of the protoplasm outside of the nucleus. The cytoplasm is enclosed in a very thin, delicate, *cell membrane* in an animal cell and an additional **cell wall** in a plant cell.

The cytoplasm of a typical *animal cell* (Fig. 4-3) contains (1) a globular **centrosome** (*sen*-truh-sohm) located near the nucleus and useful in cell division, (2) **mitochondria** (*my*-toh-*kahn*-dree-uh) composed of proteins and enzymes which carry on respiration of the cell, and (3) **vacuoles** (*vak*-you-ohls) filled with liquid containing dissolved minerals, food, and wastes. These structures may not all be present in any one cell.

Cell walls in plants are made of **cellulose,** a nonliving substance. It consists of materials secreted by the cell and gives rigidity to the plant structure. Cytoplasm of green plant cells contains living bodies called **plastids,** of which the most common are the **chloroplasts** in which is stored the green **chlorophyll** used in food manufacture. The vacuoles of plant cells are usually large and filled with **cell sap.** Centrosomes are rarely found in plant cells.

The *cell membrane* in both plant and animal cells is **semipermeable** (sem-ee-*per*-mee-uh-b'l). It contains tiny pores through which only certain kinds of molecules can pass, and regulates the movement and exchange of foods, respiratory gases, and wastes between the cells and the fluids in animal bodies. The process by which water passes through the cell membrane is called **osmosis** (oz-*moh*-sis). *Diffusion* (Sec. 1.11) is a more general term for the method by which gases and liquids pass through the cell membrane. By this method plant cells take in dissolved minerals from the soil and animals take digested food into the blood.

The *endoplasmic reticulum* forms a network of passageways from the cell membrane throughout the cytoplasm. Dense *ribosomes* along the membrane contain *ribonucleic acid, RNA,* which directs the synthesis of proteins.

The *nucleus* directs the activities of the cell. It is composed of material called **nucleoplasm** and is surrounded by the **nuclear membrane.** Within the nucleoplasm are **chromosomes** which appear as tiny threads arranged in a network of **chromatin.** A small, round body, called the **nucleolus,** is also present, which disappears when the cell divides. The chromosomes contain *deoxyribonucleic acid, DNA,* which aids in the coding of protein synthesis. DNA is the genetic material which carries the information necessary for the development, growth, and reproduction of the cell. It directs the activities of the RNA.

4.6 Single Cells

The lowest forms of animal and plant life are single cells. Yet these tiny bits of protoplasm, like the *ameba* (animal) and *bacteria* (plant), perform all the life processes. These tiny one-celled animals and plants are so small that they can be seen only with the microscope.

4.7 Many-celled Forms

While some cells live singly, most of them live together as do the members of your family. They may form colonies in which each one is somewhat independent, or they may live very close together, become attached, and help each other. Man is a many-celled animal which is highly organized. His cells work together, but are so arranged that each kind has a special work to do in helping him carry on his life processes. There are millions of cells in the human body. The higher plants are also many-celled, and these cells are arranged in groups.

4.8 Specialized Cells

Since most cells in higher plants and animals have special work to do, they differ greatly in size and shape. Such variation is known as **cell differentiation.** Thus nerve cells, which carry messages, are unlike red blood cells, which carry oxygen.

In order to carry on their work more efficiently, many cells develop special structures by modifying some parts of the cell. This is called **cell specialization. Nerve cells,** or **neurons** (*noo*-rons) (Fig. 4-5), have branches known as *dendrites* (*den*-dryts) to receive messages, and long parts called *axons* (*ak*-sons) to transmit these messages toward the next cells. Thus neurons show a high degree of specialization.

Blood cells (Fig. 4-5) have different shapes. In human blood the *red corpuscles* (*kor*-pus-'ls), which carry the oxygen, are disc-shaped. They have no nuclei when they are mature enough to enter the blood stream. The *white corpuscles* are colorless. Some can change shape. The *platelets* (*playt*-lets) are small, irregularly shaped cells. The white corpuscles, like other body cells, have nuclei.

FIGURE 4-5. *SPECIALIZED BODY CELLS*
Cells vary in size and shape, according to their function. Some also develop special structures to help them perform more efficiently.

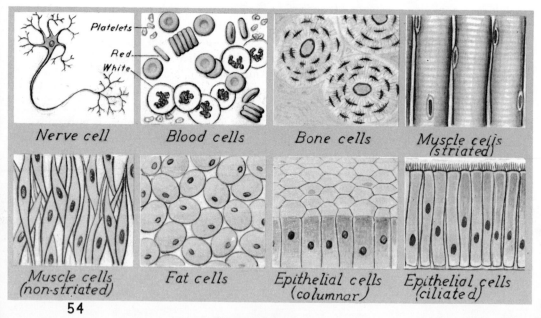

Nerve cell   Blood cells   Bone cells   Muscle cells (striated)

Muscle cells (non-striated)   Fat cells   Epithelial cells (columnar)   Epithelial cells (ciliated)

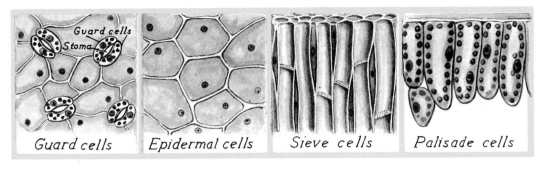

Guard cells | Epidermal cells | Sieve cells | Palisade cells

FIGURE 4-6. *SPECIALIZED PLANT CELLS*

Each has its own function. Epidermal cells cover the leaf; guard cells regulate moisture into it; and palisade cells, having many chloroplasts, are active in photosynthesis. Sieve cells carry fluids down the stem.

Bone cells (Fig. 4-5) lie in a matrix which gives support. They are very compact with the matrix between them filled with deposits of minerals.

Muscle cells (Fig. 4-5), on the other hand, are elongated and flexible in order to help in moving the bones. Note the crosslines or *striations* (stry-*ay*-shuns) on the voluntary muscle cells, such as those found in the arms and legs.

Fat cells (Fig. 4-5), which are somewhat globular, are especially arranged for fat storage. **Epithelial** (ep-ih-*thee*-lee-al) **cells** like those of the skin may be rectangular or square or flattened as in *stratified epithelium,* and may possess *cilia* (hairlike structures) as in *ciliated epithelium* (Fig. 4-5).

Plants also have specialized cells.

Guard cells (Fig. 4-6) need their particular shape in order to regulate the amount of moisture in the leaf.

You will note that cells are specialized or adapted for the work they have to do in much the same way as engineers, farmers, and mechanics are fitted for their work.

4.9 Organized Cells

In many-celled animals, cells are organized to perform the life processes. Groups of cells so organized are called **tissues.** Bone cells are arranged in groups to form *supporting tissue,* muscle cells form *muscular tissue,* and nerve cells form *nervous tissue.*

Tissues, however, are able to perform only simple tasks. In order to carry on

FIGURE 4-7. *PLANT AND ANIMAL TISSUE*

A capillary (*left*), an animal tissue composed of many cells, is a tiny tube through which blood is conducted. Sieve cells (*right*) compose a plant tissue used for the conduction of food materials dissolved in water.

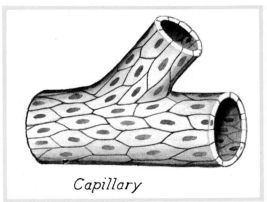

Capillary

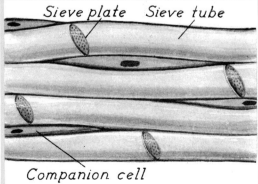

Sieve plate   Sieve tube

Companion cell

greater activity, the tissues are grouped into **organs.** One tissue alone could not digest food as does the stomach, which is an *organ* composed of epithelial (covering) tissue, muscular tissue, glandular tissue, and others. An organ is a group of tissues that does a given work in an animal or a plant.

Organs that help with similar activities are grouped into **systems.** The gullet, stomach, and intestines form the *digestive* system. The windpipe, bronchial tubes, and lungs form the *respiratory* system.

Plants also have cells grouped into tissues such as epithelial (Fig. 4-5), chlorophyll-bearing, storage, conducting, reproductive, and supporting tissues. These form plant organs like stems, roots, leaves, and flowers. Their systems include those for absorbing and conducting liquids, for manufacturing and storing food, and for producing and distributing seeds.

4.10 Organisms

The cell is the unit of structure and function in animals and plants. Cells may be grouped into tissues, tissues into organs, and organs into systems. Because of these organs all living things are called **organisms.** Most living things have cells, tissues, organs, and systems, but any living thing, whether composed of one or many cells, is called an organism. The living matter of which organisms are composed is called *organic matter,* as distinct from nonliving *inorganic matter,* like metals and minerals, for example.

FACTS TO REMEMBER

The *cell theory* states that all living things are made of cells. *Protoplasm* is the living material of cells and carries on all the life activities. All cells have a *nucleus* which is surrounded by the *cytoplasm* and a cell (plasma) membrane. The cell membrane allows exchange of various materials by *diffusion.* Plant cells are covered with *cell walls,* which are not present in animal cells.

Cells show *differentiation* and *specialization* according to their functions. Cells may live singly or they may be organized into *tissues.* Tissues in turn make up *organs* and organs form *systems.* An *organism* is any living thing.

WORDS TO REMEMBER

assimilation	chromatin	organ
cell differentiation	chromosome	organic matter
cell membrane	cytoplasm	organism
cell specialization	endoplasmic	osmosis
cell theory	reticulum	plastid
cell wall	inorganic matter	protoplasm
cellulose	mitochondria	semipermeable
centrosome	nuclear membrane	system
chlorophyll	nucleolus	tissue
chloroplast	nucleus	vacuoles

QUESTIONS

1. What are living things made of?
2. Why is the cell often called the physical basis of life?
3. Name and describe three main parts of every cell.
4. What is the function of the cell membrane?
5. Name three parts of the nucleus and give their functions.
6. Why is the cell called the unit of structure?
7. What kinds of cells are in the blood?
8. What kinds of cells are on the outside of the skin?
9. Why are people in factories organized into groups with different kinds of work to do?
10. Explain how cells are organized.
11. What is meant by the cell theory?
12. What was the chief contribution made to biology by Robert Hooke? Robert Brown?

COMPLETION TEST

As your teacher or classmate reads the following incomplete statements, with your book closed, write on a clean sheet of paper the word or phrase which correctly completes the statement.

1. Protoplasm is a _____ substance containing _____.
2. A group of similar cells performing a special function is called a _____.
3. Any living thing is known as an _____.
4. The organs that help to perform one life function form a _____.
5. A group of tissues make an _____.
6. Three plant organs are the _____, _____, and _____.
7. Blood cells which carry oxygen are called _____.
8. Some of the substances found in protoplasm are _____, _____, and _____.
9. A distinguishing characteristic of inorganic matter is _____.
10. Cells which do not have nuclei when they become active in the body are the _____ _____.

PROJECTS

I. *Use of the Microscope.*—Obtain permission to use a compound microscope and choose a suitable time to learn how to use it, for the microscope is a delicate instrument and needs special care.

1. Place the microscope on a table with the handle toward you. Then with the help of labeled charts and diagrams try to locate the following parts.

    (a) *Eyepiece.* The lens through which you will first look.

    (b) *Objective.* Note the revolving nosepiece which makes it possible to change quickly from low to high power.

    (c) *Stage.* This is to hold the slides. Note the clips to keep them in place.

(d) *Substage.* This has a moveable diaphragm to regulate the amount of light.

(e) *Mirror.* There are usually two different surfaces, one plain and the other concave. They are used for adjusting or concentrating light rays.

(f) *Coarse adjustment.* The large wheel on the side can be turned to bring the object into focus.

(g) *Fine adjustment.* When the object is quite distinct under the action of the coarse adjustment, the fine adjustment is used to bring it out in clear outline.

II. *Objects Seen under the Microscope.*
   1. *Materials Needed.*
      (a) Plain slide.
      (b) Cover glass.
   2. *Preparing the Object.*
      (a) Wash the slide and cover glass *very carefully,* as they break easily.
      (b) Place the object in the middle of the slide and put the cover glass over it.
   3. *Suggested Objects to Study.*
      (a) Piece of paper—lens paper shows the fibers very well.
      (b) Piece of cloth—try different kinds: cotton, silk, wool.
      (c) Grain of salt.
      (d) Hair.
      (e) Small printed letter such as *a* or *e.*

III. *Recording Results.*
   1. Place some paper on the table beside the microscope and try to draw the objects you see. Use the outline form of drawing rather than sketch lines.
      (a) What shape are the salt crystals?
      (b) What is the appearance of the letters under the microscope?
      (c) Does the microscope have the same effect on other objects?

IV. *Study of Cells under the Microscope.*
   1. If prepared slides are available, select some that have cells which are easily seen. Try to recognize the
      (a) *nucleus*—usually stains darker than the rest of the cell.
      (b) *cell wall* or *membrane*—around the outside.
      (c) *cytoplasm*—material outside of the nucleus.
   2. *Recognition of Cells.*
      Search your collection of slides and try to find each of the following:
      (a) Fat cell.
      (b) Columnar epithelial cell.
      (c) Bone cell.
      (d) Red blood cell.
      (e) Striated muscle cell.
      (f) White blood cell.
      (g) Cartilage cell.
      (h) Ciliated epithelial cell.
      (i) Nerve cell.
      (j) Smooth muscle cell.

THE NATURE OF LIFE

3. *Study of Living Cells.*
    (a) With a clean throat stick or other instrument suggested by your teacher, scrape gently the lining on the inside of your cheek. Place the material on a slide and study the cells.
    (b) Peel a very thin piece of onion skin and place it on a slide. Compare the general appearance of this plant cell with the cells from your cheek.

V. *Further Use of the Microscope.*
    1. Choose 5 or 10 other objects for study, such as
        (a) the wing of a fly or moth.
        (b) leaf of a plant.
        (c) pencil shaving.
        (d) chalk dust.
        (e) web of frog's foot.
    2. Look at them under the microscope.
    3. Sketch what you see.
    Note: Remember that thin objects which light will shine through are much more easily studied than opaque objects.

VI. *To Show Osmosis.*
    Method 1. Select a large carrot, sweet potato, or beet. Hollow out the inside of the root. Fit it with a large one-hole stopper. Put a glass tube 3 or 4 feet long into one end of the stopper until it reaches the lower part of the hollow root. Place the root in a large beaker of water and attach the glass tubing to a standard. Fill the hollow portion of the root with molasses or a strong sugar solution. Set aside for a time and observe. Record your observations and explain what happened.

    Method 2. Select a large hard-shelled egg, a long glass tube, and some paraffin or sealing wax. Carefully remove the shell from the large end of the egg without breaking the thin membrane. Make as small an opening in the other end of the egg as you can and insert the glass tube. Fasten the tube there and seal it with the paraffin or sealing wax. Place the egg in a beaker of water and attach the glass tube to a standard. Set aside for a time and observe what happens. Try to explain your results.

REFERENCES

Gooch, *The Strange World of Nature.* Crowell.
MacDougall and Hegner, *Biology, the Science of Life.* McGraw-Hill.
Singer, *The Story of Living Things.* Harper.
Thone, *The Microscopic World.* Messner.
Ward and Whipple, *Fresh-Water Biology.* Wiley.

CHAPTER 5

How New Cells Are Formed

5.1 Cell Functions

Because the cell is the unit of function, it must perform all of its life processes as long as it lives. The protoplasm, the living cell material, carries on the cell activities—taking food and oxygen into the cell, building and repairing the cell, secreting necessary substances, and producing more cells.

An individual cell continues to grow until it reaches the limit of its size. The cell stops growing when there exists a certain ratio between the amount of surface and its mass. Then, under favorable conditions, the cell divides to form new cells. This is **cell reproduction** or **cell division,** and occurs in all cells throughout the body.

5.2 Kinds of Cell Division

If you wanted to share a chocolate bar with a friend, there are two ways in which it could be divided. You might break it into two parts, hoping they were even, or you might measure and cut it to be sure you had exactly equal pieces.

Cells also divide in two ways. The first is by a simple or *direct cell division* called **amitosis** (ay-my-*toh*-sis), which is shown in Figure 5-2. Here the cell is pinched into two cells, giving to each half a part of the nucleus and part of the cytoplasm. This makes the two cells only approximately even, but it is a quick method. This type of cell division is frequently found in the rapidly growing cells of cancer.

FIGURE 5-1. *MITOSIS*

Indirect cell division in plants and animals is known as *mitosis.* In the resting stage, the nucleus is enclosed in a membrane, and the chromatin dis-

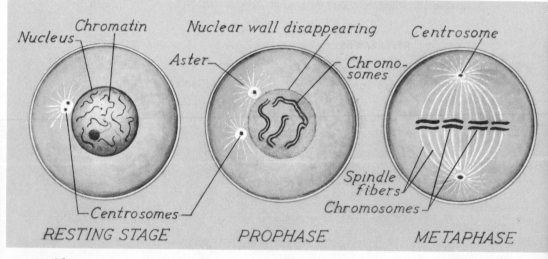

RESTING STAGE   PROPHASE   METAPHASE

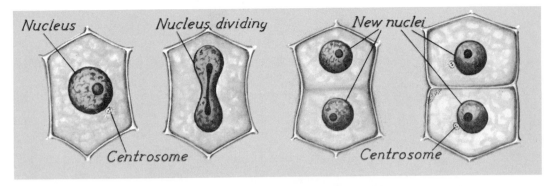

FIGURE 5-2. *AMITOSIS: DIRECT CELL DIVISION*
This rapid type of division pinches the cell into approximately two parts.
The newly formed cells are then not exactly like each other.

The second method, the *indirect* process of cell division, is slower and more complicated, but much more precise. By it there is a definite distribution of nuclear material in the new cells. This is the usual method of cell division in most animals and plants.

5.3   Indirect Cell Division

The process of indirect cell division is known as **mitosis** (my-*toh*-sis). Figure 5-1 shows the various stages of this process. You may be able to see some of these stages with the microscope.

(1) *The Resting Stage.* When the cell is not actively dividing, it is said to be in the resting stage, or *interphase.* The nucleus is enclosed in a membrane and a dense body, the *nucleolus,* can be seen. The chromosomes are indistinct and distributed throughout the nucleus in a fine network of chromatin.

(2) *Prophase.* The first stage of mitosis is called prophase. The chromosomes become much thicker and break up into distinct rods of varying lengths and shapes. Each of these rods is in two halves lying side by side and often intertwined. The centrosome, present only in animal cells, divides, and the two halves move around the nucleus in opposite directions, forming *spindle fibers* between them and raylike structures around them called *asters.* The nuclear

tributed equally; in prophase, the centrosome (present only in animal cells) divides, spindles develop, and chromosomes form. In later stages, one chromosome from each pair moves to each centrosome.

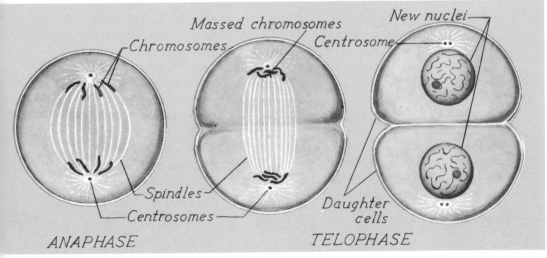

ANAPHASE   TELOPHASE

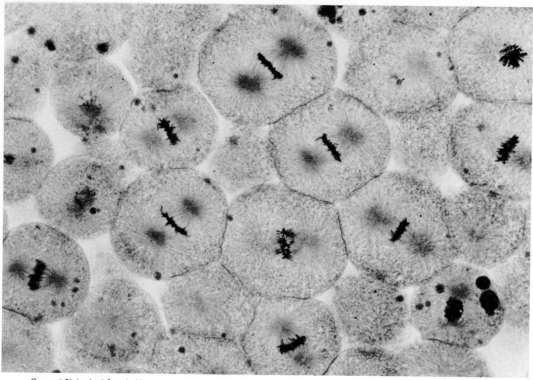

FIGURE 5-3. *MITOSIS: INDIRECT CELL DIVISION*
The exact division of chromosomes in mitosis gives to each new cell the
same nuclear material. Can you locate cells in prophase and metaphase?

membrane and the nucleolus disappear.

(3) *Metaphase.* The centrosomes are
now at opposite poles of the cell with
the spindle fibers stretching between
them. The chromosome pairs become
more or less lined up across the equator
of the cell. This is quite a short stage.

(4) *Anaphase.* The two halves of
each of the chromosome rods now separate and move in opposite directions toward the two centrosomes as if they
were pulled apart by the spindle fibers.

(5) *Telophase.* The two groups of
chromosomes mass together at opposite
poles. A cell membrane forms across
the equatorial plate and separates the
cell into two *daughter cells*. The spindle
fibers disappear and a nuclear membrane
forms in each new cell. The chromosomes become indistinct and assume the

appearance of a chromatin network.
The two new cells are now in the resting
stage.

The stages of mitosis are essentially
the same in plant cells as they are in
animal cells except that the centrosome
is lacking in plant cells.

5.4 Energy for Cell Growth

As soon as the two daughter cells are
formed, growth begins to take place by
the process of assimilation. This continues until the cells reach the size of
the original cell, when they may divide
as the parent cell did, if conditions are
favorable.

Energy for cell growth and activity
comes from oxidation of glucose. The
mitochondria in the cytoplasm synthesize *adenosine triphosphate, ATP,*

THE NATURE OF LIFE

which contains energy-rich phosphate bonds. This energy is made available to the cells as chemical bond energy when ATP changes to *adenosine diphosphate, ADP.* The energy of glucose is then transferred to ADP and changes it back to ATP. This maintains an energy cycle which enables the cell to carry on all of its various activities.

5.5 All Life from Life

An important part of the cell theory (Sec. 4.4) is the principle that all living things come from other living things by the process of cell division. Scientists have yet to learn how living things first appeared on the earth and whether some day man will be able to produce a living cell from nonliving materials.

FACTS TO REMEMBER

The *cell* is the *unit of function* because its protoplasm carries on all of the life processes. When cells reach their limit of size they divide. The usual method is by *mitosis,* indirect cell division. From the resting stage cells pass through the prophase, metaphase, anaphase, and telophase stages. Each new cell has the same amount of chromatin material as the cell which divided. This means that the new cell has the same characteristics as the original cell.

An important part of the cell theory is the principle that *all cells are produced by cell division from other cells.*

WORDS TO REMEMBER

ADP	centrosome	mitosis
amitosis	chromosome	prophase
anaphase	daughter cell	resting stage
aster	direct cell division	spindle fiber
ATP	indirect cell division	telophase
cell division	metaphase	

QUESTIONS

1. Why is the cell called the unit of structure and function in the body?
2. Which is the more common method of cell division? What are its advantages?
3. Briefly describe the stages of mitosis.
4. As a result of mitosis, how many complete cells are formed?
5. Explain in your own words what is meant by the part of the cell theory which states that life can come only from other living things.

COMPLETION TEST

As your teacher or classmate reads the following incomplete statements, with your book closed, write on a clean sheet of paper the word or phrase which correctly completes the statement.

HOW NEW CELLS ARE FORMED

63

1. Indirect cell division is known as _____.
2. During the resting stage the chromosomes are distributed in the nucleus as a network of _____.
3. Each new cell formed is called a _____ cell.
4. The split chromosomes move apart during the stage called _____.
5. Centrosomes are found only in _____ cells.
6. Cells secure energy by the oxidation of _____.
7. All life comes from _____.
8. Growth takes place by the process of _____.
9. Plants and animals are made of _____.
10. The living material of the cell that carries on the life processes is _____.

PROJECTS

I. *Studying Cell Division under the Microscope.*

Using a prepared slide which shows cell division, look carefully at different cells until you find one in each of the stages of cell division. Compare them with the diagram on page 60.

When you have learned to identify each of the stages, make a series of drawings showing *exactly what you see.* If possible, arrange them in the following order:

a.	Resting Stage	d.	Anaphase
b.	Prophase	e.	Telophase
c.	Metaphase	f.	New Cell Stage

Label the stages carefully. Then write the answers to the following questions in your notebook:

1. Why did you not find the cells in the stages of cell division arranged in the order listed above?
2. Why is it that cell division usually takes place much more rapidly in the section of a root that is near the root tip than it does in other parts of the root?

Select a slide showing a one-celled plant or animal in the process of cell division. Note that the nucleus plays a very important part in this process. Draw *two stages* of cell division in a one-celled plant or animal. Label carefully.

II. Make a series of models of cell division or mitosis. You may use such materials as (a) plasticine or clay, painted and labeled, (b) plastic wood, shaped and molded, mounted and labeled.

III. Make a series of drawings of mitosis on a chart for class use or for the bulletin board. Use colored ink or small colored objects to represent the chromosomes.

IV. Make a relief chart to illustrate the stages of mitosis showing the difference between plant and animal mitosis.

V. Make a model of an early type of microscope.

VI. Make a study of the work of Louis Pasteur with special reference to the experiments disproving spontaneous generation, an early belief that living things can come from nonliving things.

REFERENCES

MacDougall and Hegner, *Biology, the Science of Life.* McGraw-Hill.
Seifritz, *Protoplasm.* McGraw-Hill.
Smith, Gilbert, et al., *Botany.* Macmillan.
Thone, *The Microscopic World.* Messner.
Ward and Whipple, *Fresh-Water Biology.* Wiley.

COMPREHENSIVE TEST ON PART ONE

Copy these sentences, filling in the blanks. Do not mark your book.

I. 1. Biology is the study of _____.
    2. The place where a group of plants or animals live is called its _____.
    3. The particular area in which a large number of species of plants and animals occur is known as its _____ _____.
    4. Any special structure of a plant or animal that helps it to perform its life functions is called an _____.
    5. The process that includes taking in oxygen and giving off carbon dioxide is called _____.
    6. Removal of waste material from the body is called _____.
    7. Life continues from one generation to another by _____.
    8. The response to stimuli is known as _____.
    9. The process by which food becomes part of the body is _____.
    10. Changing food into a soluble form is known as _____.

II. (a) A water habitat presents certain problems for living things because of certain conditions found there. Complete the following:
    1. Locomotion in water is accomplished by means of _____ or _____.
    2. Pressure in the water varies with the _____.
    3. Most water animals breathe by _____.
    4. Water plants have flexible stems to prevent _____.
  (b) A land habitat presents other problems. Complete:
    1. Most land animals breathe by _____.
    2. Land plants breathe by openings in the _____ and _____.
    3. Land animals have legs adapted for _____, _____, and _____.
    4. Squirrels use their tails for _____.
  (c) Air offers little support for objects. Therefore, living things must be able to move rapidly.
    1. Adaptations of birds for moving through the air are _____.
    2. Rapid oxidation helps the bird to maintain a high body _____.
    3. Bats are covered with _____.
    4. Bats' wings are formed by a _____ between their long _____.

III. Without reference to your book, draw a typical plant cell and include these labels: chloroplasts, nucleus, cell wall, nucleolus, nuclear membrane, vacuoles, cell (plasma) membrane, cytoplasm, chromatin.

IV. Some of the following statements are correct and some are incorrect. Copy the numbers of the correct statements and write an explanation. Copy the numbers of the incorrect ones and write a reason.

1. The cell is the unit of structure in the body.
2. Every cell has a cell wall.
3. Indirect cell division is the usual method of producing new cells.
4. In animal cells the centrosomes help in cell division.
5. An organ is a group of cells doing the same kind of work.

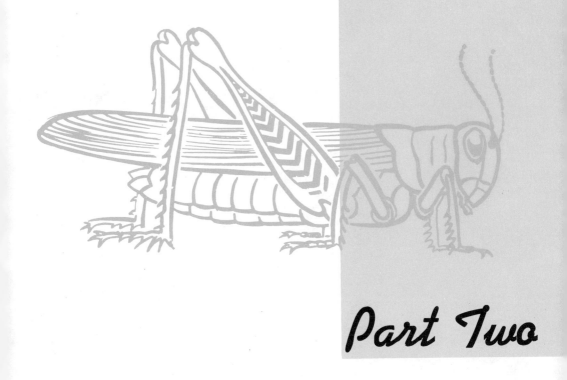

Part Two

Biology of Animal Life

UNIT III

Invertebrates—Animals without Backbones

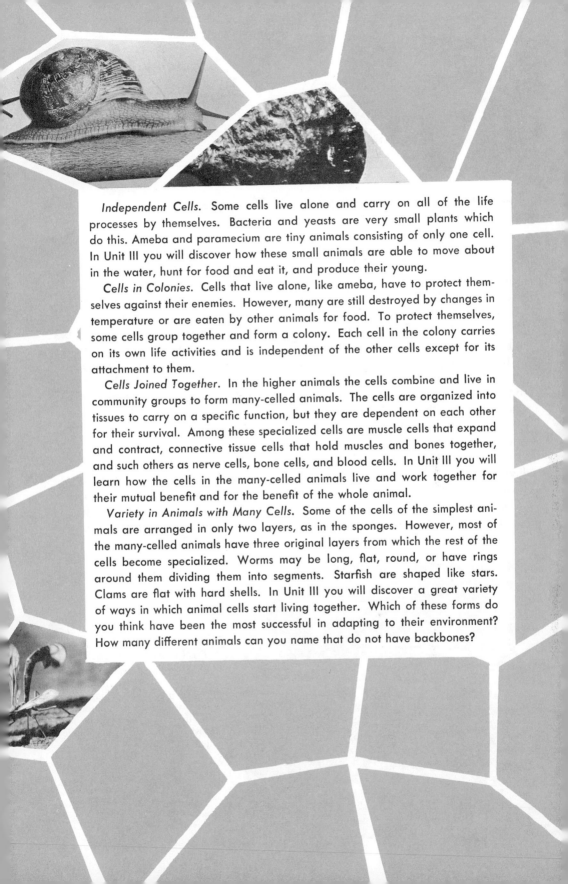

Independent Cells. Some cells live alone and carry on all of the life processes by themselves. Bacteria and yeasts are very small plants which do this. Ameba and paramecium are tiny animals consisting of only one cell. In Unit III you will discover how these small animals are able to move about in the water, hunt for food and eat it, and produce their young.

Cells in Colonies. Cells that live alone, like ameba, have to protect themselves against their enemies. However, many are still destroyed by changes in temperature or are eaten by other animals for food. To protect themselves, some cells group together and form a colony. Each cell in the colony carries on its own life activities and is independent of the other cells except for its attachment to them.

Cells Joined Together. In the higher animals the cells combine and live in community groups to form many-celled animals. The cells are organized into tissues to carry on a specific function, but they are dependent on each other for their survival. Among these specialized cells are muscle cells that expand and contract, connective tissue cells that hold muscles and bones together, and such others as nerve cells, bone cells, and blood cells. In Unit III you will learn how the cells in the many-celled animals live and work together for their mutual benefit and for the benefit of the whole animal.

Variety in Animals with Many Cells. Some of the cells of the simplest animals are arranged in only two layers, as in the sponges. However, most of the many-celled animals have three original layers from which the rest of the cells become specialized. Worms may be long, flat, round, or have rings around them dividing them into segments. Starfish are shaped like stars. Clams are flat with hard shells. In Unit III you will discover a great variety of ways in which animal cells start living together. Which of these forms do you think have been the most successful in adapting to their environment? How many different animals can you name that do not have backbones?

CHAPTER 6

The Simplest Animals Known

6.1 Biology of Animal Life

The living things which make up the animal kingdom vary in size from those of one cell to the many-celled animals. They are distinguished from each other by the characteristics which they possess and the structures which help them carry on the life processes. Some have backbones, some have shells, others have soft bodies. Some can fly, some swim, and others can do both.

The world of animals is so very large that man has divided them into large groups called **phyla** (*fy*-luh) [singular, **phylum** (*fy*-lum)], based on structure. Those with backbones, such as horses and cats, are placed in the phylum *Chordata* (kor-*day*-tuh), commonly known as the **vertebrate** (*ver*-tuh-brayt) group.

Animals without backbones, like snails and earthworms, are called **invertebrates** (in-*ver*-tuh-brayts), and are divided into several phyla. These include the tiny one-celled animals in the phylum *Protozoa* (proh-tuh-*zoh*-uh); the sponges belonging to the *Porifera* (poh-*riff*-er-uh); jellyfish, members of the *Coelenterata* (seh-len-ter-*ay*-tuh); and others which we shall study in later chapters.

6.2 Protozoa

This group of invertebrates represents the simplest animals known, yet they are able to perform all the functions necessary to life. Although they consist of only single cells, they have the ability to move, breathe, eat, and reproduce.

The Protozoa live in a moist habitat.

FIGURE 6-1. *LIFE IN A TIDEWATER POOL*

This salt water pool contains within it a variety of living things, both plant and animal. These organisms range in complexity from the many-celled crabs and starfish down to unseen, single-celled Protozoa.

American Museum of Natural History

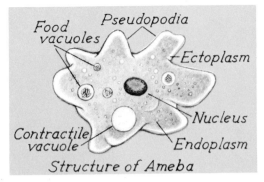

Food vacuoles
Pseudopodia
Ectoplasm
Nucleus
Contractile vacuole
Endoplasm

Structure of Ameba

FIGURE 6-2. *AMEBA*

A single-celled animal, the ameba has the same life processes as higher animals.

Some kinds live in the ocean, some in fresh or stagnant waters inland, and others in soil or decaying organic matter. Some are free-living and some are parasitic. Each individual consists of a single cell and can be seen only with the aid of a microscope. As you study these one-celled animals, compare them with the typical animal cell (Sec. 4.5).

6.3 Ameba, the Simplest Animal Known

The simplest animal of the Protozoa group is the *ameba* (uh-*mee*-buh). The living ameba (Fig. 6-2) has a faint grayish appearance when seen under the microscope. It has no definite shape, but is continually changing by pushing out from its surface blunt, fingerlike projections called **pseudopodia** (soo-doh-*poh*-dee-uh). These give an irregular outline to the body.

Near the center of the cell is a spherical mass of denser protoplasm, the *nucleus*. This governs the whole cell and is very important in the process of cell division.

The rest of the protoplasm is the *cytoplasm*. The thin and transparent outer layer of this, called **ectoplasm** (*ek*-toh-plazm), is just below the cell membrane and gives form to the cell body. The larger part of the cytoplasm is filled with numerous small granules and contains several *vacuoles* or tiny cavities. This inner mass of cytoplasm is called **endoplasm** (*en*-doh-plazm) and helps in locomotion.

The vacuoles in the endoplasm may contain food, water, or liquid waste products. The food and water vacuoles are temporary structures, but the vacuole which collects the liquid waste is always present. The functions of these vacuoles are described in the next section.

6.4 Life Processes of the Ameba

The ameba has the same life functions as the higher animals, but of course you must think of the process rather than the structure, for you must imagine a single cell as taking food, digesting, assimilating, excreting, respiring, and reproducing.

Motion.—When the ameba sends out a pseudopodium in any direction, the

FIGURE 6-3. *AMEBOID MOVEMENT*

The ameba moves about by sending out finger-like projections called pseudopodia, or false feet. The rest of the body then flows in the same direction. The ameba, therefore, has no definite shape. Compare the paramecium.

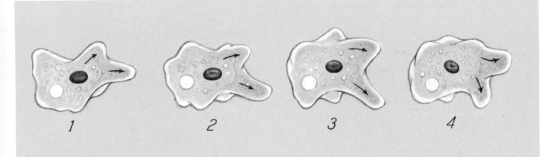

1   2   3   4

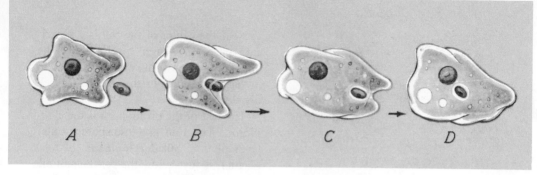

FIGURE 6-4. *AMEBA FEEDING*

The process by which the ameba extends its pseudopodia and surrounds a food particle can be seen in these successive drawings. Notice in drawing D that the food vacuole includes water as well as food.

rest of the body flows gradually, by a rolling movement, in the same direction. This creeping-rolling motion of the protoplasm enables the ameba to move.

Nutrition.—When the pseudopodium comes in contact with a minute plant or animal upon which the ameba feeds, the protoplasm of the pseudopodium surrounds the plant or animal and takes it into the cell. The microscopic food thus eaten by the ameba is inclosed, with a small amount of water, in a tiny globe called a **food vacuole.** The food vacuole is to be thought of as a stomach in which digestion can take place, for the plant or animal is digested in it. Digestion is accomplished by means of chemicals called *enzymes* (*en*-zymes). The nutritious parts are absorbed into the protoplasm and assimilated. The undigested parts are cast from the cell, and the food

vacuole disappears. Food vacuoles are not always round (Figs. 6-2 and 6-4), but take their shape from the form of the plant eaten.

Respiration.—From the air dissolved in the water, the ameba obtains by osmosis the oxygen necessary for oxidation to give it energy. The ameba also gives off carbon dioxide from the cell.

Excretion.—The term **contractile** (kun-*trak*-t'l) **vacuole** is given to a vacuole which is always present in the protoplasm of the ameba. It regulates the water content of the organism. This vacuole can be seen to expand slowly, then suddenly to contract. As it contracts, the fluid in it is forced to the outside of the body of the ameba. The expansion is caused by the collection of liquid wastes from the surrounding protoplasm. It is called a contractile vacu-

FIGURE 6-5. *AMEBA DIVIDING*

Drawings A, B, and C represent three stages in the reproduction of the ameba. What indications are there that cell A is ready to reproduce? What comparisons can be drawn between the cells in C and cell A?

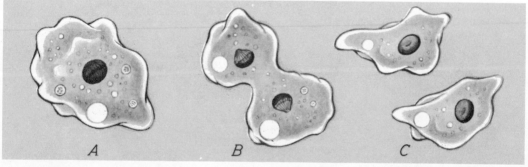

ole because it contracts and expands, but it is also called an *excretory vacuole* because it collects and expels liquid waste products.

Reproduction and Encystment.—The chief method of reproduction in the ameba is simple. The living cell divides into two equal parts by mitosis, forming two new cells (Fig. 6-5). This is an *asexual* method of reproduction known as **fission** (*fish*-un). It forms two new individuals from a single parent.

When the food or water becomes unsuited to supply the needs of the cell, some parasitic amebae, in order to live, secrete a thick wall completely surrounding the protoplasm. This process is termed **encystment** (en-*sist*-ment). After the wall has been formed, the ameba is able, for a long period, to withstand unfavorable conditions.

Irritability.—The ameba responds to the stimulus of *hunger* by moving toward food. When it touches it, the pseudopodium responds to the stimulus of *contact* and surrounds it. It moves away from bright *light* and *chemicals,* and speeds up its motion at *warm* temperatures within its range of life.

6.5 Paramecium

One of the most common forms of Protozoa is the slipper-shaped *paramecium* (pair-uh-*mee*-see-um), which is more active than the ameba. It is abundant in stagnant water and in the hay infusions prepared in the laboratory.

The paramecium, like the ameba, shows specialization of the parts of a single cell for different activities, such as the *contractile vacuoles* for maintaining water balance. The cell has also developed a **division of labor** to perform specific functions, such as the *cilia* (*sil*-ee-uh) for locomotion.

Structure of Paramecium.—The paramecium (Fig. 6-6), like the ameba, is a single cell. It has both a large nucleus, the **macronucleus** (mak-ruh-*noo*-klee-us), and one or two small ones, the **micronuclei** (my-kruh-*noo*-klee-eye.) The protoplasm composing the cell consists of *endoplasm* (inner portion), *ectoplasm* (outer portion), and a **pellicle** (*pel*-ih-k'l), a thickened membrane which surrounds the cell. Through the pellicle there extend great numbers of **cilia**, or threads of living cytoplasm. The ectoplasm contains many threadlike darts known as

FIGURE 6-6. *PARAMECIUM*

The ease with which this common protozoan can be grown in the laboratory and its comparatively large size make it a well-known organism to students of biology. Its highly distinctive shape makes the paramecium easy to locate under the microscope.

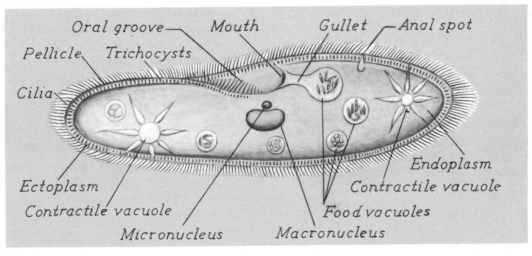

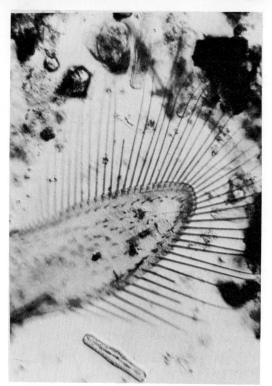

H. B. Gray

FIGURE 6-7. *DEFENSIVE ACTION*

This unusual photograph shows in detail a paramecium in the act of discharging trichocysts. For what other purpose besides defense are trichocysts used?

trichocysts (*trik*-oh-sists). These may be discharged when the paramecium is attacked or when it attacks smaller animals for food. Within the paramecium are found *food vacuoles* as in the ameba. There are two *contractile vacuoles,* one at either end of the paramecium, which open and close alternately.

6.6 Life Processes of Paramecium

The structures used in carrying on the life processes of the paramecium are not quite so simple as those of the ameba, but are much simpler than those of higher animals.

Locomotion and Defense.—The animal moves by means of the cilia, the direction depending upon the angle at which the cilia are held. Paramecia can move backward and forward, and can also rotate on the long axis. Paramecia defend themselves by discharging their trichocysts. This discharge occurs either as a result of strong artificial stimuli, such as electric currents or chemicals, or naturally because of collision with certain other Protozoa. If attacked by some animal which feeds upon them, they discharge the trichocysts in the region of the attack (Fig. 6-7).

Nutrition.—The paramecium feeds mostly on bacteria, Protozoa, algae, and yeast. These are collected by means of the cilia located on each side of the fold or depression called the **oral groove,** located near the *anterior* (front) end of the paramecium. Near the end of the oral groove is the **mouth,** which opens into the **gullet** (*gul*-it) (Fig. 6-6). The food thus collected passes into the food vacuoles. Digestion, then, is an intricate chemical process. The enzymes produced by the cytoplasm diffuse into the food vacuoles and change food materials to simpler forms.

Respiration.—Oxygen is obtained from the air in the water. It oxidizes food with the release of energy needed for cell activities.

Excretion.—Excess water is excreted

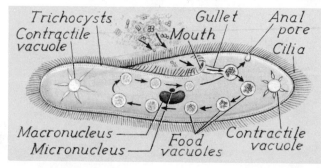

Trichocysts Gullet Anal
Contractile Mouth pore
vacuole Cilia
Macronucleus Food Contractile
Micronucleus vacuoles vacuole

FIGURE 6-8. *PARAMECIUM FEEDING*

By the action of the cilia lining the oral groove, food is swept into the mouth and gullet of the paramecium. Enzymes for digestion are found in the food vacuoles.

74

by the two contractile vacuoles and then cast from the body. Carbon dioxide gas escapes from the entire surface of the body. The indigestible parts of food are cast off from the body at the **anal spot**.

Irritability.—Paramecium responds in a definite manner to stimuli, such as contact, food, and enemies. It has no structure which can be compared to the nerve cells or brain of higher animals, but it has some special nervelike fibers called **neurofibrils** (noo-roh-*fy*-brils) which may help in the coordination of the cilia. The cilia are arranged in rows running lengthwise and need to work together if the paramecium is to move effectively.

In Protozoa generally, the ability to respond to stimuli seems to be a condition present in the whole protoplasm of the cell rather than belonging to any single structure.

Paramecium responds to *contact* by moving toward or away from the stimulus, depending on the kind of contact. It stays in *temperatures* between 24° C and 28° C, and responds negatively to *gravity,* keeping just below the surface film of the water. It swims against gentle *water currents,* and moves toward the *negative pole* of an electric current. Paramecium moves away from most *chemicals* except weak acids.

Reproduction.—Paramecia, like the ameba, reproduce asexually by *fission,* splitting crosswise. An animal divides, producing two; these divide producing four more. The process of fission goes on indefinitely (Fig. 6-9).

Both kinds of cell division (Sec. 5.2) are present for reproducing by fission. The *micronuclei* divide by *mitosis* in order that the daughter cells may have an even distribution of the chromatin. The *macronucleus* divides by *amitosis,* since an even division of the rest of the cell is less important.

Paramecia also reproduce by **conjugation** (kon-joo-*gay*-sh'n), a process of exchanging nuclear material (Fig. 6-9).

FIGURE 6-9. *FISSION AND CONJUGATION*

Fission in the paramecium is essentially the same as in the ameba, except that the paramecium has two nuclei, the micronucleus and macronucleus. The process of conjugation, in which two paramecia exchange nuclear material, rejuvenates the organisms so that they can reproduce by fission.

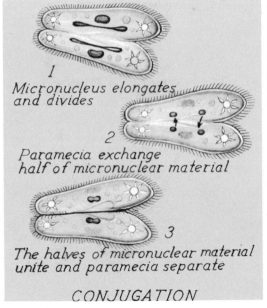

1
Micronucleus elongates and divides

2
Paramecia exchange half of micronuclear material

3
The halves of micronuclear material unite and paramecia separate

CONJUGATION

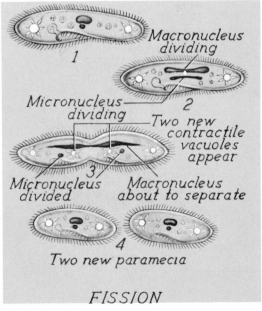

1
Macronucleus dividing

Micronucleus dividing

2
Two new contractile vacuoles appear

3
Micronucleus divided

Macronucleus about to separate

4
Two new paramecia

FISSION

No new paramecia are formed by this process of conjugation, but it does result in **rejuvenation**—a renewing of strength—of the cells since it provides for hereditary transfer. This means that the vitality of the paramecia is increased so that they are able to continue reproduction by fission. This conjugation by paramecia may be the beginning of *sexual* reproduction in animals.

6.7 Euglena, a Plantlike Animal

Most of the Protozoa move by one of three methods: (1) by *pseudopodia,* as the ameba, (2) by *cilia,* as the paramecium, and (3) by *flagella,* as the *euglena* (yoo-*glee*-nuh). A **flagellum** (fluh-*jel*-um) is a long, flexible, whiplike lash located at the front, or anterior, end. It moves in definite strokes, much as you move the oar in sculling a boat.

The euglena is especially interesting to scientists because it has characteristics of both plants and animals. Euglena appears to be an intermediate form. It can make its own food and can also move about. Perhaps animals were derived from plantlike forms.

The euglena (Fig. 6-10) has a definite shape and is covered by a pellicle. It is long and cylindrical, somewhat resembling the paramecium. The body, however, is very flexible, and when seen under the microscope, the euglena often looks like a ball.

Nutrition.—Near the front end by the flagellum is a *mouth,* leading to a *gullet* and an enlarged **reservoir.** However, the euglena seldom needs to use its mouth because it makes its own food. The euglena does this by means of green *chloroplasts,* scattered throughout its body. The starch which the euglena manufactures is stored in tiny bodies in the chloroplast called **pyrenoids** (*py*-reh-noyds). The euglena has a bright red **eyespot** which is sensitive to light and may help the animal to find the areas of diffused light which it needs.

Euglena can also absorb food materials dissolved in the water where it lives. This helps it to survive in weak light when it cannot make its own food.

Excretion and Reproduction.—Several *contractile vacuoles* excrete liquid wastes into the reservoir, which is con-

FIGURE 6-10. *EUGLENA: STRUCTURE AND REPRODUCTION*

Although the structure of the euglena (*left*) is much like that of the paramecium, it resembles a plant in being able to manufacture its own food. Reproduction in the euglena (*right*) is by means of lengthwise fission, and takes place in either the active or the encysted state.

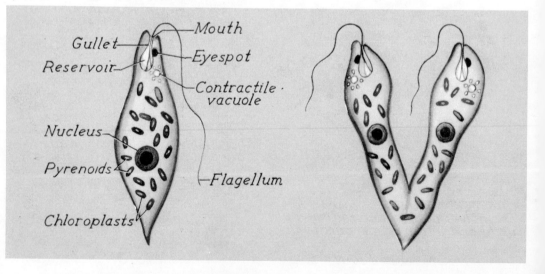

nected to the mouth by the gullet. Near the center of the cell is the *nucleus,* which is concerned chiefly with reproduction. This is by *fission,* for the euglena splits lengthwise by mitosis, one half receiving the old flagellum and the other half growing a new one (Fig. 6-10). When unfavorable conditions occur, euglena protects itself by secreting around itself a kind of envelope, and it loses its flagellum. The euglena plus this envelope is called a **cyst** (*sist*). When conditions become favorable, a young euglena emerges from the cyst.

From your study of the euglena you will note that it has green chloroplasts for food-making like a plant, and yet can move like an animal. What other characteristics of both plant and animal have you discovered? How would *you* classify the euglena?

6.8 Colonial Protozoa

Most of the Protozoa are single-celled animals and live independently. A few forms live together in colonies for added protection. Usually each cell is quite independent, as in gonium. Sometimes they specialize in certain work, as is seen in volvox. Gonium and volvox show both plant and animal characteristics.

6.9 Gonium

Gonium (Fig. 6-11) is an organism made up of sixteen separate cells held together by a mucilage-like secretion of the cells. Each cell works independently in getting food, respiring, giving off waste, and reproducing. The colony moves by lashing the water with long protoplasmic threads (flagella), two of which project from each cell. The advantage in rate of movement resulting from the union of cells is illustrated in rowing. Eight men in a large rowing shell can go faster than one man in a single, small shell. In reproduction, the

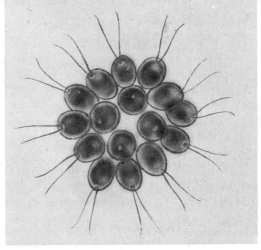

Photo by Hugh Spencer

FIGURE 6-11. *GONIUM*
 The sixteen individual cells of the gonium live together in a colony.

sixteen cells fall apart, and each one grows into a new colony.

6.10 Volvox

Volvox (Fig. 6-12) is a colony of hundreds of tiny green cells embedded in a hollow gelatinous sphere. Each cell has

FIGURE 6-12. *VOLVOX COLONIES*
 These globular mother colonies of volvox show clearly that they contain one or more developing daughter colonies.

General Biological Supply House

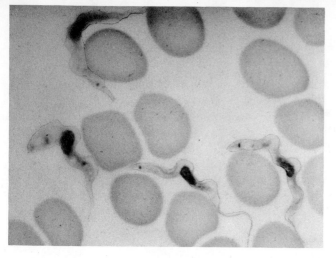

FIGURE 6-13. *PARASITES*

Large areas of Africa are made useless by the ribbon-like sporozoans in this photomicrograph. These parasites cause sleeping sickness and infect men and animals through the bite of the tsetse fly.

General Biological Supply House

two flagella, a nucleus, contractile vacuole, red eyespot, and green chloroplasts. For a time all the cells are alike and share equally in the work of the colony. But in reproduction only a few cells take part. In the simplest method of reproduction, a few cells grow larger and break away from the colony into the outer part of the hollow sphere. There, they divide and grow into new colonies. Finally, the mother colony breaks up, and the daughter colonies escape.

The more complex method is like the *sexual* reproduction of higher animals. Certain cells in the colony grow large and escape into the hollow part of the sphere. They are the **egg cells.** Other cells of the colony enlarge and divide into large numbers of slender, free-swimming cells called **sperm cells.** The sperm cells also escape into the hollow sphere and swim about. One sperm enters an egg cell and unites with it, forming a single cell, the **fertilized egg cell,** which can develop a new colony. This fertilized egg is called a **zygote** (*zy*-goht), and secretes a *cyst* to protect itself until it starts a new colony.

6.11 Parasitic Protozoa

Another group of Protozoa called **Sporozoa** (spor-oh-*zoh*-uh) have no organs of locomotion or contractile vacuoles. They are practically all *parasites* (Sec. 3.10). Some move by changing the shape of the cell body, food is absorbed directly from the host, and they reproduce by fission. These parasites are responsible for many serious diseases, such as malaria in humans, fevers in cattle, and rabbit and silkworm diseases. Some of these diseases will be discussed in later chapters.

6.12 Economic Importance of Protozoa

Since Protozoa are very tiny, they furnish food for snails, fish, and other small animals living in the water.

Protozoa are also helpful because they eat large numbers of bacteria which might become harmful to man. Some aid in the purification of filter and sewage beds.

Some tiny amebae have shells made of lime or stones fastened together. The chalk cliffs of Dover, England, were built up by the accumulation of millions of shells of tiny amebae.

Other Protozoa are harmful to man because they cause diseases such as pyorrhea, in which the gums soften and the teeth loosen, and dysentery, a disease of the intestinal tract.

FIGURE 6-14. *CLIFFS OF SKELETONS*

These famous cliffs in Dover owe their existence to the limy skeletons of certain amebae. Chalk, a soft form of limestone, is used in making putty, paints, and toothpowder.

6.13 The Sponges—Two-Layered Animals with Pores

Sponges [phylum **Porifera** (poh-*riff*-er-uh)] have their cells arranged in two layers. The cells in the outside layer are flattened for protection and support. These outside cells also form the openings, or **pores,** through which water is continually being forced in and out of the sponge.

Nutrition and Respiration.—Each cell of the inner layer has on its free end a whip called a *flagellum,* around the base of which is a collar with a mouth inside. These are the **collar cells** (Fig. 6-15) which take tiny plants and animals from the water for food. The tiny hairlike parts of these cells drive water in and out of the pores. This brings in food and oxygen and carries away the waste products.

Between the two layers of cells there is a jellylike substance, which has wandering cells capable of surrounding par-

FIGURE 6-15. *LIME SPONGE*

Unlike most of the sponges, this form of the limy sponge exhibits a definite shape. The spicules of lime that give support to the animal are usually in the form of rods or three pronged stars and are found distributed through the outer layer of cells.

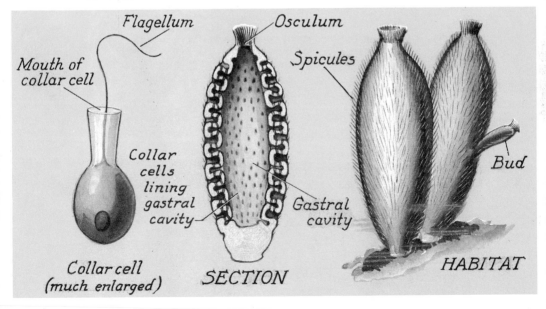

Flagellum — Osculum — Spicules

Mouth of collar cell

Collar cells lining gastral cavity

Gastral cavity

Bud

Collar cell (much enlarged)

SECTION

HABITAT

ticles and distributing them. This jelly-like substance also contains some reproductive cells and supporting spicules.

A sponge has an excurrent pore, the **osculum** (*oss*-kyoo-lum), which leads into a **gastral cavity,** and is the place where the excess water taken in through the incurrent pores flows out (Fig. 6-15).

Kinds of Sponges.—There are *three* groups of sponges, according to the kind of material they use in building the framework which supports them. **Lime sponges** have little *spicules* (*spik*-yools) (spikes) of *lime* which make them brittle. **Glass sponges** use *silica* from sand to form beautiful patterns, while the common **bath sponge** uses a much softer material containing sulphur called **spongin** for support.

Reproduction.—Sponges are found off the coast of Florida and in the Mediterranean Sea. It is little wonder that they are numerous, for they have several ways of reproduction, both sexual and asexual. When a small piece is broken off, it can grow into a new sponge asexually by **regeneration.** Sometimes a *bud* will grow at the side of the sponge and form

a new individual. Often it remains attached, resembling the branch of a tree. This is **budding,** another kind of asexual reproduction, having only one parent.

Fresh-water sponges and some others form internal buds, or **gemmules** (*jem*-yools), which is also asexual reproduction. These have protective walls which can resist the cold of the water in winter and thus can start a new generation in the spring.

Sponges have no sex organs, but they do have special cells which produce eggs and sperm. The egg cells remain in the connective layer until fertilized by the sperm cells from other sponges. These develop into tiny **larvae** (*lahr*-vee) which can move around by means of flagella. They swim near the surface of the water and continue to grow for a time. Then they drop to the bottom where they remain attached.

Symbiosis.—Sponges may look green in color owing to the presence of tiny green plants called *algae* (*al*-jee) which live within the body walls of the animals. These algae give off oxygen which the sponges use. The algae also make use

FIGURE 6-16. *DESIGN IN NATURE*

Utility and beauty briefly describe these two types of sponges. The bath sponge (*left*) is gathered commercially and has many uses. The fanciful glass sponge (*right*) is known as "Venus's flower basket."

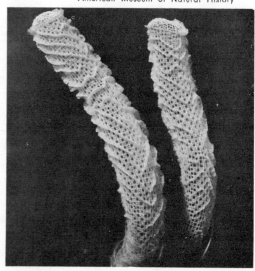

of the carbon dioxide given off by the sponges. This kind of relationship, in which two organisms help each other live, is called *symbiosis*. (Sec. 3.10).

6.14 Economic Importance of Sponges

The skeletons of bath sponges are used for washing and mopping. They are brought up by divers, by dredging, and by trawling with hooks. At the surface they are bleached, sorted, and marketed.

Some sponges grow on mollusk shells, boring into the shells and destroying the animals. Thus sponges may become destructive to oyster beds.

6.15 The Coelenterates—Two-Layered Animals with Tentacles

Jellyfish, corals, and *hydras* belong to this group, the **Coelenterata** (seh-len-ter-*ay*-tuh). They are the lowest form of animals with cells organized into definite tissues. These individuals may live singly or in colonies. They are of two types: (1) the tubular body type, called a **polyp** (*pol*-ip), with one end closed and the other having a mouth surrounded by several flexible tentacles; and (2) the umbrella type, called a **medusa** (meh-*doo*-suh), with **tentacles** (*ten*-tuh-k'ls) around the edge and the *mouth* on the underside. Each coelenterate has a *gastral cavity* and tiny stinging capsules called **nematocysts** (neh-*mat*-uh-sists).

6.16 Hydra, a Fresh-Water Form

Although most Coelenterata live in the ocean, the *hydra* (*hy*-druh) is found in fresh water (Fig. 6-17). It is about a quarter of an inch long and by close observation can be seen without a lens. Its body is long and slender, like a bag with a mouth at one end. Like the sponges, the hydra may look green because it lives in symbiosis with green algae. The hydra has six to ten hollow *tentacles* provided with stinging cells, the *nematocysts*. These are used to paralyze smaller animals so that it can eat them.

The outer layer of cells composing

FIGURE 6-17. *HYDRA*

The hydra, a fresh-water coelenterate, has a long, slender body with six to ten tentacles. The stinging cells, or nematocysts, are used to paralyze small animals for food. Three hydras in their habitat are shown at right.

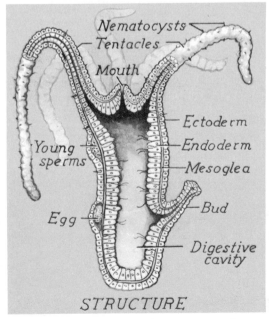

STRUCTURE

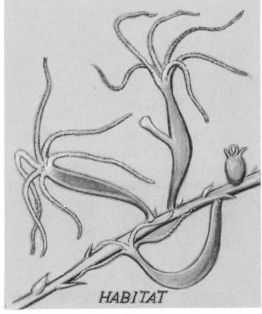

HABITAT

81

the body of the hydra is called the **ecto-derm** (*ek*-toh-derm). Some of these cells are sensitive to stimuli and help protect the animal. Others act like muscle cells, enabling the hydra to move.

The inner layer of cells is called the **endoderm** (*en*-doh-derm). These cells are adapted for digesting the food. Some of them reach out and surround food particles, some have whiplike structures to push the food along, and others secrete digestive juices.

There is also a non-cellular layer, the **mesoglea** (mes-oh-*glee*-uh), which lies between the ectoderm and endoderm and seems to help them work together.

Locomotion.—The adult hydra is usually found attached as shown in Figure 6-17. In this condition the only movements possible are such as take place in the expansion and contraction of the whole body. The tentacles wave in the water, and as the hydra expands, the body may move first in one direction, then in another. At infrequent intervals, however, the hydra detaches itself and moves from place to place by attaching the tentacles, then the base, then the tentacles, much like a boy turning handsprings or as a measuring worm moves.

Nutrition.—The hydra feeds mostly on insect larvae and other small animals, which are rendered inactive by the stinging cells, or darts, discharged from its tentacles. The paralyzed animal is then brought to the mouth by the tentacles (Fig. 6-17) and taken into the body, where the nutritive parts are digested by enzymes, as in other animals, and then absorbed. The indigestible skeleton of the animal eaten is cast out through the mouth.

Respiration and Excretion.—Oxygen is absorbed from the water by the cells of the ectoderm. The water that enters the mouth carries oxygen which is absorbed by the cells of the endoderm. At the same time the carbon dioxide from the cells is thrown off into the water.

Irritability.—The hydra is able to respond to a number of different kinds of stimuli, such as jars, a moving animal, or an enemy. It is able to contract, expand, and move the tentacles so as to bring food to the mouth, although it has no brain. When a special study of the structure of the hydra is made, a **nerve net** is found which assists it in responding to stimuli and in correlating its movements.

Reproduction.—The hydra reproduces both *sexually* and *asexually*. In sexual reproduction usually one individual has either **ovaries** (*oh*-vuh-reez), which produce egg cells, or **testes** (*tess*-teez), which develop sperm cells. These are temporary structures which form on the ectoderm during the fall. The sperm cells escape into the water and, like sperm cells of all other animals, they have the power of locomotion. The fusion of an egg cell and a sperm cell starts growth, which results in the division of the egg cell into many other cells.

FIGURE 6-18. *LOCOMOTION IN THE HYDRA*

The hydra moves not only by waving its tentacles in the water, but also by attaching its base and tentacles, in turn, as shown in these drawings.

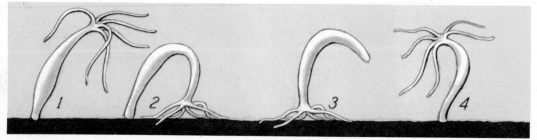

Hydras also reproduce asexually by *budding* (Sec. 6.13), a process in which a new individual is formed as an outgrowth of the old one (Fig. 6-17). The buds soon separate from the parent and begin an independent life.

Regeneration.—Like many other forms of lower animals, the hydra has the power of regeneration. This means that if a hydra is cut into pieces, a new hydra will develop from each of the individual pieces.

6.17 Jellyfish

The clear, soft, transparent, cup-shaped bodies of the jellyfish give a strange appearance as they float in the water. The *mouth* is on the underside and is usually surrounded by four *tentacles*. The jellyfish is a poor swimmer and is able to move only by waving its body and contracting its tentacles. These have *stinging cells* which irritate the skin

FIGURE 6-19. *JELLYFISH*
This jellyfish is in the adult stage and is therefore free to swim about. The tentacles help in getting food.

of bathers and form a rash. Whales and fish eat jellyfish but receive little food

FIGURE 6-20. *CORAL*
Seeming to engage the coral growth in conversation, this underwater biologist stands before the heavy arms of the elkhorn coral. The fernlike growths in the foreground are another form of coral.

Ed Fisher

83

value from them since jellyfish contain a very high percentage of water.

Adult jellyfish lay eggs which hatch into tiny jellyfish (*polyps*) resembling the hydra. They remain attached to some object for a time, eating and growing to be a half inch in length. Then they break into separate cups, forming the adult jellyfish.

6.18 Corals

These tiny animals grow in large groups or colonies, where they remain during adult life. They secrete coatings of *lime* over the outside of their bodies, and when they die these skeletons remain. Corals reproduce asexually by buds and also sexually. The young are free-swimming, but soon become attached to some object.

Sometimes other sea animals make their homes in the crevices between the coral animals. As more and more skeletons of these corals accumulate, they sometimes form fringing reefs or barrier reefs which are separated from shore by a wide, deep channel. When such a barrier reef is circular in form, it is called an **atoll** (*at*-ol). Sometimes coral islands are formed. Bermuda, the Bahamas, and the Fiji Islands are partly made of coral. Some corals are used as ornaments and for the manufacture of jewelry. Corals are also a good source of food for fishes.

FACTS TO REMEMBER

Animals are divided into large groups called *phyla*. The term *invertebrates* refers to groups of animals which do not have backbones.

The simplest animals known are one-celled and are placed in the phylum *Protozoa*. This group includes the *ameba,* with no specialized parts; the *paramecium,* with structures specialized for different functions; and the *euglena,* with chloroplasts, which makes it resemble both plants and animals. Colonial Protozoa such as *gonium* and *volvox* illustrate the simplest methods of cells living together. Volvox has two methods of reproduction, *asexual* by fission (cell division without sex cells) and *sexual* (reproduction with sex cells).

The *Porifera,* sponges, have two layers of cells with pores. Their skeletons are made of lime, silica, or spongin. Sponges reproduce sexually and asexually. They are able to regenerate themselves.

The *Coelenterata* are two-layered animals with *tentacles* bearing stinging cells called *nematocysts.* This phylum includes hydra, jellyfish, and corals.

The study of the simplest animals helps to explain how individual body cells are able to carry on the life processes, and how groups of body cells (tissues) can live together and become specialized for different functions.

WORDS TO REMEMBER

algae	budding	conjugation
asexual reproduction	cilia	contractile vacuole
atoll	collar cells	cyst

division of labor	invertebrate	pseudopodia
ectoderm	larvae	pyrenoid
ectoplasm	macronucleus	regeneration
egg cell	medusa	rejuvenation
encystment	mesoglea	reservoir
endoderm	micronucleus	sexual reproduction
endoplasm	nematocyst	sperm cell
eyespot	neurofibrils	spicule
fertilized egg cell	oral groove	spongin
fission	osculum	tentacle
flagellum	ovary	testes
food vacuole	pellicle	trichocysts
gastral cavity	phylum	vertebrates
gemmule	polyp	zygote
gullet	pore	

QUESTIONS

1. Compare the ameba and the paramecium as to methods of food-getting.

2. How does the euglena get its food?

3. Explain how the Protozoa perform each of the following functions:

     a. excretion   d. protection
     b. respiration   e. reproduction
     c. locomotion

4. Describe a colonial protozoan.

5. Mention *three* ways that the Protozoa are helpful to man and one way they are harmful.

6. How does an adult sponge obtain food?

7. What is the purpose of the osculum?

8. What is meant by regeneration? Name some animals that possess this power.

9. How do fresh-water sponges reproduce?

10. Define symbiosis. Give an example.

11. Name and describe the two layers of cells in the hydra.

12. How does the hydra get its food?

13. Describe two methods of reproduction in the hydra.

14. What characteristics do jellyfish possess that place them in the same group as the hydra?

COMPLETION TEST

As your teacher or classmate reads the following incomplete statements, with your book closed, write on a clean sheet of paper the word or phrase which correctly completes the statement.

1. Paramecium has _____ for protection.

2. The chalk cliffs of Dover were formed by ____.
3. A protozoan which contains chloroplasts is ____.
4. The eyespot of the euglena is sensitive to ____.
5. The arms of the hydra are called ____.
6. Stinging cells on these arms are called ____.
7. Sponges have little holes called ____.
8. When coral forms a circular reef, it is called an ____.
9. Bermuda Island was formed by ____.
10. Jellyfish possess ____ which may irritate the skin of bathers.

PROJECTS

I. *Study of Living Protozoa.*—You may bring in some pond water, take water from the aquaria, or make a hay infusion. To make the latter, place a handful of hay or some leaves in a jar and cover with ordinary water used in the laboratory. After a week or two, place some water on a slide with a cover glass and observe under the microscope.

1. Draw sketches of any forms which you see. Be accurate, and with the help of your teacher you may be able to find the names of the Protozoa. Record the date each time.

2. Study your culture every school day for the next two weeks and as long as you are interested. Add to your record. You may find paramecia and euglena among others. Remember that there are a great many different kinds of Protozoa. Try to find one dividing. Can you tell whether a form has flagella or cilia by the way it swims?

II. How are commercial sponges obtained? Write the complete story of sponges. Be accurate in your account.

III. *The Study of a Living Hydra.*—Bring into the laboratory some pond water containing pieces of the plants that grow under such water. Place the material in an aquarium or in some small jars.

If hydra are present, they can be seen stretching out along the glass. A gentle tap on the glass will cause them to contract to tiny balls.

1. Place a piece of a leaf in some water on a slide and observe under the low power of the microscope. It is better not to use a cover glass.

2. Watch one hydra and observe the following:
   (a) The tentacles or long arms and the mouth.
   (b) The base by which it attaches itself.
   (c) How it moves.
   (d) Whether it has any buds.
   (e) Rounded bunches on the sides which might contain eggs or sperms.
   (f) How it paralyzes smaller animals.

3. Record your observations and sketch what you see.

IV. Find out all you can about the Portuguese man-of-war. What are its closest relatives? Write a good report for the class or draw some pictures for the bulletin board.

V. The sea anemone and the hermit crab live together for mutual aid by symbiosis. Find out how they help each other.

VI. If you live near the ocean you may wish to make a more careful study of some marine life. Collect some jellyfish or sea anemone. Place them in a container of sea water and observe carefully. Study some preserved specimens also. With the aid of reference books, locate the principal structures. From your observations and references, describe how they carry on each of the life processes. Explain why they are placed in the same group as the hydra.

REFERENCES

Allen, *Microbes Which Help or Destroy Us.* Mosby.

Allen, *The Story of Microbes.* Swift.

Bayne, Jones, and Stanhope, *Man and Microbes.* Williams and Wilkins.

De Kruif, *Microbe Hunters.* Harcourt, Brace.

Disraeli, *Seeing the Unseen.* Day.

Gooch, *The Strange World of Nature.* Crowell.

Hegner, *Big Fleas Have Little Fleas, or Who's Who Among the Protozoa.* Macmillan.

Hegner, *Parade of the Animal Kingdom.* Macmillan.

Morgan, *Fieldbook of Ponds and Streams.* Putnam's.

Rahn, *Microbes of Merit.* Ronald Press.

Stokes, *Aquatic Microscope.* Appleton.

Tressler, *The Wealth of the Sea.* Century.

Walter and McBee, *General Microbiology.* Van Nostrand.

Ward and Whipple, *Fresh-Water Biology.* Wiley

Watson and Baker, *The World Beneath the Microscope.* Studio Publications.

Wieman, *General Zoology.* McGraw-Hill.

Yates, *Exploring with the Microscope.* Appleton.

CHAPTER 7

Animals with Varied Forms

7.1 Animals with Three Layers of Cells

The simplest animals, the Protozoa, described in the preceding chapter, are unable to perform the complicated tasks of the higher animals. Among the Protozoa, single cells have to perform many life functions and are unprotected to a large extent. However, colonial Protozoa, such as gonium and volvox, represent some early banding together of cells for protection and specialization.

The sponges (Porifera) and the hydra (Coelenterata) are composed of two layers of cells, each layer performing one or more specific life functions. This arrangement of cells in layers enables the animal to do more difficult things.

The next higher groups of animals have their cells arranged in three layers or in structures developed from three layers. Each layer has a particular function. The animal groups described in this chapter have their cells arranged to form many different kinds of structures.

7.2 Flatworms

This group of invertebrates belongs to the phylum *Platyhelminthes* (plat-ee-hel-*min*-theez). It includes a few inconspicuous forms occurring in fresh-water ponds and streams, and a considerable number that live as parasites within the bodies of many animals, including man. These parasites include the tapeworms and liver flukes.

Flatworms have an *anterior* (front) end or head with sense organs, and a *posterior* (rear) end or tail. The undersurface is called the *ventral* surface, and the upper surface is the *dorsal* one. Flatworms are *bilaterally symmetrical,* having their parts arranged in similar patterns on either side of a center line

FIGURE 7-1. *THE CHINESE LIVER FLUKE*

These parasitic flatworms pass their lives in the bodies of several hosts. Hatching from eggs, they begin their development in snails, but transfer to new hosts, either human beings or animals, to grow to maturity.

General Biological Supply House

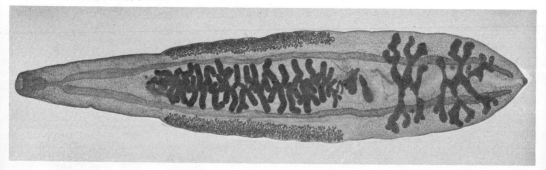

running the length of their body. Most of the higher animals are so arranged.

The common *planarian worm* (Fig. 7-2) is a flat, wormlike creature about an inch long that feeds on living or decayed organic matter and may well be termed a **scavenger**. Its *head* contains two *eyespots* and a small nerve center which acts as a *brain*. Its *mouth* is at the end of a long tube that sometimes protrudes on the ventral side of the body. There are no organs for circulation, and respiration takes place only by diffusion. Its *digestive tube* branches and carries food to all parts of its body. Undigested food is removed from the only opening, the mouth. The *nervous system* includes two ventral longitudinal nerve cords and several transverse nerves connecting them. The *muscles* are arranged in layers, making it easier to move. *Cilia* on the ventral surface also help the planaria in locomotion. The *excretory system* has two ducts and many tubules, each ending in a *flame cell* where wastes are excreted.

The free-living planaria is one of the simplest members of this group and has

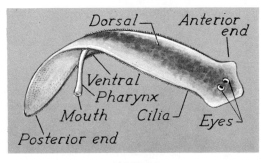

FIGURE 7-2. *PLANARIA*

The planarian worm, moves by means of cilia. The mouth projects from the body at the end of a long tube.

remarkable powers of *regeneration*. It reproduces asexually by pulling apart crosswise. It also reproduces sexually, both sexes being in the same individual.

Another member of this group is the *tapeworm* (Fig. 7-3), with the body divided into **segments**. Some tapeworms have bodies several feet long. There are *suckers* and *hooks* on their heads, which are used to cling to the walls of intestines. Tapeworms have no mouth or digestive system, but absorb their needed amount of food because, as parasites, they are constantly bathed in it in the intestine of some other animal.

The body of the tapeworm consists of

FIGURE 7-3. *TAPEWORM*

This sectional photograph shows areas of the tapeworm's body increasing in maturity from left to right. The crown on the head of the tapeworm contains the hooks that allow it to cling to the sides of the intestine. Notice the immature segments directly behind the head. These new segments will increase in size until they reach the end of the worm and drop off.

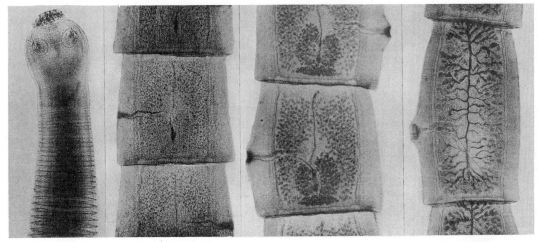

a chain of segment-like parts that are adapted for purposes of *reproduction*. The number of these segments may be two hundred or more. The segments at the free end of the body become mature, drop off, and pass out of the body of the host, ready to develop into more tapeworms. A single adult tapeworm may produce millions of eggs. Each of these eggs, which has already begun to develop before being discharged, is surrounded by a tough sac.

The young *embryo* (*em*-bree-oh) is unable to develop further unless eaten by another animal. It cannot search for the animal necessary for its further growth; so, unless accidentally eaten, it dies. When it enters the intestinal tract of a second animal, the tough sac is dissolved or digested and the worm begins to migrate into the tissues, where it passes through more changes in growth. It remains small and unlike the parent until eaten by an animal like the one from which the eggs escaped. After this happens, it becomes a mature tapeworm. When beef or pork that has been in-

fected is not thoroughly cooked, the tapeworm *cysts* are released in the intestines of man and live there until medical aid is sought. Since tapeworms take their nourishment from the body, they are said to be *parasitic*.

7.3 Roundworms

The phylum which includes the round-worms is known as **Nemathelminthes** (neh-muh-thel-*min*-theez). Their slender bodies are encased in a thin covering called a **cuticle** (*kyoo*-tih-k'l). They have a *complete* digestive tract, with a mouth at the anterior end and an opening at the posterior end called the **anus** (*ay*-nus), which is an advance in the development of animal forms.

Roundworms (Fig. 7-4) are as small and inconspicuous as flatworms, but much more numerous. One of the smallest is found in vinegar, the "vinegar eel." Most roundworms live in the soil, the water, or as parasites in the bodies of plants and animals. These are the animals that legend says come from placing a horsehair in water. Figure 7-4 shows

FIGURE 7-4. *THREE ROUNDWORMS*

Human beings are parasitized by at least 45 species of roundworm, one of which is the trichina (*right*), which encysts, or surrounds itself with a sac, within the muscular tissue of its host.

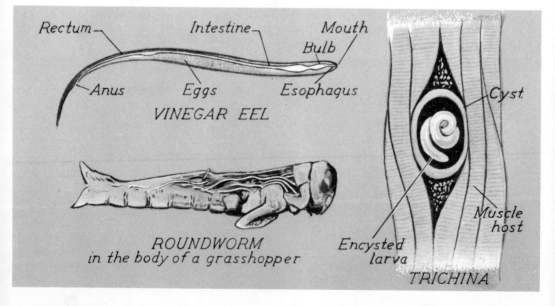

Rectum — Intestine — Mouth
Bulb
Anus — Eggs — Esophagus
VINEGAR EEL

Cyst

ROUNDWORM
in the body of a grasshopper

Encysted
larva

Muscle
host

TRICHINA

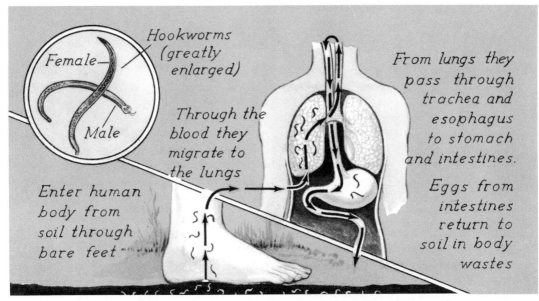

Female— Hookworms (greatly enlarged)

Male

Through the blood they migrate to the lungs

Enter human body from soil through bare feet

From lungs they pass through trachea and esophagus to stomach and intestines.

Eggs from intestines return to soil in body wastes

FIGURE 7-5. *LIFE CYCLE OF THE HOOKWORM*

Within the human body, the hookworm attaches itself to the wall of the small intestine by its hook-like teeth (inset), and sucks the blood of the host. Eggs are produced, which pass out with body wastes.

one of these worms in the body of a grasshopper, where it lives as a parasite during one of the stages in its regular life history. After it matures, it makes its way out of the body of the grasshopper into a stream, and the superstitious believe that a horsehair has become alive.

Another roundworm, *trichina* (trih-*ky*-nuh) (Fig. 7-4), lives in the intestines of mammals and from these migrates into the lymph spaces and travels in the blood to the muscles. Here, like the tapeworm, it becomes *encysted* and remains until the flesh is eaten by some other mammal. When pork, infected with this worm, is insufficiently cooked and eaten by man, the cysts are dissolved by the digestive enzymes and the worms are freed.

The worms then develop eggs and sperms which, after uniting, mature into young worms and migrate through the intestinal wall into the muscles. The activity of the worms at this stage causes a serious inflammation of the muscles of

man, resulting in the disease *trichinosis* (trik-ih-*noh*-siss).

The *hookworm* (Fig. 7-5) is another one of the roundworms. It causes the hookworm disease which occurs chiefly in a region extending about thirty-three degrees on each side of the Equator.

These areas are infested with eggs from which the young worms hatch. They bore through the skin, usually at the feet, and travel in the blood to the lungs. They enter the air sacs and move into the windpipe. When an infected person clears his throat or coughs slightly, he swallows. This allows the worms to travel down to the intestines where they remain until they mature and produce more eggs. The disease can be checked by certain medicines and by encouraging people to use sanitary toilets and to wear shoes.

7.4   Echinodermata   (eh-ky-noh-der-mah-tuh)

In this group are *starfish, brittle stars,*

STARFISH

SAND
DOLLAR

SEA
CUCUMBER

SEA
URCHIN

FIGURE 7-6. *REPRESENTATIVE ECHINODERMS*

Protecting the bodies of these sea dwellers are hard, bony plates composed
of calcium. The sea cucumber's plates are embedded in the outer memorane.

sea urchins, sea cucumbers, and *sea lilies.* They live only in the ocean. They
are quite different from other animals in
the arrangement of their organs, and in
the possession of some that are not found
elsewhere. Echinoderms are characterized by a starlike radial arrangement of
the body called **radial symmetry,** in
which the arms protrude from the center
as spokes of a wheel. The sponges and
hydra also have radial symmetry. Starfish have **tube feet** which are a part of a
water-vascular system. They are connected to canals which lead through each
ray to a central ring canal opening on
the dorsal side. When the starfish presses
the tube feet against a surface, water is
forced out and creates suction. Starfish
have a simple digestive tract, radial nervous system, a circulatory system, and
gills. They lay many eggs.

Starfish crawl for the most part at
night. An *eyespot* at the end of each
arm is sensitive to light. The rough spiny
projections which cover the body serve
as protection. Starfish are very destructive to oysters and clams. By means of
its tube feet, the starfish exerts a pull
which tires the muscles of the *bivalves,*
as oysters and clams are called, until
they relax and the shell opens. Then the
starfish turns its thin, almost transparent
stomach inside out and digests the fleshy
part of the bivalve outside its own body.

An interesting characteristic of the
starfish is its power of *regeneration,* that
is, its ability to grow new arms. Often
fishermen have broken the starfish over
the edge of the boat and thrown the
broken parts back into the water. Instead of killing the starfish, this has made
it possible for two or more to develop.

7.5 Mollusks

Clams, oysters, and *snails* are the most
familiar mollusks, and are all members
of the phylum **Mollusca** (moh-*luss*-kuh).
They have soft, unsegmented bodies protected by shells which are never shed,
but are added to, layer upon layer, as
the animal grows. These exoskeletons
in clams consist of two *valves.* For this
reason clams and oysters are called **bivalves.** Locomotion is by a wedge-
shaped muscular organ called a **foot.**
When the clam moves naturally, the
hinge between the valves allows the foot
to be extended into the mud. Thus it is
able to move slowly at an even rate.

Clams (Fig. 7-7) have two **siphons**
(*sy*-funs) at one end: the *ventral siphon*
draws in water, with food and oxygen;
the *dorsal siphon* forces out water and
waste products. The clam has **gills** for
breathing and **kidneys** for excretion.
The *digestive system* includes a stomach
and a large digestive gland, the liver.
The *circulatory system* consists of a dor-

INVERTEBRATES—ANIMALS WITHOUT BACKBONES

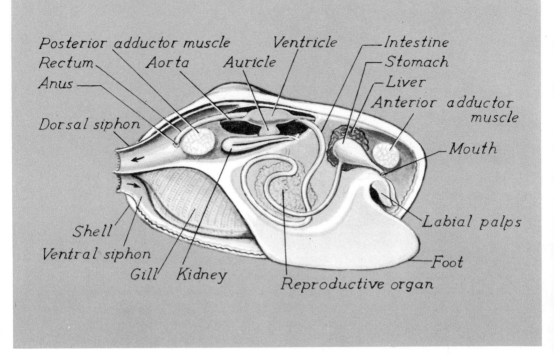

FIGURE 7-7. *FRESHWATER CLAM*

The shells or valves of the clam, one of which is removed in this diagram, are kept tightly closed by the contraction of two strong adductor muscles. The clam moves by cooperative action between the valve hinge and the foot.

sal heart, large arteries, and veins and capillaries. The blood passes through gills to obtain its supply of oxygen and through the kidneys to leave waste material. The nervous system has three pairs of ganglia. The edges of the mantle, lining the shell, contain cells sensitive to light and pressure.

Clams and oysters are valuable to man for food, and both industries are worth many millions of dollars in a single year. Even in ancient times oysters and clams were an important food source for man. Huge piles of shells have been found near man's ancient dwellings as evidence of his feasts.

Many years ago the fresh-water clam industry nearly failed because the clam's life cycle was not understood. Biologists found that very young clams swim about by opening and closing their tiny shells. When taken into the mouth of fishes, they pass out with the water through the gills. Some of them hook into the gills, but later loosen their hold and settle down to the bottom, where they develop. As soon as these facts in the life cycle of clams were understood, it was possible to make rules governing the time when clams and the kinds of fish best suited to their development could be taken from the water.

Snails are **univalves,** so called because the shell is of one piece. The foot is larger in proportion than that of a clam. The jaws move up and down, and the rough-edged tongue can be drawn in and out. By moving like a rasp against plant tissue the snail is able to eat solid food. It is a good *scavenger* (an animal

H. B. Gray

Gregor from Monkmeyer

FIGURE 7-8. *UNIVALVE AND BIVALVE*

The land snail's eyes appear at the end of two large tentacles protruding from the shell. The adult oyster can produce as many as 500,000,000 eggs per year, of which not more than one in one million will grow to any size.

that feeds on dead or decaying material) for an aquarium.

Land snails have eyes at the ends of their two large tentacles which protrude from the shell. These snails and their shell-less cousins, the *slugs,* eat fresh vegetables and are often destructive.

The *octopus* and the *squid* are also members of the mollusk group. They swim backward and when in danger send out inky liquids for defense in much the same manner as smoke screens are used.

The squid has a large head with two eyes and a central mouth. This is surrounded by ten fleshy *arms* with cuplike suckers, two of which are long retractive *tentacles.* Below the neck is a muscular *siphon* to help in swimming. The arms

FIGURE 7-9. *TWO MOLLUSKS*

The octopus (*right*) has a soft body with eight tentacles around its mouth. Notice the sucker disks with which it holds its prey. A close relative is the squid (*left*), a spindle-shaped animal from a few inches to forty feet long.

C. Limbaugh, Scripps Oceanographic Inst.

American Museum of Natural History

FIGURE 7-10. *CHAMBERED NAUTILUS*

This shell has been cut lengthwise to expose its many chambers, which are lined on the inside with mother-of pearl. The animal moves forward in the shell as it grows, and is always found in the last compartment.

American Museum of Natural History

and siphon correspond to the muscular foot in other mollusks.

Squids are eaten by fishes and marine mammals and are used as bait by fishermen, especially for cod. Squids are also used for human food in many countries.

The octopus has its muscular foot divided into eight parts called *tentacles.* They may vary from two to twenty-eight feet in different kinds of octopuses. The tentacles are filled with sucking cups which are used for food-getting and also for crawling.

The *cuttlefish* supplies cuttlebone, which may be ground up for polish or placed in the cages of canaries and other pet birds. Its ink provides the sepia pigment used by artists. The *chambered nautilus* also belongs to this hard-shelled group.

Although many mollusks are valuable for food, there are two of them which do an enormous amount of damage each year. The *oyster drill,* which is a tiny snail, gets its food by drilling a hole through the shell of the oyster and sucking the contents. The *shipworm,* a long bivalve, bores into the timber of wharves and wooden boats, thus weakening them.

FIGURE 7-11. *STRUCTURE OF THE EARTHWORM*

The digestive system of the segmented earthworm consists of mouth, esophagus, crop, and gizzard. A pair of "hearts" is found on segments 7 to 12. Each segment has four pairs of setae, used for locomotion.

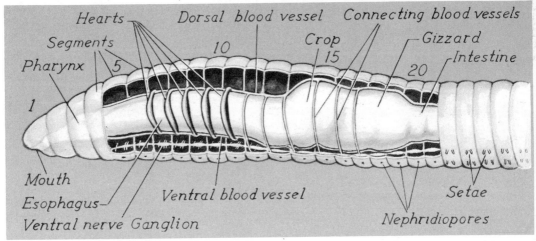

7.6 Segmented Worms

The segmented worms belong to the phylum **Annelida** (uh-*nell*-ih-duh), which includes the *earthworms, sandworms, leeches,* and many others. The arrangement of the organs in an earthworm (Fig. 7-11) indicates a well-defined digestive canal, circulatory system with closed blood vessels and capillaries, and a central nervous system.

A series of ringlike grooves divides the earthworm's body into *segments.* Each segment is separated from the next by a partition which extends from the groove to its *digestive tube.* This is a tube running the entire length of the body. Two groups of nerve cells called **ganglia** form a dorsal brain and are connected to a pair of ganglia in each segment which form a ventral nerve cord. A pair of coiled tubes to collect liquid waste, like kidneys, are in all except the first and last three segments. These tubes are called **nephridia** (neh-*frid*-ee-uh); they open to the outside through pores called **nephridiopores.**

The earthworm eats its way through the earth by means of its muscular **pharynx** (*fair*-ingks). Food particles pass through a long **esophagus** (uh-*sof*-uh-gus) into an enlarged organ, the **crop,** where they are stored. They are then forced into a muscular **gizzard,** in which they are ground up in preparation for digestion. Those food particles that are not digested are excreted through the *anus,* thus enriching the soil.

The skin of the earthworm is very thin and must be kept moist to allow the worm to breathe. When it rains there is often too much moisture and the worms, to avoid drowning, surface for air.

Locomotion in the earthworm is by longitudinal and circular muscles which expand and contract. This movement is assisted by four pairs of bristles called **setae** (*see*-tee) which project from the sides and ventral surface of each segment except the first and last. These bristles also keep the earthworm from slipping backwards in its burrow.

Earthworms produce eggs, as do the other worms, but both sexes are found in each earthworm. That is, they are *bisexual,* or *hermaphroditic.* The egg case, which holds the fertilized eggs, is left in the ground during the winter and the young worms hatch in the spring.

Earthworms are valuable to man because they bring to the surface a large amount of subsoil, because they bore many tiny holes which help in drainage and admit air, and because the earth they excrete is a valuable fertilizer.

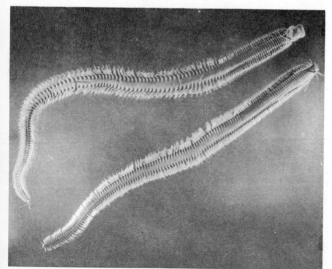

FIGURE 7-12. *SANDWORM*

This segmented worm lives in the salt water either swimming freely or submerged in the sand up to its head. What obvious differences are there between the sandworm and the earthworm?

General Biological Supply House

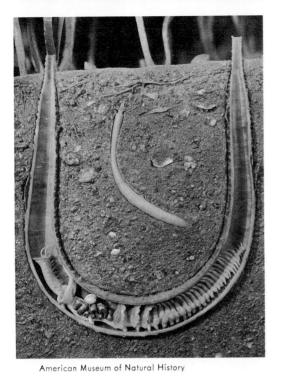

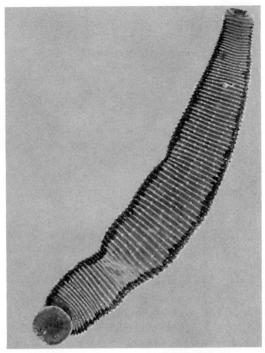

American Museum of Natural History

Photo by P. S. Tice

FIGURE 7-13. *MORE SEGMENTED WORMS*

The peculiar looking structure at the left is the tube of the parchment worm with the animal in place. The leech at the right is seen from the ventral side, showing clearly the sucking disc.

Sandworms, which live in the ocean near the shore, have on each segment paired appendages which are modified for swimming.

Leeches are commonly known as "blood suckers," because of the way they obtain their food. There are suckers at both ends of the body for clinging to objects, and they have teeth for piercing skin. A substance in the leeches' saliva prevents clotting of the blood of their victim until they have taken all they can hold.

The several groups of invertebrates listed in this chapter have another interest. Some of them produce eggs so transparent that the changes which take place in them during the early stages of growth can be seen in the living state. The exact nature of fertilization was discovered in this way.

7.7 Development of Animal Life

In this unit we have learned how the simplest of animals, consisting of only one cell, perform all of the life functions. When cells start to live together in colonies, like volvox, or in layers, like sponges and jellyfish, the cells become *differentiated, specialized,* and show *division of labor.* Some cells help with food-getting, as the tentacles of hydra, or breathing, as the gills of the clam.

When cells arranged themselves in three layers, as in the worms, the animals were able to do more difficult things. The flatworms established a digestive system with a mouth opening. The roundworms developed a digestive system with a mouth at the anterior end and an anal opening at the posterior end. The clams differentiated the digestive system into a stomach, intestine, and a

ANIMALS WITH VARIED FORMS

FIGURE 7-14. *DIFFERENT, YET ALIKE*

At first glance so different, man and the sponge have much in common. We gain understanding of man's complexities by studying life processes in simpler animals.

Courtesy of F. S. N. B.

digestive gland, the liver. Other systems, like the circulatory system, nervous system, and reproductive system, showed a higher degree of organization. The earthworms divided the body into a series of working units called segments. This type of body plan continues to be followed by the higher groups. A study of the development of these lower animal forms helps us to understand more about the complex organization of higher animals, including man.

FACTS TO REMEMBER

The *flatworms* (Platyhelminthes) and all higher groups have three layers of cells and show bilateral symmetry. The flatworms have one opening, the mouth. They include the free-living planaria and the parasitic tapeworm.

The *roundworms* (Nemathelminthes) have a complete digestive tract with mouth and anal openings. They include trichina and the hookworm.

The *starfish* (Echinodermata) have radial symmetry. This marine group includes the starfish, brittle stars, sea urchins, and sea cucumbers. They have remarkable powers of regeneration.

The clams and oysters (*bivalves*) and the snails and slugs (*univalves*) belong to the phylum Mollusca. The squids and octopuses are the most highly developed members of this group. Mollusks are of great economic importance for food and shell products. Some of them are destructive.

The *segmented worms* (Annelida) include the earthworms, sand-worms, and leeches. Their bodies are composed of segments, a plan of organization used in higher animals.

WORDS TO REMEMBER

anterior	foot	scavenger
anus	ganglion	segment
bilateral symmetry	gizzard	setae
bisexual	hooks	siphon
bivalve mollusk	nephridia	suckers
crop	nephridiopore	tube feet
dorsal	pharynx	univalve mollusk
embryo	posterior	ventral
esophagus	radial symmetry	

QUESTIONS

1. What characterizes the echinoderms?
2. How does a clam obtain food? A snail?
3. Describe the relationship of a young clam and certain fish.
4. What is the economic importance of the mollusks?
5. Briefly give the life history of the tapeworm.
6. How can trichinosis be avoided?
7. Of what value are earthworms to man?
8. Describe the life cycle of the hookworm (Fig. 7-5).
9. How do earthworms reproduce?
10. What is meant by regeneration?

COMPLETION TEST

As your teacher or classmate reads the following incomplete statements, with your book closed, write on a clean sheet of paper the word or phrase which correctly completes the statement.

1. Clams and oysters breathe by means of _____.
2. The starfish uses its tube feet for _____.
3. A _____ is a univalve because it has only one piece in its shell.
4. The tapeworm lives in the _____ of mammals.
5. A parasitic roundworm, trichina, forms a cyst in the _____.
6. Each division of an earthworm is called a _____.
7. The _____ commonly enters the body through the soles of the feet.
8. A clam moves by means of its _____.
9. The starfish has an eyespot on each _____.
10. The leech feeds on the _____ of other animals.

PROJECTS

I. *Starfish.*—If you live near the ocean, you may observe some starfish at low tide or you may bring a specimen into the laboratory. If you bring in a starfish, be sure to have a sufficient quantity of sea water and plan to study your specimen the same day. With your teacher's help you may be able to start a marine aquarium and keep your specimen several days.

1. Record your observations and include the answers to the following questions.

    (a) Note a bright yellow or orange spot on the dorsal side. This is the *madreporite,* which filters the water as it enters the vascular system.

    (b) Locate the eyespots at the ends of the arms.

    (c) Find the mouth on the ventral side.

    (d) Notice the feet in the groove on each arm. What is their use?

    (e) Is the starfish able to bend its arms?

2. Make a careful drawing of the starfish and label as many parts as you can.

II. *Study of a Living Snail.*—If you have a large trapdoor snail in the aquarium, spend some time watching it on the side of the glass. If all your snails are small, watch those, but it will be more difficult.

1. Notice the eyes on the ends of the antennae.

2. Watch the snail eat some plant material.

3. What happens when it is disturbed?

4. Can you discover the value of snails in an aquarium?

5. Record your observations carefully.

III. *Earthworms in the Laboratory.*—Collect some large earthworms, commonly known as "night crawlers." Place them in a box of moist (not wet) earth. You may be able to perform the following experiment:

1. *Object.*—To show how earthworms respond to light.

2. *Materials.*—You will need two boxes of soil or one divided box, a cover for one, and some earthworms.

3. *Method.*—Place a few earthworms on the top of the soil in each box and cover one box. Observe every few minutes and note which ones remain on the surface the longest.

4. *Observation.*—What is your observation of the reaction of earthworms to light? You may be able to devise many methods of testing their reactions. Record your observations.

5. *Conclusion.*—From your experiment what do you conclude about earthworms? Have you any idea now why people hunt "night crawlers" in the early evening or early morning?

IV. How are pearls produced? How are they artificially made?

V. Write a composition and illustrate it with diagrams, showing the life history of the liver fluke, which is a serious parasite on animals.

REFERENCES

Arnold, *Sea Beach at Ebb Tide.* Century.
Beddard, *Earthworms and Their Allies.* Macmillan.
Beebe, *Beneath Tropic Seas.* Putnam's.
Buchsbaum, *Animals Without Backbones.* University of Chicago Press.

Clark, *Animals of Land and Sea*. Van Nostrand.

Comstock, *Handbook of Nature Study*. Comstock.

Crowder, *Dwellers of the Sea and Shore*. Macmillan.

Eberson, *Microbes Militant*. Ronald Press.

Ehlers and Steel, *Municipal and Rural Sanitation*. McGraw-Hill.

Epstein and Epstein, *Miracles from Microbes*. Rutgers University Press.

Goodnight and Goodnight, *Zoology*. Mosby.

Hausman, *Beginner's Guide to Seashore Life*. Putnam's.

MacDougall and Hegner, *Biology of Life*. McGraw-Hill.

Miner, *Fieldbook of Seashore Life*. Putnam's.

Morgan, *Fieldbook of Ponds and Streams*. Putnam's.

Pratt, *Manual of the Common Invertebrate Animals*. McClurg.

Reed and Bronson, *The Sea for Sam*. Harcourt, Brace.

Rogers, *Shells*. Nature Library.

School Nature League, *Bivalves, Clams, and Their Relatives*. The School Nature League, New York City.

Storer, *General Zoology*. McGraw-Hill.

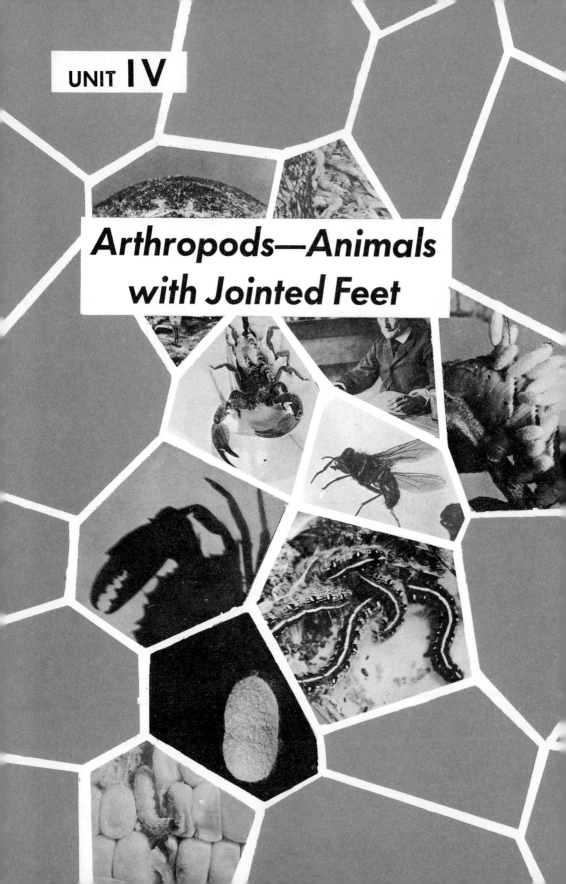

Arthropods—Animals with Jointed Feet

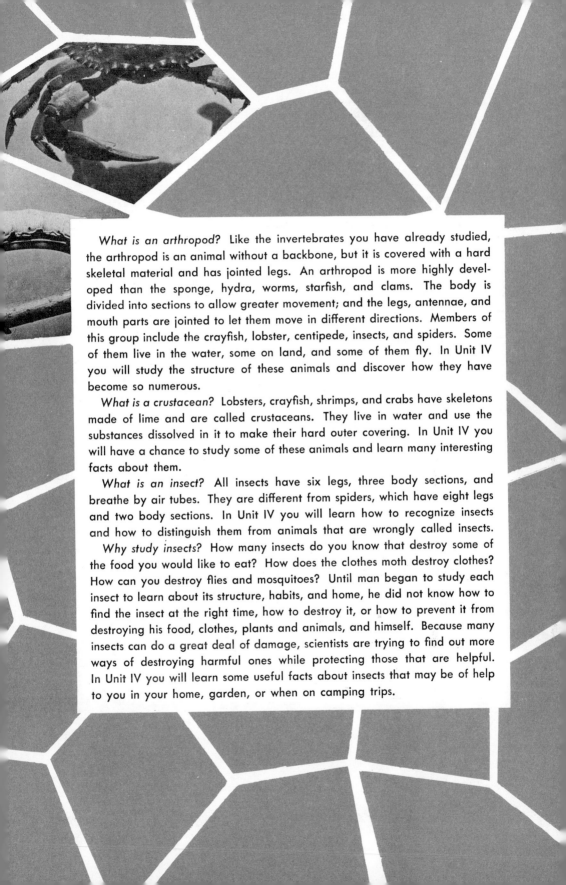

What is an arthropod? Like the invertebrates you have already studied, the arthropod is an animal without a backbone, but it is covered with a hard skeletal material and has jointed legs. An arthropod is more highly developed than the sponge, hydra, worms, starfish, and clams. The body is divided into sections to allow greater movement; and the legs, antennae, and mouth parts are jointed to let them move in different directions. Members of this group include the crayfish, lobster, centipede, insects, and spiders. Some of them live in the water, some on land, and some of them fly. In Unit IV you will study the structure of these animals and discover how they have become so numerous.

What is a crustacean? Lobsters, crayfish, shrimps, and crabs have skeletons made of lime and are called crustaceans. They live in water and use the substances dissolved in it to make their hard outer covering. In Unit IV you will have a chance to study some of these animals and learn many interesting facts about them.

What is an insect? All insects have six legs, three body sections, and breathe by air tubes. They are different from spiders, which have eight legs and two body sections. In Unit IV you will learn how to recognize insects and how to distinguish them from animals that are wrongly called insects.

Why study insects? How many insects do you know that destroy some of the food you would like to eat? How does the clothes moth destroy clothes? How can you destroy flies and mosquitoes? Until man began to study each insect to learn about its structure, habits, and home, he did not know how to find the insect at the right time, how to destroy it, or how to prevent it from destroying his food, clothes, plants and animals, and himself. Because many insects can do a great deal of damage, scientists are trying to find out more ways of destroying harmful ones while protecting those that are helpful. In Unit IV you will learn some useful facts about insects that may be of help to you in your home, garden, or when on camping trips.

CHAPTER 8

The Crayfish—A Typical Crustacean

8.1 Animals with Jointed Feet

Have you ever watched a crayfish or lobster trying to walk, crawl, or swim with so many jointed legs? Have you observed a spider making a web, or a fly crawling on a wall? All of these animals have jointed feet and belong to the phylum **Arthropoda** (ar-*throp*-oh-duh). This phylum is divided into five main *classes:* (1) **Crustacea** (krus-*tay*-shuh), including shrimps, crabs, crayfish, and lobsters; (2) **Insecta** (in-*sek*-tuh), the insects; (3) **Arachnida** (uh-*rak*-nid-uh), the spiders, scorpions, ticks, and mites; (4) *Chilopoda* (ky-*lah*-poh-duh), the centipedes; and (5) *Diplopoda* (dip-*lah*-poh-duh), the millipedes. Each class differs from the others in the number and size of the jointed feet and of the other sections of its body.

All of the Arthropoda, like many other invertebrates, have their soft bodies covered on the *outside* by a protective substance called an **exoskeleton** (eks-oh-*skel*-uh-tun). This is in contrast to the skeleton of reptiles, fishes, and man, which is *inside* of the muscles and is called an **endoskeleton** (en-doh-*skel*-uh-tun). The exoskeleton is made of a tough material called **chitin** (*ky*-tin).

The animals in this phylum are similar to the earthworm group in that their bodies are divided into segments. However, the arthropods show more specialization and are better adapted for special functions. Although many Arthropoda

FIGURE 8-1. *ARTHROPODS*

Animals belonging to the phylum Arthropoda have jointed feet and are protected on the outside by an exoskeleton. How do the classes differ?

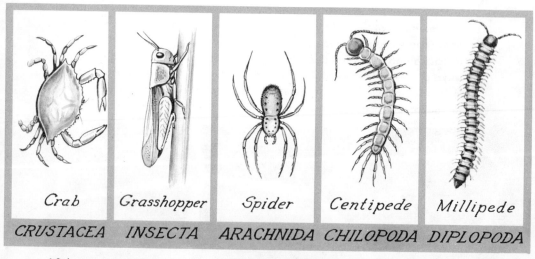

| Crab | Grasshopper | Spider | Centipede | Millipede |
| CRUSTACEA | INSECTA | ARACHNIDA | CHILOPODA | DIPLOPODA |

live in the water, some are fitted for life on land, and some are able to fly.

8.2 The Crustaceans

The crustaceans take their name from their hard outer covering, or *crust*. *Crayfish, lobsters, crabs,* and *shrimps* are familiar crustaceans.

The body of a crustacean consists of *segments,* each of which usually has a pair of *jointed* **appendages** (uh-*pen*-dih-jes). The appendages are variously modified; some are used in swimming, some in securing food, and others in walking. On the walking legs are attached most of the gills that aid in respiration. The other gills are on the thorax.

8.3 Crayfish

Lobsters and crayfish are so much alike that either one will serve as an example of the crustacean group. A description of either will indicate the chief characteristics of both. It is important to become familiar with the structure and the life habits of the crayfish and other crustacea because they are of great economic value to man.

The crayfish (Fig. 8-2) is divided into two regions, the *head-thorax* region and the **abdomen** (*ab*-duh-m'n). The segments of the abdomen are clearly defined, but those of the head-thorax, technically termed the **cephalothorax** (sef-uh-loh-*thor*-aks), are so fused that they are difficult to make out. The covering of this region is called the **carapace** (*kair*-uh-payss). This is part of the hard external skeleton which covers and protects the entire body.

FIGURE 8-2. *EXTERNAL STRUCTURE OF THE CRAYFISH*

In the dorsal view distinguish the abdomen and cephalothorax. How do the appendages of the abdomen differ from those on the cephalothorax? The largest appendage, the *cheliped,* ends in a strong pincer, the *chela.*

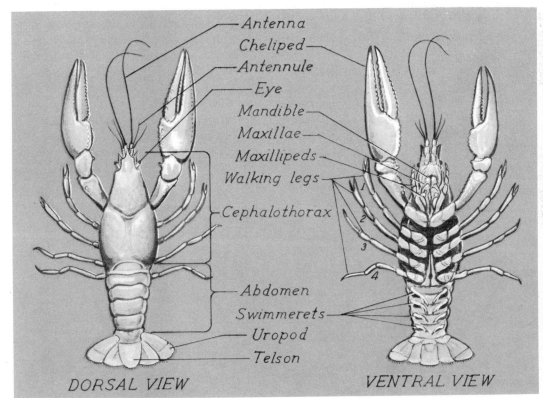

8.4 Appendages of the Crayfish

Nineteen pairs of appendages, attached to the lower or ventral surface of the body, are used for swimming, walking, protection, capturing prey, crushing food, and as special sense organs.

The appendages on the abdomen of the crayfish are simple, two-parted feet, called **swimmerets** (Fig. 8-2). There are six pairs of swimmerets on the abdomen, the first two pairs being modified for reproduction in the male. Swimmerets aid in respiration and, in the female, serve as an attachment for the eggs. The sixth pair are paddle-like and are called **uropods** (*yoo*-roh-pods). The **telson** is the tail fin which enables the animal to swim backward. The uropods and telson together form the tail.

On the thorax region, the appendages have become large, many-jointed structures strong enough to support the body in walking. Crayfish are able to walk forward, backward, and sideward. (See walking legs, Fig. 8-2). On the joints of four pairs of **walking legs** nearest the body are **gills** that absorb oxygen from air dissolved in the water. The first pair of walking legs, which are much larger than any of the others, are called **chelipeds** (*kee*-luh-peds). Each cheliped ends in a strong pincer called a **chela** (*kee*-luh). The chela is used in fighting, in defense, and in capturing food. The second and third pairs of walking legs have small pincers, but the fourth and fifth pairs end in single claws.

Just in front of the walking legs are located six pairs of appendages that assist in bringing food to the mouth after it has been crushed and torn to pieces. There are three pairs of **maxillipeds** (mak-*sil*-ih-peds), two pairs of **maxillae** (mak-*sil*-ee), and one pair of **mandibles** (*man*-duh-b'ls).

The *mandible* is short and hard and has a broad surface on the end. When the two mandibles come together, their action is mainly to crush food, but this broad surface is also rough so that they have a grinding action.

The two pairs of *maxillae* just back of the mandibles are very thin, almost leaf-like, and covered with sensory hairs. These hairs are supplied with nerves and are classified as taste and touch hairs. The second maxilla supports a special fold, scoop-shaped, which extends into the gill chamber. Its function is to help in respiratory movements by keeping the water circulating in the gill chamber. Water is drawn in from the back edge of the gill chamber and passes out near the mouth. We may show this by placing a few drops of red ink at the back edge of the gill chamber of a live crayfish, being sure to have the water cover

FIGURE 8-3. TWO *CRUSTACEANS*

A large lobster holds his prey, a crab. One lobster claw has blunt teeth for crushing, the other sharp teeth for tearing. What characteristics do the lobster and crab have in common?

American Museum of Natural History

106

its back. In what direction will the ink move?

The three remaining pairs (*maxillipeds*) are similar to the abdominal appendages. The second and third pair have gills attached. All of the maxillipeds pick up small particles of food and help in placing them near the mouth of the crayfish so that they may be sucked in and eaten.

The crayfish has two pairs of **antennae** (an-*ten*-ee) that are used for feeling and possibly tasting. When a drop of meat juice is placed in the water near the mouth parts or an antenna, the crayfish begins to move the mouth parts as it does when eating. The smaller feelers are called **antennules** (an-*ten*-yools).

In the joint by which each small antennule is attached to the body is a sac covered with a plate, the edge of which is furnished with hairs. This sac, the **statocyst** (*stat*-oh-sist), which communicates with the water, is the *balancing organ.* The crayfish is unable to swim naturally when these sacs are removed.

8.5 Eyes

The eyes of the crayfish are on the ends of a pair of short, movable stalks. They are **compound,** and each lens, or **facet** (*fass*-it), "sees" only the object directly before it. Thus, the crayfish does not have a continuous complete picture of an object as we do, but it has numerous partial and incomplete views that resemble a mosaic floor. Such vision is therefore termed **mosaic** (moh-*zay*-ik) **vision.** Insects also have this kind of vision.

8.6 Life Processes of the Crayfish

The life processes of the crayfish are very interesting. You may be able to observe some of them.

Food-Getting.—The crayfish crawls on the bottom of brooks and near the shores of ponds and hides under stones or in burrows. It faces the entrance of its hideout with the chelipeds stretched out. It catches any food that passes within reach and emerges to seize any that is near by.

FIGURE 8-4. *INTERNAL ORGANS OF THE CRAYFISH*

Food is ground up in the front, or *cardiac stomach* to prepare it for digestion in the *pyloric stomach.*

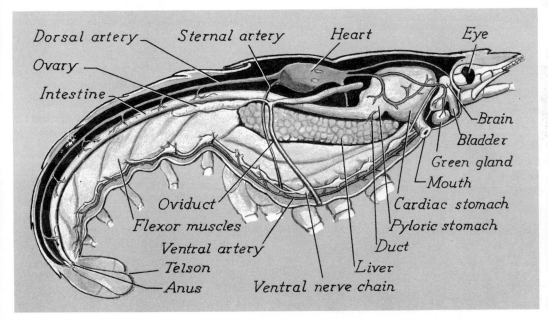

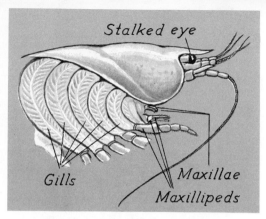

Gills

Maxillae

Maxillipeds

FIGURE 8-5. *HEAD OF THE CRAYFISH*

The overhanging exoskeleton, or carapace, has been cut away here to show the gills attached to the forward walking legs.

The crayfish feeds on live insect larvae, worms, small snails, fishes, and tadpoles. It is also a scavenger, eating some dead animal matter. Crayfish which burrow live on stems and roots of plants.

One of the simple water plants, *Chara* (*kay*-ruh), furnishes the crayfish with lime for hardening its exoskeleton after a molt. Shells of snails and the shed skins of crayfish also help to supply lime. Crayfish seize food with their pincers and move it towards the mouth. Small food

FIGURE 8-6. *GOOD EATING*

The strong muscles of the shrimp's abdomen make delicious food. Millions of shrimp are eaten by man every year.

N. C. Dept. of Conservation and Development

particles are also carried towards the mouth by currents of water produced by the movement of their mouth parts and their abdominal appendages. Particles of food are crushed by their mandibles.

Digestive System.—The *mouth* of the crayfish is just back of its mandibles, and connects with the *stomach* by a short *esophagus.* The front part of its stomach possesses a grinding structure known as the **gastric mill,** which shreds and crushes the food and makes it ready for digestion in the back part. Two large digestive glands, often called the *liver,* pour a fluid into the crayfish's stomach, which prepares the food for absorption by the walls of its stomach and intestine. The **intestine** begins at the back end of its stomach and extends to the last segment, where it terminates at an opening called the *anus.*

Respiration.—Crayfish obtain oxygen from the water and release carbon dioxide into the water by means of *gills.* Their gills are well covered by the overhanging skeleton, a protecting *carapace,* but are really outside the body. Most of the gills are plume-like in shape (Fig. 8-5) and are attached to their appendages, but some of them are attached to the thoracic region. Water is made to circulate through the gill chamber by means of the **gill scoop** or **gill bailer.**

Excretion.—The organs for excretion of waste are the **green glands** found at the base of the antennae. Each green gland consists of three parts: a green glandular portion, a thin-walled *bladder,* and a duct opening to the exterior. Blood going to these glands loses some of the waste which it has gained in its course through the body. These green glands purify the blood of the crayfish in much the same way as do the kidneys of the higher animals. The green glands also serve as a storehouse for the lime from the old exoskeleton while it is being shed and a new one is forming. This accounts for the fact that hard green glands, or "crayfish pearls," are found only in *soft-shelled* crayfish, as the animals are called after they have shed their exoskeletons.

Circulatory System.—The crayfish has a well-developed *heart* from which extend several *arteries,* which carry blood to the various parts of its body. The blood returns to its heart through *veins* and through several irregular ducts called **sinuses** (*sy*-nus-ez). As the blood flows through the body, it gives up oxygen to the cells and receives carbon dioxide. Fresh oxygen is absorbed by means of the gills, which, at the same time, pass off carbon dioxide from the blood into the water.

The crayfish, like other arthropods, has an *open circulatory system* instead of a "closed" one like that of the earthworms and vertebrates. It is called an "open system" because the blood does not flow continuously through blood vessels. There are no *capillaries* to connect the arteries and veins. Instead, there are irregular ducts, the *sinuses,* in which the blood collects. The oxygen is carried by a substance in the liquid part of the blood.

The Nervous System.—In the crayfish this is made up of a *dorsal brain, ventral nerve chain,* and many *nerves.* The special senses are well developed. These include the antennae and antennules for touch and taste, the stalked compound eyes for sight, and the special sac, the statocyst, for balance.

8.7 Life History

The males may be distinguished from the females by the larger tubular appendages on the first and second segments of the abdomen. The eggs of the female become glued to the hairs of the swimmerets and hatch in five to eight weeks. The young crayfish remain attached to these swimmerets for about two weeks after hatching, grasping the hairs with their pincers. During this time they feed on the yolk that was in the egg. By the end of the fortnight they begin to look like their parents.

The crayfish breeds annually, and those that hatch from eggs laid in the spring may, in turn, lay eggs the following spring. Crayfish usually live four or five years and sometimes grow to be six inches long.

8.8 Molting

The crayfish can shed its outside skeleton. As this exoskeleton is rigid and non-elastic, the crayfish must get rid of it occasionally in order to grow. **Molting** is a serious and dangerous operation, as it is followed by a period when the crayfish is without means of offense or defense. The animal usually hides until a new exoskeleton is partially formed. In the molting process the covering of the eyes and part of the lining of the digestive tract, as well as the whole exoskeleton, are shed. The crayfish molts every year of its life and several times during the first year.

It is an interesting fact that if one or more of the crayfish appendages are lost in the process of molting, or by accident, these lost parts grow again. This is known as *regeneration.*

8.9 Crabs

The bodies of crabs are wider than they are long, giving a rounded appearance, with the abdomen scarcely noticeable. Their method of locomotion is to walk sideways.

A few kinds of crabs have peculiar habits which may prove interesting to

FIGURE 8-7. *CRAB*

Because of its food value, the crab is of great economic importance.

8.10 Other Crustaceans

Crustaceans of less economic importance than shrimps, crabs, and lobsters are the *barnacles* which cling to rocks, wharves, and ships; the *hermit crabs* that live in the shells of mollusks; *land crabs* that feed on coconuts; and the smaller fresh-water crustaceans which are barely visible to the eye. To this group also belong *sand fleas, sow bugs, scuds, pill bugs,* and the *one-eyed Cyclops* (Fig. 8-8).

Barnacles are equipped with long stalks at the end of each of which is a **cement gland.** This gland enables the barnacle to fasten itself to objects under water. Those barnacles which attach themselves to rocks open when the tide is in and pull food into their mouths, then close when the tide is out.

watch. The *fiddler crab* has one very large claw. When frightened it walks sideways into its hiding place and then extends its large claw, waving it back and forth as if to frighten its enemies.

Shrimps and the *soft-shelled crab* are a very popular food for man, while many tiny crustaceans are an important food for fish.

8.11 Economic Value

Crayfish, shrimps, lobsters, and crabs are very important economically on account of their food value. The trade in these animals amounts to millions of dollars each year. In order that these important food animals may not become exterminated by careless and excessive fishing, the state and national govern-

FIGURE 8-8. *OTHER CRUSTACEANS*

These tiny, fresh-water crustaceans are enlarged to show their characteristic segmented bodies, jointed legs, and suits of armor.

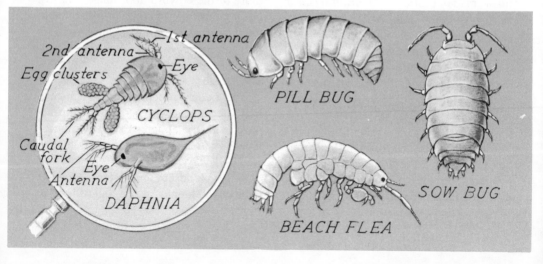

ments have attempted to control the numbers taken. Some kinds of crayfish are harmful since, by burrowing, they may cause serious damage to dams and levees. They may also injure young cotton plants and destroy young corn by eating their roots. Crayfish are helpful as scavengers, because they eat decaying vegetation and dead animals. The natural enemies of the crayfish are larger fish, water birds, muskrats, mink, and raccoons.

As a source of food the American lobster is widely used, since its body contains a large supply of delicious meat. It is in such great demand that the states of the northern Atlantic coast have made a regulation to prevent small lobsters from being taken.

In order to keep up the supply of lobsters, state and national governments have established hatcheries where the eggs are hatched artificially. During this process the eggs are protected from the animals that naturally feed on them. After the young lobsters are hatched, they are placed in the ocean.

8.12 Arachnida

Spiders, scorpions, ticks, and *mites* make up a class of arthropods called **Arachnida** (uh-*rak*-nid-uh). Spiders (Fig. 8-11) are *not* insects, as some of you may think. Watch a spider and notice that it has eight legs instead of six, as the insects have. The spider has no antennae or compound eyes, but there are several **simple eyes,** usually eight, arranged in a definite pattern on its head. This pattern arrangement varies with different kinds of spiders and is used as a basis of classification.

There are two pairs of appendages at the anterior end. One pair, the *mandibles,* connects with the **poison glands;** and the *palps* are used in crushing food.

FIGURE 8-9. *BARNACLES*
Young barnacles swim freely about, but adults attach to underwater objects and remain there the rest of their lives.

Most spiders have small appendages called **spinnerets** located under the back part of the abdomen. They contain small spinning tubes through which the silky substance is secreted. The female spiders spin the webs.

Spiders breathe by two or four **lung books,** each of which has several plates containing tiny blood vessels. Air enters a slit on the abdomen.

Spiders are the best known of the arachnids and most are harmless. Some spiders spin beautifully regular webs in the grass, in the shrubbery, and on the porches of our houses. In the fall the young of some kinds of spiders climb fences, weeds, and even telephone poles and spin long threads of silk on which they sail away. They have been caught by traps attached to government airplanes at heights of 10,000 feet. Air currents may distribute them over vast areas in a few days.

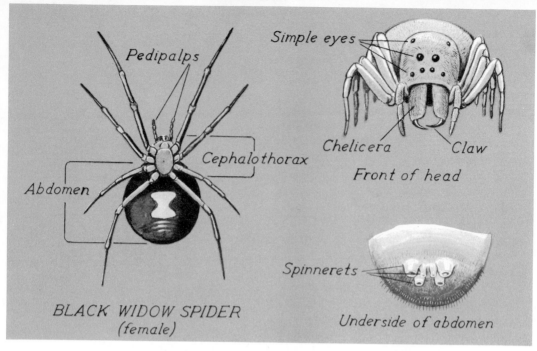

Pedipalps

Simple eyes

Cephalothorax

Chelicera   Claw

Front of head

Abdomen

Spinnerets

BLACK WIDOW SPIDER
(female)

Underside of abdomen

FIGURE 8-10. *EXTERNAL STRUCTURE OF THE SPIDER*

One pair of appendages at the anterior end of the spider, the chelicerae,
ends in a claw which connects with a poison gland. The other pair, the
pedipalps, is used to crush food. Spiders have eight legs.

FIGURE 8-11. *TRAPDOOR SPIDER*

All spiders have spinnerets, but not all
of them spin webs. This lady uses her
silk for a nest lining and a hinged door.

Lynwood M. Chace

Trapdoor spiders are found in the
southeastern part of the United States.
They dig a tubular hole in the ground,
line it with silk, fasten a hinged lip to fit
over the hole, and cleverly open and shut
this like a door, even spinning a silk
handle on the inside to hold it shut.

Spiders do not eat solid food, but suck
juices from the insects they capture.
They catch honeybees that are useful and
flies that are harmful, but we study them
because they are interesting rather than
economically important. The common
harvestman (daddy longlegs), which is
helpful, as it feeds on insects, belongs
to the spider group.

Among the few poisonous spiders are
the *black widow* spider and the *tarantula*
(tuh-*ran*-tyoo-luh), or banana spider,
both of which live best in warm climates,
but are occasionally found throughout
the temperate parts of United States.

112

American Museum of Natural History   American Museum of Natural History

FIGURE 8-12. *CLOSE RELATIVES*

The tarantula (*left*) is the largest American spider. This one has a leg spread of seven inches. The young of the scorpion (*right*) are born alive and cling to the mother with their little pincers for several days.

The small, black widow spider has a red spot, shaped like an hourglass, on the under side of its abdomen. The female has a poisonous bite and is so vicious that she kills the male after she has laid her eggs.

The banana spider, or tarantula, is very large, measuring six or seven inches when its legs are spread. Its bite is painful, but does not cause death. These spiders are sometimes brought north in shipments of bananas. They eat insects and sometimes will even attack small birds.

Scorpions live in tropical and subtropical regions. They have a pair of appendages which are modified to form pincers (Fig. 8-12) and eight walking legs like spiders. At the tip of the tail, there is a sting which is fatal to their prey, which consists chiefly of insects and spiders. Although painful, the scorpion's sting usually does not injure human beings seriously.

Mites and *ticks* are the smallest of the arachnids. The "red" spider that injures apple leaves and fruit is really a mite. Relatives of these red spiders are the "chiggers" of the South that annoy human beings. Ticks are harmful not only because they feed on the blood of various domestic animals, but because they may transfer diseases from one animal to another as well as to man. The Rocky Mountain tick carries the organism that causes spotted fever, and the Texas-fever tick spreads a disease among cattle that causes an annual loss of many millions of dollars. Vaccine is now used to protect people who have had or may have a tick bite.

Horseshoe crabs are the living relatives of ancient marine forms. They are curious creatures resembling crabs but belonging to the Arachnida. They have six additional legs on the abdomen and have both compound and simple eyes. They can walk, swim, and hop and are usually active at night. Horseshoe crabs are found on the Atlantic coast from

THE CRAYFISH—A TYPICAL CRUSTACEAN   113

FIGURE 8-13. *LIFE HISTORY OF THE TICK*
The female tick usually lays her eggs in ground rubbish, and the larvae alight on passing animals. Gorging the blood of the host, they swell and then molt, becoming nymphs. After another molting they become adults.

Maine to the southern states.

8.13 Chilopods and Diplopods

Another class of the arthropods is the **Chilopoda** (ky-*lah*-poh-duh), which includes the *centipedes* (*sen*-tih-peeds), animals having many legs. Centipedes have a flattened body and are provided with poison glands, the fluid of which is secreted in a tube in the poison claws on the first segment. This poison is fatal to some small animals and painful to man. Located at the anterior end are a pair of long, jointed antennae, a pair of mandibles to chew their food, and two pairs of maxillae. They have one pair of appendages on each segment except the last two and can run very rapidly. They feed on cockroaches and other insects. Centipedes hide by day under stones and logs and run fast at night to catch earthworms, insects, and sometimes small lizards or mice.

The class **Diplopoda** (dip-*lah*-poh-duh) includes the *millipedes* (*mil*-ih-peeds), which have cylindrical bodies,

FIGURE 8-14. *CENTIPEDE*
An adult centipede may have as many as 170 pairs of legs. The body is segmented with a pair of legs on each segment. The poison claws are located just behind the head and are used to kill their prey, usually molluscs, worms, and insects.

Black Star

114

short antennae, and two pairs of legs on each segment of their long abdomens. They crawl slowly and roll into a ball when disturbed. Millipedes are quite harmless. They live in dark, moist places under stones or logs, and they eat dead organic material, mostly the decaying remains of plants.

FACTS TO REMEMBER

The *Arthropoda* are the most highly developed of the invertebrates. The body is covered with chitin and is segmented externally. The appendages are jointed. The five main classes are the Crustacea, Insecta, Arachnida, Chilopoda, and Diplopoda.

The *Crustacea* include crayfish, lobsters, crabs, shrimps, and barnacles. The two body regions have many jointed appendages used for food-getting, sensation, and locomation. Lobsters, crabs, and shrimp are valuable for food. Barnacles attach themselves to ships and wharves, causing much damage.

The *Arachnida* include the spiders, scorpions, ticks, and mites. They have two body regions. One pair of appendages at the anterior end is connected with the poison gland. The other anterior pair helps to crush food. There are four pairs of walking legs. Spiders have simple eyes and breathe by lung books.

The *Chilopoda* include the centipedes, with long antennae and one pair of jointed appendages on each segment. *Diplopoda* are the millipedes, with short antennae and two pairs of legs on each segment.

WORDS TO REMEMBER

abdomen	endoskeleton	molting
antennae	exoskeleton	mosaic vision
antennules	facet	open circulatory
appendage	gastric mill	system
carapace	gill bailer	poison glands
cement gland	gills	simple eyes
cephalothorax	gill scoop	sinus
chela	green glands	spinneret
cheliped	intestine	statocyst
chitin	lung books	swimmerets
closed circulatory	mandibles	telson
system	maxillae	uropods
compound eyes	maxillipeds	

QUESTIONS

1. What is an arthropod?
2. How can you distinguish a spider from an insect?
3. How does a centipede differ from a millipede?
4. With what crustaceans are you familiar?
5. Why are crayfish placed in the group known as Arthropoda?

THE CRAYFISH—A TYPICAL CRUSTACEAN

6. Describe the crayfish as to external appearance.

7. Name the parts of the body of the crayfish.

8. List the different kinds of appendages of a crayfish and tell what each one is used for.

9. Describe the mouth parts of a crayfish and explain how they are used.

10. How does the crayfish breathe?

11. What are the green glands and where are they located?

12. Does the crayfish have a heart? Does it have blood vessels? Can you locate any of them from the diagram (Fig. 8-4)?

13. Describe the nervous system and sense organs of the crayfish.

14. Where do the eggs of the crayfish remain until hatched?

15. What is meant by molting?

16. How are crabs and lobsters important to man?

COMPLETION TEST

As your teacher or classmate reads the following incomplete statements, with your book closed, write on a clean sheet of paper the word or phrase which correctly completes the statement.

1. The exoskeleton of a crayfish is made of _____.

2. The gills of a crayfish are attached to the _____.

3. The organ of balance in a crayfish is located _____.

4. A crayfish may grow a new leg by the process of _____.

5. The eyes of the crayfish are on _____.

6. The organs of excretion in a crayfish are called _____.

7. The mandibles of a crayfish are used for _____ the food.

8. There are _____ pairs of walking legs on a crayfish.

9. Other edible crustacea include _____.

10. Water is forced over the gills of a crayfish by the _____.

PROJECTS

I. *Observation of Spiders.*—Collect some spiders, either with a small net or by placing a jar over them. Bring them into the laboratory and place them in an insect cage. Put a few small branches from a tree into the cage to serve as places for attaching webs.

1. Watch the spiders as much as you can and perhaps you will be able to see one spinning its web. Try to answer the following questions:

(a) What are webs used for?

(b) Why does a spider not get caught in its own web?

(c) Does a particular kind of spider spin more than one kind of web?

(d) From what part of the spider's body is the web produced?

(e) How many legs can you count on each spider?

(f) How does a spider get its food?

II. *Study of a Living Crayfish.*—Procure some living crayfish if possible, and place them in an aquarium by themselves, since they sometimes eat small fish. Supply a few snails, tadpoles, and worms, and some green water plants. Watch them carefully and try to answer the following questions:

1. What is their usual method of locomotion?
2. Can they swim? In what direction?
3. What happens when you place a stick near their claws?
4. How many pairs of legs have pincers? Which ones?
5. What do the others have on the end?
6. Compare one of the abdominal appendages with those used in walking and feeling.
7. What is the work of the large pincers?
8. Do crayfish move their eyes? What makes that possible?
9. How do they use their tail fins?
10. Can they move their antennae?
11. How many body regions do crayfish have?
12. Is the head movable?
13. How many segments are there in the abdomen?
14. What is the color of the living animal?
15. List the adaptations of the crayfish for protection.

III. *Experiment with a Living Crayfish.*—You may wish to observe for yourself how a crayfish breathes or at least how it moves the water over its gills.

Hold the crayfish in a pan of water or place it on the bottom of a dish of water. Place a drop of blue or red ink, or carmine grains, on the water at the posterior margin of the carapace. Notice where the color appears. The water is forced over the gills by the gill bailer and should be seen appearing along the lower edge of the carapace which is not attached to the legs.

IV. *Study of a Preserved Crayfish Specimen.*
1. Draw and label carefully a side view of the crayfish.
2. Remove one of the legs and examine it carefully. How many joints do you find?
3. Make a detailed drawing of a leg and label as many parts as you can.
4. With a pair of scissors, cut off the carapace on one side of the body. Describe the gills. Try to locate the gill bailer at the anterior end. How is it used?
5. Note the attachment of the gills to the walking legs. Draw and label one of them.
6. With the help of your teacher remove the mouth parts and make a drawing of each. Explain how a crayfish uses all of these in obtaining food.
7. Draw and label the abdomen, showing both dorsal (upper) and ventral (under) views.

V. *Study of the Internal Structure of a Crayfish or Lobster.*—If you like to eat lobster, you may wish to become familiar with its parts so that you can manage it better the next time it is served. If you do not like lobster or if you have never eaten any, here is an opportunity to study the internal anatomy.

Method.—1. Carefully cut away the body wall on one side. Find the tube which leads directly from the mouth. This is the *gullet,* or esophagus. Follow it to the *stomach,* which has two chambers.

You will recognize the straight *intestine* which leads to the anus.

2. An odd-shaped organ, the *heart,* lies just above and behind the stomach. Extending from it are several *arteries,* but you may not find all of them since the blood is almost colorless.

3. In the head region note the *green glands* which serve as kidneys. Locate the openings in the little elevations just in front of the mouth.

4. Very careful dissection along the under side may reveal the nervous system with its ventral chain of *ganglia.* These appear as very white threads. You may be able to follow some of them forward to the so-called *brain* which lies in the head between the eyes.

Observation.—Write a careful report of your observations. Make a drawing of the side view of your dissection, showing the location of the various organs.

VI. Find out all you can about *barnacles,* including their life history, economic importance, and other items of interest. If you live near the shore, watch some barnacles as the tide is either going out or coming in and find out how they open their shells. Bring in a living barnacle and examine it.

VII. Study other crustacea, such as sand fleas, which often become numerous enough to be pests. Look for the wood louse or pill bug under bark or loose stones. Try to explain how they breathe through their legs.

VIII. Find out all you can about crayfish which can live on the ground and build houses called "chimneys" where they can hide during the day.

IX. Make a careful study of the life history of ticks, the places where they hide, how they get on people and animals, how to avoid them, and how to prevent the diseases they cause.

REFERENCES

Carson, *The Edge of the Sea.* Oxford.
Carson, *The Sea Around Us.* Oxford.
Cockerell, *Zoölogy.* World Book.
Comstock, *The Spider Book.* Doubleday, Doran.
Duncan, *Spiders and Scorpions.* Oxford.
Herrick, *American Lobster, Study of Its Habits and Development.* United States Fisheries Bulletin, Volume XV.
Heyerdahl, *Kon-Tiki.* Rand McNally.
Morgan, *Fieldbook of Ponds and Streams.* Putnam's.
School Nature League, *Crustaceans, Armored Animals of the Seashore.* The School Nature League, New York City.

CHAPTER 9

The Grasshopper—A Typical Insect

9.1 Insects

The most highly developed of the invertebrates are the insects. They are fascinating to watch because they are always busy. Some are flying from flower to flower, others are busy on leaves or stems, and a few minutes of observation will show you whether they are friends or foes of the plant on which you find them.

The most interesting way to study insects is to watch them in their natural habitats, but when this is impossible, they can easily be studied in the laboratory. Even in the city a surprisingly large number of different insects can be collected.

Insects perform all the life functions just as large animals do. All insects must have food, all must get oxygen, all have some means of self-protection, all reproduce, and all sooner or later die of accident, disease, or old age. Therefore, when we study one type of insect, its life history and activities, we get a good general idea of how all types live.

9.2 The Work of Fabre

One of the first men to study insects in their natural habitat was Jean Henri

FIGURE 9-1. *KATYDID*

A relative of the grasshopper, the katydid is a large greenish insect with long antennae. It usually lives in trees or shrubs, feeding on the leaves and twigs.

R. L. Cassell

119

Fabre (*fah*-br), who lived in southern France in the Rhone valley (Fig. 9-2). Here he studied them so attentively that his peasant neighbors thought him strange. Little did they know that what he wrote about his studies would be read all over the world. Fabre wrote more of the behavior of insects than of their structure. Here is a quotation from what he wrote of the cricket:

"The Cricket.—In August, among the fallen leaves, in those little oases where the grass has not been wholly scorched by the sun, I find the young Cricket already rather big, black all over like the adult, with not a vestige of the white

FIGURE 9-3. *A FAMILIAR FRIEND*
Only the male cricket can "sing." How does he do it?

girdle of his early days. He has no domicile. The shelter of a dead leaf, the cover of a flat stone are enough for him; they represent the tents of a nomad who cares not where he lays his head.

"This vagabond life continues until the middle of the autumn.... It is at the close of October, when the first cold weather threatens, that the burrow is taken in hand. The work is very simple, judging by the little that my observation of the caged insect has shown me. The digging is never done at a bare point in the pan, but always under the shelter of a withered lettuce leaf, some remnant of the food provided. This takes the place of the grass screen that seems indispensable to the secrecy of the establishment.

"The miner scrapes with his fore-legs and uses the pincers of his mandibles to extract the larger bits of gravel. I see him stamping with his powerful hind-legs, furnished with a double row of spikes; I see him raking the rubbish, sweeping it backwards and spreading it slantwise. There you have the method in its entirety.

"The work proceeds pretty quickly at first. In the yielding soil of my cages, the digger disappears underground after a spell that lasts a couple of hours. He returns to the entrance at intervals, always backwards and always sweeping. Should he be overcome with fatigue, he takes a rest on the threshold of his half-finished home, with his head outside and his antennae waving feebly. He goes in again and resumes work with pincers and rakes. Soon the periods of repose become longer and wear out my patience.

"The most urgent part of the work is done. Once the hole is a couple of inches deep, it suffices for the needs of the moment. The rest will be a long-winded business, resumed in a leisurely fashion, a little one day and a little the next; the hole will be made deeper and wider as demanded by the inclemencies of the weather and the growth of the insect. Even in winter, if the temperature be mild and the sun playing over the entrance to the dwelling, it is not unusual to see the Cricket shooting out rubbish, a sign of repairs and fresh excavations. Amidst the joys of spring, the upkeep of the building still continues. It is constantly undergoing improvements and repairs until the owner's decease."

9.3 Characteristics of Insects

While Fabre was observing insects in their native habitats, other biologists were studying the structure of insects which they brought into the laboratory. They found that all insects are divided into three sections: head, thorax, and abdomen. The term "insect" comes from a Latin word meaning "cut into" describing this segmentation. All insects have three pairs of legs for moving about, and air tubes for breathing. Most insects have two pairs of wings, but this is not true of flies nor of some of the simpler forms like lice, which lack wings. While there are many differences in the size of these parts, the fact that an animal has this combination of structures defines it as an insect. The differences in these common parts are the basis on which the insect group is subdivided into twenty-five or more smaller groups.

Insects vary in size from those about 1/100 of an inch long and smaller than certain Protozoa, to grasshopper relatives more than ten inches long, beetles six inches, and moths with a wing spread of eleven inches.

9.4 A Typical Insect

The nimble, familiar *grasshopper* possesses the main features of insects and is typical of the many different kinds of

FIGURE 9-4. *SAFE*

The wispy grasshopper is hard to see in a field of ripening grain.

insects. Grasshoppers also have characteristics of their own and differ among themselves in color, in their wings, and in the shape and size of their bodies. This means that there are various kinds of grasshoppers.

If you have ever tried to catch grasshoppers, you know how difficult it is to see them when they are not in motion. The colors of their wings and upper parts blend with the grass on which they feed. These colors are said to protect the grasshopper, and the expression **protective coloration** is used to describe this protection.

The grasshopper is provided with many such adaptations as protective coloration which help it to escape its enemies. It is further protected by a pair of large eyes on its head and by simple ears on the side of its body. These sense organs enable it to know when its enemies are near. The quickness of grasshoppers in jumping also helps them to escape being eaten.

A grasshopper, like all other animals, must carry on the life processes if it is to live. It must find food and avoid being eaten. It must have oxygen to breathe and must be able to rid its body of waste materials.

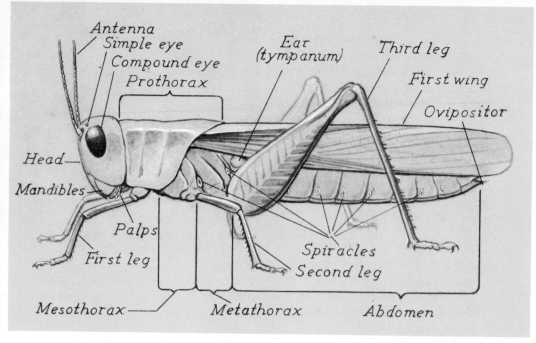

Antenna
Simple eye
Compound eye
Prothorax
Ear (tympanum)
Third leg
First wing
Ovipositor
Head
Mandibles
Palps
First leg
Spiracles
Second leg
Mesothorax
Metathorax
Abdomen

FIGURE 9-5. *A TRUE INSECT*

The grasshopper, showing the general characteristics of an insect, is an invertebrate with three well-defined body parts, six legs, and two antennae.

9.5 External Structure

As a true insect, the grasshopper has three main body regions: *head, thorax,* and *abdomen.* Each one is adapted to do certain kinds of work. The head structures are adapted for food-getting, seeing, and feeling. The thorax has appendages for locomotion: walking, jumping, and flying. The abdomen is adapted to breathing, hearing, and reproduction.

The Head.—On the front of the grasshopper's head are three *simple* eyes [**ocelli** (oh-*sel*-eye)] to detect darkness from light, and near them are two *antennae* for feeling and smelling (Fig. 9-5). On the sides of the head are two *compound* eyes, each composed of many small, six-sided structures known as *facets.* These receive stimuli of light, color, and motion. Each facet shows only one portion of the image, so that the whole picture is a mosaic (Sec. 8.5). Insects seem to have poor eyesight,

which makes it hard for them to see objects that are not moving.

The mouth of the grasshopper has several special parts for food-getting. These are called biting mouth parts (Figs. 9-5 and 9-6). They are an upper lip, the **labrum** (*lay*-brum), and a lower lip, the **labium** (*lay*-bee-um), with feelers (**palps**) for moving the food into its mouth and holding it between its jaws. Inside the mouth are a pair of *mandibles* which move sidewise for cutting and a pair of *maxillae* with palps for carrying the food. The **hypopharynx** (hy-poh-*fair*-ingks), a sort of tongue, is useful in handling the food.

The grasshopper eats leaves, particularly blades of grass. It does not need a keen sense of smell, as does the bee in its search for flowers. However, the grasshopper has special smelling organs in its antennae, those long, jointed feelers which grow out from the head.

122

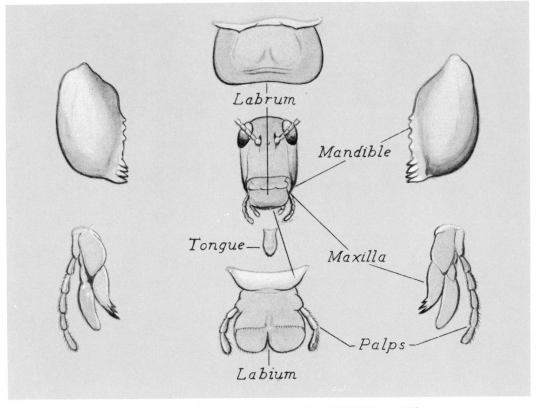

FIGURE 9-6. *GRASSHOPPER HEAD AND MOUTH PARTS*

The mouth parts of the grasshopper are well constructed for cutting and chewing vegetation. Notice the teeth-like projections on the mandibles.

The chewing parts of grasshoppers are so effective that when they come in swarms, they strip an area of all its leaves and grass and even destroy whole fields of growing grain.

The Thorax.—The middle region of the body is called the thorax. It is composed of three parts. The **prothorax** (proh-*thor*-aks), separate from the rest, is provided with the first pair of appendages, in this case *legs*. The **mesothorax** (mes-uh-*thor*-aks) is provided with a second pair of legs, one pair of **spiracles** (*spy*-ruh-k'ls), which are the openings

FIGURE 9-7. *JUMPING LEG AND WINGS*

The flying wings and jumping legs of the grasshopper are attached to the metathorax.

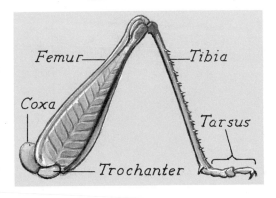

for breathing, and the first pair of wings. The mesothorax is not clearly separated from the third part of the thorax, the **metathorax** (met-uh-*thor*-aks). This last section of the thorax supports the most serviceable appendages, a pair of strong jumping legs and the second pair of wings, the flying wings (Fig. 9-7).

The Abdomen.—The third body region, or abdomen, is clearly divided into ten segments. The first segment, a partial one, contains the two sacs which probably enable the grasshopper to hear. Each auditory sac is covered by a membrane, or **tympanum** (*tim*-pan-um), which corresponds to the eardrum and vibrates with the sound waves. Nerve endings in the sac pick up the vibrations and carry them to the grasshopper's simple brain. The grasshopper produces sounds by rubbing the *tibia* (*tib*-ee-uh) of its hind leg (Fig. 9-7), which has a row of spines, against a wing vein, as a musician might pluck a stringed instrument.

There are two small abdominal openings called *spiracles,* one on each side of the first segment. Fourteen other spiracles are found on the next seven segments, seven spiracles on each side. The spiracles are used for breathing. The last two segments have no spiracles. Instead they are modified for reproduction. In the female the last segment of the abdomen is provided with two pairs of blunt spines that serve as an egg-laying organ called the **ovipositor** (oh-vih-*poz*-ih-ter).

9.6 Internal Structure

The Digestive System.—The digestive system of the grasshopper consists of an *esophagus,* leading from the mouth to the crop; a **crop** for storage; a **gizzard** with horny plates on the walls for grinding the food; a *stomach* containing special bacteria to help in the process of diges-

FIGURE 9-8. *INTERNAL ORGANS OF THE GRASSHOPPER*

Details of the digestive, circulatory, nervous, and reproductive systems can be seen here. The nerve cells, or ganglia, are located beneath the digestive canal and in the head.

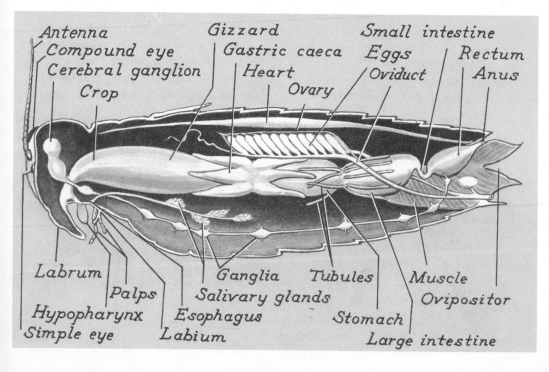

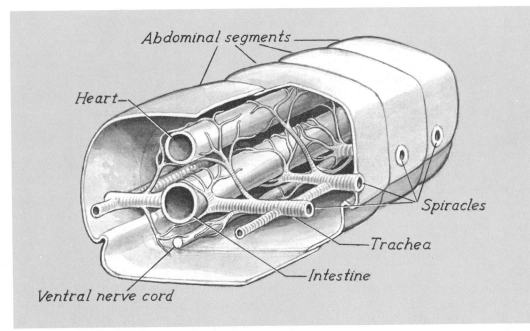

FIGURE 9-9. *RESPIRATORY ORGANS OF THE GRASSHOPPER*

Spiracles on the abdominal segments and the mesothorax are connected to branching air tubes called *tracheae*. The fine branches of the tracheae carry oxygen directly to all the tissues.

tion; and the *intestines,* ending in an enlarged portion called the **rectum.** There are also **salivary glands,** secreting digestive enzymes which act on food as it is chewed, and gastric **caeca** (*see*-kuh) which pour digestive fluid into the stomach to act on the food (Fig. 9-8). Digested food is *absorbed* directly into the blood which fills the body cavity, and is then taken from the blood by the cells which need it and is *assimilated* into a part of the insect's body.

The Circulatory System.—The grasshopper has a tube-like *heart* located along the middle of its back. When the heart contracts it forces the blood into a large vessel extending to the head. This heart is filled with and surrounded by colorless blood, and is open at the anterior (front) end. The blood is forced into the body spaces between the internal organs and re-enters the heart through narrow slits called **ostia,** which open inward. This is an *open circulatory system* because there are no capillaries. The blood serves mainly to transport food and wastes.

The Respiratory System.—All animals have some structure which brings oxygen to every part of their bodies and gets rid of carbon dioxide, a waste product. The grasshopper does not have lungs as we do, nor does it breathe through its mouth. On each side of its abdomen are eight evenly arranged *spiracles.* These lead into branching air tubes, the **tracheae** (*tray*-kee-ee) (Fig. 9-9). There are also spiracles, one on each side of the mesothorax and the metathorax. The branching tracheae are kept open by means of spiral threads, so that the pressure of the muscles and other organs cannot flatten or close them. The grasshopper breathes by expanding and contracting its abdomen, thus changing the pressure in the air tubes which lead into the air sacs which are in the abdomen.

The tracheae continue to branch until the subdivisions are so small that they can be seen only by aid of the microscope. These fine branches extend to the tiny cells of which the body of the grasshopper is composed. Here the oxygen dissolves in moisture in the microscopic tubes and passes by *diffusion* (Sec. 1.11) to the living protoplasm of the cells. Carbon dioxide is given off to the air in these breathing tubes. This use of oxygen and giving-off of carbon dioxide by the protoplasm is **respiration.**

Since a grasshopper breathes through its spiracles, it would drown in water even though its head were above the surface. An oil film or fine dust particles can clog its spiracles. This method of killing insects is used for many kinds, but poison bait is most frequently used to destroy grasshoppers.

The Excretory System.—The grasshopper must get rid of the waste substances that form in its body, or it cannot live. It has organs of excretion which remove all wastes from the body. The gaseous waste, carbon dioxide, that is formed in all animals as a result of their life processes, passes from the tracheae of the grasshopper's body out through the spiracles and into the air. The liquid wastes are collected from the blood by *Malpighian tubules* which pour them into the intestine. These wastes then leave the body through the *anus.*

The Nervous System.—In the grasshopper the life process of irritability (sensation) is performed by a nervous system. This consists of nerves and **ganglia** (*gang*-lee-uh), which are clusters of nerve cells, arranged in a row beneath the digestive canal and in the top of the head. Nerves connect this central chain of ganglia with all parts of the body. On the head are found *com-*

pound and *simple eyes,* special organs for feeling and smelling (the *antennae*), and organs of taste on the mouth parts. The organs of hearing, the *tympani,* are located on the abdomen, where they are protected by the wings when at rest.

By means of all the specialized nervous organs, the grasshopper is able to see, feel, hear, smell, and taste with a high degree of efficiency and is thus made aware of food and enemies.

The Reproductive System.—The reproductive system of the female consists of two *ovaries,* which produce the eggs, and the tubes which carry the eggs to the outside of the body (Fig. 9-8). The reproductive system of the male grasshopper consists of two *testes,* which produce sperm cells to fertilize the eggs, and the tubes which join and carry the sperm cells to the outside of the body.

9.7 Life Cycle of the Grasshopper

The female lays the eggs in the autumn in shallow holes, which she digs in the ground or in a decayed log with her *ovipositor.* The following spring the eggs hatch into small, wingless grasshoppers called **nymphs** (*nimfs*) (Fig. 9-10). The nymph has a firm outer covering, the *exoskeleton* made of chitin, which does not grow so fast as the nymph itself. Accordingly, at certain times, this exoskeleton is shed, and the nymph grows a new one. This shedding, or *molting,* continues for four to seven weeks until the fifth and last molt, when the nymph becomes an adult with wings and is fully mature and able to continue the life cycle.

Adult grasshoppers may be found during the summer in meadows, flying, hopping, crawling, and feeding on grass, grain, and other crops. The adults mate at this time, and the females lay eggs to provide for the next generation.

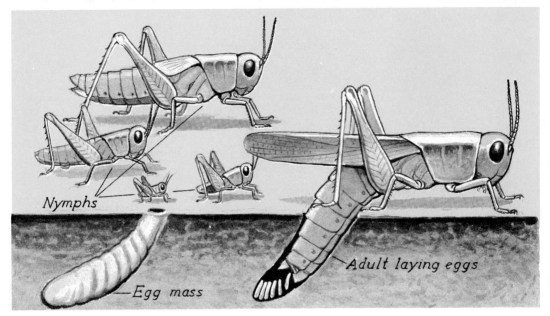

FIGURE 9-10. *LIFE CYCLE OF THE GRASSHOPPER*

Eggs laid in the fall hatch the following spring into wingless nymphs. These show little change in form as they grow, but molt several times, and finally become mature winged adults, an incomplete metamorphosis.

9.8 Metamorphosis

When animals pass through different stages of growth in which marked changes in their appearance take place, they are said to undergo **metamorphosis** (met-uh-*mor*-fuh-siss). These changes are more marked in insects like ants and bees than in the grasshopper. For this reason we speak of two forms of metamorphosis—complete and incomplete.

Incomplete Metamorphosis. — The newly hatched grasshopper, though very small, looks enough like a wingless grasshopper to be identified as belonging to the grasshopper family. Its form does not change much from the time it is hatched until it is full grown. Thus the grasshoppers become adults by the growing process termed **incomplete metamorphosis** and show no marked change in form (Fig. 9-10). Complete metamorphosis will be discussed in connection with the life cycle of the butterfly in Chapter 10.

9.9 Classification of the Grasshopper

For convenience in study, as was mentioned in Section 6.1, all known animals have been grouped into several large

FIGURE 9-11. *FARM PEST*

The grasshopper can be a serious threat to crops, especially grain.

127

groups, known as *phyla* (singular, *phylum*). Each phylum is divided into groups called **classes,** which in turn are subdivided into **orders.** The orders are broken down into **families.** The final divisions, of the families, are called **genus** and **species** (*spee*-sheez). Animals are commonly known by their *genus* and *species* names. Later in our study we shall learn more about classification.

The grasshopper has been placed in the phylum *Arthropoda,* the large division which includes all the animals with jointed feet. Such animals are insects, crayfish, spiders, and centipedes. The phylum Arthropoda is divided into five main classes. The grasshopper belongs to the class *Insecta,* which also includes beetles, butterflies, and many others. In fact, the class Insecta is the largest class of animals. Insects, as we know, have six legs and three body regions. The class Insecta is divided into orders according to wing structure. The grasshopper belongs to the order *Orthoptera* (or-*thop*-ter-uh), the straight-winged insects. This order also includes the crickets and katydids, cockroaches, walking sticks, and praying mantises. The order Orthoptera is divided into families. The grasshopper belongs to the family *Acrididae* (uh-*krih*-dih-dee). Each particular kind of a grasshopper belongs to a division of the family called the genus. A particular member of a genus has a species name. The grasshopper, then, is classified as follows:

> Phylum—Arthropoda
> Class—Insecta
> Order—Orthoptera
> Family—Acrididae

Genus and species names are different for the different kinds of grasshoppers.

9.10 Relatives of the Grasshopper

As you search for grasshoppers, you may also find some crickets, cockroaches, praying mantises, katydids, and walking sticks. All of these belong to the order Orthoptera but to *different families.* Notice how the shape and color have been modified to adapt them to their surroundings. As you study them, try to explain why the cockroach is

FIGURE 9-12. *AGGRESSIVE AND WARNING COLORATION*
The praying mantis (*left*) blends into the background, a milkweed plant, to hide from its prey. How does the wasp (*right*) use color to advantage?

Century photo   Harrison from National Audubon Society

placed in this order, or how a praying mantis appears to live up to its name. You will find out many exciting things if you decide to make a special study of the grasshoppers and their relatives.

An insect such as the praying mantis, whose colors enable it to hide and lie in wait, making it more successful in catching its prey, is said to exhibit **aggressive coloration**. Some insects that are believed to be unpleasant to taste have bright colors on their bodies to warn the animals that prey on insects that they are unsuitable as food. The conspicuous bands of color on wasps are said to warn animals that these insects have a dangerous sting. Such insects show **warning coloration**.

The walking stick, a relative of the grasshopper, is the size and shape of a small twig—a form of protection called **protective resemblance**. When frightened, it forces its antennae forward to add to its length so that it more nearly resembles its surroundings.

9.11 Economic Importance of the Grasshopper

Since the grasshopper eats the leaves of plants, a great swarm of grasshoppers causes a serious loss of crops, especially rye, oats, and wheat. The grasshopper is therefore an enemy of man. The "plague of locusts" mentioned in the Bible refers to grasshoppers. In some of the western states grasshoppers come in great swarms year after year and destroy annually crops estimated to be worth many millions of dollars. Parts of China have been devastated by grasshoppers, but they are more easily controlled there because the Chinese eat them with relish. They are also sold as food in the Philippines. The legs are usually removed and the bodies roasted. Ordinarily, because of the activities of their natural enemies,

Hugh Spencer

FIGURE 9-13. *WALKING STICK*
Can you tell this relative of the grasshopper from the twig he's sitting on?

their number does not become alarming.

Among the natural enemies of these insects are the birds, which do much to control them. Some of the grasshopper's greatest destroyers are the quail, bluebird, sparrow hawk, butcher bird, crow, red-winged blackbird, and kingbird. Skunks, toads, snakes, wasps, spiders, and certain beetles also eat grasshoppers.

There are closely related insects that are harmful, as cockroaches, which destroy food and carry disease, and crickets, that eat roots. There are also tree crickets which frequently lay their eggs in raspberry canes, killing the cane above the place where the egg is laid.

The results of the grasshopper's activities are more important than it might seem. (1) It eats plants which are useful to cattle or man. (2) It produces more grasshoppers. (3) On the other hand, it serves as food for birds and other animals. (4) It sets free waste carbon dioxide, which can be used by green plants

FIGURE 9-14. *PLAGUE*

The locusts, or short-horned grasshoppers, descend on a field by the thousands, eating every green thing in sight. This picture was taken in Tanganyika, East Africa, where the locust menace is a challenge to modern science.

Lieb from Ewing Galloway

in making food. (5) When it dies and decomposes, its chemical substances are returned to the soil and air to be used again by plants.

FACTS TO REMEMBER

The class *Insecta* is characterized by having three body regions, three pairs of legs, and breathing by spiracles and tracheae. They are similar to other members of the phylum Arthropoda by having an exoskeleton, jointed appendages, and a segmented body.

The *head* of the grasshopper, a typical insect, has two compound eyes and three simple eyes, a pair of antennae for feeling and smelling, and biting mouth parts well adapted for chewing leaves, grass, and other vegetation.

The *thorax* consists of three regions which bear the two pairs of walking legs, the one pair of jumping legs, and in addition the two pairs of wings.

The *abdomen* is divided into ten segments. The first segment contains a pair of auditory sacs for hearing, and the first eight segments have a pair of spiracles, one on each side, for breathing. The last two segments are modified for reproduction.

The *internal structure* of the grasshopper is highly specialized. It has a complete digestive system, an open circulatory system, and organs of excretion. The respiratory system consists of branching tracheae, which open to the outside through the spiracles. The nervous system is mainly a ventral nerve cord with ganglia that send out branches to all parts of the body.

The *life cycle* of the grasshopper is characterized by incomplete metamorphosis, with egg, nymph, and adult stages.

The *classification* of insects and other living things is determined by similarities in body structure. Each phylum is subdivided into class, order, family, genus, and species.

WORDS TO REMEMBER

aggressive coloration
caeca
crop
ganglia
gizzard
hypopharynx
incomplete
    metamorphosis
labium

labrum
mesothorax
metamorphosis
metathorax
nymph
ocelli
ostia
ovipositor
palps

protective coloration
protective resemblance
prothorax
rectum
salivary glands
spiracles
tracheae
tympanum
warning coloration

QUESTIONS

1. Why are the insects so important to man?
2. Name and describe the body divisions of the grasshopper.
3. In what way is the grasshopper protected from its enemies?
4. How does it get food? Breathe? Reproduce?
5. Give its life cycle.
6. What is metamorphosis?
7. What kind of metamorphosis does the grasshopper undergo? Name the stages in this type.
8. To what class and to what order does the grasshopper belong?
9. What is the economic importance of grasshoppers and their relatives?
10. Describe one relative of the grasshopper with which you are familiar.

COMPLETION TEST

As your teacher or classmate reads the following incomplete statements, with your book closed, write on a clean sheet of paper the word or phrase which correctly completes the statement.

1. Two close relatives of the grasshopper are _____ and _____.
2. Food is stored in the _____ of the grasshoppers.
3. Horny plates are found on the walls of the _____.
4. One of the first men to study insects in their home life was _____.
5. There are _____ pairs of spiracles on the abdomen.
6. There are _____ pairs of spiracles on the thorax.
7. The egg-laying organ in the female is called the _____.
8. The jumping legs are attached to the _____.
9. The grasshopper has _____ pairs of wings.
10. The smelling organs of the grasshopper are located in its _____.

PROJECTS

1. *Study of a Live Grasshopper.*—Collect a few grasshoppers and place them in a jar with a little grass sprinkled with water or in the insect cage. Choose a large specimen for special study. Keep an *accurate record* of

your observations by making notes and answering the following questions while you are looking at the specimen.

1. What are its means of locomotion?

2. Compare its jump with its length. What would be the proportional distance for a man six feet tall to jump?

3. How does the grasshopper obtain food?

4. What protection from enemies does it gain from its color?

5. Notice the division of the body into three regions: *head, thorax,* which has wings and legs attached, and *abdomen.* How large is the head compared with the thorax and abdomen?

6. The body is covered with a skin-like substance known as *chitin.* This is called the skeleton of the grasshopper, and because it is on the outside of the body, it is termed an *exoskeleton.* How does it protect the grasshopper's body?

7. When the living grasshopper is held between the thumb and finger, it "spits molasses." This is partially digested food from its crop.

II. *Examination of a Preserved Specimen.*—Since a living grasshopper is apt to move around, you may wish to continue your study by using a preserved specimen or one freshly killed. Keep an *accurate record* of your observations on composition paper and make the drawing on plain (unruled) paper.

1. Decide where the divisions of the body of the grasshopper come: head, thorax, and abdomen; the position of the eyes.

2. How are the antennae located in relation to the eyes?

3. How many distinct mouth parts are there?

4. How do the jaws work?

5. Notice the attachment of the head to the thorax. The head fits into the thorax. The loose anterior (front) portion of the thorax is the prothorax (forward thorax). The first pair of legs is attached to it.

6. Sketch the prothorax to show the attachment of its legs.

7. The portion of the thorax back of the prothorax is divided into two regions: the mesothorax (middle thorax) and the metathorax. The inner wings are used in flying. Spread out an inner wing and draw it.

8. The leg of the grasshopper consists of: a section close to the body (the coxa); a small part next to the coxa (the trochanter); a long muscular part free from spines (femur); a slender spiny part (tibia); and three segments of the foot (tarsus). The last segment of the foot is furnished with hooks which help the grasshopper in climbing; the spines on the tibia prevent slipping as the grasshopper jumps. The large muscles in the femur of the last pair of legs, the spines on the tibia, and the hooks on the tarsus are special adaptations which help the grasshopper in various ways.

9. Notice the tapering abdomen, composed of ten segments or parts of segments. Notice the depression and membrane, the tympanum, in the first segment. This is the auditory organ, but it is not a true ear.

10. The spiracles are located on the sides of the abdomen and thorax.

III. List the life processes mentioned in Chapter 1 and show how the grasshopper is able to carry on each.

IV. Study grasshoppers in the field and find out how they are fitted to their habitat. How many different kinds of grasshoppers can you find?

REFERENCES

Barlowe, *A Child's Book of Insects.* Maxton.
Buchsbaum, *Animals without Backbones.* The University of Chicago Press.
Comstock, *Handbook of Nature Study.* Comstock.
Chee, *How to Know the Immature Insects.* Brown.
Fabre, *Life of the Grasshopper.* Dodd, Mead.
Fabre, *Insect Ways.* Dodd, Mead.
Goodnight and Goodnight, *Zoology.* Mosby.
Guyer, *Animal Biology.* Harper.
Lane, *All About the Insect World.* Random House.
Lutz, *The Fieldbook of Insects.* Putnam's.
Neider, *The Fabulous Insects.* Harper.
Oman and Cushman, *Collection and Preservation of Insects.* U.S. Department of Agriculture, Publication 601.
Storer, *General Zoölogy.* McGraw-Hill.
Swain, *Insects in Their World.* Garden City.
Ward's Natural Science Establishment, Inc., *How to Make an Insect Collection.*
Zim, Cottom, *Insects: Golden Nature Guide.* Simon and Schuster.

CHAPTER 10

Butterflies and Moths

10.1 Butterflies and Moths

Butterflies and moths belong to the insect order **Lepidoptera** (lep-ih-*dop*-ter-uh*). This group of insects is characterized by two pairs of membranous *wings* covered with tiny *scales,* which produce the varied and brilliant colors for which they are noted. The adults have sucking mouth parts with which they obtain *nectar* from the flowers. The *maxillae* are lengthened to form a very long, coiled tube, called a **proboscis** (proh-*boss*-iss), through which the butterfly or moth obtains nectar from the flowers, taking it into the body in much the same way that you might use a straw to drink milk. The other mouth parts are greatly reduced in size, and the mandibles are usually absent.

Butterflies are among the most attractive insects. Many of them are helpful in pollinating flowers. As the butterfly goes from flower to flower, its head brushes against the pollen, which is carried from one to the other, making it possible for the flowers to grow seeds. Many moths, on the other hand, are destructive to food and clothing.

10.2 Life Cycle of the Monarch Butterfly

The structure of the monarch butterfly is similar to that of the grasshopper in its main features, since both are insects.

However, there are some differences in mouth parts, in life cycles, and in certain other characteristics, for these two insects belong to different orders. The grasshopper, as you know, belongs to the order Orthoptera. The butterfly belongs to the order Lepidoptera.

Complete Metamorphosis. — When June weather comes to the northern states, the monarch butterfly arrives from the South. The females begin at once to lay *eggs* on milkweed plants. The eggs hatch in a few days—the time depending on the temperature—into *caterpillars* that feed on the leaves of the milkweeds. Each caterpillar has three pairs of jointed legs near the head and five pairs of leglike structures along the posterior (rear) region that serve for clinging. The caterpillar, or **larva** (*lahr*-vuh*), sheds its skin (*molts*) and with each shedding grows larger, but does not show any signs of wings as does the nymph of the grasshopper. It merely becomes a larger caterpillar.

Just before the fourth molt it attaches itself to a leaf or stem and hangs for a few days by a knot of silk with its head down until it molts for the fourth time. After this molt it is a **pupa** (*pyoo*-puh), yellowish green with golden spots. In this stage it cannot eat, for it has no mouth, and it cannot move about, for it has no legs or wings. But the pupa can

Hugh Spencer

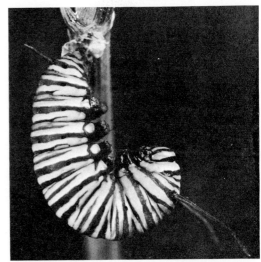

Lynwood M. Chace from National Audubon Society

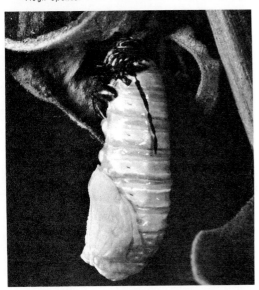

Louis Quit from National Audubon Society

Edwin Way Teale

FIGURE 10-1. *MONARCH BUTTERFLY*

The butterfly passes through stages of growth from egg (here magnified 60 times) to adult. After the fourth molting of the larva (*top right*) it becomes a pupa (*lower left*) from which the adult will emerge.

take in oxygen, so that it is able to live and grow.

During this stage the pupa lies in a **chrysalis** (*krih*-s'l-iss). There is a striking change taking place inside this hard, green covering. Wings, new legs, different mouth parts with a long, coiled tongue, and a nervous system of a differ-

ent form are growing into working order while this pupa hangs so quietly. After a few days the green pupa case breaks open, and the *adult* crawls out with its wings crumpled. Within a few hours the wings expand and smooth out their wrinkles, and the butterfly is ready to fly away to feed on the nectar of flowers.

BUTTERFLIES AND MOTHS

This development, starting with the *egg,* passing through the *larva* and *pupa* stages, and ending with the *adult* butterfly, is called **complete metamorphosis.**

Complete metamorphosis may be defined as the series of changes through which the insect passes, from egg into caterpillar or larva (plural, larvae), then into pupa (plural, pupae), and finally into a full-grown insect. Ants, bees, butterflies, and certain other insects undergo complete metamorphosis.

10.3 Migrations of the Monarch Butterfly

The monarch butterfly is one of the few butterflies that **migrate** (*my*-grayt). This means that monarch butterflies travel to different localities during different seasons. Professor John Henry Comstock (page 678) tells the story of the monarch's migrations in his book *How to Know the Butterflies:*

"The male monarch is the dandy among butterflies *par excellence.* He is not only trim in figure and gorgeous in color, but on each hind wing he carries a black sachet bag for the allurement of his ladylove. And she is as brilliant as he, but lacks the perfume pockets. "I am the monarch of all I survey," is exemplified in the confident, serene flight of this butterfly; the species is nauseous to the birds in both the caterpillar and adult stages, and by their bold actions they show the result of this immunity.

"But the monarchs have troubles of their own, even if the bird problem is eliminated. Undisturbed, they spread and flourished in their native tropic America, until it became a question of sufficient food-plants to nourish their numerous progeny. Because of this they began pushing farther north and south during the seasons of plant growth. As they could not endure the northern win-ter, they came north for the summer and went back in the autumn.

"This northern migration is accomplished thus: the mother butterfly follows the spring northward as it advances as far as she finds milkweed sprouting; there she deposits her eggs, from which hatch individuals that carry on the journey, and which in their turn lay eggs as far north as possible. Thus generation after generation pushes on until late in the season we hear of them as far north as Hudson Bay. As the cool weather approaches, these emigrant butterflies gather in great flocks and fly back to the South.

"It is quite impossible for us to understand how the flocks of butterflies are guided in their migrations. None of them are travel-wise, like the leaders of the bird flocks, but still they follow their direction as steadily as the wind will allow. Nor is the monarch satisfied with these journeys to the north and south; it is the strongest flyer of all the butterflies and does not hesitate to try its fortune over the seas. It has been found five hundred miles from shore. Either by flight or by stowaway in vessels it has pressed eastward to Europe and westward to the isles of the Pacific. Well is it named the monarch, for it is the most daring butterfly that we know, pushing back its geographical boundaries to the edges of the Arctic zone, and exploring leisurely the seas of the Occident and Orient. In the North there is but one brood during the summer, while in the South there are many more. No hibernating specimen has ever been found."

Perhaps some present-day high school student may find out how monarch butterflies are guided, or find one *hibernating* (*hy*-ber-nay-ting). **Hibernating** means passing the winter in a state of inactivity.

10.4 Coloration and Mimicry among Insects

Butterflies and moths show **protective coloration,** especially those forms that have the upper surface of the wings colored like the trunks of trees on which the insects rest. Such dull colors are effective in obscuring the insects. The contrast in color is striking in all of these insects, if we compare the brilliant colors seen on the hind wings when the insect is flying.

The brightly colored insects often have imitators which have neither an unpleasant taste nor a dangerous sting. This similarity is known as **mimicry** (*mim*-ih-kree). For example, the monarch butterfly is distasteful to birds and they soon learn to avoid it. The viceroy, a slightly smaller butterfly, has almost the same colors, but is good to eat. Nevertheless, birds do not prey upon it very much because it mimics the monarch butterfly.

Sometimes insects assume the shape of the objects on which they most frequently rest. This is called *protective resemblance* (Sec. 9.10). The walking leaf looks much like a large green leaf. The dead leaf butterfly appears so much like a dead leaf that, when the wings are folded, it even has a small space on each wing without scales which resembles a hole in a dead leaf.

10.5 Characteristics of Butterflies and Moths

Although butterflies and moths belong to the same order, there are several differences between them. Butterflies have (1) knoblike structures at the ends of their antennae, (2) slender bodies, (3) wings vertical when at rest, (4) a pupa without **cocoon** (kuh-*koon*), which is known as a *chrysalis,* and (5) are usually active by day.

137

American Museum of Natural History

FIGURE 10-2. *MIMICRY*

By resembling the bad-tasting monarch (*top*), the viceroy escapes the birds.

In contrast, moths have (1) feathery antennae, (2) plump bodies, (3) wings horizontal when at rest, (4) pupae in cocoons, and (5) usually fly at night.

FIGURE 10-3. *WALKING LEAF*

The insect lives among the leaves of trees and shrubs where it is hard to spot because of its shape and color.

Croy from Black Star

Cecropia moth

Monarch butterfly

FIGURE 10-4. *COMPARISON OF THE MOTH AND BUTTERFLY*
The feathery antennae and plumb body of the moth are here contrasted with the knobbed antennae and slender body of the butterfly.

10.6 The Importance of Moths to Man

The life cycles of butterflies and moths are similar. Both insects pass through complete metamorphosis, with four stages of development: egg, larva, pupa, and adult. Figure 10-5 shows the life cycle of the codling moth.

The larva which hatches from the egg of a moth usually forms a silklike nest (*cocoon*) around the pupa. From this

FIGURE 10-5. *LIFE CYCLE OF THE CODLING MOTH*
The four main stages in the development of the codling moth—egg, larva, pupa, and adult—are shown. The larva bores into an apple.

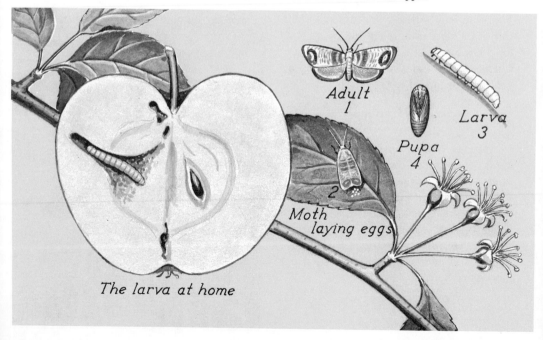

Adult
1

Larva
3

Pupa
4

Moth
laying eggs
2

The larva at home

Courtesy U.S. Dept. of Agriculture

Courtesy U.S. Dept. of Agriculture   Courtesy U.S. Dept. of Agriculture

FIGURE 10-6. *THE SILKWORM MOTH: A LIFE CYCLE*

From the newly laid eggs of the silkworm (*upper left*) are hatched the worm-like larvae (*upper right*), which feed on mulberry leaves. The adult larva spins a cocoon (*lower left*), the source of raw silk. Like the butterfly, the winged moth escapes from the cocoon fully developed (*lower right*).

cocoon the adult emerges. Some adults help to pollinate flowers. The larval stages of some moths are useful to man. For example, silkworm larvae manufacture silk for cloth. Some moths are destructive to clothing. The clothes moth eats wool, feathers, and fur. Certain moths destroy food, as the European corn borer, and the codling moth larva in the apple. The tent caterpillar, gypsy, and brown-tailed moths destroy foliage trees.

Since different moths are destructive in various stages of their life cycles, it is essential to recognize them and to know their life habits if they are to be brought under control. You will be able to help

protect your own food and clothing as you become more familiar with the insects which destroy them.

10.7 The Codling Moth

The "worm" so often seen in apples (Fig. 10-5) is the young of the codling moth and is called a *larva*. It hatches from the egg which the moth laid on the leaves surrounding the apple clusters. The larvae feed for a few hours on the leaves and then go toward the nearest fruit. The larva bores its way into the core, eats and grows, and sheds its skin (*molts*) three times before it is full grown. Then it bores its way through the side of the apple and finds some protected spot, usually under the bark of the tree, where it spins a cocoon around itself.

The larvae or "apple worms" destroy millions of dollars worth of apples each year in spite of man's effort to spray the trees.

After staying in the cocoon for a time, it sheds its skin for the fourth time, forming a *pupa*. In this pupa stage, it has no mouth, or legs, or wings. But it can wiggle and can take in air through the openings in the sides of its body. The length of time it remains in the pupa stage depends on the temperature. Finally, the fifth molt occurs, the *adult* moth emerges from the pupa, and in a few days the females are ready to lay eggs. The codling moth has then completed the four stages of its life cycle.

Codling moths may best be destroyed by applying a spray containing some poison just after the petals have fallen from the apple blossoms. Poisons commonly used for this purpose are lead arsenate or calcium arsenate. The spray should not be used while the blossoms are on the tree, because then the helpful bees which visit the blossoms are killed and no harm is done to the destructive codling moths that come later.

10.8 Silkworms

Silkworms belong to the group of spinning moths and are valuable friends to man. The silkworm larvae feed preferably on mulberry leaves, although they will eat the leaves of the Osage orange and lettuce.

After the larvae feed for about a month, they spin their cocoons. The material for the cocoon is manufactured in the **silk glands,** which open directly under the mouth of the larva. It takes three or four days for the larva to make its cocoon, which is constructed of a smooth thread usually more than one thousand feet long. In a week or two pupation ends, and the adult escapes from its silken home by moistening the cement between the silk threads on one end of the cocoon.

It takes about three thousand cocoons to make a pound of raw silk, and about ninety cocoon fibers are required to make a thread of sewing silk. Twenty-five to fifty thousand cocoons are used in securing enough material for a silk dress. The cocoons from which the silken threads are secured are baked or steamed two or three days after the larvae have completed them. This process kills the pupa, for cocoons from which the adults have escaped are unsatisfactory for the manufacture of silk.

10.9 Clothes Moths

You may have seen small moths with pointed and fringed wings, flitting about your room or clothes closet. The adults emerge from May to August, eat no food, and after depositing their eggs on woolen material, soon die. The eggs hatch into white, naked larvae about a half inch long which feed on furs, feathers, hair, woolen materials, and museum specimens. More than one generation may arise in a season.

You may help to protect your clothes by taking some of these protective measures: (1) constant watchfulness, for any treatment that kills the larva already in fabrics may not have any lasting effects in keeping other clothes moths from depositing their eggs if the material is left exposed; (2) thorough brushing and beating if possible, and placing the clothes in the sun before any treatment is applied; (3) wrapping in unbroken paper, especially newspaper; (4) use of paradichlorobenzene or other moth poisons in chests and trunks.

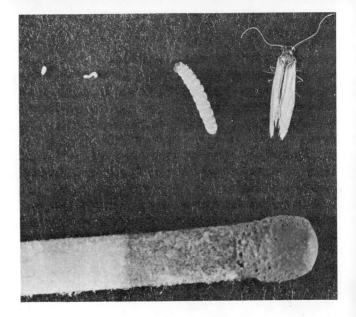

FIGURE 10-7. *PEST*

The clothes moth, familiar to every householder, goes through a complete metamorphosis from egg to adult moth. The larvae feed on wool, feathers, and fur, doing incalculable damage every year.

Courtesy Gulf Oil Corporation

10.10 The Gypsy Moth

The gypsy moth came to this country from France. In 1869 a college professor in Massachusetts imported some egg clusters for study. One day a sudden wind blew off the net which he was using to protect them and scattered all his materials. The gypsy moth had no natural enemies in this country and spread rapidly. Warning was given that it might become a pest, but the government paid little attention to this until twelve years later, when legislative action was finally taken.

In the late summer, the female moth lays about 450 eggs in a cluster. The cluster is generally laid on the bark of a tree, but often hidden under loose boards or in woodpiles. Yellowish, hairlike structures are scattered over this mass for protection. The eggs hatch the next spring, usually around the first of May. The small caterpillars eat leaves and grow to be nearly two and one-half inches long before spinning their cocoons in some sheltered place. They remain in the pupa stage for about two weeks, and then the adult moth appears. After a few days the females lay their eggs and then die, thus completing the life cycle.

The larvae of the gypsy moth and its relatives, the tussock and brown tail moths also brought over from Europe, eat the leaves of fruit and shade trees, often killing them. In some areas the loss is so great that evergreens are planted instead of shade trees, since the larvae do not destroy evergreens. Some of the natural enemies of the gypsy moth include certain wasps, flies, and European ground beetles, which have been imported to help destroy the gypsy moth larvae. Another way of fighting this pest is to cover its egg clusters with creosote. This destroys the eggs. Quarantine and inspection by the government are other control measures in use.

10.11 The European Corn Borer

This insect was introduced into the United States in 1909 and 1910, in broom corn imported from Hungary and Italy. It has spread widely throughout this country. The larva is destructive to corn, beans, beets, potatoes, Swiss chard, and many other of the food plants of

L. W. Brownell

FIGURE 10-8. *UNINVITED GUEST*

The European corn borer is responsible for the wholesale destruction of young ears of corn and other plants.

man and animals, also to dahlias, hops, cotton, and sunflowers.

The European corn borer spends the winter in a tunnel made in the plant upon which it has been feeding. In April or May the borer, which is a caterpillar, spins a cocoon in the tunnel and in about nineteen days develops into the adult moth. After mating, the female deposits her eggs on the young corn shoots in small masses, each egg overlapping the adjoining egg in the manner of shingles. The females deposit about 350 eggs, on an average, but some lay more than a thousand. These eggs hatch in about seven days. The young borer soon begins to eat its way into the inside of the plant and within fifty days has grown into an adult. Thus a second brood is ready to be hatched.

The females of this later generation lay more eggs, usually about 450, which are frequently deposited on or near the forming ears of corn. These eggs hatch

FIGURE 10-9. *TENT CATERPILLAR*

The larvae (*left*) of certain kinds of moths are harmful to forest and orchard trees. They are named for their white, tent-like web attached to tree branches (*right*). The caterpillars in one tent can eat 12,000 leaves.

Lynwood M. Chace

Carl Berger from Black Star

FIGURE 10-10. *TOMATO WORM WITH PARASITES*

These cocoons are the result of eggs laid by the female ichneumon fly in the caterpillar's body. Before the flies emerge from the cocoons, the caterpillar will die. Many insect pests are destroyed in this way.

Black Star

in seven days; then the borers begin their destructive feeding. The caterpillars of this second generation are the ones that pass the winter in the tunnels of the corn or other plant on which they have been feeding. For this reason all cornstalks should be burned after the ears have been picked and the stubble should be plowed under. Sometimes it is necessary to plant a crop that the corn borer does not readily attack until most of the borers have been destroyed from the lack of food.

The name *corn borer* is given to the larvae of several different kinds of insects that burrow into the stalks and ears of corn as well as into flowering plants and weeds.

The seriousness of the destruction caused by the European corn borer has led the United States Department of Agriculture to place strict regulations on the importation from foreign territory of plants which may be likely to contain this insect.

10.12 Other Harmful Moths

The larvae of the carpenter moths burrow into the wood of trees, those of leaf rollers roll the leaves upward and feed on the leaves, and tent caterpillars make weblike tents in the branches. The tomato, cabbage, tobacco, and cotton boll worms destroy vegetables and crops. The cutworms and army worms destroy the young roots of many garden and crop plants.

10.13 Enemies of Butterflies and Moths

Like most insects, butterflies have numerous enemies without which they would soon become a scourge. Chief among these enemies are the *parasitic flies,* the females of which lay their eggs on the bodies of many kinds of caterpillars (larval butterflies). When these eggs hatch, the larvae burrow their way into the body of the caterpillar, feeding upon the tissue of their **host,** as the victim in which they feed is called.

These parasitic larvae so weaken the caterpillar that it dies. The larvae grow rapidly, and before the caterpillar dies they reach the stage at which they turn into pupae. When they are ready to pupate, they eat their way out of the body of the caterpillar and spin a cocoon, which in some cases remains attached to the body of the caterpillar.

Other enemies of butterflies and moths are the *birds.* Many birds live entirely upon caterpillars, and some seek them as food in all stages of their development and growth. The eggs laid on the twigs and trunks of trees are eaten by chickadees, nuthatches, brown creepers, and woodpeckers. The larvae are eaten by many birds, notably cuckoos, bluebirds, wrens, blackbirds, orioles, blue jays, crows, and house sparrows. The cocoons and pupae are sought by chickadees, woodpeckers, nuthatches, and brown creepers. The adult insects are preyed upon by house sparrows, chipping sparrows, and the whole group of flycatchers.

FACTS TO REMEMBER

Butterflies and *moths* belong to the insect order Lepidoptera, the scaly-winged insects. They develop through stages of *complete metamorphosis,* with egg, larva, pupa, and adult. Butterflies differ from moths in having slender bodies, knobbed antennae, a *chrysalis* in the pupa stage, and in being active during the day.

Among the various ways that insects use to protect themselves from their enemies are *protective coloration, mimicry,* and *protective resemblance.*

Butterflies and moths are beneficial and harmful to man in a variety of ways. The butterflies help pollinate flowers and the silkworm manufactures silk. However, such moths as the codling moth, gypsy moth, and corn borer destroy foliage and grain, while the clothes moth eats certain fabrics. Natural enemies like birds and parasitic flies keep butterflies and moths from becoming too numerous.

WORDS TO REMEMBER

chrysalis	host	proboscis
cocoon	larva	protective coloration
complete	migrate	protective resemblance
metamorphosis	mimicry	pupa
hibernate	molt	silk glands
	nectar	

QUESTIONS

1. What distinguishes the Lepidoptera (butterflies and moths) from the Orthoptera (grasshoppers)?
2. Name the four stages of complete metamorphosis.
3. Describe the metamorphosis of the monarch butterfly.
4. How do moths differ from butterflies?
5. Give the life cycle of the codling moth. Why is it so important?
6. Describe the stage in the life history of the clothes moth when it is destructive.
7. Mention two immigrant pests and state how they are harmful.
8. What are the chief enemies of moths and butterflies?
9. Explain why butterflies and grasshoppers belong to
    a. the same phylum—Arthropoda

b. the same class—Insecta

c. different orders—Lepidoptera and Orthoptera

10. Name one insect that manufactures material for clothing and one that destroys clothes.

11. Give an example of each of the following:

a. protective coloration

b. mimicry

c. protective resemblance

COMPLETION TEST

As your teacher or classmate reads the following incomplete statements, with your book closed, write on a clean sheet of paper the word or phrase which best completes the statement.

1. The _____ is one of the few butterflies in this country which migrate.

2. The "worm" of the codling moth is called the _____.

3. The _____ of the clothes moth damages the clothing.

4. Silkworm larvae feed on _____ leaves.

5. Parasitic flies lay their eggs on _____.

6. Some enemies of butterflies and moths are the _____.

7. The monarch butterfly lays its eggs on the _____.

8. Adult butterflies and moths have _____ mouth parts.

9. When a larva sheds its skin, it is said to _____.

10. The _____ stage of a butterfly is called a chrysalis.

PROJECTS

I. *Study of the Monarch Butterfly.*—This butterfly is easily recognized from the pictures. Also you will no doubt find it flying around milkweed plants if you live in a region where they grow.

With your butterfly net collect a few specimens and pin them out. Study them very carefully and record your observations. Also collect a few caterpillars.

1. The adult monarch butterfly has the body divided into head, thorax, and abdomen. How do these parts compare in size with the same regions in the grasshopper?

2. Compare the legs and wings with those of the grasshopper. Which of these two insects is better adapted to flying? to jumping?

3. *Draw* the entire animal. Always *print* labels very carefully.

4. *Draw* wings and legs. Arrange neatly on your paper.

5. Gently rub your finger on the wing. As the dust comes off, the wing looks more like the wing of a fly or bee. The lines that run lengthwise are the veins. *Draw* the wing.

6. Observe the mouth parts of the caterpillar to see how they are adapted to obtaining food. Notice the antennae or feelers. Has it upper and lower lips? Compare these with the corresponding parts of the grasshopper.

7. The mouth parts of the butterfly are united into a single long tube, the coiled tongue-like structure called the proboscis. Unroll it and see how its length compares with the length of the body. The butterfly uses the proboscis to suck nectar from flowers. Compare these mouth parts with those of the grasshopper.

II. *Collection of Larvae and Pupae.*—Catch a caterpillar and *watch it change* into a moth or butterfly. You will find this a fascinating study. From late in the spring until October you can find larvae and pupae. Some of the leaves upon which the larvae are feeding should be collected.

The larvae should be placed in jars provided with moist soil and some of the leaves upon which the larvae are found. Arrange the cocoons and pupae which you find as suggested below. Copy the table and make your entries on the copy. Do not mark your book, but keep your record in your regular notebook.

Cocoon				Pupa		
Spun with Silk Only	Spun with a Leaf	Spun with Hair	Without Cocoon	Suspended from One End	Suspended from One Loop	Parasitized

Tent caterpillars spin cocoons and turn into small brown moths. Celery "worms" hang in a loop and form a black, swallowtail butterfly which feeds on the nectar of lilacs and rhododendrons.

The black spiny caterpillars of the willows and elms hang free from their knot of silk and form the mourning cloak butterfly.

Tomato "worms" burrow into the ground and form a large-bodied, small-winged moth, the sphinx moth.

REFERENCES

Comstock, *How to Know the Butterflies*. Comstock.
Comstock, *Handbook of Nature Study*. Comstock.
Fabre, *Insect Life*. Macmillan.
Fabre, *Life of the Caterpillar*. Dodd, Mead.
Farmers' Bulletin No. 1353, *Clothes Moths and Their Control*. U.S. Department of Agriculture.
Holland, *The Butterfly Book*. Doubleday.
Holland, *The Moth Book*. Doubleday.
Klots, *Field Guide to the Butterflies*. Houghton Mifflin.
Lutz, *The Fieldbook of Insects*. Putnam's.

CHAPTER 11

Social Insects—Community Life

11.1 Social Insects

Although most insects are solitary, certain kinds live in large groups or communities and depend upon each other. Such insects are called **social insects,** and most of them are members of the order **Hymenoptera** (hy-men-*op*-ter-uh). Most *bees, ants, termites,* and some *wasps* live in groups and form communities.

11.2 Community Life of the Bee

Most bees, including the *honeybee,* afford a very interesting example of community life among insects. Honeybees originally came from Asia, where they had been domesticated for years, since they furnished the principal supply of sugar. All the wild honeybees in our country which are found living in trees and caves have escaped from hives.

In a honeybee colony there are three kinds of bees—the perfect (egg-laying) females or **queens,** the males or **drones,** and the imperfect (non-egg-laying) females or **workers** (Fig. 11-2). There are generally one queen, a few hundred drones, and twenty to fifty thousand workers in a colony.

The Queen.—The queen alone lays eggs. She can lay an unfertilized egg, which hatches into a drone, or she can

FIGURE 11-1. *LIFE CYCLE OF THE HONEYBEE*

The queen bee lays her eggs in the cells of the hive. They develop into larvae and are fed and cared for by worker bees (nurses) until they spin cocoons and become pupae. Adult bees emerge in about 21 days.

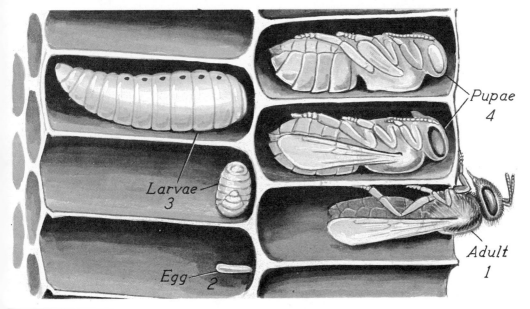

Pupae
4

Larvae
3

Adult
1

Egg
2

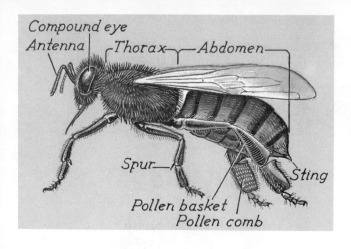

FIGURE 11-2. *WORKER BEE*

Special adaptations in the worker bee include a pollen comb and pollen basket for gathering and storing pollen; a spur on the tibia to pick up wax; and a sting for offense and defense.

lay a fertilized egg, which hatches into a queen or a worker. The queen lays her eggs according to the food and the size of the cell provided by the workers. Thus the decision as to whether the young bee shall be a queen or a worker rests with the workers themselves. They also have the power to supersede the queen, or to raise a new queen in case of the sudden death of the old one. The workers compose most of the hive.

The Workers.—The eggs are placed by the queen in special *cells* of the hive

FIGURE 11-3. *BEE STING*

When a bee stings, poison flows from the sac into a canal between the lancets.

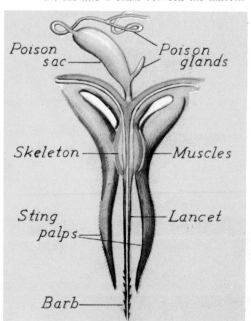

(Fig. 11-1), and after hatching are fed by the young workers, called **nurses.** The larva (Fig. 11-1) is fairly bathed in food, a jelly like substance which the nurses produce in their mouths. It is more nutritious than *bee bread,* which is made from pollen, and than *honey,* on which developing workers are later fed. In a few days the larva weaves a cocoon and changes to a pupa. The workers now cap over the cell with *wax,* secreted from their abdominal segments. In about twenty-one days the young worker bee cuts away the cap and crawls out—an adult provided with the four wings, mouth parts, antennae, and the six legs of the honeybee (Fig. 11-2). The queen hatches in sixteen days and the drone in twenty-four.

Workers are provided with the **sting,** a weapon both of defense and offense (Fig. 11-3). The queen has a small sting, but the drones have none. When a worker stings a large animal, the sting and parts of the internal organs are pulled out, and the bee dies. When a queen stings another insect or even another bee, the sting is not usually lost.

The Drones.—Drones are larger than the workers and have large eyes, strong wings, and thick, broad bodies. They have such short tongues that they are not able to get food for themselves, so they have to be fed by the workers. Drones fly with the queen and the one which mates with her soon dies. The others return to the hive and, in the autumn, the drones are stung to death by the workers.

Sometimes small swarms are attacked by bees from other colonies. It is a pitched battle until the "robber bees" are beaten back or the defenders are themselves killed. The sting is used in these battles.

Bees are instinctively sanitary. If a large bumblebee enters the hive, the honeybees kill the intruder and embalm him by stinging him repeatedly. This prevents decay and makes him harmless to the colony. Sometimes bees cover the body of a small, dead animal with **propolis** (*prop*-oh-liss) or bee glue. This is a substance they gather from certain buds to use in coating the honeycomb. The propolis serves to protect the colony from the effects of the decomposition of the dead body.

The length of the bee's life varies. The drones are usually killed at the end of their first season. Queens live for five or six or even ten years. Workers live three or four weeks in the working season and several months in the fall or winter.

Swarming of Bees.—At irregular intervals during the early spring and during the summer, bees have the peculiar habit of **swarming.** Two common reasons given to explain swarming are lack of room for the growing colony and lack of food.

When bees swarm, they usually alight on the limb of a tree and form a dense cluster. Here they hang from fifteen minutes to an hour before leaving for the woods. In a few cases bees have remained in this "cluster" state overnight, but usually they are lost to man unless

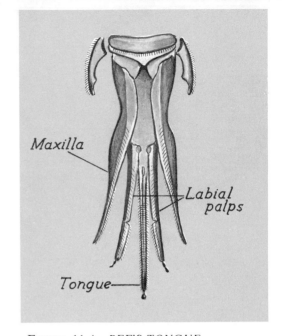

FIGURE 11-4. *BEE'S TONGUE*
The honeybee's hollow tongue is well suited for sucking nectar from flowers.

they are collected within three hours. A swarm consists of a large number of adult bees—workers, drones, but usually only a single queen.

The honey and wax produced annually in the United States are valued at many millions of dollars. The honeybee and bumblebee are both valuable as distributors of the pollen necessary to produce seed.

11.3 Adaptation in the Honeybee

The honeybee offers a fine example of adaptation. The *tongue* (Fig. 11-4) is very long, for getting nectar from certain flowers like apple blossoms, lindens, white clover, and sweet clover. It is too short to get nectar from red clover blossoms. The *mandibles* are adapted to gathering pollen, propolis from buds, for kneading the wax into **combs,** and for polishing surfaces. The *wings* are small and not easily injured when the bees are packed closely together as in swarm

FIGURE 11-5. *POLLINATING INSECT*

Whether the bee carries pollen in a pollen basket (*left*) or on other parts of his body, the flower also reaps the benefit of his visit.

clusters. To compensate for their small size, the wings are provided with *muscles* that vibrate them with a rapidity as great as 440 times a second, enough to carry the bees through the air with a load of nectar and pollen. The *legs* in the rear pair (Fig. 11-6) are flat and thin for carrying loads of pollen and propolis. These legs are provided with tiny bristles to keep their loads from slipping off.

Bees are very particular about cleanliness. They use the hairs on their legs as combs and brushes to clean their antennae, their compound eyes, and their bodies. They have other hairs which form a **pollen basket** to carry the pollen. The tibia has a **spur** to pick up wax.

The *nectar* is sucked into a **honey stomach** or **crop** where it remains until placed in the honey comb or a small part of it is used for food.

Bees have a good sense of sight and smell. They are attracted by colors. When disturbed, they produce a scent from a gland on the abdomen. When a bee returns with nectar from a flower, she does a figure "8" dance while the other bees touch her with their antennae. In this way the other workers seem to gain a sense of the direction of the food supply.

11.4 The Social Organization of Ants

These insects also belong to the order Hymenoptera and live in large families with many *workers* and a number of *queens* and *males*. Some have, in addition, **soldiers** with strong mouth parts

ARTHROPODS—ANIMALS WITH JOINTED FEET

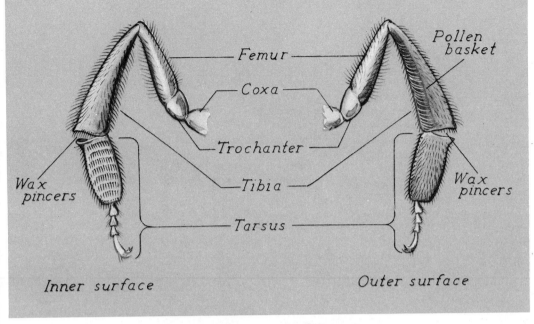

FIGURE 11-6. *HIND LEGS OF THE HONEYBEE*

The pollen basket is formed by stiff hairs attached to the tibia. Hairs on the tarsus comb pollen from the middle legs into the baskets. Only workers, which number 10,000 to 100,000 in a hive, have baskets.

(mandibles) to do the fighting for the colony. The males and females have wings, but the workers are wingless.

Life History.—In most ant colonies there are several *queens.* Unlike the honeybees, several ant queens live together in harmony. The ant eggs are so small that they are scarcely visible to the naked eye. The legless *larvae* hatch in a few days, being full grown in about two weeks. *Pupation* lasts about two weeks. The *cocoons* are the white objects which are erroneously called "ant-eggs." The adults guard these cocoons which contain the pupae, carrying them away to places of safety when the colony is disturbed. Sometimes the adult workers remove them to warmer quarters.

Behavior.—Socially, ants perhaps act more like human beings than any other animal. For example:

1. They build, under brushpiles, beaten roads with tunnels.

2. They keep plant lice (*aphids*) for the sweet fluid the lice exude; this suggests the keeping of cattle by man.

3. They carry these plant lice into their tunnels and care for them over the winter season. In the spring they carry them out and place them on food-plants. Thus, there is a *symbiotic* relationship between the ants and the aphids when they help each other.

4. If a nest is attacked by enemies, the soldiers rush around and stroke the workers with their antennae. This seems to inform them of the attack and they hurry to the rescue.

5. They wrestle and play and sometimes carry one another around. This activity looks like a football game.

6. They have battles with other colonies. This activity, unfortunately, also reminds us of man. They send out scouts and await their return before beginning the battle.

FIGURE 11-7. *LIFE CYCLE OF THE BLACK ANT*

The ant goes through a complete metamorphosis from egg to adult. The larvae are tended by workers (non-egg-laying, wingless females). Unlike the bees, several queens can live together in one colony.

7. When one colony subdues another in battle, the victors take home the larvae and pupae of the conquered and bring them up to be **slaves.** The slaves seem to be loyal to their conquerors and to take great interest in the welfare of the victorious colony.

8. Among certain kinds of ants the slaveholders have depended so long on the slaves that they are unable to build nests or even feed themselves. If the slaves are taken away, the slaveholders starve. The slaveholders are able to fight, however, to get more slaves.

11.5   The Social Order of Termites

These so-called "white ants" belong to the order **Isoptera** (eye-*sop*-ter-uh). They have a community life similar to

that of the real ants, which are their worst enemies. Some termites live in the trunks or branches of trees. They do not hesitate to eat the wood of houses, furniture, or telegraph poles, and thus are very destructive to man's property. Some of them even possess a liquid substance which will etch glass and metal, enabling them to eat canned foods if they cannot find *cellulose,* which is the natural food of termites.

Most of the termites have been found in Africa, where the huge mounds, made by millions of workers, sometimes reach as high as twenty feet. A few forms have been found in this country as far north as Massachusetts, although the normal range of temperature termites can stand is not great.

ARTHROPODS—ANIMALS WITH JOINTED FEET

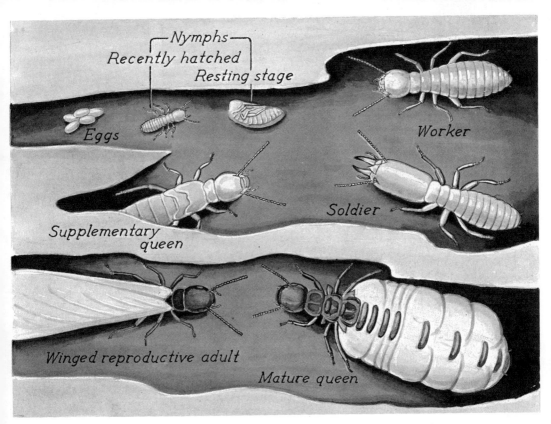

Nymphs
Recently hatched
Resting stage

Eggs

Worker

Supplementary
queen

Soldier

Winged reproductive adult

Mature queen

FIGURE 11-8. *LIFE CYCLE OF THE TERMITE*
The termite queen lays eggs which develop into blind, wingless nymphs,
the termite having an incomplete metamorphosis.

The Royal Pair.—Only a few termites are fully developed males and females, possessing wings and faceted eyes. Once a year the tiny apertures of the corridors of their mounds are opened and these fully developed termites fly out into the air to choose the **royal couple.** Just how this is done seems to be a mystery. After some time those couples which survive try to find homes to start their colonies. Usually very few succeed in finding suitable places unless received by the workers in neighboring colonies.

As soon as they return, the *king* and *queen* shed their wings and start to build their home. When the queen's room is made suitable they mate, and the queen settles down to lay thousands of eggs a day for the rest of her life. Her body

becomes greatly enlarged, reaching a size a number of times that of a normal termite. The eggs hatch into *nymphs,* as termites have incomplete metamorphosis (Fig. 11-8).

The Workers.—These tiny creatures are wingless and blind. They have no weapons, and yet they are the only termites which can receive nourishment from the food they chew. In their bodies are tiny **flagellates,** one-celled animals, which help them digest the cellulose in the wood. This is a *symbiotic* relationship, since both the termites and flagellates are dependent on each other. The workers have to chew the food and partly digest it in order to feed the queen and king, the reserves with the wings, and the soldiers.

SOCIAL INSECTS—COMMUNITY LIFE

Lynwood M. Chace

Ralph Buchsbaum

FIGURE 11-9. *SOCIAL INSECTS*

Both the ant (*left*) and the termite (*right*) live in complex social communities. In this termite colony, the dark termite is a soldier, the one on his left a reproductive termite. Sensing danger, these carpenter ants are hurriedly dragging their cocoons to safety.

The workers build galleries (Fig. 11-8) which lead to large apartments where the white oblong eggs of the queen are piled in little heaps, like grains of sand. They make corridors for ventilation to regulate the temperature of the whole dwelling. The queen's room rests upon arches. The floor is level, the ceiling low and curved, resembling a glass dome. The queen is a number of times as large as a worker, and her size makes it impossible for her to leave her chamber. The workers enter to feed her and clean the room. Soldiers are always on guard.

Soldiers.—The soldiers have long powerful jaws. The smaller kind have smaller jaws, but they can shoot out a sticky liquid which paralyzes their victim. When the workers need to pass through a dangerous area filled with ants, the soldiers form solid double lines facing outward, and the workers pass

between to safety. The workers have very soft bodies with no protection. One enemy could kill a great many, if it were not for the help of the soldiers.

When the ants attack, the soldier that first discovers the danger strikes an alarm on the ground with its mandible, and the others rush to the scene of action. If the attack is prolonged, the soldiers emit a shrill sound which is repeated at short intervals and may be answered by a similar sound from within the dwelling, meaning, perhaps, that help is coming.

11.6 Organization of the Colony

The individuals depend on each other to such an extent that none of them could live by themselves. The *queen* is limited to her job of egg-laying. The *workers* must care for the young, feed the royal pair and the soldiers, and keep the whole building in repair. *Soldiers*

ARTHROPODS—ANIMALS WITH JOINTED FEET

must risk their lives while guarding the *termitary,* as the termites' mound is called. The *reserves* lead a monotonous life and are pressed into service only when some accident happens to the king or queen. When the nymphs or the reserves become too numerous, the workers merely refuse to feed them and they starve. Thus the social life of the white ants or termites, like that of the ants and bees, is an *interdependence of individuals* for the good of the whole.

FACTS TO REMEMBER

Social insects are those which live in communities, such as bees and ants of the order Hymenoptera (insects with membranous wings), and the termites of the order Isoptera (insects with similar wings). They show division of labor in the community, and each kind of individual is adapted to the work it has to do.

Bees have queens, drones, and workers. They are helpful in pollinating flowers and producing honey. Some of the *ants* not only have queens, workers, and males, but soldiers with strong jaws for fighting their enemies. Some ants live in a *symbiotic* relationship with aphids. Others destroy food and may become household pests.

Termites are generally destructive. They also have soldiers and some reserves which may grow into kings and queens if they need them. Termites eat materials made of wood and cause much damage. Tiny flagellates live in their stomachs to help digest the food. This is a *symbiotic* relationship, since they depend upon each other.

WORDS TO REMEMBER

bee bread	nurses	soldier
bee glue	pollen basket	spur
comb	propolis	sting
drone	queen bee	swarming
flagellates	reserves	symbiotic relationship
honey	royal couple	termitary
honey stomach	slaves	wax
nectar	social insects	worker

QUESTIONS

1. Name three kinds of honeybees.
2. How does each come into being?
3. Give the life cycle of a bee from egg to fully developed adult.
4. How do bees swarm?
5. What adaptations has the bee?
6. In what different ways do ants act like human beings?
7. Describe the queens and workers.
8. Tell the life history of the ant.
9. Describe the structures of a termitary.

10. What is the work of the soldiers of the termites? Reserves?
11. What enables the workers to feed the other members?
12. What is the economic importance of termites?
13. Where are termites found?
14. Of what importance are flagellates to termites?

COMPLETION TEST

As your teacher reads the following incomplete statements, with your book closed, write on a clean sheet of paper the word or phrase which correctly completes this statement.

1. Insects that live in communities are called _____ insects.
2. The honeybee is valuable for honey and _____.
3. The workers of the ants have no _____.
4. The so-called "white ants" are really _____.
5. These insects live in _____.
6. The workers have no _____.
7. The workers feed the _____.
8. The soldiers are equipped with _____.
9. The fully developed males and females are called _____.
10. The worst enemy of the termites is the _____.

PROJECTS

I. *Building an Ant Nest.*—You may become very much interested in the activities of ants and fascinated by watching them from day to day.

With a garden trowel dig up an anthill. Place the material in a pail or covered container and bring it into the laboratory. If possible, include the large queen and some pupae (large white cases).

Either moisten the material very slightly or include a wet sponge. Place the ants in the nest. Keep it covered and in a few days they will have their new nest in order.

To feed the ants, place some crumbs, a drop or two of honey, or a few grains of sugar in one corner which may be exposed to the light and be used as a feeding chamber.

Choose some suitable time each school day to watch the ants and record your observations. You may wish to try some of these tests.

1. Blow a whistle by the anthill and note what happens.
2. Remove the dark cover and expose the nest to a bright light. How do the ants react?
3. Place some ice near one end and find out whether ants prefer to live in warm or cold places.
4. Put a few ants in a small dish of water to find out whether they can swim.
5. Do they like salt? Vinegar? Soap?
6. When ants become a nuisance, what are some ways of combating them?

II. *Fun with Bees.*—If your school has an observation beehive, you may be able to assist the teacher in starting it and placing it outside the window. Occasionally remove the covers from the glass sides and observe the bees.

Place a glass plate by the ledge and paste colored papers underneath. Put some honey or molasses above each color and notice which place the bees visit most frequently. Are bees attracted by color?

Secure from a beekeeper a bee box and a few bees. Walk a short distance from the hive and release the bees. Watch their flight if possible. Is there any truth in the statement that bees fly in a straight line? What is meant by a beeline?

REFERENCES

Emerson and Fish, *Termite City*. Rand McNally.

Ewers, *Ant People*. Dodd, Mead.

Farmers' Bulletin No. 147. *Preventing Damage by Termites or White Ants.* U. S. Department of Agriculture.

Langstroth, *Hives and Honey Bee*. American Bee Journal.

Llewellen, *The True Book of Honeybees*. Childrens Press.

Lubbock, *Ants, Bees and Wasps*. Dutton.

Maeterlinck, *The Life of the Bee*. Dodd, Mead.

Maeterlinck, *The Life of the White Ant*. Dodd, Mead.

Phillips, *Bee Keeping*. Macmillan.

Reinhard, *The Witchery of Wasps*. Century.

Root, *A.B.C. and X.Y.Z. of Bee Culture*. A. L. Root.

Tibbitts, *The First Book of Bees*. Watts.

Wheeler, *Ants, Their Structure, Development and Behavior*. Columbia University Press.

Wheeler, *Social Life Among the Insects*. Harcourt, Brace.

CHAPTER 12

Economic Insects and Their Control

12.1 Importance of Insects

There are three main reasons why we have so many insects. (1) They can *fly,* and thus escape their enemies. (2) They are *small* and have remarkable *adaptations* in color and habits, which help them to avoid being eaten and enable them to live in every conceivable place and on every variety of food. Some insects even eat tobacco and certain insecticides. (3) They *reproduce enormously,* often raising several thousand young in a single season.

Insects eat the food which plants have made and which man needs, and a few of them are the agents that spread such destructive diseases as malaria, typhoid fever, and yellow fever. Thus they not only destroy the food and economic products of man, but may directly cause his death. However, the argument is not against all insects, for some of them produce such useful articles as honey and silk.

Insects which are especially helpful or harmful to man are called **economic insects.** Some economic insects, like the silkworm, make money for man. Other economic insects, like the clothes moth, destroy man's goods.

Certain insects, like the fly which carries the germs of disease, are particularly harmful, for they cause sickness and death. Some beetles eat dead flesh or bury dead animals by tunneling under them. These insects are helpful. Others help plants that are valuable to man by carrying the pollen from one flower to another. Bees make honey. Such insects are useful. We should study insects in order to find out which ones are our friends and which are our enemies.

FIGURE 12-1. *SILKWORM EGGS*

Many eggs are produced by the silkworm moth on specially prepared paper provided by the silk farmer. In the spring they are hatched in incubators, when the first leaves of the mulberry trees appear. If the moth were living in the wild state, few of these many eggs would survive.

Sawders from Cushing

158

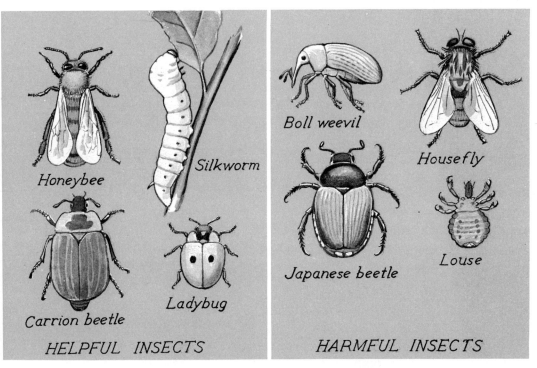

Honeybee

Silkworm

Carrion beetle

Ladybug

HELPFUL INSECTS

Boll weevil

Housefly

Japanese beetle

Louse

HARMFUL INSECTS

FIGURE 12-2. *HELPFUL AND HARMFUL INSECTS*
While some insects are so valuable to man that they are protected and
nurtured, others are enemies of man, causing disease and destruction of crops.

12.2   Beetles

The beetles belong to the order **Cole-optera** (koh-lee-*op*-ter-uh), have hard wings, and are generally noisy fliers. The first pair of wings meets in a straight line down the back. The second pair consists of a thin membrane. The mouth parts of beetles are adapted for hard biting. Among the harmful beetles are many wood borers, the May beetles, potato beetles, asparagus beetles, and boll weevils. Two of the beneficial beetles are the ladybug, which feeds on destructive and harmful insects, and the carrion beetle, which feeds on dead animals.

Hop growers like to have both the ladybug larvae and the adult ladybugs on their vines, as these insects destroy hop lice.

The harmful beetle group has many bird enemies. The most important of these are the ring-necked pheasant, the rose-breasted grosbeak, and the quail, which feeds on potato beetles. The English sparrow, cuckoo, and kingbird feed on weevils. Robins, blackbirds, and crows eat white grubs, the larval stage of May beetles. The woodpeckers catch great numbers of borers by digging holes in the trees where the borers are tunneling.

12.3   The Potato Beetle

The "potato bug" (Fig. 12-3) was first found in Colorado on wild plants of the potato family, and was named Colorado beetle. It gradually made its way east from one potato patch to another, being helped by the wild plants of the potato family that grew where there there were no potatoes. These beetles were also carried on potatoes by trains that in a few hours took them hundreds

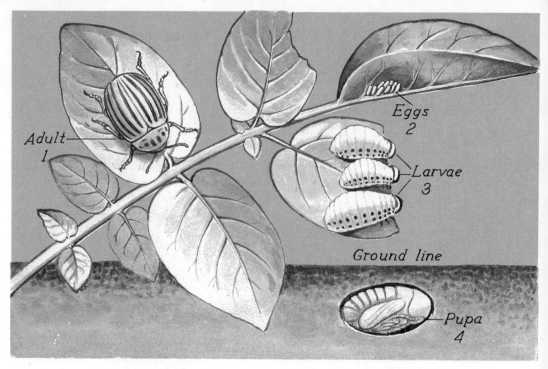

FIGURE 12-3. *LIFE CYCLE OF THE POTATO BEETLE*

The potato beetle lays its eggs on the leaves of the potato plant, which will serve as food for the larvae when they hatch. Pupation takes place underground, after which the beetle emerges as an adult.

of miles. They arrived in New York State in 1872.

The potato beetle feeds on the foliage of the potato plant, and injures the size and quality of the tubers, the parts we eat. The injury is due to the fact that most of the starch stored in the tuber is produced in the leaves, and when the leaves are destroyed, the amount of starch available for the tuber is lessened. To insure a good crop, spraying must be carried on wherever potatoes are grown.

Life Cycle.—The adult potato beetles pass the winter in the ground. In the spring they crawl out of the ground and the females lay their orange-colored eggs on the under side of the leaves of the young potato plants. In about a week or ten days the eggs hatch and the larvae eat ravenously. In two or three weeks the larvae reach their full size.

They then dig into the ground, where they pupate for two weeks or longer, depending on the temperature. At the end of this period, they emerge as adults and the females lay their eggs on the late potato leaves for a second generation. The eggs hatch into larvae, the larvae pupate in the ground, and the adults of the second generation emerge in the fall. At the beginning of the cold weather the adults enter the ground and hibernate.

Natural Enemies. — Fortunately the potato beetle has many natural enemies. Adult lady beetles, popularly called "ladybugs," and their larvae kill many potato beetles. The *tachina* (*tak*-ih-nuh) *flies* lay eggs on the potato beetle larvae and the young tachina flies, in the form of larvae, burrow into the bodies of the beetle larvae, killing them in great numbers. Birds, toads, snakes, and skunks

ARTHROPODS—ANIMALS WITH JOINTED FEET

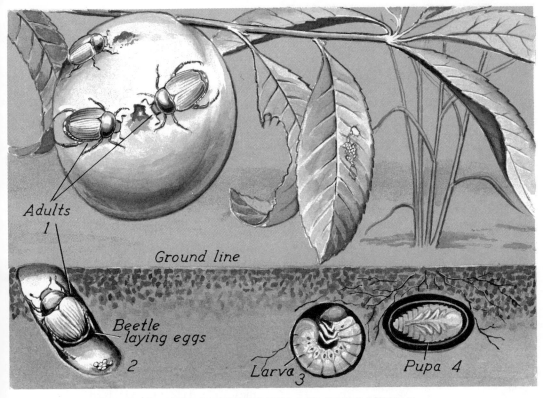

FIGURE 12-4. *LIFE CYCLE OF THE JAPANESE BEETLE*

In its adult stage, which lasts only six weeks, the Japanese beetle causes heavy damage to foliage, and sometimes to flowers and fruit.

also are enemies of potato beetles and take a heavy toll of them.

12.4 The Japanese Beetle

This foreign pest (Fig. 12-4) was brought to this country by a nurseryman who had imported some iris bulbs. Later it was discovered in the state of New Jersey, where it was causing serious damage to crops. The beetles eat and destroy the fruit and leaves of trees, shrubs, and grasses.

During the month of June the adult beetles hatch and emerge from the ground. After eating a great deal for a month, the females lay their eggs in the ground. The young hatch and remain there during the winter. They pupate in May and are ready to appear with the first green leaves.

To prevent the spread of the Japanese beetle, infected areas are quarantined, traps are set, and poison bait scattered.

12.5 Cicadas, Lice, and Scale Insects

These are the **Homoptera** (hoh-*mop*-ter-uh), the insects with "similar" wings or with no wings, and with sucking mouth parts (Fig. 12-5). The Homoptera have incomplete metamorphosis. Most of this group of insects are harmful. They feed on the sap of wild and cultivated plants, causing great loss. The lac insect, however, is used for making shellac.

12.6 Cicadas

You have probably heard of the "seventeen-year locusts" that come in swarms for a season. The name is given

Lynwood M. Chace

FIGURE 12-5. *LOCUST*

The wingless cicada nymph, a larva, (*left*) lives underground for 17 years.

them because the nymphs, the growing stage in the insect's metamorphosis, remain in the ground, feeding on roots for seventeen years before they emerge. Another kind of *cicada* (sih-*kay*-duh) that remains in the ground for thirteen years lives in the southern states.

FIGURE 12-6. *BODY LOUSE*

This ventral view of the human body louse clearly shows its hooked claws.

W. M. Smallwood

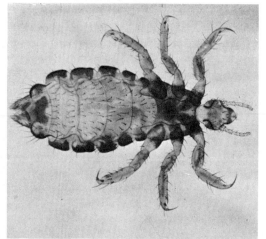

At the end of thirteen or seventeen years, generally in the month of May, the nymphs crawl out of the ground, climb trees or fences, and molt into adult cicadas. The adult females lay their eggs in tender shoots of trees, causing the shoots to die. The young cicadas, after hatching in the shoot of the tree, go into the ground and begin their long period of larval existence. These cicadas are usually found in limited areas, but in those areas they are very numerous and destructive. They do an immense amount of harm, especially to the green leaves of growing plants.

The cicadas that we hear every summer are of another kind, the nymphs of which live in the ground for two years. As there are two broods of this species that appear in alternate years, the number does not seem to vary from year to year. Birds do much toward destroying these cicadas—the kingbird, sparrow hawk, butcher bird, and great-crested flycatcher being their most common enemies.

12.7 Lice

Lice are small, wingless insects which are members of the order **Aptera** (*ap*-ter-uh). The mouth parts of some are adapted for piercing and sucking, but the bird lice have nipper-like mandibles for biting instead of sucking. The bird lice feed only on the hairs and feathers and not on the blood as do the sucking lice. The feet of lice are provided with large curved claws, which help them to cling to their victims.

The *head louse* that afflicts man deposits its eggs, about sixty in number, on the hairs of the head. The eggs usually hatch in six days. Head lice are among the most important of the external human parasites. They are commonly found in logging camps, jails,

162

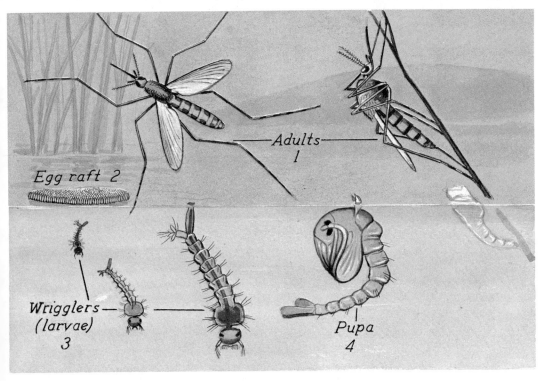

FIGURE 12-7. *LIFE CYCLE OF THE CULEX MOSQUITO*

The mosquito lays its eggs in the water, and the larvae and pupae are also adapted for life in the water. Since the larvae of Culex come to the surface to breathe, they may be controlled with chemical sprays.

slum areas, ships, in fact wherever there is close association with people who have little opportunity to keep clean.

The *body louse* (Fig. 12-6) is an insect which differs from the head louse. It hides in the clothing and deposits its eggs there. The body louse is an important carrier of the germs of typhus fever, relapsing fever, and trench fever. It is possible that as lice move from one rodent to another, they may carry the germs of the dreaded bubonic plague if their host harbors these germs.

Plant lice, known as *aphids,* are very destructive to plants. Tiny green aphids and larger white ones are frequently found in enormous numbers on house and garden plants. They suck the sap of the plants, and thus eventually destroy them.

Scale insects are small and wingless, and are very destructive to orange groves and apple orchards. They usually move about when young, but remain in a fixed position when they reach the adult stage. Ladybugs eat scale insects and plant lice, thus helping to keep them under control.

12.8 Mosquitoes and Flies

These two-winged insects belong to the order called **Diptera** (*dip*-ter-uh). They have complete metamorphosis. They also have sucking mouth parts, which is an essential factor in planning for their control. This group of insects includes some of man's worst enemies, like the harmful house flies and mosquitoes, the botfly, stable fly, cheese skipper, and the tsetse fly, which carries

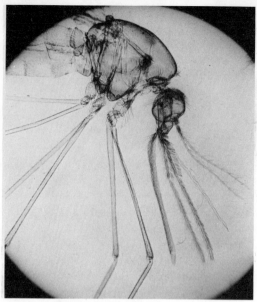

General Biological Supply House

FIGURE 12-8. *DISEASE CARRIER*
The single-celled animal that causes malaria is only carried by the female Anopheles mosquito.

African sleeping sickness. In this order we find also the beneficial bee fly, wasp fly, and tachina fly.

12.9 Mosquitoes

The common mosquito lays from two hundred to four hundred eggs in a raft-like cluster on the surface of the water in any stagnant pool or rainwater barrel. These eggs are usually laid early in the morning and, in favorable weather, hatch within twenty-four hours. The **wrigglers** (larvae) come to the surface when breathing, but swim freely in the water for food. Food is brought to the mouth by vibrating hair like cilia, which keep a current of water passing near them. After seven days the wrigglers become pupae, which, unlike most other pupae, can move about. They, like the larvae, must come to the surface to breathe. The pupa stage lasts for two days; then the adult emerges and flies away after its wings are dried (Fig. 12-7).

The length of time for these changes from egg to larva, from larva to pupa, and from pupa to adult depends on the temperature. Warm weather shortens the time and cold weather lengthens it.

In the United States there are three distinct kinds of mosquitoes. (1) The common mosquito is known as *Culex* (*kyoo*-leks). Culex carries in its body some disease germs, but not those of malaria. It is a blood-sucker and a source of great annoyance to those who frequent the woods or seashore during the summer, and it makes some districts uninhabitable. (2) The *Anopheles* (uh-*nof*-uh-leez) mosquito often carries *malaria* germs in its body. (3) The *Aëdes* (uh-*ee*-deez) is a mosquito common in the southern part of the United States. It carries *yellow fever* germs from one person to another.

Mosquitoes have their mouth parts adapted for sucking blood. In the female mosquito, some of the mouth parts form a piercing organ; other parts are combined to form a sucking organ. Thus the mosquito transfers malaria germs from the blood of one person to another.

It is fortunate for man that mosquitoes have so many enemies. The wrigglers are preyed upon by the larvae of dragon flies, by small fish, and by water beetles; the adults are eaten by night-hawks, martins, bats, and dragon flies. Certain diseases caused by bacteria (Chap. 31) attack the adults and kill them in great numbers.

The number of mosquitoes can be greatly reduced by destroying their natural breeding places in tin cans, pails, eaves troughs, sink holes, and boxes that may hold water. The larger breeding places are sluggish streams and swamps. Draining these is the most effective method of preventing mosquitoes from laying their eggs in such places.

FIGURE 12-9. *CONTROLLING MOSQUITOES*
One of the best ways to control mosquitoes is to kill the larvae by spraying the breeding places with oil. Poisons such as DDT are also effective.

When draining is not possible, the surface of the water may be covered with kerosene or other oil, which kills the larvae and pupae by preventing them from getting oxygen from the air.

12.10 The Housefly

Because of its filthy habits of breeding and because it crawls over our food, the housefly is recognized as a dangerous disease carrier and one of our worst enemies.

Each female lays from one hundred to one hundred and sixty eggs in stable manure or other refuse. The eggs hatch in a day or so into the legless larval forms called **maggots** (*mag*-uts). In five to seven days, depending on the temperature and the food supply, the larvae are full grown. They then pupate for another five to seven days. At the end of this time the adults emerge as mature flies ready to lay eggs for another generation. This continues until cold weather puts an end to their activities. Enough generations are produced every year so that a single female born in the spring could have a million descendants by October if enemies did not make this impossible.

The Housefly and Typhoid Fever.— Typhoid fever is caused by bacteria that live in the walls of the intestine. These bacteria are also found in sewage. Flies walk in sewage searching for food. Their sticky feet and hairy bodies pick up and hold all kinds of bacteria. Someone leaves a screen door open, and flies get into the dining room. The flies alight on the food. Some of the bacteria which cause typhoid fever may thus be left on the food, and one of the family may eat the food that the flies have polluted.

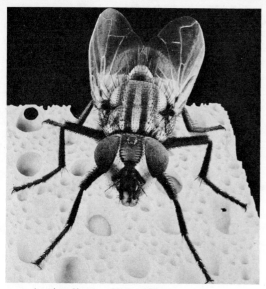

American Museum of Natural History

FIGURE 12-10. *MAN'S ENEMY*

The house fly, which is shown here on bread, may transmit serious disease to man.

Methods of Control.—The few house-flies that survive the winter are responsible for the millions that swarm about in the summer. Their numbers may be reduced by several methods:

1. Begin early to swat and kill all the flies you see.

2. Remove manure piles and garbage, and have a general cleaning up of refuse to destroy the breeding places of this menace.

3. Put flytraps on the covers of garbage cans to entrap all those that hatch as well as adults that go in to feed.

4. Keep many flytraps in operation in or about the house during the time of year that flies are active.

5. Use any good commercial poison for those flies that do come into the house.

12.11 Other Disease-Carrying Insects

The term *"bug"* to a scientist means a particular order of insects, the **Hemiptera** (heh-*mip*-ter-uh), or half-winged insect. The bedbug, squash bug, and "stink" bug are *true bugs.* The giant water bug and back swimmer also belong to this group. The bedbug is a disease carrier. It sucks the blood of man and is known to carry *relapsing fever.*

The *fleas,* order **Siphonaptera** (sy-foh-*nap*-ter-uh), are tube-winged insects that suck the blood of birds, dogs, cats, and man. The rat flea carries the disease germs that cause *bubonic plague.* Other fleas carry the *jigger,* which burrows into the skin of man, causing it to form bumps the size of a small bean.

12.12 Types of Parasitism

A plant or animal living in or on a living plant or animal is an example of

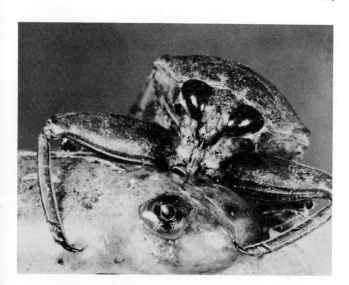

FIGURE 12-11. *TRUE BUG*

The giant water bug lives most of its life in the water, but leaves it to look for a mate or a new home. Here, it attacks a tadpole and draws its blood through the sucking tube, or proboscis.

Lynwood M. Chace

166

FIGURE 12-12. *TREMEX AND ITS PARASITE*

The thalessa (*right*) belongs to a group of parasitic flies which feed on insects harmful to man. The larvae fasten themselves to the body of the victim, a tree borer (*left*). Sometimes, both host and parasite die as a result.

parasitism. If a parasite attacks the outside of an animal, as the louse does, it is called an *external* parasite. If it feeds on the inside of an animal, as in the case of the tachina-fly larva, it is called an *internal* parasite. The animal on which the parasite feeds is called the *host.*

12.13 Parasitic Flies

This group of insects is decidedly beneficial. The *tachina fly,* which is very beneficial to man, somewhat resembles the housefly, but has differences that may be clearly seen. It has longer hairs (bristles) on its abdomen, and its antennae are considerably longer. The tachina fly lays its eggs on tent caterpillars, army worms, and many other destructive caterpillars. After these eggs are hatched, the tachina larvae bore into the bodies of the caterpillars, feed upon them, and thus they kill them. Many kinds of caterpillars are held in check by the activities of these tachina flies.

One of the larger parasitic flies is known as *thalessa* (thuh-*less*-uh) (Fig. 12-12). With long, thread-like drills this parasitic insect bores holes in trees and lays an egg at the bottom of each hole. The egg is usually laid near the burrow of one of the larger tree borers, *tremex* (Fig. 12-12). The larva of thalessa makes its way along the burrow of the tremex borer and fastens itself to the body of the borer, upon which it feeds. If the borer eats its way to the outside of the tree, the adult thalessa emerges, ready to produce another generation of larvae which will destroy more borers. But if thalessa parasites kill the tremex borer before it has eaten its way through the hard wood, all die together because thalessa cannot cut an opening for itself.

12.14 How to Control Harmful Insects

Some general measures for the control of insects are: (*a*) environmental factors, (*b*) poisons and traps, (*c*) natural enemies, and (*d*) preventing importation, or quarantine.

(*a*) *Environmental Factors.*—In order to make a definite plan for getting rid of insects, we must first understand their habits in detail. Insects that feed on roots cannot be killed by the same method used to kill those that feed on wheat and other cereals.

In turn, those insects that feed on the leaves of fruit trees require a different

FIGURE 12-13. *AERIAL WAR ON INSECT PESTS*

At tree top level, this plane sprays a western Oregon forest threatened by
the spruce budworm. One pound of DDT per acre, plus solvent, was used.

treatment from those that eat the fruit
itself. Environmental factors, such as
temperature changes, rainfall, winds,
food supply, natural enemies, and parasites, influence very much the growth
and number of insects.

One good preventive measure employed in controlling insects consists in
changing the crops so that insects that
feed on corn, for example, will not be
able to get suitable food if clover is sown
after the corn crop. The expert farmer
gives careful study to the proper rotation
of crops in an effort to prevent destructive insects from gaining too great head-
way.

Destruction of the breeding places,
such as draining of swamps, kills mosquitoes. Burning and covering dumps
for waste disposal destroys breeding
places of flies. Cleaning up around
homes, especially backyards, vacant lots,

and waste lands, keeps insects from
spreading.

Cold storage is very successful in preventing insects from developing, especially in fruit. Flour and meal are protected by heating them sufficiently to kill
the eggs or insects that may be in them.

(*b*) *Poisons and Traps.*—Most of the
above measures can be applied only to
insects that live in the soil. Poisons,
repellent substances, and traps are some
of the means taken to control insects that
live on the plants themselves. The various insect poisons are known as **insecticides.** A good insecticide must be effective, cheap, and harmless to the insect's
host (the victim on which the insect
feeds).

Before we can control a harmful insect
by poisoning, we must know how that
insect uses its mouth parts. Figure 9-6
shows the biting mouth parts of insects

that eat leaves. These insects can be killed by spraying poison, such as *Paris green* or *arsenate of lead,* on their food. These are sometimes called **stomach poisons**. But such methods are not effective with sucking insects (Fig. 12-6), whose mouth parts are modified to penetrate the surface of the leaves and suck the juices from within. These insects can be killed only by poisons that enter their air tubes as vapors, or that clog their air tubes. Such poisons are called **contact poisons,** and must be sprayed on the insects themselves. Some of these are *nicotine, lime-sulfur,* and *oil emulsions.*

The common "tanglefoot" flypaper and various traps are used with good results in capturing flies.

When insects can be confined to a small area or enclosed space, **fumigants** may be used. These are gases which pass through the spiracles and poison the tracheae. Clothes which show evidence of clothes moths may be placed in airtight containers together with the poison gas.

Sometimes a **repellent** like *camphor* or *naphthalene* is sprayed or dusted in closets to destroy the clothes moth larvae even though it may not kill the adults. This is a preventive measure.

The chemical *DDT* and other related ones are used to destroy many household pests. It is both a stomach and a contact poison and is prepared in the form of powder, sprays, and aerosol bombs. When using DDT, care should be taken to prevent the destruction of helpful insects and household pets. The person using it should be careful to follow directions to prevent any possible poisoning effect.

(*c*) *Natural Enemies of Insects.*—
The *natural enemies* of insects are the birds and other insects that prey upon

FIGURE 12-14. *LADYBUG*
Fruit growers find ladybugs very helpful because they feed chiefly on plant lice and scale insects.

them, or that live as parasites within their bodies.

The United States Department of Agriculture found in Australia a certain kind of ladybug (*Novius*) which is the natural enemy of an insect pest (cottony cushion scale) that was destroying the orange trees grown in California. This destructive scale had been imported into the United States on young trees. Being freed from its natural enemies (*Novius*), which were not imported, it had increased rapidly. The prompt importation of *Novius* put an end to the increase of the cottony cushion scale, no longer a menace to California orange growers.

(*d*) *Quarantine.*—When plants and animals native to another country are brought into this one, the "balance of nature" is upset. Their natural enemies are not present here to hold them in check, and they soon become numerous and destructive. Quarantine laws have been passed by the federal and state governments to prevent their importation. Inspections are made at the ports of entry from foreign countries and sometimes at the borders of different states.

These measures help prevent the spread of insect and plant pests.

12.15 Need for Trained Workers

Insects are so numerous and do so many different things, that it requires all the time of thousands of well-trained men and women throughout the world to make sure that the activities of our civilization shall not be seriously hindered by them. The study of insects is called **entomology** (en-tuh-*mol*-uh-jee), and scientists who devote themselves to this study are **entomologists** (en-tuh-*mol*-uh-jists). The United States Bureau of Entomology of the Department of Agriculture has a large force of trained workers, and each state has its own special staff of experts to work on the individual problems of the state.

Entomologists throughout the world are joining ranks in the war against insects. Parasites which prey upon insects and keep their numbers down in one country are constantly being drafted by scientists for use in the fight against the imported pests of another country.

The United States has had an expert in Mexico in search of parasites of the Mexican bean beetle and the Mexican fruit fly. Experts have been in Japan seeking the parasites of the Japanese beetle and the gypsy moth. Others have been in Hungary, India, and France. The experts of all these countries are also studying insect pests and then recording their discoveries in books, scientific papers, and government bulletins so that all the world may take advantage of their findings.

FACTS TO REMEMBER

Insects are numerous because they can fly to escape their enemies, they are small and able to adapt themselves to a large variety of conditions, and they have remarkable powers of reproduction.

Insects which are helpful or harmful to man are called *economic insects.* Potato beetles and Japanese beetles are destructive to leaves of low vegetation. Cicadas feed on roots. Plant lice and body lice suck juices or blood. Mosquitoes and flies suck the blood of animals and carry disease. Dragonflies and tachina flies are helpful to man because they live as parasites on the bodies of many harmful insects.

Control measures to prevent the spread of insect pests include the changing of *environmental factors,* and the use of *poisons and traps, natural enemies,* and *quarantine.*

The study of insects is called *entomology* and those who study them, *entomologists.* There is a great need for trained workers in this field.

WORDS TO REMEMBER

contact poison	fumigant	quarantine
economic insects	insecticide	repellent
entomologist	internal parasite	stomach poison
entomology	maggot	true bugs
external parasite	natural enemies	wriggler

QUESTIONS

1. What is an insect?
2. Are insects helpful or harmful to man? Illustrate your answer.
3. What is meant by *economic insects*?
4. What are some of the best-known orders of insects?
5. Name some common representatives of each order.
6. What insects do most harm to our food?
7. Are mosquitoes and flies dangerous or merely annoying?
8. Describe two kinds of lice.
9. What methods have the federal and state governments adopted to control the spread of insect pests?
10. Define parasitism, internal parasite, host.
11. Distinguish between contact poison and stomach poison.
12. Explain how the following are used: a repellent, a fumigant, a natural enemy, a poison like DDT.

COMPLETION TEST

As your teacher or a classmate reads the following incomplete statements, with your book closed, write on a clean sheet of paper the word or phrase which best completes the statement.

1. Insects use _____ for breathing.
2. Contact poisons are used for insects having _____ mouth parts.
3. _____ are insects with hard outer wings which meet in a straight line.
4. The ladybug is a natural enemy of the _____.
5. The Japanese beetle eats _____.
6. A disease carried by the body louse is _____.
7. The _____ lays its eggs in a raftlike cluster on the surface of the water.
8. The Anopheles mosquito carries _____.
9. The housefly carries _____.
10. The tachina fly lays its eggs on _____.

PROJECTS

I. *Living Insects in the Laboratory.*
  1. Land Forms.
  (a) Place a small amount of soil in the bottom of an insect cage.
  (b) Put a small dish of water in one corner and push the soil around it.
  (c) Cut some forked sticks for the insects to crawl on and fit the sticks into the cage.
  (d) Collect several different kinds of insects and include some of the leaves on which they feed.
  (e) Place the insects in the cage and keep a record of your observations.

II. *Collecting Insects for Winter Study.*—Every animal or plant must adapt itself to the winter season or perish. Some insects live through the winter in the egg stage, for example, the tent caterpillar. Others, like the Isabella caterpillar, pass the winter as larvae. The cicada, deep in the ground in nymph form, escapes the cold that way, while the cecropia moth is safe in a cocoon as a pupa. The mourning cloak butterfly hangs in some protected place, as a barn or shed. The monarch butterfly migrates to the southern states and thus escapes our severe winter weather.

How many other examples can you find? Favorable places for these various groups are old board piles and lumber piles, old buildings, fence rows, hedges, and vine tangles. Bring into class old cocoons, egg masses, larvae, and in fact any form of insect that may prove to be alive.

Individual members of the class may select one of the following problems to be studied and written up.

1. What do you find in searching near the leaves among hollow stumps and logs in the woods?

2. What do you find in searching the lilac trees and tangles?

3. What do you find in searching the hedgerows and the vines that climb on buildings?

4. What do you find in searching lumber piles and board piles?

5. What do you find in searching old buildings, especially barns, sheds, and other protected spots?

6. Make a terrarium for confining all the specimens that are brought in, but keep it outside on the window ledge.

7. Sketch a landscape, roughly, which will show the area you covered, and on it locate the places where you found your specimens.

8. Identify and classify your specimens with the aid of insect books and government agricultural reports.

III. *Special Insect Collection.*—Collect and mount insects to show coloration.

If you label your collection carefully, it may be kept in the school museum. Some of the insects to look for are:

1. *Grasshoppers.*—Green ones may be found in green fields. Make an artificial background for your specimen as much like the habitat where you find it as you can.

2. *Walking Sticks.*—Look for these on branches and twigs of trees. Use a few twigs for background to show how closely the insects resemble the twigs.

3. *Monarch and Viceroy Butterflies.*—Looking for these will test your ability to detect the difference between them and help you to understand how birds are confused and the viceroy protected.

REFERENCES

Carson, *Silent Spring.* Houghton Mifflin.

Fabre, *The Life of the Fly.* Dodd, Mead.

Farmers' Bulletin No. 1836, *The Japanese Beetle and Its Control.* U. S. Department of Agriculture.

Harvey and Hill, *Insect Pests*. Chemical Publishing Company.
Hewett, *The Housefly*. Macmillan.
Howard, *Housefly, Disease Carrier*. Ohio State Department of Health.
Jaques, *How to Know the Beetles*. Brown.
Lutz, *Fieldbook of Insects*. Putnam's.
Matheson, *Handbook of Mosquitoes of North America*. Thomas.
Ross, *The Reduction of Domestic Mosquitoes*. Lippincott.
Smith, *Our Insect Friends and Enemies*. Lippincott.
Weed, *Insect Ways*. Appleton.
Wellhouse, *How Insects Live*. Macmillan.

UNIT **V**

Animals with Backbones

What is a vertebrate? Animals with backbones are called vertebrates. These animals can grow larger without having to shed their skeletons and run the risk of being caught by their enemies during the process. The vertebrates have a nerve cord which is protected by the backbone and a brain in the head which controls the whole body. They are more highly developed than the invertebrates because the cells are more specialized and the bodies are more highly organized.

What are the classes of vertebrates? Because there are so many different kinds of vertebrates, they have been grouped into separate classes. The fish belong to the class called *Pisces*. This group includes such fish as goldfish, guppies, salmon, sharks, and sunfish. How many can you name? How do you know that a whale is not a fish?

The *Amphibia* is a class of vertebrates that lay their eggs in water and spend some of the time on land. Frogs, toads, and salamanders belong to this group. How can you tell a salamander from a lizard, which is not an amphibian? Can you tell a toad from a frog? Unit V will help you to discover the differences between these animals.

The *Reptilia* include the turtles, lizards, snakes, alligators, and crocodiles. Do you know why a turtle could not remove its shell and remain alive? Do you know where sea turtles lay their eggs? How can a snake move without legs? How can you distinguish between a crocodile and an alligator? Unit V will answer these and many other questions concerning the reptiles.

The birds belong in the class *Aves* because they have feathers and wings. Do you know any birds that do not fly? Why does a bird have a stiff backbone? Unit V will discuss these problems and help you solve them.

The *Mammalia* is the class of vertebrates which includes the dogs, cats, horses, and man. These are the most highly developed of all the animals. In Unit V you will learn many interesting facts about these mammals as well as about elephants, whales, seals, bats, and others.

dont worry about

The Fish—A Simple Vertebrate

13.1 What Is a Vertebrate?

An animal with a *backbone* is called a **vertebrate** (*ver*-tuh-brayt). Fishes, frogs, snakes, birds, and mammals belong to this group. The formation of the backbone in a growing animal is always preceded by a group of cells that do the work of a skeleton. This embryonic (before birth) group of cells is called the *notochord* (*noh*-tuh-kord). In all the true vertebrates (such as fishes, frogs, etc.), the notochord is gradually absorbed and the backbone takes its place, but between the vertebrae in the back-

FIGURE 13-1. *SIMPLE VERTEBRATES*

Both the fish and the turtle (a reptile) belong to the family of vertebrates. While the fish can live only in water, the painted turtle pictured here has claws adapted for walking as well as webbed toes for swimming.

Lynwood M. Chace

bone some of the notochord remains as cushions.

Vertebrates are found in the phylum **Chordata** which has these traits: (1) a dorsal, tubular nerve cord, (2) an internal supporting rod, the notochord, and (3) pharyngeal gill slits some time during development. The simplest Chordates have notochords but are without brains. These include tongue worms and lancelets. Chordates with backbones and brains form the vertebrate group.

Most vertebrates have a bony inside skeleton called an **endoskeleton.** It is different from the exoskeleton on the outside of crayfishes and grasshoppers.

There are usually *two pairs of appendages* (legs and wings, or fins) attached to the body at the shoulder and hip. Special bones join the limbs to the body. The bones in the *shoulder* are known as the **pectoral** (*pek*-tor-ul) **girdle**, and those in the *hip* are called the **pelvic girdle.** Snakes have only traces of legs.

The vertebrates have a relatively large brain and a nerve cord which runs down the dorsal side of the body. Their sense organs, such as eyes and ears, are better developed than in the invertebrates.

The presence of *gill slits* during development also characterizes all vertebrates. In the fishes there are external openings in the sides of the neck which thoroughly expose the gills to the water. Such structures are of use only to water animals; yet all vertebrates have them at some time in their development. This would indicate that they are closely related and perhaps all developed from some simpler form.

Oxygen is obtained by external or internal gills in most water animals and by lungs in all other vertebrates. Frogs and toads have also a thin, moist skin through which oxygen and carbon dioxide are interchanged.

In the circulatory system of vertebrates the muscular heart on the ventral side of the body forces blood carrying both red and white corpuscles to all parts of the body.

13.2   Fishes

Fishes belong to the class **Pisces** (*pihs-eez*), and are the simplest and most numerous of the vertebrates; there are about 13,000 kinds. They are adapted to live in the water. Most of them are found in the sea, but there are many in rivers or lakes, and brooks and ponds.

Fishes are found as deep in the ocean as 12,000 feet, and as high up as lakes in the Andes at 14,000 feet. Some live in very cold water and others in tropical

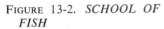
FIGURE 13-2. *SCHOOL OF FISH*

Many fish, like these having their picture taken, travel together in schools instead of striking out on their own. Can you think of reasons why?

Hass from Black Star

177

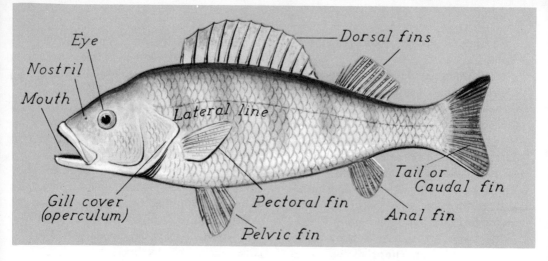

FIGURE 13-3. *EXTERNAL STRUCTURE OF A FISH*

The streamlined body of the fish enables it to swim rapidly to obtain food and avoid its enemies. The caudal fin is the main organ of locomotion.

streams. Fishes have as wide a range of distribution in the water as animals do on land. Many fishes have *seasonal migration.*

Some fish are solitary and move about alone. Others are gregarious and go in *schools.* Fish vary in size from very tiny ones less than an inch long to sharks fifty feet long. Most are under three feet.

The large divisions of fishes are: (1) the *lampreys* (*lam*-preez), (2) the *sharks,* and (3) the *bony fishes,* which also include the small group of fishes with lungs. The bony fishes constitute the most important group in numbers and economic importance. This group includes the salmon (*sam*-un), trout, bass, whitefish, pike, shad, menhaden (men-*hay*-d'n), cod, mackerel, and herring. The goldfish, perch, and sunfish are typical bony fishes but not important.

13.3 Structure of a Fish

The external parts of a fish (Fig. 13-3) consist of a well-marked *head* attached directly to the trunk; a *trunk region,* the largest part of the body; and a *tail* which is sometimes as long as the trunk.

In the *head* of a bony fish the eyes are well developed, the mouth is at the front end of the head, and the jawbones bear many small, needlelike teeth. The part of the head next to the trunk is protected by a piece of bone—the gill cover or **operculum** (oh-*per*-kyoo-lum) —that covers the gills.

The *trunk* has a number of appendages called **fins.** Each fin is composed of several bony fin rays covered by a thin fold of skin. On the shoulder and hip regions of the trunk, the fins occur in pairs, one on each side, and are called the *pectoral* and *pelvic* fins. Those fins which are called *median* fins include the dorsal, caudal, and anal fins and do not occur in pairs.

The *tail* region of the fish ends in a large median fin, the *caudal fin,* that is used chiefly in locomotion. The other fins help in balancing, steering, and stopping.

Scales cover the trunk and tail, each one overlapping the next like the shingles of a house. If you wish to know how old a fish is, simply remove several scales from the side of the body and place them

ANIMALS WITH BACKBONES

under the low magnification of a microscope or a good hand lens. Count the rays or ridges which appear in each scale. These show the yearly lines of growth. You will find that in some years the growth was more rapid, for the lines are farther apart. The skin is full of *mucous* (*myoo*-kus) *glands* that keep the fish covered with slime. Both the slime and the scales protect the fish.

13.4 Locomotion

Most fishes (Fig. 13-3) show an adaptation for swimming. The tapering head offers little resistance to the water, and the spindle-shape of the body enables it to slip easily through the water. The *paired fins* correspond to the paired legs of a frog or dog, but are used mainly for steering. They also act as a brake when the fish wants to stop, the brake being applied by simply straightening out these paired fins at right angles to the body. The *median fins* on the back and lower surface of the body keep the fish from tipping over and are chiefly for balancing, the paired fins also assisting in this process. The tail with its large *terminal fin* is often one-third of the entire length of the body of rapidly swimming fishes, and is the chief organ of locomotion. Movement is produced by a rapid sidewise motion of the tail.

An *air bladder* (Fig. 13-3) is found in most species of fish. It is a thin-walled sac, located in the dorsal part of the body cavity and sometimes connected with the throat by a tube. Its function is to allow the fish to rise or sink or keep its position at any given depth.

13.5 Respiration

Have you noticed goldfish constantly opening and closing their mouths? This is how they get oxygen. Water is taken in through the mouth and passes out

179

Photo by Hugh Spencer

FIGURE 13-4. *FISH SCALE*
To know how old a fish is, count the number of rays on one of its scales.

through two openings, one on each side of the neck. The bony fish has four pairs of **gills**. These gills are made up of many, small, very short, fleshy threads or **gill filaments** which are attached to the **gill arches** (Fig. 13-6). Into each filament a blood vessel penetrates and here the blood throws off carbon dioxide and takes oxygen by osmosis from the dissolved air in the water, just as the blood of the crayfish does. The thin-walled gill filaments are adapted to respiration in the water. The water is drawn into the mouth and forced out over the gills. When a fish opens its mouth, the water rushes in. As the

FIGURE 13-5. *OXYGEN INTAKE*
Fish obtain oxygen from water passing through the gills and out the *operculum*.

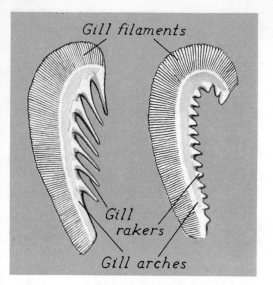

FIGURE 13-6. *HEAD AND GILLS OF THE FISH*
The structure of the fish's mouth and teeth varies with the food eaten.
Fish feeding on small food have developed gill rakers (*left*) to strain it.

mouth is closed, the floor of the mouth and throat is raised slightly, pushing the water against the side of the neck and through the gill opening. The mouth is thus emptied of water, so that when it is opened again, more water flows in.

13.6 Food and Digestion

The food of fishes consists of insects, worms, crayfish, snails, and other fish. Their teeth serve to seize, tear, and hold food. No fishes have teeth adapted for chewing food, as do most of the higher vertebrates like the dog, horse, cow, and man.

Some fish, such as lake trout, pickerel, and pike, are almost entirely fish eaters. Those that depend chiefly on insects for their food are bass, sucker, bullhead, perch, and others, although some of these occasionally eat fish. Fish like small crustaceans, crayfish, and the tiny forms of life that float near the surface. The young of bass, carp, perch, and many minnows live on this food. These tiny animals in turn gain their necessary food from the green plants, so there are most

interesting biological processes going on in all of our ponds and streams. There is a complete cycle, for plants get nourishment from animal waste products.

Among fish which eat tiny animals and plants, the four pairs of *gill arches* have many sharp-pointed projections on the throat side, called **gill rakers,** that act as strainers and gather quantities of small food as the water passes over the gills (Fig. 13-6). The development of gill rakers seems to vary in proportion as they are needed for service. Fish that feed on crayfish and on small fish have no use for strainers, and, accordingly, their gill rakers are undeveloped.

Food eaten by the fish passes into an *esophagus* which expands into the *stomach.* Digestion starts here and the process is completed in the *intestine.*

Beyond the *pylorus,* the muscular valve at the junction of the stomach and small intestine, are the *pyloric caeca* which secrete digestive fluids. Dissolved foods are absorbed by diffusion through the membrane lining the intestine and pass into the blood.

ANIMALS WITH BACKBONES

FIGURE 13-7. *FOOD CYCLE*

Some fish (1) feed entirely on other fish (2) which in turn feed on small forms of aquatic life (3) such as crustaceans. These small animals are nourished by underwater plants (4). The plants are nourished by carbon dioxide cast off by fish, thus completing the food cycle in a pond.

The *liver* is large, and secretes *bile* which is collected in the *gall bladder*. When food is ready to be digested, the bile passes through the *bile duct* into the small intestine. The *pancreas* is usually indistinct.

The main parts of the digestive system and their adaptations are similar in all the higher vertebrates (Fig. 13-8).

13.7   Circulation

The blood of fishes circulates in well-defined blood vessels. It is pumped by a two-chambered *heart* composed of one **auricle** (*aw*-rih-k'l) and one **ventricle** (*ven*-trih-k'l). The ventricle pumps the blood from the heart through the *ventral aorta* and to the gills, where it gets rid of carbon dioxide and receives oxygen. It is then carried by the *dorsal aorta* to the rest of the body, where it leaves its supply of oxygen and collects the carbon dioxide. The blood from the body is returned to the auricle of the heart through the *cardinal veins*. Because the temperature of the blood of fishes is the same as that of the surrounding water and changes with the seasons, fishes are called *cold-blooded* animals.

13.8   Excretion

In addition to **oxidation** (*the union of oxygen with certain parts of the protoplasm*), there are other vital processes taking place in all the cells of the body of the fish. These processes produce waste substances that exist in the form of liquids which are gathered up by the small blood vessels and carried to the *kidneys* of the fish. Here these liquid wastes are extracted from the blood, carried to the *bladder,* and excreted.

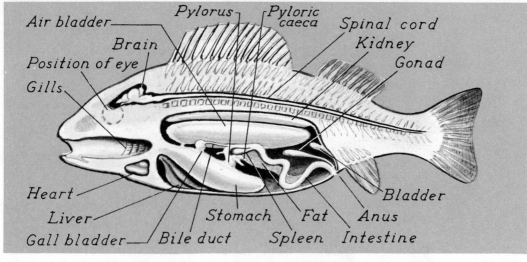

FIGURE 13-8. *BODY ORGANS OF THE FISH*

The fish, lowest form of vertebrate animals, has well-developed digestive, circulatory, nervous and reproductive systems. Note the air bladder between the digestive organs and spinal column enabling the fish to rise or sink in the water.

13.9 Nervous System

The nervous system consists of a *spinal cord,* a well-developed *brain,* and *nerves* which connect the brain and spinal cord with all parts of the body. The fish also has well-developed special sense organs.

Special Senses.—The well-developed *eye* is without lids and is somewhat moveable. It is globular and projecting and is believed to be near-sighted. The organs of *smell* are usually located in the nasal cavity. *Taste buds* are present in and around the mouth. In the bullhead, organs of *taste* are found in the feelers, on the head, and even in the skin of the tail, as well as in the mouth cavity. The *ear* is under the skin, and there is no external opening. It merely serves to give the fish a sense of balance. As water conducts sound vibrations well, the bones of the skull receive sound vibrations transmitted through water. The **lateral line** (Fig. 13-3), extending along the side of the fish, helps it to detect changes in pressure and current move-

ments. This helps when swimming close to solid objects or when determining depth.

13.10 Reproduction

The sexes of fish are distinct. The reproductive organs, knowns as **gonads** (*goh*-nads), are in the body cavity (Fig. 13-8). The male fish has *testes* which produce sperm cells called **milt.** The female fish has *ovaries* which form egg cells.

At certain seasons many fish migrate upstream to lay their eggs. This egg-laying process by a fish is called **spawning.** The eggs are small and usually float to the top of the water. They are laid in large numbers by the females, and in the same locality sperm cells are discharged into the water by the males. The sperms unite with the eggs. The fertilized eggs hatch after from seven to forty days or longer, the time depending on the kind of fish and the temperature of the water. The *yolk* of the egg remains attached to the young fish for many days after

ANIMALS WITH BACKBONES

FIGURE 13-9. *HATCHED*

The female trout lays about 500 eggs, which hatch out young fry like the one in the center of the picture. Attached to the underside of the young trout's body is a yolk sac, used for food.

they are able to swim, and supplies all the food they need during this time (Fig. 13-9).

The spawning habits of fish must be understood thoroughly if they are to be raised artificially, as in fish hatcheries. Most states have scientific game laws which protect the fish during their egg-laying period when they are easily caught and when the destruction of even a few fishes means the loss of thousands of eggs.

Spawning habits vary greatly. Some fish, like the salmon, make long journeys from the sea to the head waters of rivers and streams to deposit their eggs. The Columbia River is famous for the number of salmon which spawn there. Other fish, like shad, go up a river only a short distance to lay their eggs. Many shad, for instance, go up the Hudson River to spawn.

13.11 Care of Young

Generally, adult fish pay no attention to their young, and in many cases they devour young of their own kind as quickly as they would the young of other fish.

A few fish, like the sticklebacks, build nests of sticks and leaves in which their eggs are placed and guarded. Bass and sunfish make a circular depression about a foot in diameter near the shore and lay

FIGURE 13-10. *ON GUARD*

The male stickleback builds and then guards the nest in which the female deposits her eggs.

FIGURE 13-11. *END OF THE TRAIL*

Every spring millions of salmon return to fresh water where they spawn—
and then die. They push upstream, leaping through rapids and up waterfalls
sometimes ten feet high. Many are caught for the canning industry.

their eggs on these so-called "beds," which are guarded zealously by the males. The fresh-water dogfish males guard and care for the young until they are about four inches long.

Catfish carry the eggs in their mouths until they hatch. The male sea horse carries them in an abdominal pouch. The butterfish coils around the mass of eggs. The male paradise fish even blows bubbles which hide and protect the eggs while he circulates the water by tail and fin movements until they hatch.

13.12 Migration of Fish

Some species migrate in order to find a comfortable temperature, to seek an adequate food supply, or to escape disagreeable conditions, such as strong currents or pollutions. The swordfish moves north in the spring and south in the autumn, seeking a favorable temperature. But the salmon and the eel seem to migrate in response to the reproductive instinct, spending part of their lives in fresh water and part in salt water.

The adult salmon make their way from the ocean to fresh-water tributaries. There the eggs are laid in shallow water and are fertilized by the male's sperm cells which are deposited near them. The eggs hatch at ordinary temperatures. The adults, already weakened by the journey, do not survive very long after spawning. When the young salmon are from two to seven years old, they swim down to the ocean; there they remain several seasons until they are ready to return as adult fish.

The eel reverses the spawning habits of the salmon by traveling to salt water to lay its eggs. It is thought that both the American and European eels spend most of their lives, perhaps eight to twelve years, in fresh water. At the sexual maturity they descend to the sea to spawn. Then the young eels return to fresh water, to grow to maturity.

13.13 Enemies of Fish

Water snakes and turtles eat large numbers of fish eggs and young fish.

ANIMALS WITH BACKBONES

FIGURE 13-12. *CHAMPION ANGLER*

Fish account for 75% of the kingfisher's diet. From his perch on a tree limb, he looks for a small fish in the water and dives, either seizing or spearing it. He hardly ever misses.

G. Ronald Austing,
from National Audubon Society

Kingfishers perch on over-hanging branches of trees and are so accurate in their diving from a height that they almost always catch a fish. Wading and swimming birds such as herons and ducks eat many young fish. Minks, raccoons, and a few other mammals also feast on fish.

There are some insects that kill young fish. The fish-killing insects spend all of their time in the water except when migrating from pond to pond or during the mating period. They hide under stones or lie partly in the mud. From these places of hiding, they dart out and seize their victims with their jaws or claws. The water-tiger, a larva of one of the water beetles, is equipped with curved, sharp, hollow jaws with which it pierces its prey and sucks the juices of the body.

The largest and most destructive of these fish-killing insects is a true bug (Fig. 12-11), which, like the spider, grasps the fish with its curved forelegs, plunges its large, sharp beak deep into the fish, and then slowly sucks its blood. These and other insects feed on the eggs of fish, so that, when hatching fish artifi-

FIGURE 13-13. *FORMIDABLE FISH*

Neither of these fish has any difficulty warding off his enemies. The electric eel (right) has enough electricity to light a neon sign or make himself heard on a loudspeaker. The shark, a fast swimmer, attacks other fish and has been known to attack man.

Marine Studios, Marineland, Fla.   Science Service

A. N. Thorndike

FIGURE 13-14. *SHARK LIVERS*
These small sharks are useful for the oil extracted from their livers, which contains Vitamin A.

cially, man has to protect the eggs and young fish from such insects.

To compete against the loss of so many eggs and young, fish produce many eggs each year. A codfish lays as many as 16,000,000 in one season.

13.14 Means of Defense

A few fish have special means of protecting themselves. The bony pike has armor plates. The ray and electric eel possess enough electricity to stun and kill enemies. Bullheads and catfish have poison glands. The swordfish has a long projection from its head which serves as a weapon.

Minnows and trout have the power to change color due to pigments in special skin cells, *chromatophores,* which react to light. Some tropical fish which are brilliantly colored turn dark when alarmed, and rush for hiding places.

13.15 Importance of Food-Fish to Man

The world fisheries take from the water over 35,000,000,000 pounds of fish annually, valued at above $1,000,000,000. The hatcheries of the United States have an output of more than 4,500,000,000 eggs, fry (Sec. 13.17), and small fish. The eggs of the shad and sturgeon are eaten as food by man. Sturgeon eggs are sold commercially as "caviar." Oil from the livers of codfish and halibut is particularly rich in vitamin D and is extracted for medicinal purposes. Six million gallons of cod liver oil are used annually for vitamins and industry. Crude fish oil is used in paints and insecticide sprays. Gelatine is made from the fins of sharks.

Besides furnishing food, fish supply glue and fertilizer. Dried skins of sharks are sold as *shagreen,* a kind of rough leather, used for polishing. The large air bladders of the sturgeon are sometimes dried and then used as isinglass, a gelatin preparation for clarification in the making of wines and jellies.

13.16 Need for Fish Protection

As the human race increases in numbers it requires more and more food. Since most people are fond of fish, these animals are caught in ever-increasing numbers by the men who supply the fish markets.

The fish that are most useful as food are taken by hooks, nets, and seines, under certain restrictions. Those like brook trout, which are caught as much for sport as for food, can be taken only by a hook and line and in certain seasons, the season of the year depending upon the time of spawning. The rainbow trout spawns in February or March, while the brook trout does not spawn until toward fall.

ANIMALS WITH BACKBONES

The breeding habits and the breeding periods of fish have been the basis of all the *protective laws*. This is the reason why the closed season for one kind of fish is different from that for another.

Many streams and lakes are contaminated by sewage and chemical wastes. Dams for flood control, hydro-electric power, and irrigation create obstacles that interfere with the migration, spawning, and other activities of various fishes. *Fish ladders* have been built on some salmon and trout streams. These consist of a series of small pools at increasingly higher levels connected by small waterfalls up which the migrating adults may pass. It is important to protect fish when man uses so many for food and disturbs their life habitats.

13.17   Fish Hatcheries

In the natural state, many eggs are laid that never hatch because the sperm cells do not come in contact with them; and of the fishes that are hatched only a small proportion reaches maturity. As it is a matter of great economic importance that fish be saved from extermina-

FIGURE 13-15.   *CONSERVATION*

Ladders like this one enable fish to go around high dams or waterfalls, on their way to the spawning grounds. Even where no obstacles exist, the ladders help larger numbers to reach their goal.

tion, the governments of the world have established hatcheries where fish are raised in great numbers to be distributed to suitable waters.

FIGURE 13-16.   *ARTIFICIAL PROPAGATION*

At the fish hatchery, the eggs of the female trout are gently removed (*left*), fertilized, and set in running water until they hatch. After hatching, the young fingerlings (*right*) are kept in pools until large enough for distribution.

In these hatcheries the eggs are taken from the female and placed in a tank. The mass of minute sperm cells or *milt* is taken from the male and poured over the eggs, so that practically all the latter hatch. Then, if the developing eggs are protected and the young fish are given sufficient and proper food, nearly all these eggs develop into active fish. When they are able to take care of themselves, these **fry,** as the young hatchery fish are called, are taken to natural feeding grounds.

It is not sufficient simply to know how to hatch fish and feed the fry; one must have an accurate knowledge of the kinds of food available for the fry when they are placed in a stream, pond, or lake. This means that one must know a great deal about the general life of the waters that are to be stocked. What are the enemies of the fry? What plants supply the most food for the young fish? Is the water polluted by the wastes of some manufacturing process? These are some of the more important problems that must be solved before it is wise to set the fry free.

FACTS TO REMEMBER

Vertebrates have (1) a backbone, (2) usually two pairs of appendages, (3) a brain and dorsal nerve cord, (4) a ventral heart, and (5) gill slits sometime during life.

Fish belong to the simplest group of vertebrates. They have (1) fins, (2) gills, (3) scales, (4) two-chambered heart with one auricle and one ventricle, (5) body temperature like its surroundings, (6) usually an air bladder, and (7) well-developed brain and sense organs.

Fish are adapted to live at the surface and at great ocean depths, in fresh and salt water, and in Arctic and tropic seas.

Fish are of great economic importance, furnishing man with food and many other products. It is important to know their habits of migration and life histories in order to protect and raise them in hatcheries.

WORDS TO REMEMBER

air bladder	gill rakers	oxidation
auricle	gills	pectoral girdle
endoskeleton	gill slits	pelvic girdle
fin	gonad	scales
fish ladder	lateral line	spawning
fry	milt	ventricle
gill arch	notochord	vertebrate
gill filaments	operculum	

QUESTIONS

1. What are the characteristics of vertebrates?
2. Of what three parts does the body of a fish consist?
3. Name the fins of a fish and state the function of each.
4. What is the advantage of the overlapping scales of the fish?
5. How can you estimate the age of a fish?

6. What is the purpose of the gill rakers?
7. Explain how a fish breathes.
8. What is the food of most fish?
9. Give the life cycle of the salmon.
10. How does the life cycle of the eel differ from that of the salmon?
11. What are the chief enemies of fish?
12. Name some fish protectors and their methods.
13. How do some fish care for their young?
14. Name several uses of fish to man.

COMPLETION TEST

As your teacher or classmate reads the following incomplete statements, with your book closed, write on a clean sheet of paper the word or phrase which correctly completes the statement.

1. The egg-laying process of fish is called _____.
2. Young hatchery fish are known as _____.
3. Fish breathe by means of _____.
4. The heart of a fish consists of _____ chambers.
5. The nasal cavities of fish are used for _____.
6. The fish has no _____ ear.
7. The temperature of the fish is the same as its _____.
8. Fish use their teeth for _____ food.
9. The eggs of fish are known as _____.
10. The gill cover is called the _____.

PROJECTS

I. *Study of a Living Fish.*—Observe the fish in the aquarium and carefully record your observations.
1. Note the shape and relative sizes of the head, trunk, and tail regions.
2. The operculum or gill cover moves as the fish breathes. Can you find it?
3. Where are the eyes located? Do they move?
4. Locate each of the following fins:

(a) pectoral   (d) caudal
(b) pelvic   (e) dorsal
(c) anal

5. Which of the fins are paired?
6. Find out how the fish uses each of its fins.
7. Locate the lateral line sense organ.

II. *Study of a Preserved Fish Specimen.*
1. On a preserved fish specimen locate the following parts:

(a) fins   (d) eyes
(b) lateral line sense organ   (e) nostrils
(c) operculum   (f) scales

Draw a side view and label carefully.

2. Cut away the operculum on one side and expose the gills. Note the following parts:

   (a) gill filaments   (b) gill rakers   (c) gill arch

3. Open the mouth and observe the type and kind of teeth. What is their use?

4. If you are interested, you may dissect the fish, and with your teacher's help you may be able to locate the digestive and other organs.

III. *Details of Structure.*

1. Remove a few scales. Examine under the low power of the microscope. Count the main curved lines and estimate the age of the fish.

2. With a hand lens study the lateral line sense organs. What is the purpose of these?

3. Remove one of the gills and look at the filaments with a hand lens or low power. How are they adapted for removing oxygen from the water? Draw one in detail.

IV. *Tropical Fish.*—Look up reference material on tropical fish. You may wish to start a small aquarium with guppies. They are especially interesting because they produce living young.

V. *Fishing as a Sport.*—If you like to fish, find out all you can about the fish in your vicinity, including the laws about open seasons and size of fish. Write a report and illustrate it if you can.

VI. *Fish Hatchery.*—Visit a fish hatchery and write an account. Your whole class may decide to go there on a field trip.

REFERENCES

Beebe, *Half Mile Down.* Harcourt, Brace.

Boardman, *Guide to Higher Aquarium Animals.* Cranbrook Institute of Science (Michigan).

Bureau of Fisheries, Fish Manuals of the United States Commission of Fish and Fisheries.

Carson, *Under the Sea-Wind.* Oxford University Press.

Harris, *Salmon and Trout.* Macmillan.

Hausman, *Beginner's Guide to Fresh-Water Life.* Putnam's.

Henshall, *Bass, Pike, Perch, and Others.* Macmillan.

Jordan, *Fishes.* Appleton.

Kay, *A Child's Book of Fishes.* Maxton.

Lane, *All About the Sea.* Random House.

Mellon, *Fishes in the Home.* Dodd, Mead.

Morton, *Boy's Guide to Fishing.* Greenberg.

Reed and Bronson, *The Sea for Sam.* Harcourt, Brace.

Romer, *The Vertebrate Body.* Saunders.

Roule, *Fishes, Their Journeys and Migrations.* Norton.

Williamson, *Salar, the Salmon.* Little, Brown.

Zim, Smith, *Seashores: Golden Nature Guide.* Simon and Schuster.

CHAPTER 14

Land and Water Animals

14.1 Amphibia

The class **Amphibia** (am-*fib*-ee-uh) bridges the gap in the development of living things from a water environment to a land environment. Amphibia live two kinds of lives. On land there are less pressure, greater changes in temperature, and less food than in water. Amphibians have (1) two pairs of legs for locomotion, (2) lungs, gills, or skin for breathing, (3) a three-chambered heart with two auricles and one ventricle, (4) a moist, glandular skin without scales, (5) nostrils leading to the mouth cavity, and (6) external fertilization in frogs and toads, internal in salamanders.

Familiar amphibians are *frogs* and toads; but the *salamanders* also belong in this group. Amphibian means *both lives,* and suggests that habit which frogs, toads, and some salamanders have of spending their larval life (tadpole stage) in the water, and their adult life on land, or partly on land and partly in water.

The *amphibians* are all small vertebrates, the largest one found in America being a salamander which is rarely more than 2 feet long. One giant salamander grows to be 5 feet long, and a very tiny one is only 1½ inches in length. The giant African frog may have a body length of 12 inches, and a small Cuban one only ⅜ of an inch when full grown. Most toads and frogs are from 2 to 5 inches long.

14.2 Habitats of Amphibia

Amphibians live in fresh water or moist places. Their habitats cover a wide range of distribution. A few live at an altitude of 12,000 feet in California. Toads can exist over 15,000 feet in the Himalayas, and some frogs within the Arctic Circle. Some toads live where it is quite dry, as in Texas, but they stay in underground burrows by day and come out only at night. Certain salamanders live only in the water while

FIGURE 14-1. *AMPHIBIAN*

The bullfrog (*left*), which may reach a length of 8 inches, and the spotted leopard frog are both familiar in the U.S. The muscular jumping legs of bullfrogs are considered delicacies by many.

Lynwood M. Chace

191

others live some of the time in moist woods. There is great variety in habitats among this group of animals. Over many years they have tried to adapt themselves to a change in environment from water to land.

In regions with cold winters, frogs and certain types of salamanders **hibernate** (pass the winter in inactivity) by going deep into the lakes or ponds. Toads and other kinds of salamanders burrow below the frost line. In regions such as the lowlands of California, where the summers are hot and dry, the amphibians **estivate** (pass the summer in inactivity) by digging into the ground.

14.3 Frogs

The general form of the body, the shape of the head, and long hind legs adapted for jumping, and the webbed toes for swimming are much the same in all frogs. There are several kinds, one of which, the *leopard frog,* is found generally distributed throughout the United States. It can be recognized by the many brownish or greenish spots, edged with white, on the back, which help the frog to escape the notice of its enemies as it squats among the water weeds. These colors form rather definite bands on the hind legs, though there is much variation. There is no green pigment in the skin; the green color is due to the reflection of light by other pigments.

Like other animals, frogs carry on all the life processes. They are typical vertebrates, with many structures similar to those of higher animals.

14.4 Food and Digestion

Frogs are greedy; they eat almost any animal small enough to be swallowed, such as insects, worms, snails, tadpoles, and small frogs. These are caught alive and often when in motion. The frog's mouth has short lips covering the short teeth in the edge of the upper jaw. The sticky tongue has two fleshy horns at the back end, and is attached at the front

FIGURE 14-2. *DIGESTIVE SYSTEM OF THE FROG*

From the esophagus, food passes into the rather large stomach, where it is acted upon by digestive juices containing enzymes. With bile from the liver and a pancreas secretion the process is continued in the small intestine.

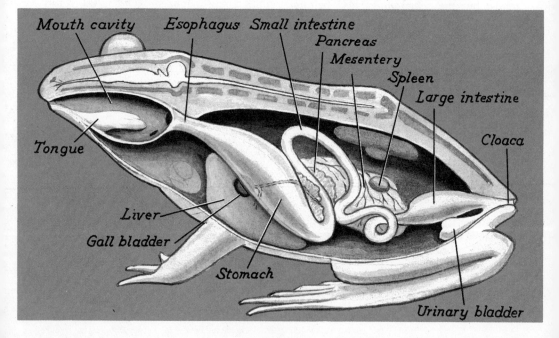

end to the floor of the mouth. The frog can throw its sticky tongue over the tip of either jaw and use the forked end to catch insects, which are then carried into the back of the mouth. Two groups of vomerine teeth in the roof of the mouth aid in preventing the escape of the prey. The food is swallowed whole.

In the frog, the *esophagus,* also called the *gullet,* enlarges at the lower end to form the *stomach.* This is a long spindle-shaped sac (Fig. 14-2), larger than the rest of the digestive tube. It has gastric glands in the walls and secretes gastric fluid.

The *small intestine* begins at the pylorus at the end of the stomach. It is a small tube which makes several turns, finally enlarging into a region called the *large intestine,* the last part of which is termed the **cloaca** (kloh-*ay*-kuh). The cloaca is where wastes from both the intestine and kidney collect before being excreted through the *anus.*

Two important glands belong to the digestive organs—the **liver** and the **pancreas** (*pan*-kree-us). The liver is a large, dark-red, three-lobed organ that covers the *ventral* (lower) surface of the stomach. The pancreas is a whitish, small, irregularly shaped body attached between the stomach and the first loop of the intestine. Both these glands drain into the intestine just beyond the stomach through tubes called *ducts.* The *bile* secreted by the liver is at first collected in a sac called the **gall bladder,** from which it passes through the **bile duct** into the small intestine. The **pancreatic duct** leads directly from the pancreas to the small intestine (Fig. 14-2). The fluids secreted by these glands are necessary for intestinal digestion.

All these parts of the digestive canal are held in place by a thin membrane, the **mesentery** (*mes*-en-ter-ee), one edge of which is attached on the *dorsal* (upper) side along the line of the backbone and the other to the stomach and intestine. A small gland (the **spleen**) is found in this mesentery; it has no duct connecting it with any other organ in the frog, and is called a *ductless gland.* It is closely related to changes in the blood.

14.5 Respiration and Circulation

The *lungs* are hollow sacs that lie back of the stomach, one on each side. Each lung connects by a short tube, the **bronchus** (*bron-kus*) (Fig. 14-3), to the voice box, or **larynx** (*lair*-inks), which contains two vocal chords. When air is forced from the lungs, the cords vibrate and the frog croaks.

The oxygen from the air passes directly through both the thin, moist skin and the lungs into the blood of the frog, and the carbon dioxide of the blood is thrown off through these same two organs. The frog has large blood vessels close to the skin, especially along the back. These send out many fine branches which enable the frog to respire through its skin, as it is accustomed to do when staying below the surface of the water.

When the frog remains under the water for a long time, as during the winter, all the oxygen used enters the blood through the skin. Air can be taken directly into the blood through the lining of the mouth cavity. It can also be forced into the lungs by the muscles on the floor of the mouth rather than breathed in, as a frog has no diaphragm (a muscular partition between the chest and abdomen). Experiments have been made which show that the frog can get oxygen in sufficient quantities to maintain life, even when it cannot use its lungs. The frog thus has two respiratory organs, the *skin* and the *lungs;* and can take through the mouth oxygen from

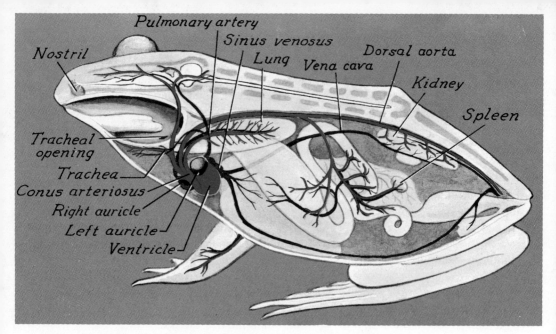

FIGURE 14-3. *FROG RESPIRATION AND CIRCULATION*

When the gills disappear, the frog, now adult, takes in air through the lungs, which are connected with the mouth by the trachea. While underwater, it respires through the skin. The organs of circulation are a three-chambered heart (ventricle and two auricles), arteries, veins, and capillaries.

the open air and from the dissolved air in the water.

The Circulatory System.—Amphibians possess a three-chambered heart: two *auricles* which receive the blood,

FIGURE 14-4. *HEART OF FROG*

Blood is pumped throughout the body by the muscular *ventricle.* Some of it enters the lungs through the *pulmonary artery,* and returns by the *pulmonary vein.*

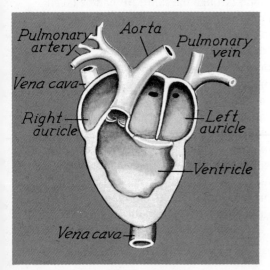

and one *ventricle,* a muscular organ which pumps blood throughout the body by contracting (Fig. 14-3).

The ventricle forces blood into the *conus arteriosus.* This large blood vessel on the front side of the heart forms two main branches, each one subdivided into three smaller branches: (1) the *carotid arteries* to the head, (2) the *aortic arches* which bend around the body and join to form the *dorsal aorta* and (3) the *pulmocutaneous arteries* which supply the lungs and skin. The arteries continue to subdivide to form capillaries in all parts of the body where the cells receive food and oxygen and send back nitrogenous wastes and carbon dioxide. The capillaries unite to form small veins, the *venae venosus.* These empty into the *sinus venosus,* a thin-walled sac at the back of the heart, then enter the right auricle. As the blood circulates, branches lead out to the

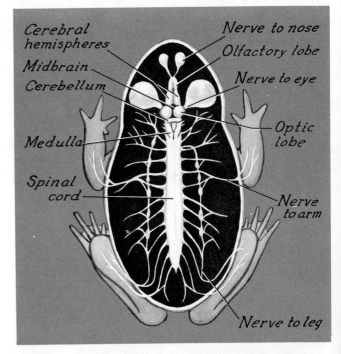

Nerve to nose
Olfactory lobe
Nerve to eye
Optic lobe
Nerve to arm
Nerve to leg
Cerebral hemispheres
Midbrain
Cerebellum
Medulla
Spinal cord

FIGURE 14-5. *NERVOUS SYSTEM*

Nerves leading from the brain are shown, as well as the ten pairs of nerves from the spinal cord. Locate the parts of the brain. What functions does each have?

digestive organs where it receives food which it carries by the *portal vein* to the liver and on to the *vena cava.* Other branches pass through the kidneys, where nitrogenous wastes are removed.

The blood consists of clear fluid *plasma,* large oval-shaped *red cells,* usually with nuclei, several kinds of *white cells,* and *spindle cells* for blood clotting. Blood cells are formed in the *marrow* inside of the bones and also in the *spleen.*

14.6 Nervous System

All vertebrates have a well-developed nervous system, which includes brain, spinal cord, nerves, and sense organs. They are able to do more things and with more precision than invertebrates, such as a worm, for example. The brain of a frog is really a very simple organ when compared with the brain of a dog. This is why a dog can be taught to do more things than a frog.

The nervous system of the frog is more highly developed than that of the cray-

fish and in some respects more than that of the fish. The **central nervous system,** sometimes designated the cerebro-spinal system, as in all vertebrates, is divided into the *brain* and the *spinal cord,* from which nerves extend to all parts of the frog's body.

The brain of the frog is not as highly developed as that of man, but the parts are similar and much easier to study (Fig. 14-5). The **olfactory** (ohl-*fak*-tuh-ree) **lobes** receive the smell stimuli; nerves go from these lobes to the nostrils. The **cerebral** (*seh*-ruh-brul) **hemispheres** may have some control over muscular action. Studies have been made on the functions of the nervous system by removing parts of it. Removal of the cerebral hemispheres is not fatal, but the frog loses the ability to initiate movement and will sit still in a dry, warm room for hours unless disturbed. It never sits like this when the cerebral region of the brain is uninjured.

The **midbrain** region is the passageway for all nerve-pathways that travel

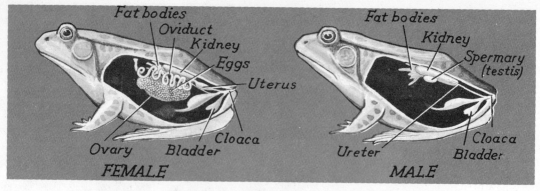

FIGURE 14-6. *REPRODUCTIVE AND EXCRETORY SYSTEMS*

Liquid wastes are removed from the body by the *kidneys,* which are connected with the *cloaca* by the *ureter.* The male sperm also passes through the kidney and ureter. The *testes* are attached to the kidneys.

to and from the brain. The midbrain and **optic lobes** explain to the frog the sight stimuli. The **cerebellum** (ser-uh-*bel*-um), which is poorly developed, coordinates the muscles. The **medulla** (meh-*duhl*-uh) gives off more nerves than any other region of the brain, leading to the face, tongue, ear, heart, and lungs, and controls automatic functions.

The medulla of the brain merges imperceptibly with the **spinal cord.** Ten pairs of **cranial** (*kray*-nee-'l) **nerves** leave the brain proper. These go to the special senses of the head and direct the moving of the muscles of the throat and head. The frog has ten other pairs of **spinal nerves** extending from the spinal cord (Fig. 14-5).

The sense organs of the frog include the taste buds on the tongue, the nerve endings in the skin for touch and in the nasal cavities for smell, the ears for hearing and balance, and the eyes for sight, but without depth perception.

14.7 Excretion and Reproduction

Like the fish, the frog has a pair of **kidneys** that remove wastes from the blood in the form of liquids, while the skin and lungs allow such wastes as carbon dioxide gas to be discharged from the blood.

The kidneys are small red bodies lying close to the back. Each one is connected with the cloaca by a tiny duct, the **ureter** (yoo-*ree*-ter) or **urinogenital** (yoo-ree-noh-*jen*-uh-t'l) **duct.** The **urinary bladder** is attached to the cloaca (Fig. 14-6).

The fundamental process of reproduction in amphibians is like that in other animals, but it also passes through the *tadpole stage.* This makes their life cycle different from that of other vertebrates.

The male frog has a pair of **testes,** one attached to the front (anterior) end of each kidney (Fig. 14-6). Each testis, or *spermary* (*spur*-muh-ree), is yellow in color. The sperms pass through the kidney, through the urinogenital duct, into the cloaca, and out into the water. In the female frog, **ovaries,** sometimes filled with eggs, are easily seen. A long, closely coiled pair of **oviducts** (*oh*-vih-dukts) opens in front near the forward end of the stomach and in the back into the cloaca. The eggs break through the wall of the ovary and then pass through the oviducts, where they are coated with a jelly that swells in the water (Fig. 14-7), protecting the eggs which are stored in the *uterus* until they are laid.

At the front end of each kidney in both the male and the female frog is an irregular mass of stored fat that the

Lynwood M. Chace

FIGURE 14-7. *LEOPARD FROG AND EGGS*

Although thousands of tadpoles will be hatched from this egg cluster (*left*), few will reach maturity. At right are tadpoles shortly before hatching.

frog uses as it begins to grow eggs or sperms in the early spring before there is plenty of food (Fig. 14-6).

14.8 Life Cycle of the Frog

In the early spring the frogs gather in ponds to lay their eggs. These are surrounded by a jellylike substance which holds them together. As the eggs are being laid by the female frog, the male frog spreads a large number of sperm cells over the whole mass. These sperm cells make their way through the soft jelly, and one of them must enter each egg if the egg is to grow normally into a *tadpole.*

Scientists have been able to make an unfertilized egg develop, under special care, until the tadpole stage, but normally or in nature the egg will not grow unless a sperm cell unites with it. The development of unfertilized eggs is known as **parthenogenesis** (pahr-then-oh-*jen*-eh-sis).

Fertilization of the Egg.—As soon as the sperm cell enters the egg (Fig. 14-8), the solid, pointed body of the sperm cell changes into a round nucleus which is so much like the nucleus already in the egg cell that none but experts in this study can tell which came from the sperm cell and which from the egg cell. These two nuclei come in contact and unite, forming one nucleus in the egg (Fig. 14-8). This last change is **fertilization,** which is defined as *the union of the egg and the sperm nuclei.* This union consists in bringing the **chromosomes** (bodies within the nucleus which are formed from the chromatin) of the two nuclei together into a single nucleus so that there is a definite part of each present in this fusion. After this union is completed, the egg begins to divide into more cells, as shown in Figure 14-8, and finally the tadpole is developed, and eventually matures into a frog.

Growth of the Tadpole.—As soon as the young tadpole hatches, it attaches itself to plants and lives for the first few days upon the food-yolk within its own body, while the mouth forms and horny jaws develop (Fig. 14-9). Then the tadpole begins to feed upon tiny plants and

LAND AND WATER ANIMALS

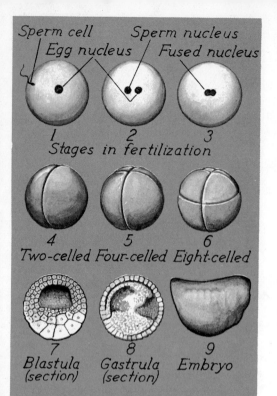

Stages in fertilization

1   2   3

Sperm cell   Sperm nucleus
Egg nucleus   Fused nucleus

4   5   6
Two-celled   Four-celled   Eight-celled

7   8   9
Blastula   Gastrula   Embryo
(section)   (section)

FIGURE 14-8. *FERTILIZATION AND DEVELOPMENT OF A FROG EGG*

In 1-3, the stages of fertilization are shown from the entrance of the sperm to the union of sperm and egg nuclei. In 4-6, the egg divides into eight cells. After this point, the blastula, a ball of unspecialized cells, is formed, a portion of which pushes in to form the two-layered gastrula. The egg flattens out, a third layer of cells forms between the first layers, and the embryo begins to take shape.

becomes dependent upon its own skill to get food and to escape its enemies.

For a time the tadpole respires through external gills. A fold of skin grows over the gills except for a small opening on the left side. The tadpole respires with these external gills until lungs develop during metamorphosis.

As the tadpole develops, the hind legs appear first. Later the front ones begin to show; and as they develop, the tail is

gradually absorbed. While these external changes are going on, there are many complicated internal changes taking place; internal gills are disappearing, and lungs, nerves, blood vessels, and muscles are being formed to give the new legs life and action. The internal lungs take the place of the gills in the throat before the legs are fully grown, and such tadpoles must rise to the surface to breathe air. Can you explain which tadpoles in Figure 14-9 breathe by lungs and which by gills? This complicated way of growing into a frog by first forming a tadpole is called *metamorphosis* and this term was also used to describe the life history of insects.

The tadpoles of leopard frogs become small frogs in a single summer, but the tadpoles of bullfrogs and green frogs require two seasons to complete their development. These latter tadpoles hibernate in the mud with adult frogs and toads.

Toward the end of fall, frogs prepare to spend the winter dormant or sleeping. Sometimes in the middle of the day they may be seen sunning themselves on a bank, but as soon as ice forms on the water they remain on the bottom or buried in the mud. The lungs are emptied of air, the heart beats decrease, and all the usual life processes take place more slowly. In cold regions, amphibia and reptiles, and several of the mammals *hibernate,* that is, pass the winter in an inactive state.

14.9 Protection from Enemies

Frogs are seldom found far from the marshy edges of some pond or stream. When disturbed, they jump into the water, swim to the bottom, stir up the mud, and quietly come to rest a short distance from the place where they entered. They are protected also by their

198

FIGURE 14-9. *METAMORPHOSIS OF THE FROG AND TOAD*
    The life cycles of frogs and toads are similar in many ways. Eggs are laid in the water, and the tadpoles remain until they have matured. Tadpoles breathe by external gills first, and later, by internal gills. How do adult frogs and toads breathe?

color, which usually resembles the grass and rocks among which they live. When away from water, frogs often escape their enemies by their remarkable leaping ability. Man is the worst enemy of the larger frogs, as he considers their hind legs a delicacy. Next come the snakes, birds, and fish. The leech kills frogs by sucking their blood. Fish eat many of the tadpoles, and, strange to say, some water beetles also eat tadpoles.

14.10   The Toad

The toad is one of our best friends, for it lives on insects and slugs that destroy the plants in our gardens. It captures its food by throwing out a sticky tongue just as the frog does. The toad has no teeth.

One often hears the expression, "Don't touch a toad; you will have warts." Of course this is not true. The rounded *warts* over the back, sides, and legs of toads contain mucus and other bitter substances. Their enemies dislike the bitter taste and learn to avoid the toads. Nor is it true that toads are found alive in solid rocks. They require food like any other animal and soon starve unless they can secure it.

14.11   Life Cycle of the Toad

In many respects the toad's life cycle is similar to that of the frog. In the spring, the eggs of the toad are laid in stagnant water in strings of a jellylike substance (Fig. 14-9). The eggs hatch in from five to ten days into wriggling

Robert C. Hermes from National Audubon Society

Henry B. Kane

FIGURE 14-10. *DOWN THE HATCH*
Flicking out a long, sticky tongue, both the tree frog (*left*) and his cousin the toad (*right*) aid man in his struggle against insect pests.

tadpoles, which feed on the microscopic plants in the water and swim by means of their tails. Respiration is by means of the outside gills, which allow the oxygen from the dissolved air in the water to reach the blood, and the carbon dioxide to enter the water. Later the inside gills take over the work of the outside gills, and the outside gills disappear. Still later, as lungs begin to develop, the tadpoles come to the surface for air, so that for a time they are getting the oxygen from both the open air and the dissolved air in the water.

About this time the hind legs begin to appear, the tail shortens, and, soon after, the front legs may be seen. Before much longer the tail has entirely disappeared and the small toad begins to hop around on the bank, having the same form and habits of the toad as we see him in the garden. From the bank they begin to travel away from the water

and scatter over the country in all directions. After a rain or during a shower, thousands of them are sometimes found hopping along a ravine or highway. Here they are run over by man and beast and eaten by crows and other enemies. Of the hundreds that leave the pond only a very few ever live to be a year old. Although slow-moving, the toad is able to feed upon flying insects as they rest on plants or crawl over the ground by striking out and seizing them with his quickly moving tongue.

14.12 Salamanders

These amphibia have long tails. Their two pairs of weak legs are about the same size. In the eastern part of the United States there are small *newts* which frequent ditches and sluggish water. The *spotted salamander* (Fig. 14-11), about six inches long, has a series of round, yellow spots along each edge of the

200

Lynwood M. Chace

FIGURE 14-11. *HANDLE WITH CARE*

The *necturus* (*left*) is an aquatic salamander with external gills behind the head. The spotted salamander (*right*), also an amphibian, gives off a milky substance when handled which is poisonous to some of its enemies.

back. When handled, the adult may protect itself by ejecting a poisonous fluid.

Some forms, like *necturus* (Fig. 14-11), found in the rivers of the upper Mississippi Valley and the Great Lakes, keep their gills throughout life. They grow to be about sixteen inches long. The siren or "mud eel," so common in the ditches of the South Carolina rice fields, also keeps its gills, but it retains only its front legs.

14.13 Care of the Young

Like fish, amphibians pay very little attention to their eggs after they are laid. Some amphibians in Brazil and Java build nests filled with foam in holes in banks. Others make enclosures near the shore to keep the eggs from floating away. A few lay their eggs in resin-lined holes in trees. Some salamanders coil around their eggs or hide them under logs and stones.

The female Surinam toad of South America carries the eggs in separate pits on her back. Others carry them in pouches, around the hind legs, and even in the vocal sacs.

14.14 Economic Value of Amphibians

Frogs and toads are of value to man. They eat many destructive insects. Bullfrogs are used as food. The smaller frogs are used as bait by fishermen. They are also used for biological specimens and as convenient forms for dissection in biology courses.

FACTS TO REMEMBER

Amphibia are cold-blooded vertebrates having (1) two pairs of weak legs, (2) a moist, glandular skin, (3) gills in the water-living larval stage and lungs as air-breathing adults, and (4) a three-chambered heart.

Frogs, toads, and salamanders belong to this group. Frogs and toads have complete metamorphosis. Many of them are of value to man as food, bait for fish, and as specimens for biological study, since their body structure is typical of the vertebrate body.

WORDS TO REMEMBER

amphibian
bile
bile duct
bladder
bronchus
capillaries
central nervous system
cerebellum
cerebral hemispheres
chromosomes
cloaca
conus arteriosus
cranial nerves
dorsal aorta
estivate
fertilization
gall bladder

hibernate
kidneys
larynx
liver
lungs
marrow
medulla
mesentery
metamorphosis
midbrain
olfactory lobe
optic lobes
ovaries
oviduct
pancreas
pancreatic duct
parthenogenesis

plasma
portal vein
pulmocutaneous arteries
red corpuscles
sinus venosus
spermary
spinal cord
spinal nerves
spleen
tadpole
testes
ureter
urinogenital duct
vena cava
warts
white corpuscles

QUESTIONS

1. What is an amphibian?
2. Name the three main groups of amphibia.
3. Explain how they breathe.
4. How can you recognize toads' eggs? How could you distinguish them from frogs' eggs?
5. Explain how a frog catches insects.
6. Compare the life cycle of a frog with that of a toad.
7. What is the function of the frog's olfactory lobes?
8. Name the male and the female frog's reproductive organs.
9. Describe the metamorphosis of the frog.
10. Discuss the economic value of amphibians.

COMPLETION TEST

As your teacher or classmate reads the following incomplete statements, with your book closed, write on a clean sheet of paper the word or phrase which correctly completes the statement.

1. The union of the contents of the egg and sperm nuclei is called _____.
2. The frog eggs are protected by a mass of _____.
3. Liquid wastes are removed from the blood in the frog by the _____.
4. Bile is secreted by the _____.
5. The frog's tongue is attached at the _____ end.
6. The frog breathes by _____ and _____.
7. The _____ legs of a frog have webbed toes.
8. The _____ legs of a tadpole appear first.

PROJECTS

I. *Study of a Living Frog.*—Place one or two frogs or toads in a small jar or box. Watch them for a time and carefully record your observations. Be sure to include the answers to the following questions:

1. How does the general shape of the frog differ from the general shape of a fish?

2. How do the colors differ?

3. How are the legs and feet adapted to the way the frog lives? Can it walk? Can it hop? How far can yours jump? Count the toes on each of the frog's feet.

4. Is the frog sensitive to touch in various parts of the body?

5. Can a frog wink? Lightly touch the eye. In what way does the frog protect its eye?

6. How does a frog get air? Can you account for the motion of the throat?

7. Hold the frog under the water and gently rub its sides. It will usually croak. Thus we can prove that the frog is able to make the air travel from its lungs to its mouth and back again while under water.

8. Locate the ears. These correspond to the middle ears of higher animals. The inner ears are underneath and cannot be seen.

9. Note the elongated glands extending along either side of the back. Find out what they are used for.

10. Put some flies in the jar and watch the frog catch one.

II. *Study of a Preserved Frog Specimen (External).*—Locate the following structures. Make a drawing of the frog, showing all the parts.

1. Head
2. Trunk
3. Eye
4. Ear
5. Nostril
6. Front leg
7. Hind leg
8. Toes
9. Mouth
10. Glands (if possible)

III. *Dissection of a Frog.*—If you can bring a living specimen into the laboratory, your teacher may help you etherize it so you can watch the heart beating.

1. Place the etherized frog on its back and fasten it.

2. With scissors, cut through the skin of the under side, making a slit down the middle of the body and fasten back the skin.

3. With scalpel or scissors, cut through the muscle layer very carefully and expose the heart.

4. If you are careful, you may be able to watch the heart beat for several minutes after the animal seems dead. Notice the two auricles (top) and the one muscular ventricle (below).

5. Carefully move aside the muscle layer and with your teacher's help identify the digestive and respiratory systems.

6. If your frog is a female, you may note a large egg mass on each side nearly filling the abdominal cavity.

7. The pancreas can be seen as a small whitish structure in the loop between the stomach and the intestine. The spleen is a round, red organ usually found near the large intestine.

8. A pair of narrow kidneys lies close to the back. They are connected by ducts with the cloaca. A spermary (in a male frog) is attached to each kidney near the front end, and the sperm cells escape to the exterior by the kidney ducts.

9. The nervous system is enclosed in bone that is easily removed from the dorsal surface. The brain should be studied and the following divisions recognized: cerebral hemispheres ending in front in the olfactory lobes, which are not clearly marked; just back of these, the two large roundish optic lobes, which are attached to the midbrain; the cerebellum, which is small; and the medulla, which passes into the spinal cord without any sharp dividing line.

IV. *Development of Tadpoles.*—Bring a mass of frogs' or toads' eggs into the laboratory. Be sure to bring some of the pond water in which you found them floating.

1. Change the water every day if you can. Avoid chlorinated water. At least be sure there is enough water to supply the necessary oxygen.

2. Watch the development of the eggs by looking at them every school day. Place a few of them in a watch glass of water and observe under a microscope.

3. From day to day make sketches of what you see and compare them with those shown in Figure 14-9.

4. After a few days, tiny tadpoles will appear. Place some green water plants in the jars with the tadpoles. Be sure to keep plenty of fresh water in the jars. If you care for them very faithfully, you may be able to keep the tadpoles alive until school is out.

5. If you are still interested, you may be able to take your tadpole home and watch the metamorphosis as it changes to a frog.

6. Record your observations. Write an account of what you did and include your sketches in your report.

V. If you live in a region where you are unable to obtain amphibia and you are also unable to study any preserved specimens, here are a few suggestions:

1. Make a booklet of stories and pictures of frogs. Find out how and where they are raised for food.

2. Using reference books, write a detailed account of the care of the young.

3. Compare salamanders with fishes. What adaptations does each kind of animal show? How would you have to change a salamander in order to make it into a fish?

4. Explain how a lung fish can live during the dry season buried in the mud and how a frog can live under the water all winter.

5. Which has the more highly developed sense organs, the frog or the grasshopper? Explain.

6. Can you suggest how animals came to live on land?

REFERENCES

Barbour, *Reptiles and Amphibians*. Houghton Mifflin.

Bishop, *Handbook of Salamanders*. Comstock.

Dickerson, *The Frog Book*. Doubleday.

Hodge, *Nature Study and Life*. Ginn.

Morris, *They Hop and Crawl*. Cattell.

Swenson, *A Child's Book of Reptiles and Amphibians*. Maxton.

Wright, *Handbook of Frogs and Toads*. Comstock.

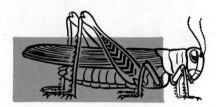

CHAPTER 15

Reptiles

15.1 Early Reptiles

The class **Reptilia** (rep-*til*-ee-uh), which includes the turtles, snakes, lizards, crocodiles, and alligators, are fast disappearing. They have many enemies among the birds and mammals. As a group, reptiles have been the greatest in number, greatest in size, and most complete in dominance. For 10,000,000 years the dinosaurs and other huge reptiles held sway over the earth. They ranged in size from that of a lizard to the Brontosaurus (bron-tuh-*sor*-us), which measured 75 feet long and 15 feet high. It weighed 30 tons or more. Most of these early reptiles disappeared as a result of great changes of the earth and its climate, the inability to compete with smaller, but more intelligent forms of life, and possibly for other reasons still unknown.

15.2 Characteristics of Reptiles

Reptiles are land animals, breathing entirely by lungs and having dry, scaly skin which is relatively thick. The mandibles, or jaws, are composed of several bones, usually not more than six. All except the snakes have two pairs of legs ending in claws. Some snakes have traces of hind legs during the embryonic stages, but all snakes throughout their lives use only their ribs and scales in moving.

FIGURE 15-1. *DINOSAURS*

These huge duck-billed dinosaurs were once very numerous on the earth. Their large tails and webbed feet were helpful in swimming. Why do dinosaurs no longer exist?

Hugh Spencer

Century Photos, Inc.

Figure 15-2. *BOX TURTLE*
The box turtle is so called because the plastron, or undershell, is hinged to bend
tightly over the carapace, or upper shell, boxing in the body. (*right*)

Reptiles have a **sternum,** or breast-bone, to protect the heart and lungs. They are cold-blooded, but their temperature seldom drops below 32° F. This is due to the fact that in most reptiles the ventricle of the three-chambered heart has a partition which almost separates it into two parts. Thus there is less mixing of the pure and impure blood. Alligators and crocodiles have a four-chambered heart like the higher animals.

15.3   Life History

The reptiles hatch directly from eggs into the adult form, only much smaller. They do not go through several larval stages like the insects and amphibians. The young snake or alligator just out of the egg is readily recognized by its resemblance to its parents. The reptiles lay their eggs in protected places, but exhibit no parental care to either eggs or young. The eggs of some snakes are hatched in the body of the parent and the young are born alive.

15.4   Turtles

The common *spotted turtles* are easily recognized by their outer skeleton, which is unlike that of insects or crabs or any other group of animals. The skeleton of the turtle is composed mostly of epidermal plates with bony plates underneath. When the turtle is disturbed, the legs, the head, and the tail are withdrawn, and the cover is pulled down tightly by muscles.

A turtle cannot be removed from its shell without killing it, because the ribs and backbone are fused into the shell of the back, which is called the **carapace.** The sternum, or breastbone, fuses into the under shell, which is known as the **plastron** (Fig. 15-2). A bony bridge connects the carapace and plastron.

Turtles have no teeth, but the horny jaws have sharp cutting edges. They have well-developed eyes and keen eyesight. The tympanic membrane is at the angle of the jaws. The nostrils are near the front of the head. The skin covering the limbs and tail has scales and most turtles have five toes with claws.

Sea turtles attain a length of six or eight feet and weigh sometimes as much as a thousand pounds. The female comes to shore once a year, at night, to lay her eggs in the sand. She covers them and

REPTILES

Lynwood M. Chace

Monkmeyer

FIGURE 15-3. *UGLY DUCKLINGS*

Two lizards found in southwestern U.S. and in Mexico are the horned lizard (*left*) and the Gila monster (*right*). The tail of the Gila monster is a storage place for fat, which enables it to go for months without food.

then goes back to the water leaving them to be hatched by the heat of the sun.

The flesh of the *green turtle* and of the diamond-back *terrapin* (*tehr*-uh-pin) is considered a delicacy. The *snapping turtle* common in the United States has sharp horny jaws capable of a severe bite. It is **carnivorous** (kahr-*niv*-er-us) (flesh-eating) and lives on fish, frogs, and waterfowl.

15.5 Lizards

These are the most numerous of the reptiles and are mostly tropical. They are covered with dry scales. Some are noted for swiftness, others are sluggish. There are several varieties of lizards, one of the commonest of which is the *chameleon* (kuh-*meel*-yun), which has the extraordinary ability of changing the intensity of the color of its skin by moving the color material nearer the outer surface or drawing it away. The *horned lizard* (Fig. 15-3) of the western United States is a lizard with scales of varying length which give it a horny appearance. Some horned lizards lay eggs; some hatch their eggs while they are in the oviducts, and the young are born alive. A poisonous lizard is the *Gila* (*hee*-luh) *monster* (Fig. 15-3) that occurs in New Mexico

and Arizona. It is deep black with blotches of orange, and grows to be about twenty inches long. The poison glands are in its lower jaw. The bite is unpleasant, but seldom causes death among human beings.

Some lizards easily break off their tails in order to escape from the hold of an enemy. Later new tails grow by regeneration. The *glass snake* is not a snake at all, but a lizard without legs. It easily breaks into two parts. The *ring-neck lizard* can stand upon its hind legs and walk. The *frilled lizard* has such good suction pads for climbing trees that it can walk on a vertical sheet of glass.

15.6 Snakes

Snakes are legless vertebrates with long, cylindrical bodies covered with scales. They move by means of the scales, or **scutes** (*skoots*), on the under side of the body, and by the action of a large number of muscles. Since snakes eat insects, mice, rats, and rabbits, they are generally considered beneficial to man.

The mouth of a snake is large and has several rows of sharp teeth pointing backward. The tongue is long and forked. This may be thrust out through

ANIMALS WITH BACKBONES

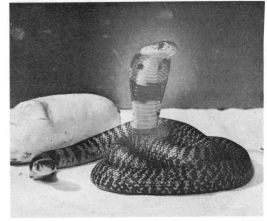

G. E. Kirkpatrick

Black Star

FIGURE 15-4. *TWO POISONOUS SNAKES*

The Western diamondback rattlesnake (*left*) is easy to recognize by the rattle and by its diamond-shaped yellow-edged splotches. Two Indian cobras (*right*) are shown here with the egg from which one of them hatched.

a small opening when the mouth is closed. The tongue is harmless and aids in the sense of smell, but many people have mistaken it for a fang. The eyes have no eyelids but are covered with transparent scales. Snakes cannot close their eyes but they can move them.

Rattlesnakes (Fig. 15-4), *copperheads,* the *cotton-mouthed moccasin,* and the *coral snake* are the most common poisonous snakes of our country. Their jaws are provided with **fangs** (Fig. 15-5), by means of which a poison **(venom)** is injected into their prey.

The venom of rattlers is secreted by two glands located under the upper jaw. These glands connect with the long slender fangs, which are hollow. When the mouth is closed, the fangs lie flat against the roof of the mouth, but are thrown forward when the snake strikes.

Large snakes, like the *boa constrictor* of South America and the *python* (*python*) of Asia, are **constrictors.** This means that they are able to wind their bodies around their prey and crush it to death. The most deadly snake in the world is the *cobra* (*koh*-bruh) of India (Fig. 15-4). Thousands of inhabitants

die annually from its bite. It is the only snake that pursues man when not attacked by him.

Snakes swallow their food whole. Their teeth point backwards because they are used merely for holding prey. They can eat animals larger than themselves because their lower jaws are attached to a separate quadrate bone which acts as a hinge allowing the jaws to drop downward and forward. They are held together by elastic fibers.

Fear of Snakes.—Small children seldom fear snakes until they are told snakes are poisonous or that they will bite. In fact small garden snakes will

FIGURE 15-5. *RATTLESNAKE*

The hollow fangs are shown as the snake prepares to strike. When not in use they are folded back into the mouth.

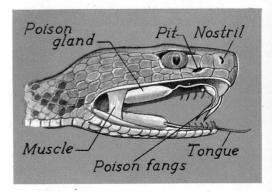

209

FIGURE 15-6. *REPTILES IN THE SUN*

   The unusual picture on the left shows baby black snakes just hatching from their eggs. The alligator (*right*) is a close relative of the crocodile, but has a broader snout and is much less vicious, seldom growing to more than twelve feet. Alligators are found in southeastern United States.

not bite when carefully touched, but seem rather to like being handled. When one stops to think that snakes, like all reptiles, are cold-blooded, while our hands are warm, it is not strange that they might come to enjoy the human hand. It is unwise to put fear where there should be none.

   Snake Bites.—When traveling or living in a region where there are poisonous snakes, wear suitable clothing and take wise precautions. It is well also to carry a first-aid kit for snake bites and know how to use it. Snake venom affects the blood, certain body tissues, and may affect the nervous system. It is therefore important to take first-aid measures immediately after a bite to prevent the venom from traveling through the body.

15.7   Crocodiles and Alligators

   These reptiles are covered with large, bony scales, and the limbs are fitted for crawling and swimming, the toes being partly webbed. The jaws have cone-shaped teeth. Crocodiles are found in the southern United States, South America, Africa, and India. Alligators are found chiefly in pools and sluggish streams in the southern United States. They are usually 10 to 12 feet long but a few longer ones have been caught. Crocodiles resemble alligators but have narrower heads, more pointed snouts, longer, sharper teeth, and more fully webbed feet. Alligator hide is used for shoes, handbags, and luggage.

15.8   Adaptations of Reptiles

   Reptiles are well adapted to their environment. Snakes that live in trees are sometimes the color of leaves or bark. Some that are harmless are colored much like poisonous snakes. An adaptation found in the crocodile is a fold of skin which shuts off the mouth from the throat and prevents water from entering the throat while the crocodile is drowning its prey. The old-world chameleons have their feet modified for clasping branches. Marine turtles have paddlelike feet for swimming, while those that live partly on land and partly in the water have toes with webs. Lizards are almost always of about the same color as their surroundings.

ANIMALS WITH BACKBONES

FACTS TO REMEMBER

Reptilia characteristics are (1) a dry, scaly skin, (2) a sternum, or breastbone, (3) a three-chambered heart with two auricles and the ventricle partly or wholly divided, (4) body temperature seldom below freezing, (5) two pairs of legs with claws (except snakes), and (6) only lungs for breathing.

The prehistoric reptiles were very important in the development of animal life, but only four groups of living reptiles remain. The adaptations to environment vary from the *turtle* with its shell, the *lizard* adapted for dry regions, *alligators* and *crocodiles* for water life, and the legless *snakes* of many regions.

Some reptiles, such as turtles, are used as food. Many snakes are poisonous, and great care should be taken to prevent injury.

WORDS TO REMEMBER

carapace	fang	sternum
carnivorous	plastron	venom
constrictor	scutes	

QUESTIONS

1. Why have most of the reptiles disappeared from the earth?
2. Name five characteristics of reptiles.
3. Can a turtle crawl completely out of its shell? Why?
4. Where do sea turtles lay their eggs?
5. In what ways are most snakes beneficial?
6. How does the boa constrictor kill its prey?
7. How do crocodiles differ from alligators?
8. Explain how a crocodile is adapted for killing its prey by drowning.
9. How could you distinguish a lizard from a salamander?
10. Discuss the life cycle of reptiles.

COMPLETION TEST

As your teacher or classmate reads the following incomplete statements, with your book closed, write on a clean sheet of paper the word or phrase which correctly completes the statement.

1. The horned toad is a _____.
2. Snakes move by means of _____.
3. The _____ appears to change color.
4. The most deadly snake of India is the _____.
5. The glass snake is a _____.
6. Reptiles take no _____ of eggs or young.
7. The upper part of the shell of a turtle is called the _____.
8. The under part of the shell is the _____.

9. The frilled lizard has _____ for climbing trees.

10. The _____ snake in this country is very poisonous.

PROJECTS

I. *Study of a Living Reptile.*—Bring a turtle into the laboratory. If it is small, you may put it in a small aquarium, but it should have a place to crawl out of the water and rest. A large turtle can be kept in the terrarium.

If you live in a dry region where there are lizards, include them in your desert terrarium.

If you are able to secure a small alligator or snake, bring that into the laboratory.

Study your specimen very carefully and answer the following questions:

1. How does it move? How is it fitted to do this?
2. With what is it covered?
3. Locate the eyes. Can they be closed? Can you find any ears?
4. Locate the nostrils.
5. Is the tail of any particular use?
6. Find out what your specimen eats.

II. *Study of a Preserved Reptile Specimen.*—1. Identify the following parts:

(a) External covering   (d) Nostrils
(b) Appendages   (e) Mouth (teeth)
(c) Eyes

2. Make a careful sketch of your animal, showing the external features.

3. If you have an abundance of material, you may be able to dissect a freshly killed animal with your teacher's help. Identify as many parts as you can and record what you see.

III. *Poisonous Snakes.*—1. Find out whether there are any poisonous snakes in your region. If so, get pictures of them and learn to recognize them.

2. Make a booklet with drawings and pictures of these.
3. Find out the proper first-aid treatment for snake bite.
4. Learn where the poisonous snakes live and are apt to be found.

IV. *The Age of Reptiles.*—Look up reference material and write a report on the Mesozoic Age, also called the Age of Reptiles.

V. List as many differences as you can between a frog and a turtle. Why are they classified in different groups?

REFERENCES

Andrews, *All About Dinosaurs.* Random House.

Barbour, *Reptiles and Amphibians.* Houghton Mifflin.

Colbert, *The Dinosaur Book—Handbook #4.* American Museum of Natural History.

Curran and Kauffeld, *Snakes and Their Ways.* Harper.

Disney, *Living Desert*. Simon and Schuster.

Ditmars, *Reptiles of North America*. Doubleday.

Ditmars, *Reptiles of the World*. Macmillan.

Ditmars, *Snakes of the World*. Macmillan.

Ditmars, *The Reptile Book*. Doubleday.

Linville and Kelly, *General Zoology*. Ginn.

Morris, *Boy's Book of Snakes*. Ronald Press.

Pope, *Snakes Alive and How They Live*. Viking.

Pope, *Turtles of the United States and Canada*. Knopf.

Reese, *The Alligator and Its Allies*. Putnam's.

Schmidt and Dwight, *Fieldbook of Snakes of the United States and Canada*. Knopf.

Smith, *Handbook of Lizards*. Comstock.

Walter and Sayles, *Biology of the Vertebrates*. Macmillan.

Zim, Smith, *Reptiles: Golden Nature Guide*. Simon and Schuster.

CHAPTER 16

Birds

16.1 Birds

Early in the history of the world and long before man roamed the earth, a strange creature, looking like an ancient reptile with wings, succeeded in flying through the air. Its name was Archeop-teryx (ar-kee-*op*-tehr-iks). This strange-looking bird was very heavy and probably did not fly very far or very fast. Yet through this ancient bird, our modern birds trace their ancestry to the reptile family.

FIGURE 16-1. *AROUND THE WORLD*

Birds are found in all parts of the world. They live on land, near the water, in mountains and fields; they inhabit arctic regions and the tropics.

Allan D. Cruickshank

FIGURE 16-2. *EXTERNAL STRUCTURE OF THE BIRD*
A bird's body is ideally constructed for flight. The coat of feathers helps the streamlined body glide through the air and also keeps it warm. The bones are hollow and light, the skeleton rigid, and the neck flexible.

In your study of the structure of modern birds [class **Aves** (*ay*-veez)] you will learn some of the reasons why they can remain in the air so long and can ride out most of the storms, why they are able to fly at night, and why they usually make safe landings. Some birds fly high, others remain low; some glide long distances, others can remain poised in the air for a short time. Birds vary in size from the ostrich of Africa which stands 7 feet tall and weighs 300 pounds, to the tiny hummingbird, 2¼ inches long and weighs about 1/10 of an ounce.

16.2   Characteristics of Birds

The outstanding feature of birds is the presence of **feathers.** These afford much surface with very little weight. They also keep a layer of warm air next to the skin.

The skeleton of birds is light in comparison with that of other animals. It is very compact, and the backbone is rigid except for the neck. There is a prominent ridge in the breastbone called the **keel,** which serves as a place of attachment for the large, active wing muscles. Air tubes extend into the bones, so that the body is lighter than that of animals with solid ones.

16.3   How Birds Live

Birds are very active using a great deal of energy. This energy comes from the oxidation of food that goes on in the body. In birds, oxidation is more rapid than in other vertebrates, because their lungs are small, and they change the air almost completely with each breathing movement. Thus they secure a greater supply of oxygen. The rapid oxidation requires that a large supply of food be digested and assimilated rapidly, and it makes the normal body temperature of birds higher than that of other vertebrates. The four-chambered heart is large and powerful, and is completely

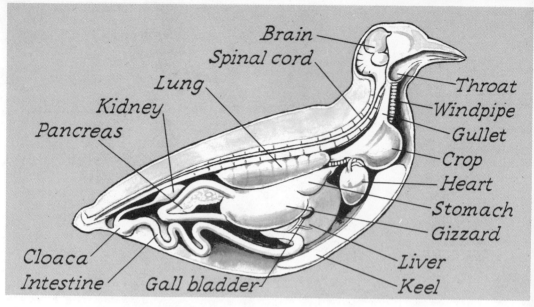

FIGURE 16-3. *INTERNAL STRUCTURE*

The internal systems of the bird are much like those of other vertebrates. The digestive system includes a crop, gizzard, and stomach. The bird is a warm-blooded animal, with a large, four-chambered heart.

separated so that pure and impure blood do not mix. The heartbeat is rapid.

Birds do not have teeth. Instead they use horny **beaks.** The tongue is small and pointed, with a horny covering. It has taste buds to help in the selection of food. Most birds cannot extend the tongue, but woodpeckers are able to protrude their tongues to catch insects, and hummingbirds to obtain nectar.

FIGURE 16-4. *VOICE BOX*

Air passing through the syrinx causes it to vibrate, producing "songs."

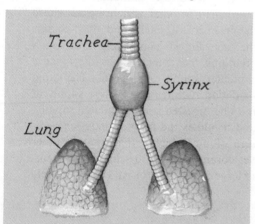

The food passes down the *esophagus* and into the **crop,** an outgrowth of the esophagus, where it is stored. It then moves into the *stomach* where glands secrete digestive juices. From there the food goes into the *gizzard* to be mechanically ground. Birds swallow small stones and gravel to aid in this process. The *intestine* is slender with many coils, and leads to the *rectum* and *cloaca* where the waste matter is excreted as soon as it is formed. The *liver* and *pancreas* are well developed (Fig. 16-3).

Birds do not have a very keen sense of smell, but their eyesight is the best of all the vertebrates. They can see small objects at great distances. The eagle is especially noted for its keen sight. If your eye were as large in proportion to your body as the owl's, it would weigh three pounds. The eyes have upper and lower lids and an additional membrane, the **nictitating** (*nik*-tih-tay-ting) **membrane,** which can be used for protection.

The voice box of a bird is called a **syrinx** (*sihr*-inks). It is located at the lower end of the trachea. The loudness of the voice is determined by the length of the muscle cord, and the pitch by the tenseness. Although there is no external ear, the sense of hearing is very keen. The opening of the ear canal is located under special feathers.

The brain is well developed. The *cerebrum,* or thought brain, is broad, and the *cerebellum* is especially large. Birds have good muscular coordination and definite patterns for nestbuilding.

16.4 Plumage of Birds

The **plumage** (*ploom*-ij) of birds shows great variety in form and color. In some species there are certain colors which always predominate on the males, while the females have little color; in other species it is hard to distinguish between the sexes. The brilliantly colored males are supposed to attract the females at the mating season, while the dull-colored females are inconspicuous and less likely to be attacked by enemies while hatching their eggs or caring for their young. We may say, therefore, that birds are *protectively colored.* The color of birds varies during the first two or three years. Birds shed their feathers (*molt*) at least once a year, so that new ones may replace those that have been lost or damaged.

FIGURE 16-5. *NESTBUILDING*

The purpose of the nest is to provide a place to hatch eggs and protect the young. The black-necked stilt (*lower right*), a wading bird, builds its nest by lining a low place on the ground with grasses. The Eastern phoebe likes to have its nest in a protected spot near a house or barn (*center*). The baby robins (*top*) eagerly await dinner in their efficient, mud-lined nest held together with dried grasses.

All photos by Allan D. Cruickshank
from National Audubon Society

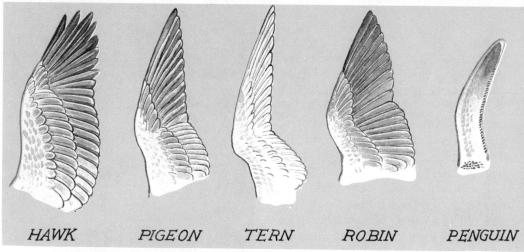

HAWK · PIGEON · TERN · ROBIN · PENGUIN

FIGURE 16-6. *KINDS OF WINGS*

Bird wings are modified for different kinds of flight. The hawk's are for soaring, the pigeon's for speedy trips, the tern's for gliding and diving, the robin's for long migrations, and the penguin's for swimming.

16.5 Habits of Birds

Birds show a wide variation in size and mode of life, from the tiny nectar-eating hummingbird to the broad-winged eagle. They are usually classified according to their *structure.* The shape and size of the beak, feet, and wings are the characteristics most used. Birds are also studied in the light of their habits, such as groups based on their **migratory habits.** Birds like the downy woodpecker and English sparrow are *permanent residents* throughout their range, while bobolinks and hummingbirds are *summer residents* in the northern section of the country. Birds like wild geese and fox sparrows are *transients,* stopping along their migratory route for rest or food or to escape unfavorable weather; while such birds as the snowy owl, northern shrike, and evening grosbeak (*grohss*-beek), are *winter residents.*

Birds can be grouped also by their **nesting habits.** Some, like the meadow lark and bobolink, nest in the open field, and their nests are made difficult to see rather than difficult to reach; others, like certain hawks and eagles, build their nests in tall trees, making them conspicuous, but inaccessible. Still others, like the oriole, build at the end of slender branches, where they are out of reach of animals. Birds like the kingfisher and bank swallow build their nests at the bottom of a burrow in a bank.

16.6 Structure and Adaptations of Birds

Wings.—The front limbs of birds are modified into wings (Fig. 16-6). Three bones support the wing of a bird, instead of two as in one of our arms. The muscles which control the bird's wing are very strong and are located in the breast, attached to the sternum, or breastbone. These muscles are connected to the wings by **tendons,** tissues which connect muscles to bones. The downward strokes of wings help to raise the bird's body in the air and the tilting and banking movements assist in changing the manner of flight.

Among some birds, like the penguins (*pen*-gwinz) of the Antarctic region, the wings are used not for flying but to assist in swimming. In others, like the eagles

218

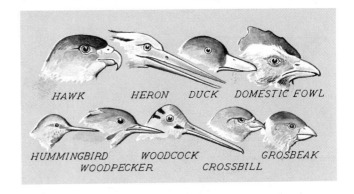

FIGURE 16-7. *BEAK ADAPTATIONS*

Each beak is constructed according to the work it must do. The woodpecker's beak is like a chisel, used for cutting holes in trees and digging out wood-boring insects for food. How is the domestic fowl's bill specially adapted?

HAWK   HERON   DUCK   DOMESTIC FOWL

HUMMINGBIRD   WOODCOCK   GROSBEAK
WOODPECKER   CROSSBILL

and condors, the expanse of the wings is enough to enable the birds to fly away with young lambs and young deer. Between the wings of the penguin and those of the hawk there are many variations.

Sailing birds, like the gulls, have long, slender wings, while ground birds, like the partridge and pheasant, have short wings capable of only rapid, short flights. Birds that use their wings most, naturally have them best developed. An example of the underdevelopment of wings is the domestic fowl, a ground bird, which makes little use of its flying powers and is incapable of long flights.

Adaptations of Beaks.—The beaks of birds show great variation as well as adaptation for defense and food-getting (Fig. 16-7). Hawks, owls, and eagles have the upper jaw curved over and hooked for tearing their food; herons and bitterns have the beak modified into a long, pointed weapon of offense and defense; grosbeaks and finches have a short, stout beak for crushing seeds and

other hard foods; and hummingbirds have a long, slender beak which in some kinds is curved so that they may reach the bottom of certain flowers.

Adaptations of Legs.—Legs also show many variations (Fig. 16-8). When a bird is at rest or asleep on a perch, its claws grasp the perch and are held there because the leg is bent. The weight of the body of the bird on its legs helps maintain a closer grasp on the perch and prevents the bird from falling. Perching birds usually have three toes in front and one behind. Climbing birds have two toes in front and two behind. In the case of eagles, hawks, and owls, the toes end in powerful claws called **talons** for seizing and holding prey, while ducks and geese have long and webbed toes, adapted to swimming. Seed-eating birds have weak toes, which serve merely for perching.

Adaptations of Tails.—The tail serves as a rudder in flight and as a balance in perching. Some birds spread their tails

FIGURE 16-8. *FOOT ADAPTATIONS*

The feet of birds show much variation. Can you find those adapted for scratching, swimming, climbing, grasping and running?

219

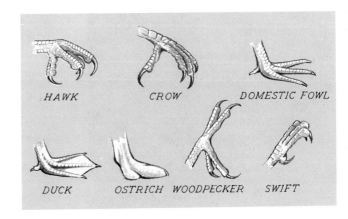

HAWK   CROW   DOMESTIC FOWL

DUCK   OSTRICH   WOODPECKER   SWIFT

FIGURE 16-9. *FUNCTIONAL*

The blue jay (*left*), a wild bird that is helpful to man because it feeds on grasshoppers, has a long tail for balancing on a precarious perch. The penguin, because it swims rather than flies, has a very short tail.

during courtship. Jays have long tails for balancing on limbs of trees. Pigeons have broad tails for sudden stops. Woodpeckers have stiff tails to support them on tree trunks when climbing or catching insects. Ducks and geese have small tails.

16.7 Nest-building and Egg-laying

Birds lay very large eggs, in which food is stored. The sexes are distinct and the eggs fertilized *internally*. The shell is formed just before the egg is laid. Nests vary from very elaborately con-

structed ones to mere depressions in the ground. Some birds build large nests with materials loosely put together, others build small nests of neatly woven material, and some birds, like cowbirds, build no nest at all, but lay their eggs in the nests of other birds and leave the work of caring for their young to the foster parents.

The number of eggs laid in a nest varies from one to as many as thirty or forty. The eggs hatch in from ten days to six weeks. Birds whose eggs hatch in ten days or two weeks are called **altricial**

FIGURE 16-10. *HATCHED*

The ovenbird (*left*), an altricial bird, builds an elaborate nest somewhat resembling an oven and carefully nurtures its young. The common tern (*right*) is precocial and lays its eggs on bare ground, rocks, or sand.

FIGURE 16-11. *GUANO ON THE CHINCHA ISLANDS*

Guano is an unusually rich fertilizer found off the coast of Peru, on the Chincha Islands. The waste matter of millions of sea birds, it is rich in nitrate and phosphate compounds, and is sold commercially to fertilize farm lands.

J. Barnell from Shostal

(al-*trish*-ul), from a Latin word meaning *nourish,* for such young are hatched helpless, blind, and with little down. Eggs that hatch in from three to six weeks develop well-formed young, able to run around within ten or twelve hours after hatching. These are known as **precocial** (preh-*koh*-shul), from a Latin word meaning *early ripe.* Such birds have little need for a substantial nest, and only a few of them build one. The robin is altricial, and the domestic fowl precocial.

16.8 Economic Importance of Birds

The chief food of many birds is insects, and so they are beneficial to man, for they kill insect pests that destroy crops, especially in the South and West.

It has been estimated that insect-eating birds are worth $350,000,000 a year to farmers. Other birds, however, that eat food needed by man, or that destroy small and more useful birds, may be termed harmful. Domestic birds are valuable for the food which they supply or for the beauty of their songs or plumage.

Beneficial Wild Birds.—Birds such as quails, crows, red-winged blackbirds, kingbirds, shrikes, bluebirds, blue jays, pheasants, and many others feed on grasshoppers. Army worms, which are harmful almost without exception, are food for vesper sparrows, song sparrows, and pheasants. The flicker eats ants by the thousands. Cuckoos are the enemies of caterpillars and canker worms.

FIGURE 16-12. *DOMESTICATED BIRDS*

The domesticated turkey has been bred to have a fleshier body and shorter legs and neck than his wild cousin. The brilliantly colored parrot (*left*) is very popular as a pet because he can learn to talk.

Among the hawks and owls are found many beneficial birds, for the screech owls, red-tailed hawks, and red-shouldered hawks, together with shrikes, destroy such harmful rodents as mice, shrews, moles, prairie dogs, woodchucks, and rabbits. The hawks prey upon them during the day, and at night the owls continue the slaughter. The shrikes feed upon mice and small birds.

Aside from their value in destroying insects, birds are valuable as scavengers. The buzzards and vultures of the south and west eat dead animals. The gulls of the sea and lakes eat refuse thrown upon the water. Crows and herons eat dead fish.

One group of birds lives largely on seed, and these birds, for example, the tree sparrows, redpolls, song sparrows, juncos, pheasants, and quails, destroy tons of weed seed during the fall, winter,

and spring. In doing this, such birds have a distinct value to agriculture.

Harmful Birds.—Not all birds are beneficial to man. Some birds are beneficial a part of the year, and more or less harmful at other times. Whenever the taste of a bird is like our own, it takes our foods. For example, a robin will eat cherries, grapes, and berries which we are raising for ourselves. Robins also prefer the beneficial earthworm to harmful caterpillars.

Some of the smaller hawks, such as the sharp-shinned hawk and the Cooper's hawk, are fond of small insect-eating birds and the young of our domestic fowls.

Game Birds.—These include quail, pheasant, partridge, grouse, ducks, geese, and wild turkeys. Game birds are protected by law, and hunters must observe "open" and "closed" seasons. Each bird

ANIMALS WITH BACKBONES

FIGURE 16-13. *SNOWY EGRET PLUMES*

In past years, egrets were killed in great numbers to satisfy the demand for their plumes. Since the plumes appear only on adults during the nesting period, many young egrets were left helpless and unable to feed themselves. Now, however, many public and private agencies protect the egret, which are again numerous in the southern states.

Allan D. Cruickshank
from National Audubon Society

may be shot only during the open season on it. During the closed season on a bird, it may not be harmed. Game birds are hunted for both food and sport. Pheasants and quail are raised on suitable farms.

Domestic Birds.—Man has domesticated many kinds of wild birds. Chickens, turkeys, ducks, and geese have been developed for meat and eggs. Peafowls (peacocks), pheasants, and canaries have been developed for their beauty of color or song. Parrots and parakeets have been trained to speak.

All the kinds of chickens have been developed from the wild jungle fowls of India. Some of these chickens are used as food, others as egg-layers. Most of our ducks and geese have been developed from the wild forms of Europe and Asia. Doves have come from the wild pigeons of Europe and Asia. From Africa we have taken the guinea fowl. The turkey is the only popular domestic bird that our own continent has contributed.

Canaries have been developed from the wild birds of various parts of the world. Most parrots have been captured in the wild state; they are not bred as canaries are. Parakeets and finches are raised in captivity and are enjoyed as pets.

16.9 Bird Protection

As the population increases, it encroaches on forest and waste land and other favored nesting sites of birds. To prevent the extermination of desirable birds, we must protect them against the losses caused by man. The available agencies for this work of *conservation* may be divided into three classes: (1) federal, (2) state, (3) private.

Work of the Federal Government.— The government of the United States has passed laws that have greatly helped conservation of birds.

The Lacey Act, as amended in 1909, enables the Secretary of Agriculture to regulate the importation of birds and forbids the shipping of birds from a state where it is illegal to kill them.

The Federal Migratory Bird Treaty Act of 1918, passed to give effect to the convention of 1916 between the United States and Great Britain, makes it unlawful to capture, kill, sell, or transport any migratory bird, or any part, nest, or egg of such a bird, except during the *open seasons* established by the Secretary of Agriculture. (A similar law is in force in Canada.) Under this law, open seasons are provided for ducks, geese, swans, rails, sandpipers, and others. Thrushes, orioles, swallows, wrens, and woodpeckers are always protected and cannot be taken at any season. For example, the robin, which is a thrush, may not be killed anywhere in the United States. A state law making an open season for robins would be a violation of the federal law.

Another aid to bird protection is a section of the tariff act of 1913 by which "the importation of aigrettes, egret plumes or so-called osprey plumes, and the feathers, quills, heads, wings, tails, skins, or parts of skins, of wild birds, either raw or manufactured, and not for scientific or educational purposes, is hereby prohibited." This act does not apply to ostrich feathers or feathers of domestic fowls.

Yellowstone National Park contains more than 2,000,000 acres. This is a famous *game preserve* and all animals are protected there. Glacier National Park contains over 800,000 acres. The Wichita National Game Preserve in Oklahoma contains 57,000 acres. Yosemite National Park in California contains 719,000 acres. No hunting is allowed in any of these parks and preserves.

Throughout the United States, including Alaska and various islands in the Atlantic and Pacific, there are many *bird refuges* and game preserves. Is there a bird refuge near your home?

Work of the States.—Each state has the power to extend protection through laws which aid in the propagation of birds within its borders.

New York has a splendid conservation law on its books, which forbids the sale of all native wild game birds in New York State no matter where they are taken.

Most states have special officers called game wardens to enforce the *game laws*.

Work of Private Organizations.—The laws passed by the federal government and the various states have originated and have been pushed by organizations of citizens interested in saving the birds. The National Association of Audubon Societies is one of the most energetic and powerful of these organizations. Junior Audubon clubs are very active in schools and communities. Students learn to recognize birds, attract them to the school grounds and to their homes, and to protect them.

Work of Individuals.—A government may pass conservation laws, but it is public sentiment that compels their enforcement. In other words, it is necessary for the individual to do his part in supporting and respecting the various laws.

Some individuals of means have purchased lands suitable for breeding grounds, where ample protection is afforded either by state officials or by privately hired protectors. Marsh Island, Louisiana, with an area of 77,000 acres was one of the first bird *sanctuaries*. It was established in 1912.

The Ward-McIlhenny Bird Preserve of 13,000 acres, in Louisiana, is another sanctuary. Here thousands of ducks, geese, herons, and egrets are allowed to breed and live without being disturbed in any way. The Mountain Lake Sanctuary, established by Edward Bok, is located in Florida and is one of the most beautiful spots in the United States. The Kellogg Bird Sanctuary in Michigan consists of 180 acres where over 5000

Hal H. Harrison from National Audubon Society

FIGURE 16-14. *BABY CHICKADEES*

The chickadee is a quick, active, friendly bird that grows to a length of only about four or five inches. A friend of the farmer, it feeds on moths, caterpillars, beetles, and other insects. It will also eat weed seeds.

wild Canadian geese and several thousand ducks may be seen each fall.

16.10   Some Common Birds

In most states there are probably between 200 and 500 kinds of birds found during the year. California, with its great extent from north to south, offers a larger variety in environment than any other state in the Union. No doubt it leads in this aspect of its bird life, for more than 500 varieties have been identified in this state.

We may select from these large lists certain representative birds for study.

The *bluebird,* often taken as a symbol of happiness, is found in orchards, fields, roadsides, and second-growth woods throughout the greater part of the United States. It is a perching bird about seven inches long. The upper part of the male, including wings and tail, is bright blue. The breast and throat are of cinnamon color. The female is grayish blue above and paler than the male below. This bird nests in holes in trees and fence posts and is readily attracted by nesting boxes put up in orchards and woods. Its food consists of caterpillars, grasshoppers, crickets, and, in cold weather, some flying insects that are benumbed by the cold.

The *chickadee* is only 5½ inches long, but its great activity makes it valuable out of proportion to its size. It eats the eggs, larvae, pupae, and adults of many harmful insects. A permanent resident within its range, it does most effective work every month of the year. The bird is attractively marked with black and white. The top of the head has a black cap. It comes to dooryards and orchards freely in the wintertime, and its spirited notes of "chick-adee-dee-dee-dee" make it a conspicuous and welcome visitor. It builds its nest in a hole of a tree or stump and sometimes in a man-made nesting box.

FIGURE 16-15. *NESTING HABITS*

The yellow warbler (*left*) usually nests in bushes or trees near the water, while the crow (*right*) builds its nest high on a cliff or in the tree-tops, sometimes as much as 30 feet from the ground.

The *crow* is a bird very well described by the expression, "black as a crow," though it has bluish and purplish lights on its black feathers. A mature crow is nearly twenty inches long. It is usually classed as a permanent resident in the northern states. It is quite likely, however, that the crows which nest in the northern states go south in the winter and that their places are taken by winter visitants from Canada. These winter crows usually roost together in rookeries, where thousands are sometimes seen. They live in the deep woods, roadsides, orchards, and parks. They feed upon grasshoppers and other insects and young birds. They have been known to eat the eggs of some of our valuable songbirds, and they love the farmer's freshly planted seeds. Hence the quaint "scarecrows" seen in newly planted fields. The crow, therefore, is partly helpful and partly harmful.

The *yellow warbler* is one of our smallest warblers, measuring about five inches in length. The male is greenish yellow above and bright yellow beneath. The lower parts are streaked with dull red. It likes man's company and keeps well to the yards, gardens, and roadsides.

It is a summer resident. The nest is compactly built of fine grass and fibers and lined with plant down or hair. This bird is frequently victimized by the parasitic cowbird. The eggs of the cowbird are sometimes buried beneath another nest which the yellow warbler builds in an effort to avoid hatching a cowbird's egg. The cowbird does not build a nest of its own.

Robins are rather large birds, ten inches in length, and rated as summer residents in the north. A few remain over the winter in favorable locations. In the male the top of the head is black. The back and tail are dark, and the breast of the characteristic dull reddish color. The females are of lighter color. Robins are found widely scattered in yards and orchards, along the roadside, in the parks, and in second-growth woods. Usually two broods are raised each season. They feed upon earthworms, caterpillars, crickets, and other insects. In some regions they are unpopular because they eat the smaller fruits, but this damage they help to pay for by destroying insects.

The *house* (*English*) *sparrow* is an imported product, like its European

FIGURE 16-16. *FAMILIAR BIRDS*

No other birds are more familiar than the friendly robin (*right,* coming in for a landing) or the English sparrow (*left*), which likes to build its nest on houses and in trees.

cousin, the starling. It was brought over from England about 1851 for the purpose of destroying certain insects, and has now spread to the Pacific coast. It eats many weed seeds and destroys such insects as cutworms, tussock moths, some weevils, cabbage worms, and white grubs. The male has a gray crown. Its back is streaked with black and chestnut. A part of the throat and breast is black; the under parts are whitish. The bird is a little more than six inches long. The chief fault found with the English sparrow is that it uses the nesting sites of more desirable birds and so drives them away. It has no song.

The *downy woodpecker* is the best known and smallest of all woodpeckers in the United States. The principal markings are in black and white. The adult male has a scarlet band on the nape of the neck, but the female lacks this mark. The under parts are white. There is a white stripe above the eye and another below it. In the winter season the downy woodpecker frequents our orchards and yards, cleaning the trees of insects. He is often found also in the woods. Being a permanent resident, he renders a 365-days-a-year service. Every day he must obtain food enough to support his active body, and by doing so he renders an important service to us.

The *herring gull* is aquatic, nesting on islands and the shore of the mainland, and getting its food largely from the water. Our inland streams and lakes are frequented in certain seasons by these birds. As its name indicates, it feeds on fish, but it is not limited to that diet.

FIGURE 16-17. *AN INSECT EATER AND A SCAVENGER*

The downy woodpecker (*left*) nests in cavities cut in dead trees and eats boring beetles and other insects. The herring gull (*right*) is a useful scavenger.

Gulls are scavengers, and they are found in large numbers near garbage dumps. In the lower part of New York harbor, gulls follow the scows which are carrying garbage. Mr. Frank M. Chapman (page 678) estimated the number he saw here at one time as three hundred thousand. The herring gull is twenty-four inches long. The colors of the male in summer are deep pearl-gray and white with spots of black. In winter, the male has many spots of gray.

The *screech owl,* a bird of prey, is one of our smallest owls, having a length of only nine and one-half inches. The bird has two color phases, a rufous (dull-red) and a gray. In the former phase the colors are rufous above with streaks of black and white below. In the gray phase the rufous is replaced by gray. These color phases do not depend on age, sex, or season. Screech owls are permanent residents and mostly beneficial, as they feed largely on mice and insects. They sometimes eat earthworms. During the day they rest in hollow trees, conifers, old buildings, and caves. They also nest in hollow trees or bird boxes. Their screech is blood-curdling.

The *mockingbird* is typical of the Southern states, and is the country's greatest songbird. It not only has its own

FIGURE 16-18. *SCREECH OWL*

The characteristic ruff around the face of the owl is called the *facial disk,* and helps in identifying it. Screech owls may be either reddish or grayish in color and are among the best friends of the farmer, since they feed on mice and insects.

228

General Biological Supply House   General Biological Supply House

FIGURE 16-19. *SONGBIRDS OF THE SOUTH*
Commonly found in the southern states, the mockingbird (*left*) and the cardinal are both famous for their beautiful songs.

songs, but mimics the calls and songs of scores of other birds as well. One observer has recorded a mockingbird that imitated the notes of no less than thirty-two different bird species.

It has a gray back, grayish white breast, and dark wings and tail spotted with white. It nests in thickets and orange trees. The nest is built of twigs, weed stalks, and cotton. The eggs are greenish-blue, or bluish-white, and are from four to six in number.

The *cardinal* male is bright rosy red, which makes it conspicuous wherever it occurs. It is commonest in the Southern states, where its famous singing powers give it a rank close to the mockingbird. These birds have strong, thick beaks for eating seeds. Feeding them sunflower seeds in winter helps them to adapt to the northern winter season. They nest in bushes. The nest is made of twigs, grass, and rootlets. The eggs, three to four in number, are white, or bluish-white, with brownish spots.

The *magpie* is a bird of the Western states and ranges as far north as Alaska. It is a close relative of the crows and

blue jays of the East. It is unpopular because of its feeding habits; it attacks the backs of sheep to pick out the warble larvae that live in the skins of sheep. It also sets upon animals caught in traps. The magpie is a rather large bird, about nineteen inches in length. It is black and white with steel-blue scattered through. Its tail is bronzy green. Its nest, found in trees and bushes, is a bowl of mud and grass surrounded and covered by many variously sized sticks. There are six to nine grayish or greenish eggs, spotted with brown and purple.

The *road runner* is a striking bird of the Western states from Kansas to California. It is rather large, from twenty to twenty-four inches long. The predominating color is olive streaked with tawny brown and buffy white. It has a strikingly long tail. It is known also as "snake killer" and "lizard bird," which gives a clue to its feeding habits. The nest is found in the cactus plants and the desert bushes. It lays four to six white or yellow eggs. It gets its name from its habit of running like a chicken instead of hopping like most birds.

BIRDS

229

FIGURE 16-20. *THE MAGPIE AND THE ROAD RUNNER*
A cousin of the crow and jay, the magpie is known as a noisy, quarrelsome
bird that eats the eggs and young of other birds. Related to the cuckoo, the
road runner is found in the southwestern states and northern Mexico.

16.11 Migration of Birds

In spite of man's effort to conquer the air, birds are still the champions. Not only do they fly great distances, but they do so at speeds ranging from 20 to 50 miles an hour. Some of the flights that they make are almost beyond belief. For example, the golden plover nests on the shores of the Arctic Ocean and winters in Argentina, 8000 miles away. The arctic tern may travel 11,000 miles between its winter and summer homes (Fig. 16-21).

Most migration is north and south. Some birds migrate from lowlands to highlands for the summer and return in the winter, as in the Rocky Mountains and Sierra Nevadas.

Small warblers, thrushes, and sparrows migrate at night, and stop to rest and feed by day. Crows and geese travel by day. Shore birds migrate either day or night. Much as with airplane flights, some travel close to the earth and others fly at 3000 to 5000 feet.

Careful studies made of starlings are suggestive in explaining a possible origin of the migration habit in birds. The English starlings of the northern states, after more than thirty years of residence there, finally learned to migrate. Huge flocks of these birds now go south in the fall and return with the coming spring. Their first knowledge of migration, bird students believe, probably came from their contact with flocks of blackbirds and purple grackles, with which latter species they are confused by many people, though they are easily distinguished by their yellow bills. They mingled with flocks of these and other species, and doubtless began to drift southward with them in the fall and back again in the spring.

Birds seem to be guided by *instinct*, inherited characteristics impressed on

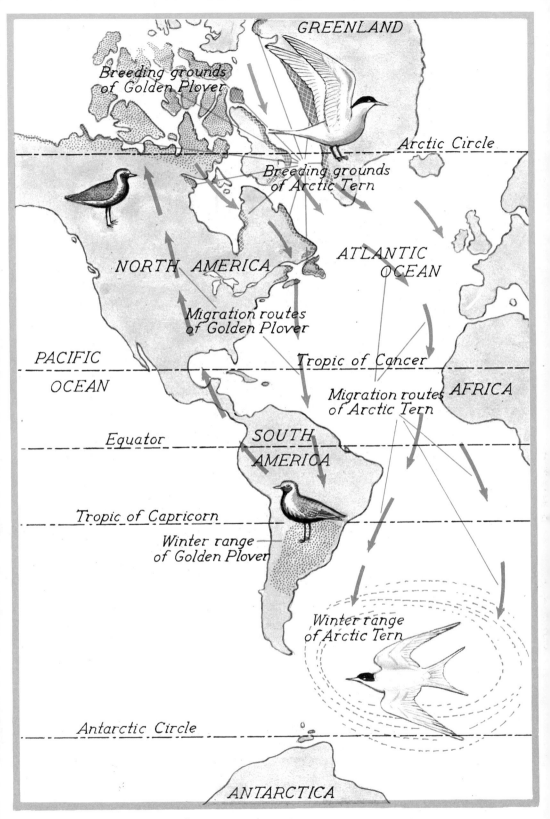

FIGURE 16-21. *MIGRATION ROUTES*

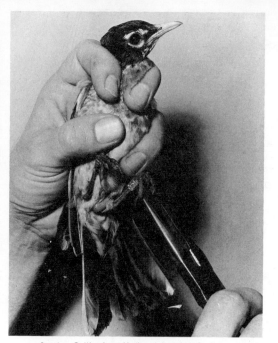

FIGURE 16-22. *LEARNING ABOUT BIRDS*

Ornithologists learn a great deal about the migratory habits of birds by banding them (*left*). Providing bird houses is a good way to observe bird behavior and also helps to conserve the bird population.

their nervous systems over many generations. The urge to migrate is also related to the activity of the ductless glands, particularly the sex glands. These in turn may be affected by light or the length of day.

Many birds are *banded* each year and careful records kept of the numbers on the bands. Whenever the birds are found or caught, the numbers are sent to the address indicated. In this way migration routes are traced and bird habits are studied.

16.12 Methods of Attracting Birds

It is pleasant to coax the birds near our windows so that we may enjoy and study them at close range. There are several ways of getting the birds to come near a building. One method is to plant fruiting shrubs, such as elderberry, sumac, raspberry, dogwood, mountain ash,

and cherry. The best method is to feed the birds. Foods such as suet, bread crumbs, hemp, canary seed, sunflower seeds, and raisins are attractive to birds. The feeding station should be where cats cannot get at it. A broad shelf attached to a window ledge makes a simple and convenient feeding ground.

When it is not convenient to have a window shelf, suet may be attached by a wire loop to a branch or trunk of a tree. Bird seed and crumbs may be scattered on the ground, but a better way is to put them in a box with a wide entrance and a cover several inches above to keep out the snow. This box should be placed on a post, as squirrels will raid it if it is attached to a tree trunk. There are many attractive and ingenious feed boxes that may be purchased or made.

Bird Houses.—Putting up bird houses in the yard is another way of attracting

232

birds. But they must be guarded against cats and squirrels. These will climb to the houses if they can and strike the birds as they leave the nest. Houses put up on the ends of posts and away from trees seem to be preferred to those put up in the trees. Poles and posts may be covered with tin or sheet iron to keep cats from climbing them, or ordinary small iron pipe instead of poles and posts may be used. The size of the opening and the amount of inside space will determine what birds will be most likely to make use of the houses.

Bird Baths.—During the dry weather of July and August, the supply of water is greatly reduced. Sometimes the water that is available is in a place where the birds have no chance of escaping a cat that may be lying in wait for them. A shallow plate or dish of water placed on a stump or post in the shade is frequently used by the birds. Bird baths placed in the garden make an attractive center.

FACTS TO REMEMBER

Birds have (1) wings, (2) one pair of legs, (3) beaks, (4) high body temperature, (5) feathers, (6) four-chambered heart, (7) rigid skeleton with air spaces in the long bones, (8) well-developed optic lobes which are useful in eyesight, and (9) a large cerebellum, making it possible for birds to form many habits.

Birds have many *adaptations* of the feet, beaks, legs, wings, and tails which make it possible for them to have a wide range of distribution. Flight makes long *migrations* possible. Birds may be permanent, summer, or winter residents, or transients.

Birds build a variety of kinds of *nests,* and care for their young. Many are beneficial to man and are protected by laws.

Many people enjoy such birds as canaries and parakeets as pets. Others raise pigeons and poultry for eggs and other products. Some people attract birds with feeding stations, bird houses, and bird baths.

WORDS TO REMEMBER

altricial	game laws	open season
beak	gizzard	precocial
bird refuge	instinct	preserve
conservation	keel	sanctuary
crop	plumage	syrinx
domestic bird	migratory habits	talon
feathers	nesting habits	tendon
game bird	nictitating membrane	

QUESTIONS

1. Name at least five characteristics of birds.
2. In what ways are birds classified?
3. For what purpose is the beak used? The claw?
4. How does the penguin use its wings?

5. Why do birds migrate?

6. What are the best ways of attracting birds?

7. In what ways are birds beneficial to man? How are they harmful?

8. Why do you think the Lacey Act was passed?

9. Why do you approve of the migratory bird treaty act? What are its provisions?

10. What is the value of the tariff act of 1913?

11. Where is the Ward-McIlhenny Bird Preserve? the Mountain Lake Sanctuary established by Edward Bok?

12. Name in order the parts of the digestive tube of a bird through which the food passes, and state the important function of each part.

COMPLETION TEST

As your teacher or classmate reads the following incomplete statements, with your book closed, write on a clean sheet of paper the word or phrase which correctly completes the statement.

1. Ducks and geese have _____ for swimming.

2. Thick, stout beaks are characteristic of birds that eat _____.

3. Hawks and eagles have curved upper beaks for _____.

4. Herons and other wading birds have _____ legs and necks.

5. Sailing birds have _____ wings.

6. Chimney swifts have feet adapted for _____.

7. Birds whose eggs hatch in a short time and whose young are helpless are called _____.

8. Birds, like the chicken, which are well developed when hatched are called _____.

9. An imported bird which has learned to migrate is the _____.

10. Methods of attracting birds are _____, _____, and _____.

PROJECTS

I. *Study of a Living Bird.*—Have a member of your class bring a canary or other caged bird to school for observation. Questions about the bird may be asked and answered by members of the class. The following are typical questions that may be used:

1. How many toes has the bird?

2. Are these toes grouped, two in front and two behind, or three in front and one behind?

3. Are the toe nails long or short? Are they used for taking food, for holding food, for perching, or for what?

4. How are the feathers distributed?

5. Where are the long feathers? Where are the short feathers?

6. Does the bird walk or hop?

7. Are the feathers evenly colored? Examine the molted feathers in the cage.

8. Examine the beak. Is it adapted for crushing seed, tearing flesh, catching insects, drilling?

9. Examine the feet. Are they adapted for tearing flesh, scratching, wading?

10. Examine the eyes. Does the bird wink?

11. Does the bird have eyelashes? Describe them, if any are found.

12. Can you find a third eyelid? Describe it, if it is found.

13. What are the colors of the head, back, tail, breast, throat?

14. Are there any special markings, such as head bands, shield spots, splashes of color, or any other striking color features?

15. How many kinds of sound does the bird make, such as different songs, alarm notes, call notes?

16. How does the bird drink?

17. How does the bird eat?

18. What and how much does it eat?

19. How does the bird bathe?

20. How does the bird "dust"?

II. *Methods of Bird Study.*—The following are the usual methods of studying birds. You may wish to choose one of these methods and make it not only a project but let it become a lasting hobby.

1. *The Naturalist Method.*—The naturalist studies birds wherever and whenever he sees them.

2. *The Sportsman's Method.*—Whether or not a sportsman hunts game birds for food, he needs to learn as much as he can about the habits of the birds.

3. *Camera Method.*—It is fascinating to watch birds and try to take pictures of them, especially if you have a movie camera. This requires patience, but the results are well worth while.

4. *Egg Method.*—Students learn to recognize the eggs of different birds. Sometimes they collect a few for their museums.

5. *Mord Method.*—This is the study of dead birds. They can be identified, stuffed, and mounted for museums.

6. *Detective Method.*—You can be a good detective if you have patience enough to watch a family of birds and learn how they feed and care for the young.

7. *Stomach Contents.*—Sometimes scientists investigate the contents of birds' stomachs to find out how helpful the birds are to man and what harmful things they eat.

8. *Nature Walk.*—A naturalist or bird student often takes a group of interested people for a walk to study birds.

III. Make a feeding station and keep a record of the number and kinds of birds which come there.

IV. If you are studying birds in the spring, you may keep a record of the date of arrival of each kind of bird you recognize.

If you are studying birds in the fall and your school year begins early enough, you may be able to watch some birds congregating and getting ready to leave on their migratory flights. You may also be watching for the arrival of some of the birds from farther north, which come to spend the winter with you.

V. Make and erect some nesting boxes or birdhouses and keep a record of what happens.

Size of Bird Houses

Bird	Diameter of Opening	Size of Cavity	Location
Chickadee	1⅛"	4 × 4	In protected spots
House wren	1⅛"	4 × 4	Trees and arbors
Nuthatch	1¼"	5 × 6	On buildings or trees
Bluebird	1¼"	5 × 6	On buildings or trees
Tree-swallows	1¼"	5 × 6	In trees near ponds
Red-headed woodpecker	2½"	6 × 7	On posts or trees
Flicker	3"	6 × 8	On posts or trees
Wood-duck	6"	10 × 18	Trees or stumps

REFERENCES

Allen, *The Book of Bird Life.* Van Nostrand.
Allen, Fuertes, and Pirnie, *Laboratory Notebook for Intensive Bird Study.* Comstock.
Bodsworth, *Last of the Curlews.* Dodd, Mead.
Curtis, *Our State Birds.* Lyons and Carnahan.
Henderson, *A Child's Book of Birds.* Maxton.
Job, *How to Study Birds.* Outing.
Lemmon, *All About Birds.* Random House.
McKenny, *Birds in the Garden.* Grosset and Dunlap.
Neurath, *The Wonder World of Birds.* Lothrop, Lee, and Shepard.
Peterson, *Birds Over America.* Grosset and Dunlap.
Peterson, *Field Guide to the Eastern Birds.* Houghton Mifflin.
Peterson, *Field Guide to the Western Birds.* Houghton Mifflin.
Pough, *Audubon Bird Guide.* Doubleday.
Saunders, *A Guide to Bird Songs.* Doubleday.
Serdel, *A Child's Book of Wild Birds.* Maxton.
University Society, *Birds of America.* Garden City.
Williamson, *The First Book of Birds.* Watts.

CHAPTER 17

Mammals

17.1 Characteristics of Mammals

Of all animals, mammals have the best-developed brains. For this reason, they have ruled the animal world ever since the huge reptiles became extinct, thousands of years ago. Mammals vary in size from the tiny mice and shrews, two inches long, to elephants eleven feet tall and whales 105 feet long. The weight also varies from a part of an ounce to more than one hundred tons.

Mammals make up the class **Mammalia** (muh-*may*-lee-uh). They are generally warm-blooded (the body temperature remaining the same in winter and in summer), have hair, two sets of teeth, fleshy lips, breathe by means of lungs, give birth directly to young, and are provided with **mammary** (*mam-er-ee*) **glands** for producing milk to

FIGURE 17-1. *INTERNAL STRUCTURE OF A MAMMAL*

In this diagram, the nervous, digestive, respiratory, and circulatory systems of a male mammal are shown, as well as the organs for reproduction and excretion. All mammals are fundamentally alike in body structure.

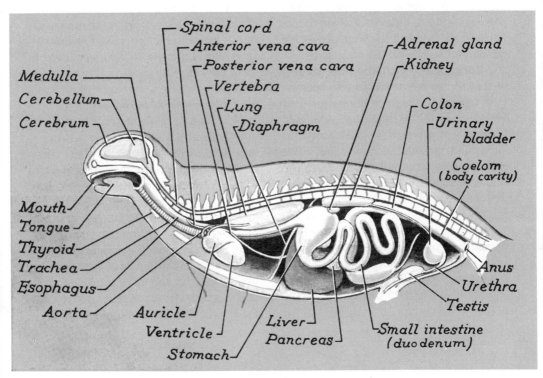

Black Star

Lynwood M. Chace

FIGURE 17-2. *MAMMALS AT HOME*

The gibbon (*left*) is a small ape from the Indo-Malay countries. A tree dweller, it has very long arms and no tail. The gopher, on the other hand, lives underground and can dig a tunnel 300 times its own length in one night.

suckle their young. A muscular wall, the **diaphragm** (*dy*-uh-fram), subdivides the body cavity into two parts. The anterior contains the four-chambered heart and the lungs; the posterior contains the stomach, intestine, liver, pancreas, spleen, kidneys, and reproductive organs. At birth the young resemble the parents in having the same parts.

All the animals that you have studied in this course were able to live because they secured food which nourished their bodies, carried on respiration, excreted waste, were adapted to their environment, and reproduced their kind. You have become so familiar with these life functions that it is necessary only to say that they apply in the same way to mammals.

Mammals have a distinctive method of reproduction. Their eggs are very small and do not have enough yolk to nourish the growing embryo. Thus the egg becomes attached to the wall of the **uterus** (*yoo*-ter-us), a structure in the female reproductive system. There the young animal receives food and a supply of oxygen through the mother's blood system until it is born. After birth it is dependent on its mother, who nurses it until it can get its own food. It is because of this nursing, or suckling, that animals of this highest order are called mammals, from the Latin word *mamma,* which means *breast.*

17.2 Habitats of Mammals

Mammals have a wide variety of habitats. Seals and walruses live in the Arctic seas, whales and porpoises in the open ocean, and beavers and muskrats in fresh water. Monkeys and tree squirrels live in trees; bats spend much time in the air and cling to high places as trees or roofs of caves to rest. Mountain sheep and goats live high on the mountains, and lions and tigers in jungles. Woodchucks live in and on top of the ground, and deer roam the frozen wastes and temperate woodlands. Different mammals have

ANIMALS WITH BACKBONES

habitat limitations of food and climate but each kind of mammal has a definite *geographic range.*

17.3 Homes and Habits of Mammals

Some mammals are *solitary,* like the bears which wander alone except when a mother protects her cubs. Wolves live in packs and deer in herds. Can you name other similar social groups?

Mammals are among the most interesting animals to watch. Do you know where a rabbit stays at night or how it sleeps? Have you ever seen the home of a beaver, or a dam that it had helped to build? Have you seen or read about a pack rat? When you find a hole in a tree, how can you tell whether it is inhabited by a mouse, chipmunk, raccoon, opossum, or a black bear? Burrows are also exciting to find. They may be the homes of rabbits, ground squirrels, badgers, coyotes, or skunks. Some of these animals build runways and tunnels, provide storage for food, make nests for their young, and have signal systems. They have their own subway entrances, blind alleys, and exits. Many of these animals are excellent engineers.

Some animals, like bears, bats and chipmunks, *hibernate* in the winter. Others, like the mule deer in the western states, *migrate* up the Sierra-Cascade and Rocky Mountains in summer and go farther south in the winter. The cony cuts and dries various plants, like hay, during the summer and *stores* them among the rocks for winter use.

Certain mammals, like cattle and horses, which *graze* on grasses and herbs and those which *browse* on leaves and twigs of trees are called **herbivorous** (er-*biv*-er-us) mammals. Those like cats, whales, and weasels which eat flesh are **carnivorous** (kahr-*niv*-er-us). Some mammals, like man, bears, pigs, raccoons, and rats, eat both plants and animals. They are called **omnivorous** (om-*niv*-er-us).

17.4 Special Adaptations of Mammals

Most mammals have two pairs of limbs; the *fore limb* (Fig. 17-3) may be variously modified for different uses, as for running on hard ground in animals like the horse, for tree-climbing and for food-getting in the squirrel, for burrowing in the moles, for flying in the bats, and for swimming in the seals. In all fore limbs of mammals, even those as different as the leg of the squirrel, the flipper of the whale and seal, and the wing of the bat, the bones are the same.

The *hind legs* (Fig. 17-4) of mammals do not show so much variation as the forelegs, but in some cases, as in the whale, the hind legs have disappeared through disuse, and there is no external evidence of their existence. Almost the reverse is true of the kangaroo, which moves by hopping on its big hind legs. Some animals, like bears, walk on the soles of their feet, and some, like cats and dogs, walk on their toes only. Animals vary in the number of toes; for example, the cow walks on two toes, the horse on one toe, the hoof being a modified toenail. In such cases the other toes are entirely lacking or not perfectly developed (Fig. 17-4).

The *skeleton* of mammals is built on a similar pattern in all cases. In the vertebral column there are generally several regions, such as neck, rib, back, hip, and tail. The number of the separate vertebrae in the neck region is seven in all mammals except the sloth and the sea cow, but the neck region is not of the same length. Each of these vertebrae in the neck of the giraffe is very large, and this adaptation helps him in securing his food, which consists of tree leaves.

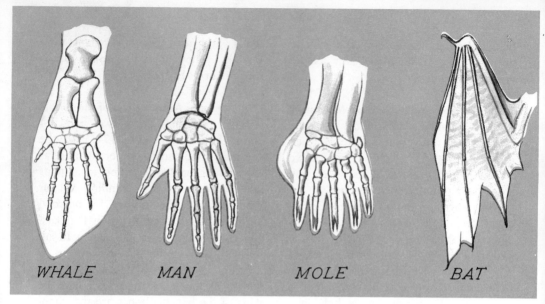

WHALE   MAN   MOLE   BAT

FIGURE 17-3. *MAMMALIAN FORELIMBS*

    Man's hand and fingers are capable of precise movements. Other mammalian forelimbs have similar bones modified for other uses. Can you explain these modifications in the whale, mole, and bat?

FIGURE 17-4. *HIND LIMBS*

    Notice that the same bones occur in the leg of a man and the leg of a horse, but that their arrangement is different.

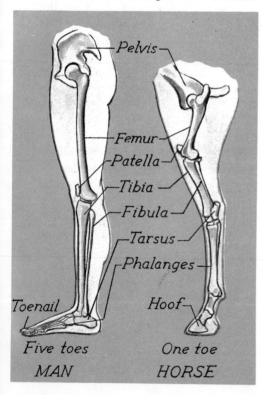

Pelvis

Femur
Patella
Tibia
Fibula
Tarsus
Phalanges

Toenail   Hoof

Five toes   One toe
MAN   HORSE

    The fold of skin of the flying squirrel is another strange adaptation, which enables the squirrel to glide easily through the air.

    Adaptations for Protection.—Mammals are found all over the earth, living in the frozen north and the humid tropics, or roving over plains and mountains. Everywhere mammals show adaptations in habits and form.

    The color of the white polar bear and arctic fox renders them inconspicuous against the ice and snow. Deer are among our swiftest runners, and the possession of such speed helps them escape when they are chased. In marked contrast to the habit of the deer when it is in danger is that of the opossum, which often rolls up into a ball and feigns death. After the animal which has been annoying the opossum goes away, it deliberately and slowly begins to move.

    Whales are water mammals that have lost most of their protective coat of hair but have developed instead a thick layer

240

H. Armstrong Roberts   Courtesy Michigan Conservation Department

FIGURE 17-5. *OPPOSITES*

The porcupine (*right*) is adequately protected from its enemies by its formidable barbed quills, even though it is slow and not very clever. The fleet-footed deer (*left*) avoids its enemies by outrunning them.

of protective fat beneath the skin. This fat is whale blubber. The porcupine has its hair enlarged and stiffened into sharp spines. These special hairs protect the porcupine effectively from lynxes and wild cats. Such spiny hairs are in marked contrast to the sheep's protective coat of wool, which also is modified hair.

There are many more examples of protective adaptation in mammals. How many can you name?

17.5   Origin of Mammals

Among the vertebrates there are intermediate forms between the different groups. These intermediate forms seem to indicate an orderly development from simple to complex forms.

Just as birds trace their ancestry to the reptiles through Archeopteryx (Sec. 16.1), the reptilian bird, so the mammals claim relationship to reptiles through a few fossil intermediate forms. The duck-billed platypus is the most primitive of the present-day mammals.

17.6   Classification of Mammals

Since you are already familiar with a great many different kinds of mammals, you may be interested in knowing some of the *orders* to which they belong. The following classification of mammals is for reference and need not be memorized:

1. Egg-laying mammals (Monotremata): duckbill, spiny anteater.
2. Pouched mammals (Marsupialia): kangaroo, opossum.
3. Insect-eating mammals (Insectivora): hedgehog, mole, shrew.
4. Flying mammals (Chiroptera): bat.
5. Flesh-eating mammals (Carnivora): cat, dog, civet, mink, raccoon, fox, bear, seal, lion, wolf, tiger.
6. Gnawing mammals (Rodentia): rabbit, squirrel, beaver, rat, porcupine, mouse.
7. Toothless mammals (Edentata): sloth, anteater, armadillo.

MAMMALS   **241**

FIGURE 17-6. *PLATYPUS*

An egg-laying mammal, the duck-billed platypus nourishes its young through pores on the stomach. An odd combination of mammal, bird, fish and reptile, it has short fur, webbed feet, a duck's bill, and feels at home on land or in the water.

Sawders from Cushing

8. Hoofed mammals (Ungulata): cattle, horse, deer, giraffe, pig, rhinoceros.
9. Trunk mammals (Proboscidea): elephant.
10. Marine mammals (Cetacea): whale, dolphin.

FIGURE 17-7. *MARSUPIAL*

A pouched mammal native to Australia, the kangaroo leaps forward with the aid of its powerful hind legs and tail.

Courtesy Australian News and Information Bureau

11. Flexible-fingered mammals (Primates): lemur, monkey, ape, man.

17.7 Egg-laying Mammals—Monotremata (mon-uh-*tree*-mah-tuh)

The duckbilled platypus of Australia is the best known of this group of primitive mammals. It is eighteen to twenty inches long and lives in the water. It has a ducklike bill, webbed feet, flat tail, and a heavy skeleton. The male has a poison gland. The female builds a nest in a burrow and lays from one to three eggs with flexible white shells. As she has no uterus, the young develop within the eggs after they are laid. Following incubation, the young are about an inch long after they hatch. They get their food by lapping up a nutritious substance secreted by scattered, modified glands on the abdomen of the mother. These glands do not have openings localized at nipples.

The brain of the duckbill is little more than a bundle of nerves, and the body temperature is very low.

The spiny anteater is another egg-laying mammal. It has long claws for digging into the nests of ants.

17.8 Pouched Mammals—Marsupialia (mahr-soo-pih-ay-lih-uh)

Kangaroos in Australia and opossums in the United States are the best known of the pouched mammals. The young

242

are developed in the uteri of the mother but are quite helpless when they are born. They are put in the mother's pouch near the milk glands, which have nipples, and where for several weeks milk is pumped into their mouths by the mother. Because of their true milk glands and the presence of the two uteri, the marsupials are more highly developed than the duckbilled platypus.

Except for the opossums in the United States and two groups of pouched mammals in the Andes of South America, the marsupials make their homes in Australia. The koala or "teddy bear," the wallaby, resembling a jack rabbit, and the wombat are interesting members of this group.

17.9 Insect-eating Mammals— Insectivora (in-sek-*tiv*-er-uh)

The "insect eaters" include the hedgehogs, moles, and shrews. These and later groups of mammals have a **placenta** (pluh-*sen*-tuh) for attaching the embryo to the wall of the uterus. The hedgehogs are not porcupines, as many people call them. They are small insect-eating mammals with long, quill-like hair, and are found only in Europe. The moles and shrews eat large numbers of grubs. They burrow into the ground by means of their sharp noses and forelimbs, which are adapted to digging. Moles have very fine hair, and their eyes are concealed under the skin. They are sightless, but are sensitive to light. Shrews have eyes and are able to see.

17.10 Flying Mammals—Chiroptera (ky-*rop*-ter-uh)

Bats, the shadowy creatures that fly about at night, differ from all other mammals. They have the bones of the fingers greatly elongated, but there are no more joints or bones in each finger than in a

Figure 17-8. *FLYING MAMMAL*
The bat has a small body in proportion to its wingspread. A nocturnal animal, it "sees" with its ears in the dark.

man's hand. Over these greatly lengthened fingers is stretched a thin, rubbery wing-membrane which is double in thickness. It is also attached to the side of the body, hind legs, and tail.

When the eyes of bats are covered with wax so that they cannot see and they are set free, the bats fly about freely, never touching objects, even avoiding and passing between silken threads. The hearing of bats is very keen. Their ears are very sensitive to the echoes of vibrations thrown back from objects. This helps them to avoid touching things as they fly at top speed. The voices of bats have a high range of pitch and can make sounds too high for man to hear. They can listen to the echoes of their own voices to help locate objects. The leaf-nosed bat of the Southwest has an erect membrane, or "leaf," on its nose which records sensitive vibrations set up by

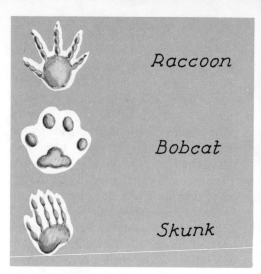

Raccoon

Bobcat

Skunk

FIGURE 17-9. *LAND CARNIVORES*
Flesh-eating land mammals are grouped by the way they walk. *Upper left:* the raccoon walks flat-footed; *center:* the cat walks on its toes; *lower left:* the skunk combines both methods.

insect wings. It is also stimulated by the rebound of the air from the objects which the bat is approaching.

It was from the study of bats that the echo sounder was invented. This device is used for finding obstacles hidden from a ship by darkness or fog. This method of detecting vibrations has been used in such other devices as the depth finder, which gives ocean depths by "bouncing" sound off the bottom, and radar, which uses the echo of electrical waves to detect unseen objects.

Bats are strong fliers and most of them can catch their food while in flight. They drink while flying by taking a tongue full of water as they dip down in flight.

A bat's food consists of insects, which are captured with both the mouth and the wing-membrane where it is attached to the body. The feeding time varies with the kind of bat, some seeking their food in the early evening, others early in the morning.

244

The young are born in early summer and among some kinds are carried around by the mother for the first two or three weeks as she flies at night. After this they are left "hung up" in some retreat while the mother gathers food for them and herself. When the young are three months old, they are able to fly and forage for themselves.

The group of bats includes the insect-eating bats which we have already described; the fruit bats, sometimes called "flying foxes," found in Africa, Asia, and Australia; and the vampire bats in the American tropics. The vampire bats suck blood and may carry disease.

17.11 Flesh-eating Mammals— Carnivora (kahr-*niv*-er-uh)

The term "Carnivora" means "flesh-eating"; in this order of mammals we find that the *canine* (*kay*-nyn) *teeth* are well developed and the jaws strong. There are the aquatic carnivores, sea lion, walrus, seal; and the land carnivores, which in turn are divided into three well-known groups: (1) bear and raccoon, which walk flat-footed; (2) wolf, coyote, lion, tiger, hyena, cat, dog, etc., which walk on their toes only; (3) weasel, otter, skunk, and mink, which walk partly on the toes.

Skunks and Weasels.—The skunk is the commonest of the wild, flesh-eating animals. Close relatives are the minks and weasels. All these animals, especially the skunk, are capable of discharging a strong and almost suffocating odor when annoyed or angry. This offensive odor is manufactured in glands located near the tail and is an adaptation that has had a decided influence on the habits of the skunk. The skunk is no longer required to be alert to escape its enemies and so has become fat and lazy. Its muscles are soft, and rapid exertion ex-

hausts it sooner than any other member of this group.

The food of the skunk consists of grasshoppers, crickets, frogs, snakes, rabbits, eggs, the young of birds, and field mice. It is only occasionally that a hen is captured, and the general habits of this animal are beneficial. Skunks hibernate for short periods in the winter in the holes of other animals. They usually come out in February, and at this time their food consists of mice and moles.

By May the young are able to begin foraging for their own food, and it is not unusual in the early evening to see the mother and her brood slowly wandering about as they capture insects.

Skunk fur is made up chiefly in neck pieces and coat trimmings, and the demand for it has become so great that regular skunk farms are conducted at a profit, due to the increasing demand for fine furs.

Closely related to the skunks are the *weasels,* which are very destructive to birds, rabbits, squirrels, and poultry. Their thin, muscular bodies enable them to move with great rapidity, and their endurance may carry them many miles in a single night. Weasels should be killed whenever possible.

17.12 Gnawing Mammals—Rodentia (roh-*den*-she-uh)

The rodents are the gnawing mammals which have the *incisor* (in-*sy*-zer) *teeth* chisel-shaped and much enlarged. These gnawing teeth of the rodents do not wear out because they keep growing, and they also keep sharp because the front edge is harder than the back. Rodents lack the canine teeth of the Carnivora. It is only necessary to name the more common members of this order to realize how very destructive the rodents are, for

Ewing Galloway

FIGURE 17-10. *THE INDUSTRIOUS BEAVER*
On each jaw the beaver has two sharp-edged incisors which continue to grow throughout his lifetime, replacing parts worn away by constant gnawing.

here are included the rat, mouse, rabbit, porcupine, chipmunk, squirrel, muskrat, beaver, and woodchuck.

The Beaver.—Its social habits and architectural ability make the beaver one of our most interesting mammals. The demand for its fur has led to its extermination in many parts of the country. Beavers live in colonies and work industriously in building dams and houses. They live on the bark and shoots of tender young trees. Some damage is done by their cutting trees and damming up streams, but the great popular interest in beavers and their work, and the value of their fur more than outweigh the little harm they do.

The Rat, the Worst Mammalian Pest. —Early in our life as a nation the black

rat was introduced from Norway. For a time it spread rapidly and soon became a nuisance. Some time later the brown rat came from Europe, escaping from the boats. This animal exhibited great versatility in its habits and ate various foods. It was so much more savage than the black rat that it was but a few years before the earlier immigrant was almost completely exterminated by this later arrival.

In the United States the damage which the brown rat causes to cereals and grains is estimated at a billion dollars annually. The rat is the active agent in the spread of the dreaded disease known as *bubonic* (byoo-*bon*-ik) *plague*, which has an almost world-wide distribution. The rat becomes infested with fleas, blood-suck-

246

FIGURE 17-11. *CARRIER OF DISEASE*

The rat is a destructive, disease-carrying mammal that thrives in trash and garbage heaps like this one. In waging war on rats, it is important to destroy their food supply and prevent them from breeding.

Post-Dispatch pictures from Black Star

ing insects, which bite persons and thus spread the germs of the plague (Fig. 17-11). This disease spreads rapidly and usually results in death. During a single twenty-year period, this disease killed over 11,000,000 people in India alone.

Rabbits.—Rabbits and hares are rodentlike animals. They differ from true rodents in having four large front teeth on each jaw. These enable rabbits to do much damage to orchards. They also do considerable damage to truck gardens and other farm areas.

The cottontail rabbit breeds several times each year during the warmer months, with litters averaging five or six young. The nest is placed in a hollow or depression in the ground and is composed of dead grass lined with fur which the mother pulls from her own body. These animals breed so fast that, despite their many enemies who hunt them for food, they may become so numerous as to constitute a serious hindrance to food production.

The carnivorous birds and mammals are usually successful in keeping rabbits from becoming a menace. Hawks, owls, and eagles are the chief birds that destroy rabbits, while foxes, minks, weasels, skunks, dogs, and cats are the mammals that prey upon them.

17.13 Toothless Mammals—Edentata (ee-den-tay-tuh)

The name of this group means "without teeth," yet the hairy anteater is the only mammal which does not have any. The sloths of South America, though members of this group, have primitive teeth. They are among the slowest animals known; they could walk about half

FIGURE 17-12. *TWO-TOED SLOTH*

The sloth seldom comes down from the trees. It walks hanging upside down from branches and sleeps in this position too.

Arthur W. Ambler from National Audubon Society

247

Jorgensen from Three Lions

FIGURE 17-13. *WILD HORSE*

With its striking pattern of dark stripes on a white background, the zebra differs from other members of the horse family.

a mile in twenty-four hours if they kept going that long. Most of the time they hang head downward in trees and move so little that green algae grow in their coarse brown hair.

The armadillos are interesting to study because their young are born either as twins or quadruplets. They are covered with heavy, overlapping, bony scales.

One species lives in the southern part of the United States. It is two and a half feet in length, lives in burrows, and eats leaves, fruit, and some buds.

17.14 Hoofed Mammals—Ungulata (ung-yoo-*lay*-tuh)

This important group of mammals takes its name from the Latin word *ungula,* hoof. It includes our most useful domestic animals. They are called the hoofed mammals and are divided into two great subdivisions:

1. Odd-toed, as the horse, rhinoceros.
2. Even-toed.
   (*a*) Those that do not chew the cud, as the pig and hippopotamus.
   (*b*) Those that do chew the cud, as the cow, sheep, and deer.

The expression "chew the cud" refers to the habit of hastily swallowing food which is later forced again into the mouth and then thoroughly chewed. Such animals are known as **ruminants** (*roo*-mih-n'nts) and have a modified stomach with four divisions. The first section, the rumen, holds the unchewed food.

FIGURE 17-14. *VALUABLE ANIMALS*

These cattle are prize milk producers. Other types of cows are bred specifically to supply meat, as are these pigs. Why is pork cheaper than beef?

Courtesy U.S. Department of Agriculture

J. C. Allen & Son

Some of the ungulates have horns. Oxen, sheep, and bison have hollow horns which are never shed. Deer, moose, and caribou have solid horns which are shed every year. When full grown, these horns have many branches.

Horses and Mules.—The horse has been associated with man since the Stone Age, and next to the cow has been his most useful animal. It has been suggested that man first hunted horses for food, then drove them, and finally used them for riding and as beasts of burden. The fine animals which we see today have gradually developed over a long period of time from a small animal about the size of a fox terrier.

The mule, offspring of horse and donkey, has been known for many centuries. Even in the days of ancient Greece and Rome mules were used in agriculture because they are more enduring, live longer, and are surer-footed than horses.

Pigs.—The pig has been developed from the wild boar of the Old World. Meat is obtained more cheaply from the pig than from any other animal, because it adds more weight for a certain amount of food than either sheep or cattle and does it in a shorter time. Two types of pigs are the lard type (Poland China) and the bacon type (Hampshire or Tamworth).

The Cow.—Cattle are descended from wild oxen of Europe and Asia, and practically all our popular breeds have been developed in the Old World, mainly in the British Isles.

There are two chief types of cattle: the beef type used for food, and the dairy type most valuable for the milk, butter, and cheese that it produces. The beef type is characterized by "blocky" bodies, a form which yields the greatest quantity of meat. The beef cow is not expected to produce much milk. The dairy type presents a different appearance from the beef type, having a bony, angular body and a very large udder.

The island breeds, Jersey and Guernsey, are famous for the production of butterfat rather than for the quantity of milk. The Ayrshires, a Scotch breed, are known for the superiority of their milk for cheese, for the large proportion of butterfat, and for the fact that they yield more beef than any other dairy breed. Dutch cattle, the Holstein-Friesian breed, are famous for the quantity of milk that they produce. Their milk is also superior for cheese-making and, on account of the large quantity they produce, these cattle rank foremost in supplying cities with milk.

Sheep and Goats.—The shepherd has been a famous character in literature. Sheep in the Old World were possibly the first mammals domesticated by man. They thrive in nearly all climates and can find food where other mammals can scarcely live. Sheep furnish wool and meat. Three classes, based on the quality of the wool, are: (1) the fine-wool breeds like the *merino,* which has its origin in Spain, from where it has been carried to all countries where sheep raising is an important industry; (2) the medium-wool breeds like the Shropshire; and (3) the long-wool breeds like the Leicester. The latter two are English breeds. The fine-wool breed is raised principally for the wool, the meat value being a secondary consideration, while the medium-wool breeds are raised principally for meat, and the wool is a secondary consideration; in the long-wool breeds the mutton and the wool are of equal importance.

Closely related to sheep are goats, which are the main supply of milk and meat in the island of Malta, in Switzerland, southern Italy, and Asia Minor.

FIGURE 17-15. *JUNGLE BULLDOZER*

The elephant's trunk is amazingly strong and versatile. It can lift a ton's weight or pick up a peanut.

17.15 Trunk Mammals—Proboscidea (proh-buh-*sid*-ee-uh)

The most important of these animals with trunks are the elephants. They are the largest of the land mammals, often weighing six or seven tons. The general body structure is simple. The trunk is formed by the upper lip and nose being drawn out. Elephants have long memories and are intelligent and teachable.

17.16 Marine Mammals—Cetacea (seh-*tay*-she-uh)

These are the whales and the dolphins. Whales are the largest of the mammals. Although they live entirely in the water, they breathe by lungs and have to come to the surface for air. Whales use their tails to move through the water and their flippers to balance. They have very little hair, mostly around the snout. The young, usually one or two, are born alive and are nourished by the mother's milk.

The sperm whale is sixty feet long. It has teeth with which it can eat fish and squid. The dolphin is seven feet long and also feeds on fish. The baleen whale grows to be 105 feet long and produces young twenty-three feet long at birth and fifty-two feet long when old enough to be weaned. This whale strains small animals from the water for its food.

17.17 Flexible-fingered Mammals— Primates (pry-*may*-teez)

The primates are a distinct group of mammals with the brain especially well developed. This is the main reason that we regard the animals in this group as the highest mammals. All have nails in place of claws on the fingers and toes.

Lemurs and monkeys live chiefly in trees, while most apes seldom leave the ground. The higher apes are similar in structure to man. They do not have tails. The body is completely hairy. The fore

FIGURE 17-16. *KILLER WHALE*

These are not the largest whales—they usually reach a length of about 30 feet, as compared with the sperm whale (60 feet) or the blue whale (100 feet), but they are among the most fierce. They hunt in packs, often attacking whales two or three times their own size.

Ernest P. Walker

250

feet are grasping hands as a rule, and the hind feet are walking as well as grasping appendages. Chimpanzees can be taught as much as a child of three years. They can communicate ideas but do not have a language.

Man has a much more highly developed brain than any other primate. His feet do not have opposable large toes, his lips are rolled outward, he has a well-developed chin and forehead. He stands erect, and his arms are much shorter than his legs.

17.18 Economic Importance of Mammals

Man finds some mammals helpful, some harmful, and some neither. The domesticated mammals, especially the horse, cow, sheep, goat, and pig, are of the greatest use to man in this part of the world. In cold regions, reindeer are the main source of food and clothing, and are also used as beasts of burden. In desert regions, the camel is the most useful, and in hot regions, elephants are of great value as beasts of burden. It is not too much to say that these domesticated mammals are almost indispensable to man's existence.

Dogs and cats have long been man's companions, and the former were much used in olden days to hunt down and kill man's animal enemies as well as to protect his livestock from their ravages. Of the wild animals, seals and walruses, which live in the water, furnish food, fur, and leather. The whale furnishes whalebone and oil.

Man is profiting by learning the habits of other mammals; for example, we build roosts in the vicinity of swamps and marshes to furnish shelter for bats by day. At night the bats fly about, catching insects which annoy both man and animals.

FIGURE 17-17. *EDUCATED*

The most intelligent of the apes, the chimpanzee has an excellent visual memory and learns rapidly by trial and error. He is also a good imitator.

Rats and mice carry disease, eat our food, and ruin much that they do not eat. Red squirrels damage beds and furniture if they gain access to the house, and out of doors they destroy the eggs and young of birds and the seeds of evergreen trees. It has been estimated that rodents alone, such as mice, rats, prairie dogs, gophers, and jack rabbits, each year eat or otherwise cause the loss of crops worth more than a billion dollars.

Rats, mice, and guinea pigs have proved of great use in laboratories where the causes and effects of diseases are studied. Their reaction to diphtheria, tuberculosis, cancer, and other diseases is similar to that of man. These experiments have taught doctors much about the treatment of disease in man.

Bauer from Cushing

FIGURE 17-18. *GUINEA PIG*

Widely used as an experimental animal, the guinea pig has small ears, no tail, and feeding habits like that of a rabbit. Its real name is "cavy."

17.19 Conservation of Useful Mammals

With the steady growth of population, more and more wild animals have been killed to supply the increased demand for food and clothing. In fact, so great has been the slaughter of the most valuable ones that laws have been passed to protect them from total extinction. Some of these laws make it illegal to kill certain kinds of mammals at any time of the year; others protect them only while they are rearing their young. In the first class, in New York State, we have the elk and beaver, and in the second the deer, fox, and raccoon. The laws protecting mammals are not the same throughout the United States.

Many of our common mammals were not extensively killed for their fur until 1919. During three years for which a record was kept, over fourteen million muskrats were sold as Hudson seal, and nearly twenty-four million insect-eating moles and over thirteen million American and Australian opossums were marketed. These are but three of the kinds of fur bearers introduced by the fur trade to replace the original fur bearers whose supply is diminishing. The entire world is being searched to meet this abnormal demand.

Fur Farming.—In order to help meet the demand for furs many fur-bearing animals are being raised on farms. There they receive excellent care, good food, and are protected from their enemies. These factors keep the fur in good condition for use in fur garments. Silver fox, mink, muskrats, and some chinchillas are raised on farms for this reason.

Mammal Sanctuaries. — Yellowstone National Park in the state of Wyoming is the best-known sanctuary in the United States for large mammals. Here the bison, moose, elk, mule deer, white-tailed deer, and black and grizzly bears

FIGURE 17-19. *BUFFALO*

The American buffalo (bison) almost became extinct after vast numbers were slaughtered for their meat and fur. Efforts to preserve them from extinction began about 1889 when only 551 remained in this country. Now, there are about 10,000 scattered in many herds on fenced game preserves.

Rose from Fish and Wildlife Service

FIGURE 17-20. *THE BEAR AND THE FOX*

Breeding foxes in captivity (*left*) for their fur has become an important industry. There are now about 78,000 black bears (*right*) left in this country.

are protected during the entire year. Even such predatory mammals as the timber wolf, coyote, and mountain lion are partially protected in this park. The number killed is determined by the destructiveness of the animal to the other animals in the park. As soon as the predatory animals become too numerous, a few are killed in order to keep them from becoming a serious menace. Yellowstone Park was one of the first sanctuaries in our country to preserve destructive animals in a wild state for educational purposes.

The federal government now operates more than four hundred game preserves where both birds and mammals are protected. About a quarter of these are in national parks and monuments. The Fish and Wildlife Service, the chief government wildlife conservation agency, maintains many other game sanctuaries.

17.20 Other Products Furnished by Mammals

Many of the animals we have just been studying supply us with food, fur,

and wool. But mammals also furnish us with various other things, such as leather, oil, and buttons.

Leather.—Tanning, or leather manufacture, is a very ancient art, and was practiced with considerable skill by the earliest of civilized peoples. The Babylonians and Egyptians made leather much as it is made today.

This large industry depends upon the structure of the skin in mammals, especially the arrangement of the fibers in the *dermis* (*der*-mis) (the inner layer of the skin). In the skin of a fish or an alligator, the fibers of the dermis run parallel and at right angles in the several layers. This makes an interlacing network, thus producing a strong skin which resists tearing or flaking. In the hairy animals these same fibers do not follow any order of arrangement.

Most of the leather that is used in shoes today comes from the hides of cattle. The hides must be removed with care to avoid cutting, as all such injuries destroy the fibers of the dermis. These hides are then sent to tanneries, where

MAMMALS

FIGURE 17-21. *PRODUCING COWHIDE LEATHER*

Although all hides and skins can be tanned, cattle hides are the most important raw material. The first step at the tannery is soaking the hides to remove all traces of curing agents or preservatives. About 80% of U.S. production of leather is for shoes; other uses include saddles, gloves, luggage, and upholstery.

George H. Davis Studio

each is made into a certain grade of leather, such as sole leather or the leather for the upper part of the shoe. This difference in thickness and firmness is produced largely by the method employed in tanning. When a vegetable tan is used, such as hemlock bark, oak, or sumac, sole leather results; and when a mineral tan is employed, leather suitable for the upper part of the shoe is secured.

Two common parasites, the white grub and the southern cattle tick, live in the skin of cattle and render it unfit for leather. The United States Department of Agriculture has greatly assisted cattle raisers in ridding their cattle of these destructive parasites.

Another biological factor in the production of good leather is the care that the cattle receive. If they are well fed and properly housed during the winter and kept free from disease, their hides have a better texture and are finer-grained. The coarser grades of leather are made from older cattle and those that have little or no shelter in winter.

Oil.—Oil is the name for fat in liquid form. The edible animal fats are butter,

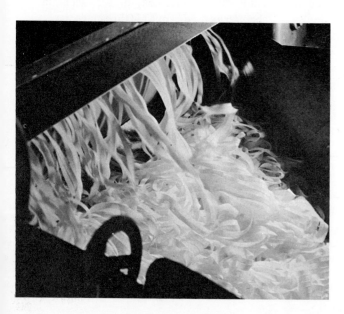

FIGURE 17-22. *SOAP FLAKES*

A product of animal fats, soap flakes are made by passing a hot soap mixture over water-cooled rollers (shown here). It is then put through a dryer and scraped off in thin chips, or flakes, and packaged by machinery.

Courtesy Procter & Gamble

lard, and margarine. Mutton tallow is used in the manufacture of candles. Tallow, bone fat, horse fat, and the fat squeezed from the skins of animals are used in the dressing of leather. Animal oils are used in the manufacture of soap, and a large amount of grease is of animal origin.

Buttons.—In addition to the immense number of buttons manufactured from clam and mussel shells, there is a large industry manufacturing other kinds of buttons. In expensive tailoring, real horn buttons are used, sliced from the horns of cattle. (However, many of the buttons used on clothing are made from "vegetable ivory," which is a nut and not an animal product.) Great numbers of so-called bone buttons are made from the casein in skim milk. The casein is coagulated, colored, and combined with certain chemicals which give it solidity.

These buttons are made by compression. Not only buttons are made by this process, but also umbrella handles, hairbrush handles, and similar products.

17.21   Contributions of Mammals

Our lives are probably more influenced by mammals than by almost anything else. Of the three essentials of life, food, clothing, and shelter, more of the first two comes to us from mammals than from any other single source. While grains and fruits are important elements of diet, they can hardly compare with milk and its products and the different kinds of meat.

In clothing production, cotton is an important vegetable item, but the wide use of woolens and worsteds in outer garments, belts, buttons, and shoes make the contributions of mammals in this field particularly important.

FACTS TO REMEMBER

Mammals, the highest class of the phylum Chordata, have (1) the best-developed brains, (2) a four-chambered heart, (3) breathe by means of lungs, (4) are warm-blooded, (5) have hair on their bodies, (6) possess a muscular *diaphragm,* (7) give birth to living young (except the egg-laying group), and (8) nourish the young with milk from the *mammary glands.*

Mammals trace their ancestry to the reptiles. The most primitive mammal, the duckbilled platypus, lays eggs; the next higher group, the pouched mammals, possess *uteri* where the young begin their development; and the insect-eating mammals and higher groups have a *placenta* to attach the young to the wall of the uterus where it receives its food supply from its mother.

Mammals have many adaptations for life in the water, on land, underground, and in the air. They live in climates ranging from the Arctic to the tropics. Many are useful to man in supplying food, clothing, and other commercial products. Some mammals, like rats, carry disease, and others, like horses and cattle, supply materials used in the manufacture of medicines.

Many mammals are protected in sanctuaries and by laws. Others, like fox and mink, are raised on farms for their valuable fur. Some, like rats and mice, need to be destroyed because they are disease-carriers.

WORDS TO REMEMBER

canine teeth	herbivorous	placenta
carnivorous	incisor teeth	ruminant
dermis	mammary glands	solitary
diaphragm	omnivorous	uterus

QUESTIONS

1. What characteristics distinguish a mammal?
2. Name as many wild animals as you can which live around your home. Give the order to which each belongs. *Example:* Fox—Carnivora.
3. Why is the rat called the worst mammalian pest?
4. Tell what you can of the ancient horse.
5. Which animals chew their cud? What is meant by "chew the cud"?
6. Name some animals with solid horns. Name some with hollow horns.
7. What are the two chief types of pig? Of cattle? Which are raised near your home?
8. Discuss the three classes of sheep. On what basis is the classification made? Give examples of each.
9. Why is the duckbilled platypus considered the most primitive mammal? Describe it.
10. What part of the body of the bat has special adaptations for flying? Do bats have hair? Do they nourish their young with milk?
11. What is a mammal sanctuary and where are some located?
12. Discuss the economic importance of mammals.
13. What game laws are in force in your state for the protection of mammals?
14. List as many products as you can which are derived from mammals.
15. Explain the difference between a porcupine and a hedgehog.

COMPLETION TEST

As your teacher or classmate reads the following incomplete statements, with your book closed, write on a clean sheet of paper the word or phrase which best completes the statement.

1. An animal with a trunk is the _____.
2. The slowest mammal known is the _____.
3. A pouched mammal is the _____.
4. Man belongs to the group of _____.
5. Ungulata are called _____ mammals.
6. Gnawing mammals are the _____.
7. The _____ sleeps upside down.
8. Buttons are manufactured from the _____ of mammals.
9. The _____ industry depends on the arrangement of the fibers in the dermis.
10. An animal which eats both meat and plants is called an _____ animal.

PROJECTS

I. *Mammals in Their Native Habitats.*—1. Many interesting studies can be made based on the lives of mammals in their native habitats. The different kinds of mammals can be detected by their tracks, the distance between footfalls, claw marks on trees, logs, or ground, tooth marks on wood or bone, their nests, shelters, runways, holes, trails, and dust paths—all tell something about each kind. Where do they live—in the soil, among the rocks, in the water, or in the air? What effect do unusual conditions in nature, such as storms, floods, or forest fires, have? Which animals are active in the winter and which animals are inactive during that season?

2. Choose a particular mammal for study. How is it related to other animals? Who are its enemies and its friends? Does it have the same enemies in youth, middle age, and old age? When does it begin to be active each day? How long is it active and when does its activity cease? Does the animal spend the entire year in one locality or does it migrate? If it migrates, in which direction and how far does it go? Try to find out any of the causes of migration, such as food supply and changes in climate.

3. For those animals that hibernate, the times of entering and emerging from hibernation should be observed. Are they completely inactive during this period? As these animals move about during the active season what is their method of locomotion? Do they run, jump, climb, dig in the ground, swim, or fly? What foods do they eat? Do these foods differ at different seasons? Do they store up any food? Are they dependent on water? What are the various sounds and calls made? Do they have warning calls and alarm calls?

II. The following observations were made within a few miles of a large city and indicate that a great deal can be learned about the winter life of our common wild mammals:

"The home of the cottontail is where its food grows, and in the winter this consists of more than seventy different kinds of shrubs and trees. Among the forms more extensively eaten are the following: bark and soft wood, sumac, bittersweet, high blackberry, bush honeysuckle. The bark only is eaten of sugar maple and barberry, while the young shoots of nearly fifty different kinds of shrubs and trees supply them with food."

III. The recent great demand for fur coats has enabled many people to start fur farms. If you wish to take up fur farming, write to the Bureau of Animal Industry, Washington, D.C., for information concerning this subject.

IV. *Study of a Domestic Animal.*—You may wish to observe a farm animal or your own dog or cat and make a careful study of the characteristics of mammals. Make a written report of the external features and include the classification. A snapshot of the animal you choose will add to your report. Then observe its reactions to heat, cold, noise, light, darkness, approach of other animals and of people. Learn all you can about it and decide whether your animal is typical of the group.

V. Record of Mammals Observed.—The following form should be copied. Begin entering your observations now on the copy, and keep the report up to date during the year.

REPORT ON MAMMALS

To Be Filled Out First from General Knowledge, Later Extended by Trips to Fields, Woods, or Parks

Kinds	Where Found	Food	Kind of Food	Life in Winter	Life in Summer	Benefi- cial	Harmful

VI. Study of Internal Structure.—Mammals are complicated animals and much more difficult to dissect than the frog. But if you have a white rat which can be sacrificed for dissection or if any other small mammal is available, you may be able to do the work with your teacher's supervision. However, before you begin, make very careful plans as to what you would like to do and have your outline carefully checked. In this way your project may prove to be very much worth while.

VII. Comparison of Mammals.—If you are unable to spend much time out of doors, you may be able to consult some reference books. Collect or draw pictures to represent each of the animal groups, or, if you wish, make a detailed study of one of them. You will find this a fascinating hobby that you will enjoy for a long time.

REFERENCES

Ashbrook, *Fur Farming for Profit.* Macmillan.
Bauer, *Animal Babies.* Donahue.
Cahalone, *Mammals of North America.* Macmillan.
Colbert, *Evolution of the Vertebrates.* Wiley.
Daglish, *Life Story of Beasts.* Morrow.
DeVoe, *Speaking of Animals.* Creative Age Press.
Dodd, *Mark Trail's North American Mammals.* Hawthorn.
Dreamy, *A Child's Book of Horses.* Maxton.
Eipper, *Animals Looking at You.* Viking.
Fletcher, *Driftwood Valley.* Atlantic, Little, Brown.
Frost, *A Child's Book of Jungle Animals.* Maxton.
Henderson, *A Child's Book of Dogs.* Maxton.
Ivah, *Animals Under Your Feet.* Grosset and Dunlap.
Lane, *The Story of Mountains.* Doubleday.

Moore, *The Book of Wild Pets.* Putnam's.

Murie, *A Field Guide to Animal Tracks.* Houghton Mifflin.

Nelson, *Wild Animals of North America.* National Geographic Society.

Neurath, *The Wonder World of Animals.* Lothrop, Lee, and Shepard.

Palmer, *The Mammal Guide.* Doubleday.

Piper, *Animal Story Book.* Platt and Munk.

Sanderson, *Animal Tales.* Knopf.

Sanderson, *Living Mammals.* Hanover House.

Scheinfeld, *The New You and Heredity.* Lippincott.

Schmidt, *Homes and Habits of Wild Animals.* Donahue.

Seton, *Wild Animals at Home.* Doubleday, Doran.

Stone and Cram, *American Animals.* Stone.

Voter, *All About Whales.* Random House.

Warren, *The Beaver: Its Works and Ways.* Williams and Wilkins.

Ylla, *Animals by Ylla.* Hastings House.

COMPREHENSIVE TEST ON PART TWO

I. On a separate piece of paper, list the numbers of the following sentences, and opposite these numbers place the word from the right-hand column which makes the statement correct.

1. The tadpole gets oxygen in its early stages by means of _____ gills.	four
	complete
2. Insects have three body regions: head, _____, and abdomen.	temperature
	bison
3. The abdomen and _____ of certain insects have spiracles.	nest
	tachina
4. Birds have a higher body _____ than reptiles.	six
5. The _____ bones of birds increase their buoyancy.	trichinosis
6. Clothes moths are destructive in their _____ stage.	permanent
7. Diptera have _____ wings.	nymphs
8. Lepidoptera have _____ wings.	larval
9. Adult insects generally have _____ legs.	pectoral
10. The young cicadas are called _____.	hollow
11. Lice are insects without _____.	ocean
12. The _____ fly is a valuable insect which lays its eggs in other insects.	precocial
	thorax
13. The monarch butterfly has a _____ metamorphosis.	summer
14. A disease known as _____ is contracted by eating undercooked ham or pork containing certain larvae.	wings
	thorax
15. The anterior pair of fins on a fish is known as the _____ fins.	external
	altricial
16. The gill arches of some fish bear sharp-pointed projections known as _____ rakers.	two
	mammals
17. A small fish, the stickleback, builds a _____ and lays its eggs.	gill
	diaphragm

18. Eels lay their eggs in the waters of the _____.

19. Frogs lack a _____, so that they are unable to take a breath.

20. Birds, like pheasants, that are active when hatched are called _____.

21. Birds that are inactive when hatched are _____.

22. The chickadee is known as a _____ resident.

23. The bobolink is known as a _____ resident.

24. Bats are placed in the class of _____ because they suckle their young.

25. A mammal recently saved from extinction by man's knowledge of conservation is the _____.

II. On a separate piece of paper, list the numbers of the following sentences, and opposite them place the word from the right-hand column which makes the statement correct.

1. Malaria and yellow fever are carried by _____.	molt
2. In the life history of the monarch butterfly there are the egg, _____, pupa, and adult stages.	exoskeleton
	regeneration
3. The butterfly takes its food by means of a _____.	stomach
4. The outside covering of an insect is called an _____.	dinosaurs
5. Insects take air into their bodies by means of _____.	oxygen
6. Sucking insects are controlled by _____ poisons.	lobster
7. Biting insects are controlled by _____ poisons.	legs
8. The study of insects is known as _____.	alligator
9. The parts of an insect's compound eye are known as _____.	webbed
	mammal
10. Larvae of insects _____ several times in their development.	mosquitoes
	spiracles
11. The head and thorax of crayfish together are called _____.	larva
	facets
12. The _____ of a crayfish are protected by the carapace.	contact
	proboscis
13. The crayfish gets _____ by means of gills.	entomology
14. The eyes of crayfish are on the ends of _____.	four
15. Spiders have four pairs of _____.	gills
16. Crustaceans may restore lost parts by means of _____.	cephalothorax
	stalks
17. The largest known crustacean is a _____.	skin
18. The hind legs of frogs have _____ toes.	serum
19. Hibernating frogs get oxygen through the _____.	Audubon
20. A group of reptiles known as _____ are now extinct.	
21. The largest reptile found in the United States is the _____.	

22. Snake bites are no longer fatal to man if the proper _____ is promptly administered.

23. The earliest bird artist of the United States was
_____.
24. The heart of mammals is a _____ chambered heart.
25. The whale is a _____ because it suckles its young.

III. Some of the following sentences are true and some are false. On a separate piece of paper, list the numbers of sentences that are true and write an explanation of each. List the numbers of the sentences that are false and state the reason in each case.

1. Bees make food for man.
2. All insects are adapted for cross-pollination of flowers.
3. A spider is a true insect.
4. Some ladybird beetles help to protect orange trees.
5. Bees and butterflies belong to the same order of insects.
6. Some ants and some aphids are mutually helpful.
7. Boll weevils destroy the leaves of the cotton plant.
8. Codling moths eat the apple-tree leaves.
9. Both the adult and the larva of the potato beetle eat potato leaves.
10. The monarch butterfly migrates in the fall of the year.

IV. The invertebrates show a wide variety in structures and in the methods of carrying on their life processes. Some of the characteristics which distinguish them from vertebrates are: (1) no backbones—exoskeletons present when needed for protection and attachment of muscles, (2) dorsal heart with both open and closed circulatory systems, and (3) ventral nervous system consisting of a chain of ganglia in the head sometimes called a "brain."

Under the life processes given below are listed various structures which different invertebrates use in their activities. For each structure try to recall as many different kinds of animals as you can which you have studied in Units III and IV which use them.

LIFE PROCESSES OF THE INVERTEBRATES

1. Food-getting		2. Irritability	
a.	Siphon	a.	Antenna
b.	Pseudopodia	b.	Antennules
c.	Cilia	c.	Tympanum
d.	Tentacles	d.	Statocyst
e.	Mouth	e.	Compound eye
f.	Cheliped	f.	Simple eye
g.	Maxilliped	g.	Eye spot
h.	Proboscis		
i.	Mandible		

3. Digestion	a. Stomach	7. Locomotion	a. Cilia
	b. Food vacuole		b. Flagella
	c. Crop		c. Pseudopodia
	d. Intestine		d. Tentacles
	e. Gizzard		e. Muscular foot
			f. Setae
4. Circulation	a. Sinuses		g. Tube feet
	b. Closed system		h. Walking legs
	c. Open system		i. Swimmerets
			j. Jumping legs
5. Respiration	a. Tracheae		k. Wings
	b. Outer covering		
	c. Gills	8. Reproduction	a. Fission
	d. Lung books		b. Conjugation
			c. Both sexes in same individual
6. Excretion	a. Green glands		d. Sexes separate
	b. Nephridia		e. Incomplete metamorphosis
	c. Contractile vacuole		f. Complete metamorphosis
	d. Tubules		
	e. Anus		

V. Both the state and national governments expend large sums of money for the conservation of natural resources. Describe:

1. Two ways in which the conservation of fish is being promoted.
2. Four ways in which insects are being controlled.
3. Two ways in which bird life is being controlled.
4. Two ways in which mammals are being controlled.

Part Three

Biology of Man

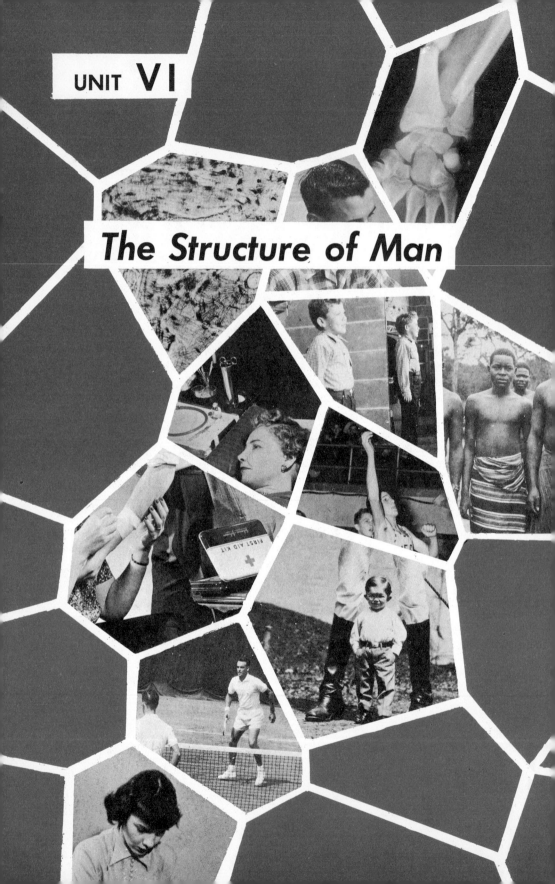

UNIT **VI**

The Structure of Man

What are your physical features? Are you tall or short? Are you light or dark-complexioned? Is your hair curly or straight? In some of these ways you may differ from your parents, your brothers or sisters, and your classmates. Can you explain this? How long have your ancestors been in this country? Some groups of people have come from Asia, some from Africa, and others from Europe. Can you guess where they came from by looking at them? In Unit VI you will study the physical features of ancient and modern man. You will also learn which characteristics are the most important in tracing ancestry.

Why is your skin an index to your health? Is your skin clear and smooth? Is your hair soft and glossy? Are your fingernails smooth and well-formed? Are your eyes bright and shining? Do your cuts and scratches heal quickly? Your skin is nourished by your whole body and protects it from disease germs which are found everywhere. It also regulates the temperature of the body. In this unit you will discover many reasons why your skin serves as a thermostat in your body as well as an index to your health.

What does your posture indicate about you? Do you stand as straight and tall as you can? Do you walk gracefully? Do you know the correct posture for sitting at a desk? Your bones and muscles help you to stand, walk, sit, climb, and run. If you try to keep good posture when you are growing, your bones will be held straighter by your muscles. Proper food and exercise will keep your muscles firm so that you will become a good athlete, a lively dancer, and an energetic student. In Unit VI you will discover how bones are formed, how they move, and what food they need to keep them strong. You will also learn how the muscles and bones work like levers, what really happens when your muscles are tired, and how you can recover more quickly from such fatigue.

CHAPTER 18

The Development of Modern Man

18.1 Prehistoric Man

To study the earliest men, we must go back more than two million years. Our knowledge of primitive man is based on a very few remains found in various parts of the world. From these, **anthropologists** (an-thruh-*pol*-uh-jists)—men who specialize in the study of man's physical characteristics—built theories to explain man's development.

The remains on which these theories rest are often limited to as little as part of a skull and a bone or two. From these, scientists reconstruct certain types of primitive men, which are named from the places near which their remains were found: *Zinjanthropus, Java, Peking, Heidelberg, Neanderthal,* and *Cro-Magnon.* Zinjanthropus, the earliest human skeletal remains, was discovered in Tanganyika in 1959. It was determined that Zinjanthropus lived about 1,750,000 years ago.

18.2 The Java Man

In 1891, in Java, four fragments of a skeleton were found: a skullcap, two upper molars, and a femur (the thigh bone). By studying these bones we have learned a great deal about early man.

From the remains, it is possible to judge how tall early man was. It has been estimated that the Java man was about 5 feet 7 inches tall. He probably walked erect and had the power of speech. His forehead was low and flat, with ridges of bone over his eyes. His brain was much larger than that of an ape but much smaller than that of modern man (only about two-thirds as large).

Since no other remains were found with the Java man, it is supposed that his weapons were made of wood and had decayed. It also indicated that wood was used long before stone in making weapons.

NAME	DATE OF DIS-COVERY	TIME OF EXISTENCE
Zinjanthropus	1959	About 1,750,000 B.C.
Java	1891	Early ice age—1,000,000 B.C.
Peking	1929 and 1930	Ice receding from the continent—500,000 B.C.
Heidelberg	1907	After second glacier—300,000–350,000 B.C.
Neanderthal	1856	Last glacial period before interglacial stage—90,000–80,000 B.C.
Cro-Magnon	1868	Retreat of last glacier—25,000 to 40,000 B.C.

18.3   The Peking (pee-king) Man

In 1929 and 1943 remains of nearly a dozen human beings were found in a cave north of Peking, China. These fossil remains consisted of skulls and teeth. Peking man had a larger brain and he lived during the period when the ice was receding from the continent and the climate was warmer. He could speak, but had little power of thought. The civilization of the Peking man was more advanced, for among the remains were found quartz implements which were used in scraping skins, and also charred bones which indicated that fire had been discovered. The use of fire, which was one of man's greatest discoveries, was essential to the advancement of culture.

18.4   The Heidelberg (hy-d'l-burg) Man

Before the discovery of Peking man, a lower human jaw was found in some ancient river sand in Germany in 1907. Teeth present in the jaw made scientists think that the prehistoric remains belonged to a much stronger human race. This specimen was called Heidelberg man. No implements were found in this region, but other remains show that the Heidelberg man lived in a country inhabited by bear, deer, and moose. This indicates a forested country and a moist climate, the conditions in the period after the second great glacier.

18.5   The Neanderthal (nee-*an*-der-tahl) Man

In 1856, skeletal remains were found in the Neanderthal Valley in Germany. In 1908, a complete skeleton was excavated at LeMoustier, France. Other skeletons have been found in Asia and Africa.

All these remains had the same characteristics. The Neanderthal man was

American Museum of Natural History

FIGURE 18-1.   *DISCOVERY*

The remains of primitive Peking man were found in this quarry in China.

THE DEVELOPMENT OF MODERN MAN

probably covered with hair and had broad shoulders and a large chest. His arms were of moderate length, and he had large hands with short fingers, powerful legs, and clumsy feet. The features of his face were coarse, with prominent eye ridges and a low, flat, receding forehead. His jaw was massive, and he had almost no chin.

The Neanderthal man lived in caves during the last glacial period. He hunted mammoths and the woolly rhinoceros, which were used for food and clothing. He also used fire, evidence of which has been found in his caves. Stone scrapers and spear-shaped points were buried with the remains, suggesting that the Neanderthal man believed in life after death. Most scientists believe that he disappeared and became extinct.

18.6 The Cro-Magnon (kroh-*man*-yon) Man

In 1868, skeletons of the Cro-Magnon man were discovered in the Dordogne Valley in France. He lived during the last ice age. His lower jaw and chin were well developed, and his long, narrow forehead indicated greater intelligence than any of his predecessors. He was rather tall and more slender than some forms of early man. From implements

FIGURE 18-2. *PREHISTORIC MEN*

Arranged chronologically (*top*) are casts of restored skulls (*left* to *right*) of the Java, Neanderthal, and Cro-Magnon men. The dark portion of the skull at the far left are the fragments from which it was restored; the other two were restored entirely from original material, except for the jaws and teeth. The models (*bottom*) are based on these skulls; they represent what the prehistoric men are believed to have looked like.

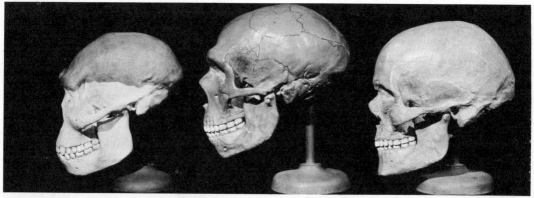

FIGURE 18-3. *CAVE DWELLERS*

Primitive man lived in caves for about one million years. He discovered fire, which he used to light and heat his home. Caves have been found decorated with pictographs, the earliest form of written communication.

which were found with the skeletons, it is evident that a great deal of care was taken in the burial of the dead. Cro-Magnon men also probably believed in an after-life. They have made a great contribution to students of prehistoric life, for they were skilled artists and have left a record of their observations carved upon the walls of caves in France and Spain (Fig. 18-3).

The Cro-Magnons were among the first prehistoric people to band three or four families together for hunting groups and to form settlements or communities. Remains of a large outdoor hunting station have been discovered in France, where there may have been annual roundups of wild horses. Man may have used these horses for food, clothing, and other products. This shows an advance in the social organization of mankind.

Some believe that the Eskimos are descendants of the Cro-Magnon man, others think that the race died out, and still others believe that Cro-Magnon blood is found in some modern Europeans.

18.7 Home of Ancient Man

Man's earliest home was probably the shelter of trees and an overhanging cliff or a cave. Sometimes branches were added to keep out wind and rain, and this gradually led to the weaving of branches and placing them in several layers, making a thatched roof. The famous cliff dwellers represent another class of human beings who have adapted themselves to living in excavations in the face of cliffs. The Eskimo's ice hut represents another one of the crude, simple forms of protection.

The early lake dwellers built their homes over the edge of lakes by using wooden posts to support their houses. They made nets and cloth from the flax plant for use in fishing and they grew wheat, barley, and other grains. They made clay dishes and they polished stones for tools and weapons.

FIGURE 18-4. *NEW STONE AGE*

These stone age people, with their polished spears and crude bows and arrows, are grouped around a newly-killed stag. Notice the baked clay pot.

A great change in climate since man first appeared has been one of the important forces in causing him to adopt different forms of protective shelter.

18.8 Discoveries Made by Ancient Man

The earliest men were dependent on raw plants and animals for food, open shelters for protection, and simple tools. The discovery of *fire* made it possible to (1) cook his food, (2) help to keep warm, (3) bake his clay dishes, and (4) melt metals from the rock to form better dishes and better tools. The discovery of *tools* and the invention of *weapons* made it possible for ancient man to progress from the Old Stone Age, with chipped stone tools, to the New Stone Age, with polished weapons, to the various ages of metals, such as copper, bronze, and iron.

The discovery of *signs* for communication and *speech* for relating ideas made it possible to (1) explain to others how things could be done, (2) give advance warning of danger, and (3) give directions. The development of *writing* made it possible to (1) leave records for the next generation, (2) leave formulas and directions for doing things, and (3) express ideas. This was the beginning of civilization.

18.9 Classification of Man

For a great many years, scientists have regarded man as an animal, but it was not until about 1750 that he was given a permanent name and place in the animal kingdom. As you know, all animals with an internal vertebral skeleton are grouped as *vertebrates*. You have studied the subdivisions of this large group: fishes, amphibians, reptiles, birds, and mammals.

An animal whose body is partly or wholly covered with hair and which supplies milk for its young in glands located on the ventral region of the body belongs in the class of *mammals*. There are several orders of mammals, the last or highest being the *primates,* the one to which man belongs.

Hundreds of different species of recent primates are known, and almost every year new fossil species are discovered.

In primates the thumb can be placed opposite the other fingers. Primates have flat fingernails and toenails, not claws like the dog or cat. A complete bony rim surrounds the eye, and the shoulder bones are well developed. These and other technical features clearly define the primates.

There are various terms in common usage for the higher primates, such as *ape, baboon, gibbon, orangoutang, chimpanzee,* and *gorilla.* In all schemes of classification, man is placed in a separate family distinct from the apes, gorillas, and others. The name of this family is *Hominidae* (hoh-*min*-ih-dee), and we have only one living species in the world. It is called *Homo sapiens* (*hoh*-moh *say*-pee-enz), the Latin words for *thinking,* or *intelligent, man.* The marvelous discoveries of fossil men which you have just studied reveal that some of the earlier men were so different from modern men in bodily proportions that scientists describe them as belonging to other species.

18.10 Man's Power of Adaptation

Man somehow learned to make fire and to use it. This great discovery revealed to him a new world. Our early records indicate that man was using fire before the close of the glacial period. He could now remain in the cold cave when winter came. Thus he began to live under artificial conditions and entered a period of what we call **domestication.** Now began a series of adaptations that have continued until today. The use of fire, implements, and words places man in a separate class from the other animals. His biological activities are similar to those of the higher animals, but we cannot study his biology without considering the influence which his culture has had upon it.

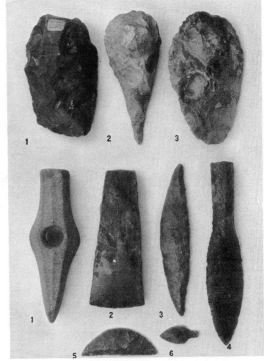

American Museum of Natural History

FIGURE 18-5. *STONE AGE TOOLS*
Weapons and implements were made of stone, wood, bone, and horn in the Stone Age. *Top row:* early tools; *lower row:* polished tools of the New Stone Age.

As men grew more numerous, they had to go farther afield for their necessary food. The same forces that compelled early man to migrate have continued to impel later man to move out into unknown regions where he tries to make a living more easily.

We now realize how man can live in all parts of the earth. When we discussed the places where frogs, fish, and grasshoppers lived, we saw that these animals are kept within certain limits.

This is much less so with man. He is *Homo sapiens;* he possesses what no other animal has—the power to think and to reason, to rise above the limitations of his environment. This he does by building a house of snow in the northlands and spreading a tent in Arabia.

Man's constructive ability has led him to invent various devices for his protection, such as stone, brick, wood, or concrete houses, something that no animals are able to do. One of the reasons that man is able to do many more things than other animals is that he has a better mind, a mind that can adapt itself to many kinds of work, such as that done by carpenters, engineers, teachers, and surgeons. He can also profit by past experience.

Man's brain is the fourth largest in weight in the animal kingdom. It has a greater blood supply and gives man six times more intelligence than any other animal. Man also has *binocular* (by-*nok*-yoo-ler) *vision*, which enables him to see one picture of an object instead of two separate ones with each eye. With this type of vision, man can see in three dimensions (depth perception) and in colors.

Man's erect position and the kind of hands he possesses are other structural adaptations which have aided greatly in man's development.

Scientists give four reasons in explaining why certain animals and plants are not adapted to living in all parts of the world: (1) lack of suitable food, (2) failure to adapt their lives to the peculiarities of climate, (3) too many enemies, (4) inability to raise their young. Most of these man has been able to overcome.

FIGURE 18-7. *DESERT NOMADS*

The Berbers are a nomadic people who move around in search of grazing land for their sheep. They live in tents that are not only easily moved, but also provide protection from the blowing sand and intense heat of the desert.

Burton Holmes from Ewing Galloway

FIGURE 18-8. *LAKE DWELLERS*

Relics of primitive man's crude houses have been found preserved in the lakes of Switzerland and Southern Europe. The houses were built on posts in the water to protect the occupants from the huge land beasts of the time. The wooden platforms provided a haven for domestic animals.

Exhibit in Museum of Science, Boston

18.11 Modern Man

Although modern man is classified as belonging to one species, this has been subdivided into three **stocks,** namely, the *Caucasian* (kaw-kay-zhun), *Negroid* (*nee*-groyd), and *Mongolian* (mon-*goh*-lee-an). The origin of these stocks was probably Central Asia. Groups of people migrated to the Western Hemisphere. The ancestors of the American Indians may have traveled over a land bridge near Bering Strait from Asia to Alaska.

The characteristics used as a basis of classification are skin color, hair form, shape of the head, facial features, and types of stature.

These traits vary within a stock which is further subdivided into *races*. A race has common ancestry and physical characteristics within a stock.

Thus the **Caucasian** or *white* stock is subdivided into the Nordic, Alpine, Mediterranean, and Hindu races. Study Figure 18-9 and the facing chart carefully and try to form a picture of a person of each type.

The **Mongolian** or *yellow* stock includes the Asiatic, Malay, Eskimo, and the American Indian. The **Negroid,** which is the *black* stock, has the Negro, Oceanic, Pigmy races, and the Bushmen

of South Africa. There are some authorities who refer to these races as **Ethiopian** stock.

The Australian aborigines, probably of Caucasian origin, do not fit with certainty into any of the stocks. They are living today much as the men of the Old Stone Age. Studies are now being made of their ways of life to help us better understand ancient peoples.

18.12 Stock Variances

Practically no stock is pure or unmixed at the present time. This fact has been brought about by (1) wars and invasion, (2) migration to new lands, (3) trade with foreign countries, (4) emigration and colonization, and (5) travel.

Because of better means of communication and transport of men and materials to distant lands, stock variances are now taking place at a more rapid rate than ever before.

18.13 Environment Most Favorable to Man

While man can live for a time in all parts of the world from the Arctic to the Equator, he is not equally energetic everywhere. Temperature and humidity

FIGURE 18-9. *THE RACES OF MAN*

CAUCASIAN

Nordic

Alpine

Mediterranean

Hindu

Indian

Asiatic

Malay

MONGOLIAN

Negro

Oceanic

Pigmy

NEGROID

SUBRACE	HAIR	SKIN	EYES	STATURE	HEAD	LIPS
Nordic	Light, fine	White	Blue	Tall, large	Long, narrow	Long, thin
Alpine	Darker, straight	Little darker	Light to dark-brown	Thick-set medium	Short, broad	Thicker, larger
Mediterranean	Wavy, dark-brown	White, olive		Shorter, slender	Shorter than other Caucasians	Thicker; large mouth
Hindu	Dark, thin	Olive with brown		Slim, light frame		Close-set, thin
Indian	Straight, black	Medium-brown, red	Small, dark, deep-set	Very tall to short	High cheeks, long head	Medium to thick
Asiatic	Coarse, straight, black	Yellow	Dark-brown	Shorter than Caucasian	Short, broad, high forehead	
Malay		Medium-brown, yellow		Short, light frame	Small, round	
Negro	Black, kinky	Dark-brown, black	Dark-brown to bluish-black	Tall, light frame	Long, narrow, low forehead	Thick, large, puffy
Oceanic	Black, curly, short	Gray-black, brown		Shorter than Negro	Smaller than Negro	Less thick
Pigmy	Black, spiral clumps	Gray-black, brown		Shortest	Smaller than others	Smaller than others

FIGURE 18-10. *GOOD TRAINING*

The human body is a marvelously complex organism, able to adjust and adapt to its environment. An understanding of its mechanisms will help you make it work for you more intelligently. These champions have superior physical equipment, but they have also had rigorous training.

United Press

affect his activities so that the limits within which he is at his best physically and mentally are rather narrow. The most comfortable temperature for most people is about 66° F.

When men live in regions that are considerably colder or hotter than this, their activities are restricted. The extra vitality of the men who live in the *temperate belt* of the world permits a higher standard of living and yet leaves additional energy for new experiments in all aspects of human activity. The mere fact that **men have had time and energy for such experiments has given to us the solar-heated house, lighted by electricity, in** which we sit and enjoy all sorts of programs on radio and television. See if you can find whether or not we are using any inventions that were discovered by men living in regions of extreme heat or cold.

18.14 The Body of Man

As we turn our attention to the working of the several organs in our own bodies, we shall find that many of the facts which we have learned in the preceding sections of this book are of great help to us. If we are to live free from

pain, the organs in our bodies must work in a natural manner. If we are to work efficiently, we must give our organs proper care. They can be made to do too much work as well as be permitted to do too little.

Every person has some features peculiar to himself, which must be adjusted to the social group in which he lives. As we try to understand this matter of adjustment, we should keep in mind our physical inheritance and the equipment which nature has given us. Through man's invention of language and the records of his experience, we learn of this inheritance and equipment, and through reason and initiative we adjust ourselves to the new conditions which affect our own lives.

Our forefathers settled this country by numerous adjustments, although handicapped by lack of railroads, telephones, radios, and airplanes. Yet these men pushed their settlements from the Atlantic to the Pacific. Your task is to adjust yourself to the social environment in which you live. In doing this, one of the first steps you need to take is to get an intelligent understanding of how your own body behaves.

FACTS TO REMEMBER

Modern man's development began with such *primitive men* as Zinjanthropus, Java, Peking, Heidelberg, Neanderthal, and Cro-Magnon. It is

276

THE STRUCTURE OF MAN

believed that these prehistoric races later became extinct except for possibly some Cro-Magnon blood which may still exist in some groups of man. However, the body structure of modern man is so different from that of primitive man and the other primates in certain features that scientists have classified him in the species *Homo sapiens.*

Such changes in *man's physical structure* as (1) walking erect, (2) full use of arms, (3) large brain case, and (4) binocular vision have led directly to changes in his culture. These physical characteristics, as well as *man's ability to think and to reason,* aided his *cultural development* by enabling him to (1) build shelters suitable to his environment, (2) grow crops, and (3) discover how to make tools and weapons from stone and, later, metals. Because man can adapt to his environmental conditions, he has succeeded in living in certain parts of the world where other living things cannot.

The discovery of *fire* was probably the first important event in man's history. However, *civilization* really began when man learned how to (1) make signs, (2) talk, and (3) write.

Modern man is divided into three *stocks*—Caucasian or white, Mongolian or yellow, and Ethiopian or Negroid. These stocks are further divided into the many *races* of man which inhabit the earth. Those races that live in the *temperate region* have contributed the most to modern man's standard of living.

WORDS TO REMEMBER

anthropologist	*Homo sapiens*	primates
binocular vision	Java man	race
Caucasian	Mongolian	stock
Cro-Magnon man	Neanderthal man	temperate belt
domestication	Negroid	Zinjanthropus
Heidelberg man	Peking man	

QUESTIONS

1. What advances in civilization were made possible by the discoveries of fire, of speech, and of writing?
2. Describe the Java man.
3. What were the climatic conditions during the time of the Heidelberg man?
4. What indications are there that the Peking man knew the use of fire?
5. Describe the Neanderthal man.
6. What contributions to civilization has the Cro-Magnon man left behind him?
7. Name the three stocks of mankind. What races are included in the Caucasian?
8. List five physical traits used in classifying man and beside each write your own characteristic. (For example: hair color—black.)

9. Name as many factors as you can that have brought about racial mixing of types.

10. What is the most suitable environment for man? Why?

11. Give four reasons why certain animals and plants are not adapted to live in all parts of the world.

12. What is the scientific name of man?

COMPLETION TEST

As your teacher or classmate reads the following incomplete statements, with your book closed, write on a clean sheet of paper the word or phrase which correctly completes the statement.

1. A typical Nordic has _____ eyes and _____ hair.
2. The American Indian is now classified as a race of the _____.
3. Flat fingernails and toenails are characteristic of the _____.
4. The family name of man is _____.
5. Man has existed for at least _____ years.
6. The earliest known fossil man is the _____ man.
7. Man is able to do more things than animals because he has a better _____.
8. Man belongs to the order of _____.
9. A period of domestication began when man started to live under _____ conditions.

PROJECTS

I. Are you brachycephalic (brak-ih-seh-*fal*-ik), mesocephalic (mes-oh-seh-*fal*-ik), or dolichocephalic (dol-ih-koh-seh-*fal*-ik)? Are you round-headed, medium-headed, or long-headed? These terms are from the Greek *brach-*, short; *mes-*, medium; *dolich-*, long; and *cephalos*, head.

Work with another student to determine your *cephalic index,* which is the relation of the length to the width of your head. You will need at least one ruler and two flat pieces of cardboard.

1. Place the flat pieces on either side of the subject's head and ask him to hold them there, keeping them parallel to his head and at right angles to your ruler.

2. With the ruler measure (a) the width of the head and (b) the length of the head.

3. Compare the result according to the following:

$$\frac{\text{width} \times 100}{\text{length}} = \text{cephalic index}$$

If this number is 80 or above, you are brachycephalic.
If this number is between 75 and 80, you are mesocephalic.
If this number is less than 75, you are dolichocephalic.

THE STRUCTURE OF MAN

II. *To Determine Your Nasal Index.*—Do this exercise with the help of another student. Measure the width of your nose at eye level. Then measure the length.

Compute your nasal index according to the following:

$$\frac{\text{width} \times 100}{\text{length}} = \text{nasal index}$$

III. Using reference books, describe the culture of such primitive tribes as—
   a. the Tasmanians of Australia.
   b. the Patagonians of Argentina.
   c. the New Caledonians, tribes of Ceylon, and New Guinea.
   d. the Bushmen—Hottentots of South Africa.

IV. Find out all you can about—
   a. Pigmies.
   b. Eskimos.
   c. desert tribes.

V. Make a study of the migrations of people and explain how the American Indians were able to spread along the west coast.

VI. Trace your own ancestry as far back as you can and try to discover why you happen to live in your own particular part of the country.

REFERENCES

Benedict and Weltfish, *The Races of Mankind.* Viking.
Cassils, *The Amazing Story of Your Wonderful Human Body.* World Publishing.
Cleland, *Our Prehistoric Ancestors.* Coward-McCann.
Haskins, *The Tides of Life.* Norton.
Lee, *Stories in Stone.* Van Nostrand.
Life, *The Epic of Man.* Life Magazine.
Lucas, *Animals of the Past.* American Museum of Natural History.
Montague, *Statement of Race.* Schuman.
Nash, *Races of Man.* Thomas Rockwell.
Newburgh, *The Exchange of Energy Between Man and the Environment.* Charles C. Thomas.
Osborne, *Men of the Old Stone Age.* Scribner's.
Van Loon, *The Story of Mankind.* Garden City.
Wells, Huxley, and Wells, *The Science of Life.* Doubleday, Doran.
Wilder, *Man's Prehistoric Past.* Macmillan.

CHAPTER 19

The Covering of Man

19.1 External Features of Modern Man

Modern man stands erect, with head held high enough for good vision and with free-swinging arms. His body is only partially covered with hair, and his skin serves as a protective and excretory organ. The fingernails and toenails are modifications of the skin for added protection. Sense organs responsive to heat, cold, and touch are located in the skin.

FIGURE 19-1. *HUMAN SKIN*

The outer layer of the epidermis sloughs off, as the germinal layer (black area) makes replacements.

Courtesy General Biological Supply House

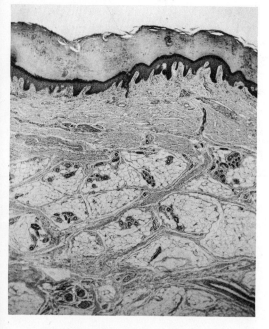

19.2 The Skin of Animals

Every mass of living protoplasm has some form of protective covering. Even the outer layer of an ameba acts in this capacity. A paramecium has a thin cuticle (the pellicle) which covers the entire animal and through which the cilia protrude. The starfish and crayfish have hard skins which form external skeletons. The skins of invertebrates vary greatly; but all vertebrates have a skin that is built on the same general plan. In order to understand how our skin works, we must first know of what it is composed.

19.3 Parts of Our Skin

There are two main parts: the outer layer called the **epidermis** (ep-ih-*der*-mis), or **cuticle** (*kyoo*-tih-k'l), and the deeper layer, the **dermis** (Fig. 19-2).

The *epidermis* is made up of three or more layers of cells. The **surface layer** consists of dead cells which are constantly being shed, as in the case of dandruff in the hair. When these cells are shed, their place is taken by others which are pushed up from below, growing harder and flatter as they approach the surface. These come from the middle or **mucous** (*myoo*-kuss) **layer,** a strong spongy membrane. Below this is found the innermost or **germinal** (*jer*-min-al) **layer,** which is continually un-

280

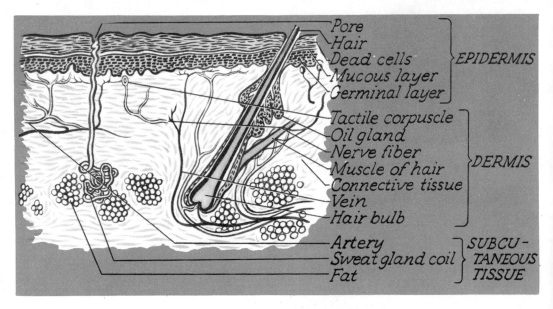

FIGURE 19-2. *CROSS SECTION OF THE SKIN*

This diagram shows the many layers of which the skin is composed. Nerve endings, blood vessels, and sweat glands are distributed throughout the connective tissue. Since the deeper layers of the epidermis contain nerves but no blood vessels, an injury to the epidermis will not draw blood.

dergoing cell division in order to replace dead cells.

The inner surface of the epidermis is in contact with the second layer of the skin, the *dermis*. The dermis consists of interwoven bundles of strong connective tissue containing blood vessels, nerves, oil glands, and sweat glands. These inner lining cells of the epidermis contain coloring matter, or *pigment*. Exposure to sunlight increases the production of pigment resulting in freckles or suntan. Just under the epidermis the outer part of the dermis forms many projections called **papillae** (puh-*pil*-ee), arranged in rows or ridges. It is the arrangement of papillae that makes fingerprinting possible. They are most prominent and numerous in the palms of our hands and the soles of our feet. In the skin of the face the papillae are poorly developed and may disappear in old age. Below these papillae the dermis merges with the subcutaneous tissue.

19.4   Functions of the Skin

The skin has at least four important functions. (1) It forms a protective covering which prevents the entrance of bacteria. The skin also prevents excessive loss of moisture except at the sweat glands. The color of the skin, due to pigment in it, helps protect it against the sun's rays. Hair and nails guard against injury to some parts of the body. (2) The sweat glands and blood vessels regulate body temperature, and (3) the sweat glands excrete minerals and nitrogenous wastes. (4) Many nerve endings in the skin warn man of danger. In short, the skin functions as an organ of *protection, heat regulation, excretion,* and *sensation.*

19.5   Sweat Glands

In Figure 19-2 is shown a long, slender tube opening on the surface of the skin and ending deep in the dermis in a closely coiled mass. Into this coiled part,

Ewing Galloway

FIGURE 19-3. *PROTECTION*

One of the functions of the skin is to prevent the entrance of bacteria. Breaks in the skin should be bandaged.

blood vessels penetrate in close contact with the cells of the sweat gland. These sweat glands are very numerous; there are more than one million of them in the skin of the average man. They are distributed over practically the entire surface of the body and are most numerous in the palm of the hand, sole of the foot, and under the armpits.

The sweat glands take water containing some minerals and nitrogenous wastes from the blood stream and discharge it on the outer surface of the skin as **perspiration**, where it evaporates. This process of evaporation uses up heat, thus cooling the body when it is too warm. More than a quart of water is given off in a day by a man who sweats freely. There are also some wastes in this water, so that we have in this process of sweating one of the methods of excretion.

The heat in our bodies may also be modified by changes in the blood vessels. When the skin capillaries are enlarged, the amount of blood exposed to the cooling action of the surrounding air is increased. The skin appears red and often remains so until we have cooled off. *Blushing* is due to the same cause—the sending of an extra amount of blood to the skin. When we are cold, these same skin capillaries contract and the skin looks pale or even bluish, due to the lack of the usual amount of red blood.

Man can be comfortable in a dry, hot room at a temperature much higher than he can endure in a room where there is much moisture. This is due to the fact that the evaporation of sweat in the dry, heated room is more rapid than in the moist room and so tends to keep him cool.

Some animals have few sweat glands. Dogs excrete water when hot by panting and pigs by wallowing in the mud.

19.6 Hair

Figure 19-2 shows the relation of hair to the other parts of the skin. The outer end of each hair is dead, but the root is alive and is nourished by blood vessels. Unlike all other mammals, man lacks feeling, or *tactile* (*tak*-t'l), hairs; and he differs from the higher apes, such as the chimpanzee or gorilla, in the total absence of hair on the last joints of his fingers and toes. Man likewise has much less hair on his body than do any of the hairy animals. The average number of hairs per square inch in the scalp of adult man is 312, though it may run as high as 400.

All birds and mammals are termed "warm-blooded," because their temperature is fairly constant, winter and summer. Both of these groups of animals have special skin covering, *feathers* or

THE STRUCTURE OF MAN

hairs, that modify their temperature. In very cold weather, the fur or hair of an animal tends to rise, and a bird ruffles up its feathers to increase the thickness of the air jacket. We have to rely on our clothes to do what nature enables some animals to do without such help.

The hair is in part a distinguishing characteristic between the different races of men. Mongolians have straight, coarse black hair, while the Negroes have short, wiry, closely curled hair. There is a marked difference in cross section between straight and kinky hair. You should note that those who have naturally curly hair have a biological basis for it, and on the other hand no amount of artificial treatment will give a permanent natural curl to the hair that is round when seen in section.

The color of the hair, like the color of the skin, is due to the presence of *pigment.* Man and animals derive this pigment through inheritance, and their surroundings do not cause any marked change. Hair pigment tends to be light in children's hair, to grow darker in middle age, and to become gray, or disappear by the time old age is reached. Cutting the hair does not make it grow faster or change its character. The various agents advertised, as well as exposure to the sun, have little or no effect on hair growth.

19.7 Skin Color

There is great variety in skin color. The fair skin of Swedish people contrasts sharply with the ebonylike blackness of the aborigines of parts of Africa and Australia. Between these two extremes are all gradations. The *pigments* that are found in the skin of the various races of man occur also in the animals. You have but to recall the beautiful colors of insects or of many of the vertebrates to

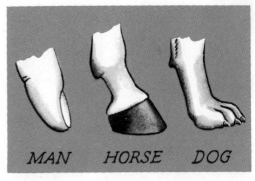

FIGURE 19-4. *NAIL, HOOF, CLAW*

Nails, like hair, are modifications of the outer skin or epidermis. The horns, claws, talons, and hoofs of birds and animals are made of the same material as the nails of the human body. How else are nails, hoofs and claws alike?

realize the wide variety of pigments. The several shades of color in our skin are due to a small proportion of a yellow pigment, abundant in the yellow races of Eastern Asia, and a black pigment, abundant in Negroes.

19.8 Nails

The nails on our fingers and toes are flat, but otherwise similar to the claws of a dog or cat. Nails are modifications of the outer layer of the epidermis. The nails are held in place by the papillae, which are arranged in rows, and by the curvature of the nail. Our fingernails require about 250 days to grow one inch in length while those on our toes need nearly three times as long. Nails should never be bitten off, but should be carefully trimmed, preferably with scissors.

19.9 Some Skin Diseases

During the winter we frequently have *chapped hands,* due to excessive dryness. This is usually caused by the failure of the *oil glands* in the skin to keep the skin protected. If one has to use soap and water a great deal, chapping can be prevented by replacing the natural oil by rubbing the hands with glycerine, cold

Ewing Galloway

FIGURE 19-5. *GOOD CARE*

Skin care begins with a soap and water routine to remove body wastes and stimulate the circulatory and nervous systems.

cream, petroleum jelly, or olive oil. Rinsing them in cold water, after washing with soap and hot water, helps to prevent chapping.

Warts are local excessive growth of the outer layer of the epidermis. Some may be caused by a virus. It is unwise and useless to cut them off as we do our fingernails. When warts occur on the soles of our feet, they are very painful and require the attention of a physician. There are many superstitious cures for warts, but all such superstitions are as foolish as the belief that toads cause warts.

Moles, pimples, and *boils* are some of the additional skin disorders that require intelligent treatment. A mole that is left undisturbed is usually harmless, as the mass of pigment cells will remain inactive; but when irritated by a collar or belt, the mole may take on an active stage of growth that frequently leads to serious consequences.

During adolescence the skin shows excessive oiliness, and sometimes the oil gland openings become clogged with dirt, causing *blackheads.* Pimples occur not only on the face but also in the skin of the shoulders and chest. This is a difficult trouble to cure. It may be due to hormone imbalance. The best remedy is to keep the skin clean and to watch the diet. Eat foods that are low in fat content.

Many boils are due to infections in spaces around the hairs. The bacteria come from outside and not from bad blood. In addition to these changes in the skin, parasitic fungi cause ringworm, and the itch-mite and lice occasionally live on the hair and on the body. Lice feed on the blood of the people they bite, and are the chief carriers of typhus fever. If Napoleon had known this fact, it might not have been necessary for him to retreat from Moscow. During more recent wars extensive plans were devised to keep the soldiers free from lice.

19.10 Fingerprints

If you press your thumb on an ink pad and then place the inked thumb on a paper, you will leave a pattern of ridges that exist in just this shape in no one else. These ridges are due to the form which the *papillae* take. One of the spider monkeys that uses its tail to hang from limbs of trees has similar ridges in the hairless skin covering that part of the tail. Fingerprints constitute a valuable method of identifying human beings, and most states have laws requiring fingerprints to be taken of all criminals. Because this is such a certain means, many other people wish to have their fingerprints taken and kept in a record file for identification in case of serious accident or injury.

THE STRUCTURE OF MAN

FIGURE 19-6. *FINGERPRINT IDENTIFICATION*

An expert, preparing court testimony, compares a *latent* print left carelessly on an object with an *ink* print, made by pressing the finger in ink and rolling it. Both are greatly enlarged. The fingerprint is considered positive identification.

Courtesy Federal Bureau of Investigation

19.11 Skin, an Index of Health

We judge the health of a person by the appearance of the skin. No amount of face decoration can conceal what lies beneath it. The appearance of good health does not come in packages. The skin can best be kept healthy through proper *bathing, diet,* and *exercise.* It is good advice to "paint your face from the inside." Bathing not only removes dirt but also stimulates the circulatory and nervous systems.

FACTS TO REMEMBER

The *skin* is the protective covering of the body and consists of two layers: the *epidermis* and the *dermis.* The functions of the skin are (1) to prevent entrance of bacteria and other disease germs, (2) to protect and cover the delicate tissues of the body, (3) to protect the body by warning of danger through the nerve endings in the skin, (4) to regulate the body temperature through evaporation of moisture from the surface of the skin, and (5) to remove nitrogen and mineral wastes from the body.

The *sweat glands, hair,* and *nails* are structures in the skin to help carry out these functions. As an important organ of the body, the skin and its structures should be kept free of disease. This can best be done by proper *bathing, diet,* and *exercise.*

WORDS TO REMEMBER

blackhead	fingerprint	pimple
blushing	germinal layer	surface layer
boil	mole	sweat gland
chapped hands	mucous layer	tactile
cuticle	oil gland	toenail
dermis	papillae	warm-blooded
epidermis	perspiration	wart
fingernail	pigment	

QUESTIONS

1. Describe the parts of the skin of vertebrates.
2. What structures are found in the skin of birds that are lacking in that of man?
3. What are sweat glands? State two of their important uses.
4. How do the nails of primates differ from those of other animals?
5. Compare the hair of man with that of other mammals.
6. How does the skin protect our bodies?
7. What causes the different shades in color of the skin?
8. Explain why cleanliness is so important in the health of the skin.
9. Mention some skin disorders and their probable causes.
10. To what is the color of hair due?

COMPLETION TEST

As your teacher or classmate reads the following incomplete statements, with your book closed, write on a clean sheet of paper the word or phrase which correctly completes the statement.

1. The outer surface of the _____ consists of dead cells.
2. Blood vessels, nerves, and fat are distributed through the _____ of the skin.
3. Blushing is due to _____.
4. The outer end of each hair is _____.
5. Mongolians and Negroes have _____ hair.
6. Short, wiry, coiled hair is characteristic of the _____.
7. Infections in spaces around the hairs often cause _____.
8. Fingerprints are a valuable method of _____.
9. The hoof and claw are modified _____.
10. Oil glands are located in the _____.

PROJECTS

I. *Microscopic Study of the Skin.*—Examine a prepared slide of the skin. Identify as many parts as you can. Draw and label what you see.

II. *Modification of the Skin.*—1. Compare the types of hair found among mammals. Notice that some animals have two kinds of hair. Porcupines have the hairs modified into quills. Armadillos have horny plates for coverings.

2. Make a comparison of the fingernails of man and the claws of a cat, the hoofs of horses, cows, and deer.

III. *Special Study of a Hair.*—With a microscope, study hairs of several different people. Note the difference in size and shape. Make a report of your observations.

IV. *Experiment to Determine the Rate of Growth of Fingernails and Toenails.*—Place a very small drop of nitric acid at the base of one fingernail and one toenail. Record the date. At the end of two weeks measure the distance from the spot to the edge of the nail. Continue at intervals until the yellow stain is cut off.

Make a careful report of your conclusions as to which grow faster, your fingernails or toenails, and how fast each grows.

REFERENCES

Best and Taylor, *The Human Body and Its Functions*. Holt.

Cassils, *The Amazing Story of Your Wonderful Human Body*. World Publishing.

Clendening, *Common Sense Health Chats*. Blue Ribbon Books.

Clendening, *The Human Body*. Knopf.

Jenkins, Bauer, Schacter, *Teen Agers*. Scott, Foresman.

Meredith, *The Health of Youth*. Blakiston's.

Phillips, *Skin Deep*. Vanguard.

Tokay, *Fundamentals of Physiology*. Garden City.

Wellman, *Beauty Begins at Home*. Covici Friede.

CHAPTER 20

The Framework of Man

20.1 Bones for Support

Man, like the rest of the vertebrates, has an *endoskeleton* for support. The size and strength of the *bones* determine his height and general structure. In addition to support, the bones serve for the attachment of muscles and form protective structures which enclose such delicate organs as the heart, lungs, and brain.

20.2 Body Regions

The body of man, like that of all the mammals, is divided into head, trunk, and limbs (Fig. 20-1). These are the *regions* of the body. The trunk is divided into the *chest,* or *thorax,* and the *abdomen.*

In the human body there are three important cavities; namely, the **cranial** (*kray*-nee-al), which is the brain case, the **thoracic** (thor-*ass*-ik), and the **abdominal** (ab-*dom*-uh-n'l). In the *cranial cavity* is found the brain, the base of which passes through a large opening to continue as the spinal cord of the central nervous system. The *thoracic cavity* contains a pair of lungs and the heart. The thoracic cavity is separated from the abdominal cavity by a muscular sheet called the diaphragm (Fig. 20-3). In the *abdominal cavity* are the stomach, intestines, liver, pancreas, spleen, kidneys, and reproductive organs.

20.3 Skeleton

The skeleton of man has more than two hundred separate bones. Those of the **skull** are (1) the *cranium* (*kray*-nee-um) proper, which is the bony case that surrounds the brain, and (2) the bones that form the skeleton of the face. In the adult skull the bones have grown together or become fused and their outline is often recognized with difficulty. In early youth the joints between these bones are movable to allow for growth. The arched structure of the skull gives it great strength and thus makes the brain the best-protected organ in our body. The deep sockets in the front protect the eye, and the delicate parts of the ear are so inclosed as to be completely out of danger.

The bones of the face are mostly paired. The prominent cheek bones are just below the eye sockets and are separated by the bones of the nose. The eyes, and the delicate parts of the inner ears are enclosed within the bones of the skull.

The **spinal column** consists of thirty-three segments, or **vertebrae** (*ver*-tuh-bree). The different vertebrae permit a limited amount of movement, which enables us to turn and bend the trunk in various directions. At the same time these vertebrae, piled one on top of another, form a strong support for the

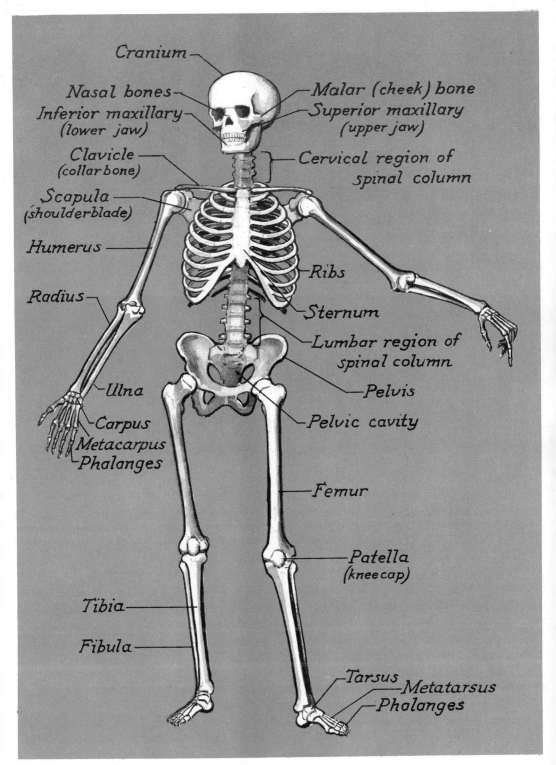

Cranium

Nasal bones

Inferior maxillary
(lower jaw)

Malar (cheek) bone

Superior maxillary
(upper jaw)

Clavicle
(collarbone)

Cervical region of
spinal column

Scapula
(shoulderblade)

Humerus

Radius

Ribs

Sternum

Lumbar region of
spinal column

Ulna

Carpus

Metacarpus

Phalanges

Pelvis

Pelvic cavity

Femur

Patella
(kneecap)

Tibia

Fibula

Tarsus

Metatarsus

Phalanges

FIGURE 20-1. *THE HUMAN SKELETON*

Man's bony framework is made up of over 200 separate bones. An internal, or *endoskeleton*, it protects the vital organs and supports the body.

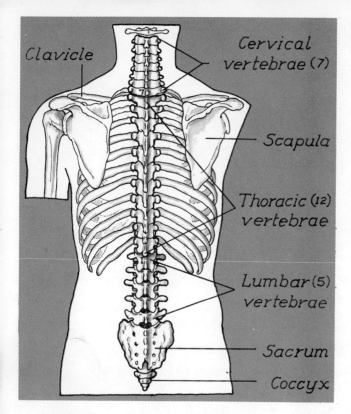

Clavicle

Cervical vertebrae (7)

Scapula

Thoracic (12) vertebrae

Lumbar (5) vertebrae

Sacrum

Coccyx

FIGURE 20-2. *SPINAL COLUMN AND CHEST*

The spinal column, which surrounds and protects the spinal cord, is composed of five kinds of vertebrae. What are they? Each vertebra is separated from the next by a pad of cartilage which provides flexibility and acts as a shock absorber. Notice the scapula (shoulder blade) and clavicle (collar bone).

weight of the body and head. The vertebrae also surround and protect the spinal cord.

The seven neck vertebrae [*cervical* (*serv*-ih-k'l)] make it possible to turn the head and change its position to aid in balancing the body. Below these are the twelve chest vertebrae (*thoracic*), which serve for the attachment of the ribs. The five vertebrae in the lower back (*lumbar*) make it possible to bend at the waist and twist the body in many directions. The *sacrum* (*say*-krum) in the pelvic region consists of five fused vertebrae which are immovable. At the tip end of the spine, also in the pelvic region, are four more vertebrae fused to form the *coccyx* (*kok*-siks), which in lower animals grows much longer to form a tail. In humans this remains rudimentary in form.

There are twelve pairs of **ribs**—all attached to the vertebrae of the spinal column. Of the upper seven pairs, the other ends are attached directly to the breastbone, or *sternum* (Fig. 20-2), by flexible cartilage. This permits the freedom of movement necessary in breathing. Of the other five, the upper three are indirectly attached to the sternum. The two lower, having no cartilages, are called *floating* ribs and are attached only to the spinal column.

The breastbone, or sternum, in man consists of a single piece which serves for the attachment of the ribs and protects the heart. In childhood this bone consists of several distinct parts, which allows for growth.

The arm and the leg of man are built upon the same plan. In the arm there is the long bone, the *humerus* (*hyoo*-merus), which extends from the shoulder to the elbow; the two bones in the forearm, the *radius* (*ray*-dee-us) and *ulna* (*ul*-nuh); the row of small bones in the

THE STRUCTURE OF MAN

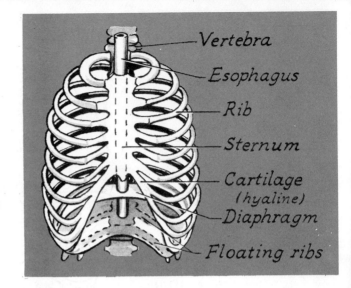

FIGURE 20-3. *DIAPHRAGM AND RIBS*

Part of the axial skeleton, the ribs encircle the chest cavity, protecting the heart and lungs. All but the floating ribs are attached to the sternum in front and to the vertebrae in back. The diaphragm, a muscular sheet separating the abdominal and thoracic cavities, helps in lung expansion and contraction.

wrist, the *carpus* (*kahr*-pus), which move freely upon each other; the bones of the hand, the *metacarpals* (meh-tuh-*kahr*-p'ls); and the bones of the fingers, the *phalanges* (fuh-*lan*-jeez). Corresponding to these are the long upper bone of the leg, the *femur* (*fee*-mer), that extends from hip to knee; the two bones, the *tibia* (*tib*-ee-uh) and *fibula* (*fib*-yoo-luh), that go from the knee to the ankle; the several bones in the ankle, the *tarsus* (*tahr*-sus); the bones of the feet, the *metatarsals* (meh-tuh-*tahr*-s'ls); and the bones of the toes (the *phalanges*). The knee-cap, the *patella* (puh-*tel*-luh), is an extra bone (Fig. 20-1) to protect the knee.

Two bones join each arm at the shoulder. One of these is the collar bone, the *clavicle* (*klav*-ih-k'l), which connects the upper end of the sternum with the shoulder. The second bone is the shoulder blade, the *scapula* (*skap*-yoo-luh), which is a large flat bone at the back of the shoulder, serving as a most important surface for the attachment of the powerful muscles that help move the arm.

The hip girdle (*pelvis*) joins a number of the vertebrae, furnishing a firm base of support for the body and at the same time permitting a large range of movement in the legs.

20.4 Bone and Cartilage

The skeleton appears first in the form of **cartilage** (*kahr*-tih-lij) or of membrane, both of which are gradually replaced by true bone. This transition from soft material to hard bone begins before birth and is not completed in certain bones before the twenty-fifth year. This hardness is due to the deposits of such minerals as calcium phosphate and calcium carbonate. The process is called *ossification*.

Bones are covered with a membrane, the *periosteum*. This provides a place for attachment of muscles and a blood supply for nourishment of the cells in the bony layer beneath. The blood vessels connect with the *Haversian canals,* the channels penetrating the bony layer.

There are cells in the bones (Fig. 20-4) just as there are cells in the liver, the muscles, and the nervous system. Like the other parts of the body, the bones grow because the bone cells are supplied with food from the blood.

Many bones have hollow interiors.

THE FRAMEWORK OF MAN

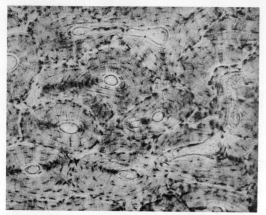
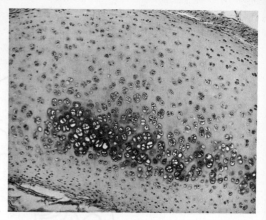

FIGURE 20-4. *BONE AND CARTILAGE*

Bone tissue is made of living cells (*left,* black dots) embedded in a calcified substance. They are arranged around canals which contain blood vessels. Cartilage cells (*right*) are embedded in a softer, protein substance.

Red marrow fills space found in the ribs, vertebrae, sternum, and long bones. It forms red corpuscles and some white ones. Yellow marrow found in the long bones is composed mostly of fat cells.

Cartilage occurs near the ends of the bones, in the ear, and in the nose. It is prominent in the wrists and ankles of children. Young children should not be lifted by their hands or allowed to stand for any length of time, until a certain amount of bone has taken the place of this soft cartilage.

The cartilage found in the ear, nose, and between the vertebrae is called *hyaline* (*hy*-uh-lin) cartilage. It never changes to bone, but remains quite soft and flexible throughout life.

FIGURE 20-5. *FRACTURES*

X-ray reveals broken bones. In simple fracture the bone does not break through the skin as it does in compound fracture.

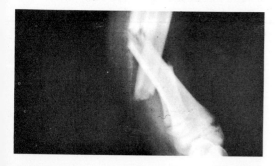

20.5 Mending Broken Bones

Man has never been free from accidents; he frequently falls or slips and breaks a bone. Those present at the scene of an accident should try to keep the broken bone from being moved in order to prevent further injury to the muscles, nerves, and blood vessels. Usually splints are applied and the victim moved very carefully to a hospital.

The first measure taken to learn the extent of the injury is to have the bones photographed by X-rays. This gives an accurate picture of the injury (Fig. 20-5), which helps the surgeon to proceed intelligently. When the bones of a limb are broken, they are set; that is, the broken ends are brought together, and the limb is placed in splints or a cast to keep the broken ends from slipping. The splint must be left on until new cartilage forms and has time to change to bone.

20.6 Joints

The place where two bones meet is termed a **joint**. The joints are divided into three classes: *immovable joints, movable joints,* and *mixed joints.* **Immovable joints** are formed along sutures

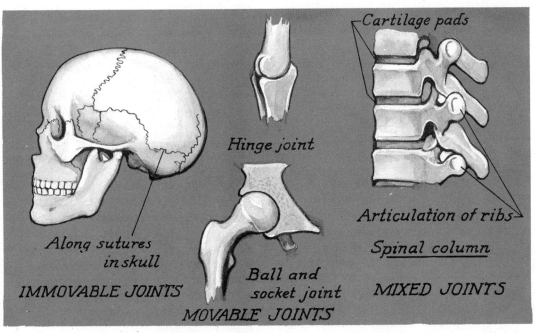

FIGURE 20-6. *TYPES OF JOINTS*

The skull's many bones are connected by immovable sutures to protect the brain. At the hip, where motion is required, a movable ball and socket joint exists. A mixed joint provides both flexibility and protection.

(*soo*-chers) in the skull of the adult. The bones of the skull do not become firmly united until the head has reached full size, after which no movement takes place between these bones.

Movable joints are the *ball-and-socket joints* (shoulder and hip) and the *hinge joints* (elbow, knee, and ankle).

Mixed joints allow only a limited movement such as sliding joints in the vertebrae and the pivot joint for the rotation of the head on the spine.

The bones of movable joints are bound closely together by strong bands of connective tissue. These bands are called **ligaments** (lig-uh-ments). The tearing of these ligaments is called a *sprain*. The stretching of ligaments is a *strain*. Joints are lubricated by a secretion called the *synovial fluid*.

20.7 Muscles for Movement

Movement is involved in the locomo-tion of animals. The movements of breathing and the beating of the heart sustain our lives, and the movements of our lips and tongue reveal to us the stranger or friend. But neither stranger nor friend would recognize us were it not for the fact that our bodies keep a constant shape, due mainly to the number and arrangement of the bones and their covering of muscles and skin. Muscles exist in every part where movement is needed in the body processes. Muscles are found not only in the arms, legs, and back, but also in the walls of the heart, the arteries, and the digestive canal.

Muscles are of three kinds: **voluntary** (governed by the will), such as those which we use in walking or in moving the arms; **involuntary** (over which we have no control), such as those that move the food along the digestive tract; and **cardiac** (kahr-dee-ak), or heart muscles.

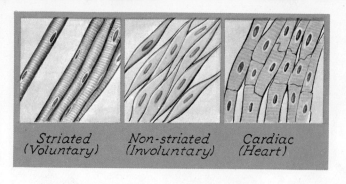

Striated *(Voluntary)* Non-striated *(Involuntary)* Cardiac *(Heart)*

FIGURE 20-7. *KINDS OF MUSCLES*

Muscles are present in the body wherever movement is necessary. The voluntary muscles such as those in the legs are striated. Involuntary muscles are made of smooth spindle-shaped cells and operate internal organs and blood vessels. Cardiac muscles are both striated and branched and are found only in the heart.

The *voluntary muscles* consist of many long muscle cells (fibers) bound together by connective tissue into a distinct bundle. Usually the muscle bundle is attached at each end to the bones by a **tendon** of connective tissue. A single muscle moves the arm in one direction only; so in order to lift the arm from the desk to the back of the head, for instance, several muscles must act at the same time.

FIGURE 20-8. *STRIATED MUSCLE*

It takes many muscle cells to make one fiber and many fibers to make one muscle.

General Biological Supply House

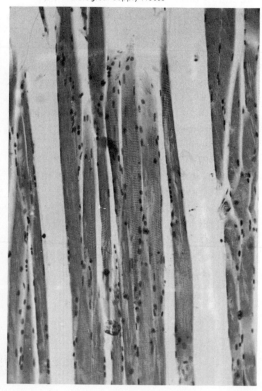

The cells of *voluntary muscles* are **striated** (*stry*-ayt-ed); that is, small cross streaks can be seen under the microscope. The cells of *involuntary muscles* do not have these cross-striations; hence, they are called **smooth** muscles. These muscle cells are found in layers in the walls of the digestive tract, the blood vessels, and the like, and they are not under the control of the will. The cells of the *cardiac muscles* of the heart are branched and, like voluntary muscles, striated.

20.8 Nerve and Blood Supply of Muscles

The muscles are richly supplied with many blood vessels, large and small, and it is the blood that gives the deep red color to muscles. Each muscle fiber is supplied with a fine branch of the main nerve that enters the muscle. This shows us how the nervous system controls our muscles.

20.9 Food of Muscles

The blood flowing through the muscles carries food to the muscle cells. **Glycogen** (*gly*-kuh-j'n), or *animal starch,* is stored in the liver and to a limited extent in muscle tissue. This is changed to **glucose** (*gloo*-kohss) and is carried to muscle tissue where it is oxidized to furnish energy for muscular contraction. A small amount of *fat* is present in muscles and may be used up during their contraction. Usually the

294

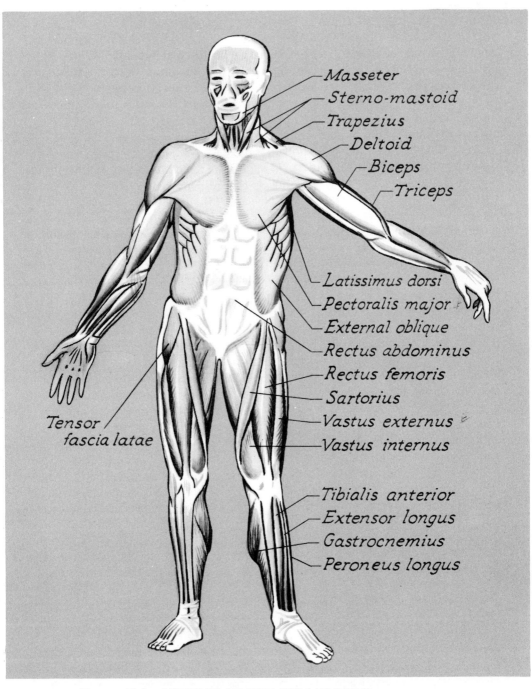

Masseter
Sterno-mastoid
Trapezius
Deltoid
Biceps
Triceps

Latissimus dorsi
Pectoralis major
External oblique
Rectus abdominus
Rectus femoris
Sartorius
Vastus externus
Vastus internus

Tibialis anterior
Extensor longus
Gastrocnemius
Peroneus longus

Tensor
fascia latae

FIGURE 20-9. *MUSCLES OF THE HUMAN BODY*

There are many muscles in the body, each with a specific function. One group of muscles is for flexing the arm and another group for extending it again. Muscles almost always occur in opposed groups, one for prime movement, the other for recovery. As the diagram shows, many muscles are necessary to move the arms and legs; they tend to become enlarged and strengthened by use and to atrophy with disuse.

protein foods do not furnish energy for contraction, but are used to repair the actual wastes that take place in the muscle cells as they work.

20.10 Action of the Voluntary Muscles

When you place your left hand around the upper right arm and raise the right forearm toward the shoulder, you feel the muscle under the hand become shorter, thicker, and firmer. This is the *biceps* muscle, which is made up of possibly 260,000 voluntary muscle cells held in place by connective tissue. These cells must receive a message from the brain if they are to contract. Each cell in a muscle contracts as hard as it can when the order from the brain is given. Thus when you move your forearm slowly or rapidly, the difference seems to depend on the number of muscle cells that you order to contract. You may order 100 or 1000 of the cells in the biceps to contract, and it is possible for you to combine them with as few cells or with as many cells in other muscles as you like. You rarely use all of the cells in any one muscle at the same time.

When you stand on your feet and throw a baseball, you use parts of almost every muscle in your body. If you wish to throw the ball faster, you call on a few hundred thousand more muscle cells than you use when you throw a slow ball.

Muscles which bend joints are **flexors** (*fleks*-ers), as the *biceps* in the upper arm. Muscles that straighten joints are **extensors** (ek-*sten*-sers), as the *triceps* muscle at the back of the upper arm (Fig. 20-9). You may also feel the large *deltoid* muscle on the top of your shoulder. If you have climbed a mountain or many flights of stairs, you may have felt the large *gastrocnemius* (gass-trok-*nee*-mee-us) muscle in the back of your lower leg (Fig. 20-9). Locate the *sartorius* (sahr-*tor*-ee-us) muscle (Fig. 20-9). This word means "tailor" muscle, because it makes it possible for you to sit cross-legged as tailors sometimes do when they sew.

20.11 Fatigue of Muscles

When you are feeling well, your muscles respond quickly to your desire to walk or run. If you are accustomed to regular exercise, your muscles respond even more quickly, but after playing or working hard, you become tired. Then you need to rest, for the muscles are fatigued. When you are taking your physical exercises, some of the movements may make your arms ache, so that you do not do them in good form. That is because you are using muscles that do not get much exercise, and so they quickly become **fatigued**. You may continue to move your arm until you find it impossible to move it any longer.

What really happens? Each time that you move your arm, *heat* and *lactic acid* are produced and work is done. If you move your arm long and hard enough, even without lifting or pushing anything, you soon begin to perspire from the heat produced. Energy is required for muscular contraction. During this muscular contraction some of the *glucose* brought to the muscle by the blood stream is changed to lactic acid. One of the causes of the fatigued muscles in your arm is the presence of too much lactic acid.

You recover from this fatigue by changing some of the lactic acid back into glucose. *Oxygen* is necessary for this process; so you need to breathe deeply and rapidly until the extra demand of oxygen has been supplied. Some of the lactic acid, however, is changed to *carbon dioxide* and *water,* and these are carried away by the blood. As these

296

FIGURE 20-10. *AN ENERGETIC PASTIME*

For exercise as strenuous as this, a great deal of energy is required. The muscles expand and contract rapidly and oxidation takes place in the cells of the body. Lactic acid accumulates and causes fatigue.

wastes are removed and the extra oxygen changes more lactic acid back to glucose, your muscle ceases to be tired.

When muscles become stiff and sore, rubbing helps to increase circulation and heat relaxes the blood vessels to hasten the removal of wastes.

20.12 Importance of Exercise

During exercise the heart sends six to nine times as much blood through the muscles as during rest periods. The walls of the large blood vessels in the abdomen contract and those of the skin and working muscles relax, so that more blood enters them. This tends to increase the size and strength of the muscles and improve muscular control. Exercise should be taken regularly and in proper amount to be of real value.

20.13 Posture

If you bought a pre-fabricated house and wished to erect it, you would make sure that the framework, whether made of wood or steel, was securely fastened to hold it upright. This would not only protect the building itself but everything that you wished to put inside. So it is with your body. If you do not insist that your muscles hold the bones straight, your internal organs will be cramped and thus unable to do their best work. Poor posture is as unpleasant to behold as the sagging lines of a tumble-down building. For these reasons at least, you should consider your own posture.

Sitting.—Today more and more people have to work in a sitting position. The correct sitting position is with the trunk of the body straight, resting squarely on the hips, and not sliding down into the seat. The trunk should be kept at right angles to the long bones of the leg. It is easier to sit correctly in a shallow than in a deep seat. One can also sit correctly so far as the trunk is concerned and still become fatigued by bending the head too far forward at the neck.

FIGURE 20-11. *GOOD POSTURE*

When given a chance, the muscles will hold the bones of the body upright so that the internal organs will not be cramped. Some common posture defects are slouching, curvature of the spine, and round shoulders. Many health problems are the result of incorrect posture.

Standing.—The correct positions of the body in standing and walking are similar. The head should be held straight, the chin drawn in, the chest raised, the abdomen flat, and the weight of the body resting on the balls of the feet. In such a position the head is balanced with the least strain upon each of the muscles. All the defects which are caused by incorrect position of the body require very definite exercises to correct them.

Walking.—Walking is a pleasure when the whole body is in correct position and the weight thrown forward on the ball of the foot. The feet should point forward instead of at an angle. It is easy to practice correct walking by simply holding the body in proper standing posture, and then walking forward along a line, each step of the foot directed forward with the front foot close against the toes of the rear one.

20.14   Mental Attitude

Our mental attitude has much to do with our posture. How much straighter we stand when we are cheerful than when we are unhappy! And our posture also reacts on our mental attitude. When we are gloomy and downcast, we can often make ourselves more cheerful by standing erect, breathing deeply, and throwing out our chests. Taking a brisk walk in the fresh air will do much to change our attitude.

298

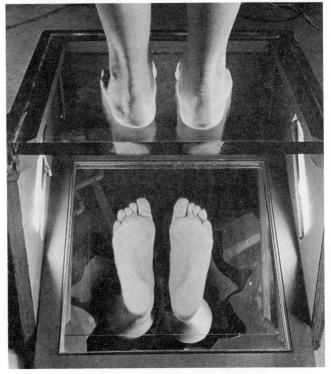

Figure 20-12. *FOOT MIRROR*

The arches of the foot, which can be seen in the foot mirror, are formed by the tarsal and metatarsal bones. They aid in the natural elastic spring of the foot. Improper shoes cause many ills which might be avoided.

Monkmeyer

20.15 Hygiene of the Foot

The human foot is an ingenious arrangement of bones, muscles, and tendons, which support the weight of the entire body. There are two arches in the foot, one in the forward part, the *anterior metatarsal,* and the other running lengthwise, called the *longitudinal arch.* Both of these arches act as shock absorbers, and they must be in perfect condition for the feet to work properly.

If, as often happens, one arch is depressed or broken down, we get what is called **flat foot**. This condition generally causes a feeling of unusual fatigue and weariness at night.

Flat foot may be prevented by using a little care. The proper method is to walk with the feet parallel, not with the toes pointed out. Walking with the toes pointed straight ahead strengthens the muscles.

FACTS TO REMEMBER

Man's bony *skeleton* is designed to (1) support the body and give it form, (2) serve as an attachment for muscles, and (3) protect the delicate internal structures. In development, bone first appears as *cartilage* which later hardens to become bone.

Whenever two bones meet, they form a *joint*. There are three kinds of joints: *movable, immovable,* and *mixed. Ligaments* hold the bones in place at the joints.

Muscles make it possible to move. The three types of muscles found in the human body are *voluntary* or *striated, involuntary* or *smooth,* and *cardiac* or *heart. Tendons* connect muscles to the bones.

In order to produce motion, muscles require *energy. Glucose* is

THE FRAMEWORK OF MAN

brought to the muscles by the blood stream and is oxidized to produce the energy for motion. *Proteins* are also supplied by the blood stream for the repair and growth of the tissue.

As the muscles contract and relax, they become *fatigued* due to the accumulation of *lactic acid* and certain waste products. Rest is necessary in order to change the lactic acid back to glucose and to eliminate the wastes.

Exercise, good posture, and a *healthy mental attitude* are all necessary for the proper development of muscles and for a pleasing appearance.

WORDS TO REMEMBER

abdominal cavity	glucose	ribs
anterior metatarsal arch	glycogen	sacrum
ball-and-socket joint	hinge joint	sartorius
biceps	humerus	scapula
cardiac muscle	hyaline cartilage	skeleton
carpus	immovable joint	skull
cartilage	involuntary muscle	smooth muscle
cervical vertebrae	joint	spinal column
clavicle	lactic acid	sprain
coccyx	ligament	sternum
cranial cavity	longitudinal arch	strain
cranium	lumbar vertebrae	striated muscle
deltoid	marrow	suture
endoskeleton	metacarpals	tarsus
extensor	metatarsals	tendon
fatigue	mixed joint	thoracic cavity
femur	movable joint	tibia
fibula	patella	triceps
flat foot	pelvis	ulna
flexor	phalanges	vertebrae
floating ribs	radius	voluntary muscle
gastrocnemius	red marrow	yellow marrow

QUESTIONS

1. What is the function of the skeleton?
2. Name the three body regions.
3. List the organs found in each of the three body regions.
4. What are the functions of the different groups of vertebrae in the spinal column?
5. Why is the breastbone attached to the ribs by flexible cartilage?
6. What is meant by voluntary muscle? Involuntary muscle? Cardiac muscle? How can you tell the difference when you look at them under the microscope?

300

7. Name three kinds of joints and give an example of each.

8. Explain what is meant by muscle fatigue. How can this condition be relieved?

9. Describe the correct posture for sitting and standing.

10. How do bones grow? Why do they grow?

11. How should a person walk in order to prevent foot troubles from arising?

12. What is the relation of the nervous system to muscles?

13. What is the importance of blood vessels to the muscles?

14. What is the value of physical training?

COMPLETION TEST

As your teacher or classmate reads the following incomplete statements, with your book closed, write on a clean sheet of paper the word or phrase which correctly completes the statement.

1. The place where two bones meet is called a _____.

2. Strong bands which hold bones together are called _____.

3. Starch stored in the liver is called _____.

4. _____ acid forms in the fatigued muscles.

5. There are _____ pairs of ribs in the human body.

6. _____ cartilage never changes to bone.

7. Soreness can be taken out of a muscle by rubbing and by applying _____.

8. Glycogen must be changed into _____ before it can enter the blood stream.

9. The collar bone connects the sternum with the _____ _____.

10. The eyes and ears are both protected from injury by deep _____ in the skull.

PROJECTS

I. *Study of a Skeleton.*—If your school has a human skeleton or a good chart, examine it carefully. Note the following:

1. The membrane bone of the skull with wavy lines showing where it grew together.

2. The cartilage connecting the ribs.

3. Find the two pairs of "floating" ribs, which are attached only to the backbone.

4. Count the vertebrae beginning at the skull and locate the following: 7 cervical, 12 thoracic, 5 lumbar, 5 sacral, and 4 coccyx or tail (bones fused together).

5. Note three kinds of joints. Locate at least one of each.

6. Observe the fingers and toes. Man has an opposable thumb (opposite to fingers) for grasping.

7. Notice how well the pelvic bones are fused to make a firm support for the body organs.

8. Make a careful report of everything you have observed about the human skeleton.

II. *Study of a Long Bone.*—If possible, obtain from the meat market or slaughterhouse a long bone of some animal. Observe the following points on the bone.

1. Attachment of the muscles.
2. Ligaments.
3. Pieces of tendons (tissues which join muscles to bones).
4. Joints.
5. Cut the bone crosswise and look at the severed end.
6. Cut one piece lengthwise and find the bone marrow where the red blood corpuscles are made.
7. Make a careful report of what you find on your bone.
8. Draw a cross section of the bone.
9. Sketch the longitudinal section, showing the marrow.

III. *To Show the Composition of Bone.*—Obtain some *small* bones of a chicken or other small animal.

1. Place *one* in dilute hydrochloric acid for a day or two or until it becomes soft enough to bend. Then wash it and show to the class. In your report explain that the acid dissolved the minerals, leaving the animal matter of the bone.

2. Place *another* bone on a rack or wire gauze over a Bunsen burner. Burn the bone for an hour or more, depending on its size. When it is covered with a grayish-white ash, extinguish the flame and let the bone cool. Write your report and explain that you have burned all the animal matter, leaving only the minerals in the bone.

IV. *Homologous Structures.*—Visit a museum or obtain pictures of the skeletons of a man, horse, and dog. Compare the position of the arms and legs. What are the advantages and disadvantages? Structures arranged in the same place in the body and used for different purposes are *homologous* structures. For example, the wing of a bat and the arm of a man are both attached to the shoulder girdle, but these structures are used for different purposes.

V. *Comparison of a Monkey with Man.*—By means of pictures or skeletons compare the structures one at a time. Note the similarities and differences. List as many as you can. Do you think they should both be placed in the order Primates?

REFERENCES

Carlson and Johnson, *The Machinery of the Body.* University of Chicago Press.

Cassils, *The Amazing Story of Your Wonderful Human Body*. World Publishing.

Clendening, *The Human Body*. Knopf.

Elwyn, *Yourself, the Story of the Human Body*. Grosset and Dunlap.

Harvey, *Simple Lessons in Human Anatomy*. American Medical Association.

Kimber and Others, *Textbook of Anatomy and Physiology*. Macmillan.

Newell, *The Human Body*. Holt.

UNIT VII

Nutrition in Man

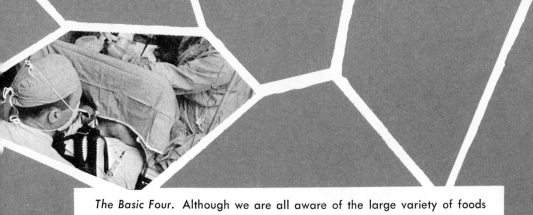

The Basic Four. Although we are all aware of the large variety of foods available to suit any individual taste, how many people realize just what foods constitute a well-balanced diet to maintain healthy and vigorous bodies? After many years of study to determine the nutritional needs of the body and which foods best fill these needs, food experts have found that the foods we require to keep us healthy can be placed in four groups, which they call the "basic four." If a person eats the proper amount of foods taken from each of these four groups every day, he is receiving a balanced diet. In Unit VII you will have an opportunity to learn more about the basic four. How many of these foods do you eat for breakfast? Do you have a balanced lunch at school? If you were to select some foods from each group for your dinner, which would you choose?

Digestion and You. Your stomach takes whatever you send down to it. How kind are you to your stomach? You may carefully choose the basic four but the way you eat your food is also important. Do you eat your meals as fast as you can and run out to play; or do you rest and enjoy your meal, giving your stomach a chance to take care of the food? Do you eat regularly and chew your food well? Your stomach wants working hours and rest periods. In Unit VII you will learn how your digestive system changes the foods so that they will dissolve and go into the blood. You will then be able to trace the pathway of the food through the blood stream until it reaches the cells of the body.

Energy for Living. Every living cell in your body produces a certain amount of heat. The oxygen taken in through the lungs is carried to the cells by the blood. Just as in a furnace or a stove, when the temperature is high enough, the oxygen in the air burns the coal or the oil; so in the cells, the oxygen burns the food and provides the body with heat energy. Do you know how high your body temperature is? How much oxygen do you need? How much food do you need? What are the body wastes? In Unit VII you will learn how the body regulates its heating system and what you can do to take care of it.

CHAPTER 21

Food and Nutrition

21.1 Nutrition

The human body has skin to cover it, a skeleton to support it, and muscles to move it. These all depend on various organs and systems within the body cavity which supply them with food and remove the wastes. The body has structures for receiving food, digesting it, carrying it around to the cells, burning the food for energy, and taking away parts that cannot be used. *The process by which the body uses food to repair tissue and carry on its activities is called* **nutrition** (noo-*trish*-un). In this chapter we shall study the kinds of food the body needs and how to protect our food supply.

21.2 Nutrients and Foods

A **nutrient** (*noo*-tree-ent) is a substance which furnishes heat and energy to the body or builds tissues. A **food** is a substance which in addition to this contains some roughage and adds bulk to the diet. All living things must have food to keep them alive.

The foods people eat differ greatly in different parts of the world. People who eat large amounts of protein grow taller, heavier, and stronger than those living

FIGURE 21-1. *FAMILY DINNER*

Normal growth and energy depend on a continuous supply of food materials. A well-balanced diet contains many body-building foods.

Underwood & Underwood

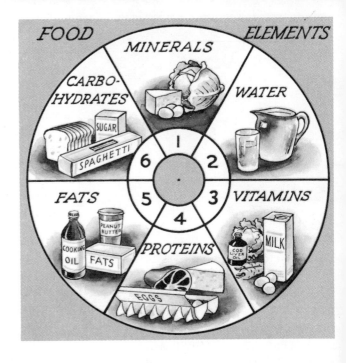

FIGURE 21-2. *FOOD
ELEMENTS*

Carbohydrates, proteins, and fats are actual foods because they generate energy and heat as well as building tissue. The accessory foods (minerals, vitamins, and water) help to promote growth and serve as body regulators. It is important to eat a variety of foods containing these elements to nourish the body adequately.

mostly on fruits and vegetables. Nevertheless, people will live and be healthy in any part of the world if they have the right balance of proteins, minerals, fats, carbohydrates (starches and sugars), and vitamins. You may eat potatoes, the Chinese may enjoy rice, but both of you will be supplying your need for starch. Whether you drink milk from a goat, a llama, or a cow, you will be helping to meet your basic food needs. Have you ever eaten cactus fruit, turtle steak, or fried octopus? Some people eat roasted grasshoppers; others eat snails. Each food is helping to supply some basic need.

There are three classes of foods: **proteins** (*proh*-tee-ins), **carbohydrates** (kahr-boh-*hy*-drayts), and **fats.** *Mineral salts, water,* and *vitamins* are called **accessory foods.** Each food has its own particular function. *Proteins* build and repair muscles and other tissues. Proteins are found in lean meat, cheese, eggs, fish, gelatine, and some vegetables, such as beans and peas. Before proteins

can be used by the body, they must be changed into **amino** (uh-*mee*-noh) **acids,** which are nitrogen compounds. Different foods contain different combinations of these acids. It is very important to eat a variety of foods to make sure that all these acids are included in the diet. About one-fifth of the diet should be proteins.

Carbohydrates include starch and sugar, and are made by green plants from the carbon, hydrogen, and oxygen supplied by water and carbon dioxide. They are oxidized in the body and release heat and energy to keep us warm and enable us to move. Cereals, bread, potatoes, macaroni, and rice contain large amounts of starch. Honey, cane and beet sugar, maple sugar, and various products such as candy, ice cream, and pastry are listed in the sugar group. Carbohydrates should compose about three-fifths of the diet.

Fats also contain carbon, hydrogen, and oxygen, but in different proportions than in the carbohydrates. They also

FOOD AND NUTRITION

FIGURE 21-3. *AFTER MEALS*

This teenager is demonstrating one of the most important health routines.

furnish heat and energy to the body and can be stored in layers under the skin. Butter and lard are almost pure fat. Bacon, salad dressing, nuts, and fried foods contain a great deal of fat. Fats should make up about one-fifth of the diet.

21.3 Minerals

These are needed for growth and repair of body tissues. *Calcium, phosphorus, iron,* and *iodine* are the most important in building body tissues. Other elements, such as copper, zinc, and manganese, are needed in small amounts, but they are usually found associated with the more common minerals in foods.

Calcium found in milk, cheese, nuts, celery, and leafy vegetables is needed to build strong bones and teeth. It helps in regulating the heartbeat through its control of the contracting and relaxing of the muscles.

An adequate supply of *iron* is essential to our health at all ages. It is found in eggs, liver, lean meats, some dried fruits, and beans. Iron forms an important part of the coloring matter of the red blood cells, which carry oxygen to all the cells of the body. Small amounts of *copper* are necessary for the utilization of iron. Copper is found in liver, oysters, nuts, leafy vegetables, and whole grains.

Sodium and *potassium* are necessary for the blood, as they aid in regulating the fluid balance of the body. Both of them are found in vegetables.

Iodine plays a very important part in regulating body activities. It helps the thyroid gland to regulate the oxidation or burning of the food. It is found in sea foods and in iodized salt.

Fluorine is a mineral that is proving to be very important for healthy tooth development and in preventing the formation of cavities. Many cities are now adding small amounts of fluorine to their water supply.

Phosphorus, like calcium, is essentially concerned with building bones and teeth; and *sulphur,* with making general protoplasm. These minerals are supplied by leafy vegetables, liver, chocolate, peanuts, peas, eggs, cheese, and whole grains.

21.4 Water, a Regulatory Substance

The body needs water to digest and absorb food properly, to carry it to all parts of the body, to remove wastes, and to regulate body temperature. The cell processes need water as a medium of exchange in which they can work. The amount of water needed depends upon the climate, clothing, activity, and water content of the foods that are eaten. For good health, an adult should drink at least six glasses of water each day.

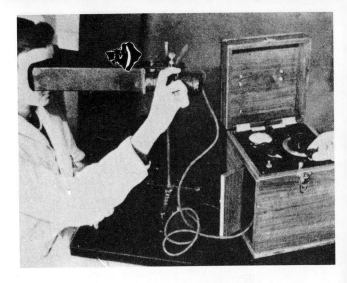

FIGURE 21-4.

ADAPTOMETER

The ability to adapt to dim light can be tested with the adaptometer. Sensory cells in the eye called *rods* contain a substance, *visual purple* which enables the eye to see in dim light. A deficiency in Vitamin A may lead to "night blindness."

Journal of the American Optical Society

21.5 Vitamins, the Body Regulators

Vitamins are chemical substances in food which definitely regulate some body activity. Without them different types of diseases occur. Doubtless many vitamins have not yet been discovered, and on those reported a great deal more work still needs to be done. Those definitely known now include vitamin A, the vitamin B complex (B_1, B_2, B_6, B_{12}, and others), vitamin C, vitamin D, vitamin E, and vitamin K. As the chemical parts are being learned, new names are gradually taking the place of the letters of the alphabet in designating vitamins.

Vitamin A is essential to growth and development. It maintains the normal structure and functioning of the membranes which line the nose, mouth, ears, frontal sinuses, digestive tract, lungs, and other parts of the body, thus helping to prevent colds and other infections.

When there is not enough vitamin A, the eyes gradually lose their ability to adapt themselves to dim light. This is called *night blindness* and is very dangerous to airplane pilots who fly at night, engineers on railroads, and any person driving a car after dark. Failure to see clearly in dim light may cause many accidents.

In severe shortages and food restrictions an eye disease known as *xerophthalmia* (zee-rof-*thal*-mee-uh) occurs. This may lead to total blindness.

Good sources of vitamin A are oil from livers of cod and halibut; butter, cream, and milk; egg-yolk and liver. Yellow vegetables, such as apricots, carrots, squash, sweet potatoes, and corn, contain *carotene* (*kar*-oh-teen), a substance from which vitamin A is produced.

Fairly large reserves of this important vitamin can be stored in the body. Since vitamin A is only slightly destroyed by canning, the daily needs can be easily met. An adult needs an egg, a pint of whole milk, butter, green and leafy vegetables every day.

Vitamin B is now usually referred to as the vitamin B complex. What was formerly thought to be one substance that prevented nervous disorders has since been found to consist of several complex substances. The most important are: B_1, thiamin; B_2, riboflavin; niacin; B_6, pyridoxine; and B_{12}, cobalamin.

Vitamin B_1, *thiamin* (*thy*-uh-min), prevents *beriberi* (*behr*-ee-*behr*-ee), a serious nervous disorder. Before 1880, it was very common among the Japanese

FOOD AND NUTRITION

FIGURE 21-5. *VITAMIN DEFICIENCY*

These birds are the same age. The chicken on the left was fed a vitamin deficient diet while the one on the right had a sufficient supply of vitamins. The result is a graphic illustration of the importance of the body's need for vitamins.

Courtesy Ohio Agricultural Experiment Station

and Chinese, who lived chiefly on a diet of polished rice with very little whole grain cereal. When taken in proper amounts, vitamin B$_1$ stimulates the appetite, maintains normal muscle tone, and promotes the health of the nervous system. It is also required in the oxidation process by which energy is released for use in the body. Mild deficiency in vitamin B$_1$ results in loss of appetite, indigestion or poor digestion, headaches, lack of endurance, fatigue, and irritability.

Thiamin is found in whole grain cereals and bread, green leafy vegetables, lean pork and beef, beans, peas, milk, and eggs. It is soluble in water and easily destroyed by heat if cooked in an open pot. Very little water should be used in cooking the vegetables, and it should be served with them. Bread which has been enriched by the addition of vitamins is also a good source.

Vitamin B$_2$, *riboflavin* (ry-boh-*flay*-vin), is essential for growth, health, and cell respiration. It maintains healthy skin and proper co-ordination of the muscles. It prevents a disease of the mouth, in which the lips and tongue become cracked, and a kind of skin disease.

Riboflavin is abundant in lean meats, liver, kidneys, milk, eggs, yeast, green leafy vegetables, nuts, and fruits. It is water soluble and is destroyed by light.

Pantothenic (pan-tuh-*then*-ik) *acid,* a substance closely associated with riboflavin, is found in liver, egg yolk, cheese, milk, whole grain cereals, green leafy vegetables, and fruits.

FIGURE 21-6. *VITAMINS*

Pressure cooking vegetables is one good way to preserve their nutritive substances. Proper preparation of food helps ensure a vitamin balance in the diet.

Courtesy National Pressure Cooker Co.

310

Niacin (*ny*-uh-sin) is called the *pellagra* (peh-*lay*-gruh)-*preventive* vitamin. This disease was prevalent in the South until Dr. Joseph Goldberger (page 680) of the United States Public Health Service discovered its cause, cure, and prevention. In cases of pellagra, there are reddened blotches on the skin, which often break out into open sores. These also occur in the mouth. Digestive disturbances, nervous disorders, and smoothness of the tongue often develop.

Niacin is found in lean meats, liver, eggs, yeast, milk, and green and leafy vegetables.

Vitamin B₆, *pyridoxine* (py-rih-*dok*-zeen), is thought to play an important part in the oxidation of the food and the health of the skin. Lack of it causes severe *anemia* (uh-*nee*-mee-uh), extreme nervousness, insomnia, irritability, abdominal pain, weakness, and difficulty in walking. Vitamin B₆ is found in dried yeast, liver, rice polishings, meat, fish, and whole wheat. It is destroyed by light.

Vitamin B₁₂, *cobalamin,* was isolated from liver in 1948. It is used as a treatment for *pernicious* (per-*nish*-us) *anemia,* a serious disease in which the red blood cells are destroyed. Its principal sources are animal proteins, including liver, eggs, milk, and muscle meats.

Still other vitamins of the B complex group are: *folic acid, biotin, and para-aminobenzoic acid.* The functions of these are not fully understood.

Vitamin C, *ascorbic* (uh-*skor*-bik) *acid,* prevents *scurvy,* a disease once prevalent among English sailors on long voyages when they lacked fresh fruit and vegetables. Vitamin C is necessary in building and maintaining well-developed teeth and healthy gums. It also helps to prevent infections. Lack of this vitamin causes restlessness and irritability in chil-

Pinney from Monkmeyer

FIGURE 21-7. *ON THE BEACH*
Vitamin D, formed by the sun's rays, helps the body utilize calcium received from various food sources.

dren, and fatigue in adults. In severe cases teeth and bones may be damaged, joints become stiffened and swollen, the teeth loosened, and interior bleeding developed in the muscles.

Ascorbic acid can only be stored in the body in very limited amounts and it easily oxidizes in the air. Thus it is important to have a fresh daily supply. Citrus fruits such as lemons, oranges, and grapefruit are important sources. Tomatoes, both canned and fresh, strawberries, cabbage, green peppers, and uncooked leafy vegetables contain it.

Vitamin D is sometimes called the "sunshine" vitamin, because it can be manufactured in the body by the ultra-violet rays of the sun. This vitamin aids in the metabolism of calcium and phosphorus. Without it *rickets* develops in children and leaves them with leg and chest deformities. "Knock knees" or

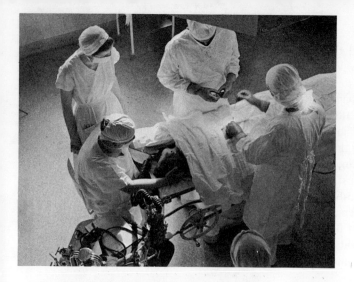

FIGURE 21-8. *SURGERY*

Vitamin K, found in certain vegetables, liver, egg-yolk, etc., is essential for blood clotting. A deficiency in this vitamin means that a wound would not stop bleeding.

Cushing

"bow-legs" develop from this weakness and may remain throughout life. It also causes weakening of the bones in adults and may be a contributing factor in arthritis.

Foods rich in vitamin D are liver and yolk of egg, especially in the summer when the animals furnishing these foods have been out of doors. Fish liver oils such as halibut and cod contain considerable quantities. Milk and a few cereal products are being reinforced with vitamin D through irradiation.

Vitamin D can be stored in the body, but there is real danger in overexposure to the sun's rays in an effort to receive a coat of tan. The sun can burn the skin and thus prevent any benefit from exposure.

Vitamin E prevents sterility in animals. It may help to prevent failure of growth, muscular dystrophy, injuries to the nervous system, and interference with normal heart action. Its effect on humans is not known, but wheat germ oil, which is its best source, is used in the treatment of some cases of developing the young of animals. Vitamin E is fat soluble and is also found in lean meats, animal fats, green leaves, and embryos of seeds. It is not easily destroyed in cooking and can be stored in the body.

Vitamin K, *menadione* (men-uh-*dy*-ohn), helps to build a protein substance, *prothrombin,* necessary for clotting of the blood. It prevents loss of blood in injuries and in surgical operations. Green leafy vegetables, such as cabbage, kale, and spinach, and certain fruits, especially tomatoes and chestnuts, are good sources of vitamin K.

21.6   Meaning of Calorie

Heat is a form of energy, and one of the reasons for taking food is to keep up the supply of this energy. The more work a person does the more energy he uses, but even a resting body uses some energy, for the heart beats and the muscles of the chest move. The amount of this form of energy a person uses is measured by a unit of heat named the **Calorie** (*kal*-er-ee). A Calorie represents the amount of heat required to raise the temperature of a pint of water about four degrees Fahrenheit. A man in rising from a chair, walking eight feet, and returning to the chair uses about one Calorie of energy.

Note that this Calorie should always be spelled with a capital C. This is to

Nutrient	Use to the Body
Protein . . . . White (albumen) of eggs, curd, casein of milk, lean meat, gluten of wheat, etc.	Forms tissue
Fats . . . . Fat of meat, butter, olives, nuts, oils of corn and wheat, etc.	Are stored as fat · All serve as fuel to yield energy in the form of heat and muscular power.
Carbohydrates . . . . . Sugar, starch, etc.	Are transformed into fat
Mineral matter (ash) . . . . . Phosphates of lime, potash, soda, found in milk and fresh vegetables	Shares in forming bone, assists in digestion, etc.
Vitamins . . . . In milk, eggs, meat, fruit, vegetables, potatoes, and whole grains of wheat, corn, and rice	Keep the body healthy and promote growth of children

distinguish it (the great Calorie) from the lesser calorie, which is used in physics as the unit of heat. The lesser calorie is the amount of heat that will raise one gram of water one degree Centigrade. The great Calorie is equal to 1000 lesser calories and is the unit used when discussing food energy.

The number of Calories we need depends on our age, sex, size, the region of the world where we live, and our daily occupation. The following are average amounts of Calories required per day by several kinds of people:

Girl sixteen years old	2400 Calories
Boy sixteen years old	2700 Calories
Man partly sedentary	3000 Calories
Workman (manual)	4000–5000 Calories

Each portion of food eaten contains a certain number of Calories. You can find a Calorie chart in the library from which you will be able to determine whether you are eating the proper number of Calories for your age. How does this compare with the average given in this chapter?

21.7 Meeting the Body's Needs

To determine how much use the body is making of the food it receives, a **basal metabolism** (muh-*tab*-uh-liz'm) test is taken. This shows the rate at which the body is releasing energy and is expressed in terms of Calories per hour. A person is placed in a respiration *calorimeter* (kal-oh-*rim*-eh-ter) of the type best suited to the purpose of the particular test. The amount of oxygen he breathes and the heat given off by the body are measured.

The *basic metabolic rate* is used in determining the amount of Calories a person actually needs in a day. Then, by a study of the heat energy which certain foods produce, it is possible to make out a diet that will suit his needs.

21.8 Balanced Diet

A *balanced diet* is one which has the proper proportion of the various food elements consumed over a period of time. It should be a *mixed diet*, with a large variety of foods, since no one food

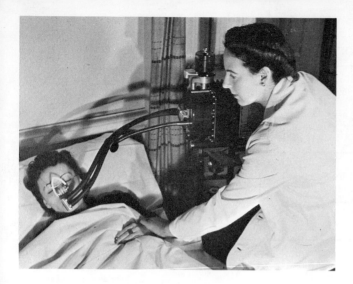

FIGURE 21-9.
CALORIMETER

The basal metabolism is found by measuring the amount of oxygen taken in and the amount of heat generated by the body while it is resting. This information is useful in prescribing diets, and to diagnose certain diseases.

Gregor from Monkmeyer

contains all of the necessary food elements, vitamins, and minerals. A diet should also be selected with regard to the *cost* in money. The cost is affected by food value, amount of water, and amount of waste.

The Basic Four Food Groups.—In selecting foods and deciding which kinds to eat regularly, look at the "Wheel of Health" (Fig. 21-10). Many noted food authorities working with the United States Government found that all of the essentials for a well-balanced diet were included in these four groups of foods. Use these foods each day:

1. Vegetables and fruits—At least two vegetables besides potatoes. A green, leafy vegetable at least four or five times a week. Two servings of fruit, one of which should be fresh and uncooked, but more may be used.
2. Meats, fish, and poultry—At least once a day.
3. Milk and other dairy products—One quart of milk for each child;

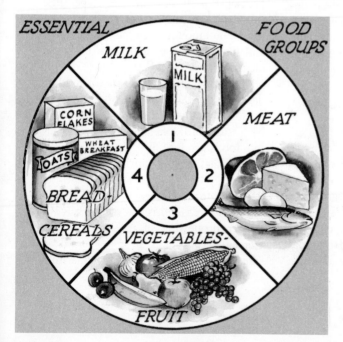

FIGURE 21-10. *THE FOUR BASIC FOODS*

Food from each of these basic groups should be eaten every day, to ensure an adequate supply of food elements (proteins, carbohydrates, etc.). Malnutrition can result not only from eating insufficient food, but also from eating the wrong kinds of food.

314

FIGURE 21-11. *MILK PROCESSING*

Certified milk is produced by dairies under strict regulations which require medical supervision of employees, veterinary supervision of cows, barn hygiene and herd management. Standards are set for the composition and sanitary quality of milk.

National Dairy Council

at least one pint for each adult. Others such as butter and eggs at least once a day.

4. Bread and cereals—Use a whole cereal product at least twice a day.

21.9 Milk

Milk and cream make up about one-sixth of the weight of all of the food eaten by the average American family. We use cow's milk; but where cows do not thrive, as in the hilly districts of Europe, goat's milk is used. In some parts of India buffalo's milk is common, while in South America the llama furnishes milk. Camel's milk in desert countries and mare's milk on the steppes of Russia are as natural to the inhabitants of those places as cow's milk is to us in this country.

Milk is unlike most of our foods because it contains no refuse or indigestible material. It is valuable because it contains: (1) materials that children need for growth, (2) materials that young and old alike need for the repair of the body machinery, and (3) materials that all need for fuel, to provide heat and the energy necessary for work.

Since milk is especially valuable for the variety of its nutrients, nutrition ex-

perts recommend that every child have a quart of milk a day and that an adult take at least a pint a day. We should not make the mistake, however, of thinking that milk can serve as the only food for a grown person or even for a child after the nursing age. Iron is needed in greater abundance than is furnished by milk. Other foods, therefore, are necessary to supplement milk in the diet of both children and adults.

21.10 Green Vegetables and Fresh Fruit

Vegetables and fruits are needed to balance the diet. Green vegetables contain a large proportion of mineral matter. For very young children, spinach, asparagus tips, string beans, carrots, and peas, when well cooked and mashed, are highly nutritious. For children who are older as well as for grown-ups, potatoes, beets, cabbage, onions, and squash are also valuable.

Fresh fruits are especially good for children. There is much truth in the old saying, "An apple a day keeps the doctor away."

21.11 Food Habits and "Hidden Hunger"

Every year many cases of *pellagra,*

Hays from Monkmeyer

FIGURE 21-12. *HIDDEN HUNGER?*

Busy, active students need the energy provided by a balanced diet.

rickets, and scurvy are found among the people in this country, among families with average incomes. Some people select the foods they like without regard to

FIGURE 21-13. *MEAT INSPECTION*

Under the terms of the Pure Food and Drug Act, meat is inspected by the federal government and graded for quality.

Owen from Black Star

the importance of the vitamins, minerals, and milk products. Take a look at your own food habits. Do you eat a good breakfast so that you feel energetic during the morning? Do you drink four glasses of milk a day? Do you eat your fruit and vegetables every day?

Your low-cost school lunch program is made possible through the United States Government. This is an effort to help you maintain a balanced diet and a mixed diet. Do you select your lunches carefully? Are you a healthy student or are you showing the effects of "hidden hunger" from too much candy, fried foods, or other reasons? Someone has said, "You are what you eat." Try to explain this.

21.12   Adulteration of Foods

Foods are **adulterated** either by subtracting some of the nutritious parts and substituting less valuable parts, or by adding materials which cannot act as a food.

In white flour the coating of the wheat kernel which contains essential mineral salts and roughage has been removed. This greatly reduces the food value of the flour.

Milk formerly was much adulterated. This adulteration was accomplished by adding water to make the milk go farther when measured, and by adding *formalin* (*for*-muh-lin) to keep it sweet.

For a time many cereals were adulterated with sawdust or peanut shucks. It would require a long description to enumerate all the foods that have been found by the Department of Agriculture to be unsatisfactory for nourishment.

Pure Food Laws.—The Federal Food, Drug, and Cosmetic Act requires manufacturers of foods, drugs, and cosmetics to make a definite statement as to their composition and weight. Manufacturers

316

must also list any preservatives that have been added. A number of special regulations and rules have been issued from time to time.

The Federal Food, Drug, and Cosmetic Act established standards for meats, meat extracts, milk, cream, butter, cheese, ice cream, grains, meals, flour, fruits, vegetables, flavoring extracts, tea, coffee, cocoa, vinegar, and salt. Before the adoption of the Act, manufacturers were not required to reach any standard in their products. The regulations about the manufacture of cosmetics are similar to those for food and drugs. Another federal law, the Wheeler-Lea Act, makes it unlawful to issue false claims in the advertisement of a product. When the needs arise new regulations are made to maintain health standards.

FACTS TO REMEMBER

The human body needs *foods* and *nutrients* to provide it with energy, to provide for the growth and repair of tissues, and to keep healthy. The substances which fulfill these needs are proteins, carbohydrates, fats, water, minerals, and vitamins.

The three nutrient foods are proteins, carbohydrates, and fats. *Proteins* build and repair tissues. *Carbohydrates* and *fats* are the sources of energy and heat for the body.

Water, minerals, and *vitamins* are *accessory foods*. They are essential for the proper functioning of all the life processes and for normal physical and mental development. Vitamins also prevent certain *deficiency diseases*.

In order to maintain a healthy and sound body, it is necessary to eat a *well-balanced* and *mixed diet*. This diet depends on a person's age, state of health, physical activity, and climate.

The United States Government has passed *Pure Food Laws* to protect the American public from *adulterated* and impure foods. These laws regulate the purity of foods and fitness for consumption by establishing certain standards that all foods must meet.

WORDS TO REMEMBER

accessory food	deficiency disease	pantothenic acid
adulterate	fat	pellagra
amino acid	Federal Food, Drug,	pernicious anemia
anemia	and Cosmetic Act	protein
ascorbic acid	folic acid	prothrombin
balanced diet	food	pyridoxine
basal metabolism	menadione	riboflavin
beriberi	mineral	rickets
Calorie	mixed diet	scurvy
calorimeter	niacin	thiamin
carbohydrate	night blindness	vitamin
carotene	nutrient	xerophthalmia
	nutrition	

QUESTIONS

1. Define: food, nutrient, nutrition, vitamin, Calorie.
2. Name the three classes of food and three types of accessory foods. Mention something you have eaten that belongs to each class.
3. What is the value of protein to the body? Name *three* foods which contain it.
4. Into what must protein be changed before it can be used by the body?
5. Mention *two* classes of foods that furnish heat and energy. What elements do they contain?
6. What are the most important minerals which the body needs? Give at least one source of each.
7. Why are minerals necessary to the body?
8. List *five* known vitamins of the B complex and state their functions.
9. Why is vitamin D sometimes called the "sunshine vitamin"? What happens from the lack of it?
10. What foods prevent scurvy? How does this disease affect children and adults?
11. Why is milk considered such a valuable food? Why would it not be a complete food for an adult?
12. What is meant by a "balanced diet"? A "mixed diet"?
13. What has been done by the government to prevent the adulteration of food?
14. What is meant by a "basal metabolism" test?

COMPLETION TEST

As your teacher or classmate reads the following incomplete statements, with your book closed, write on a clean sheet of paper the word or phrase which correctly completes the statement.

1. Night blindness is caused by the lack of vitamin _____.
2. Sterility in animals is prevented by vitamin _____.
3. A disease from the lack of vitamin D is _____.
4. You should drink at least _____ glasses of water a day.
5. Lack of vitamin _____ causes beriberi.
6. Vitamin _____ helps in clotting the blood.
7. A high school boy needs about _____ Calories a day.
8. Iodine helps the _____ gland.
9. _____ is used to build or repair tissue.
10. Fluorine helps to prevent _____.

PROJECTS

I. *The Test for Starch.*—For this experiment you will need several test tubes, a test-tube holder, and a test-tube rack; some iodine; a few grains of starch; and some bits of food to be tested, such as bread, potato, carrot, cookie, and rice.

1. Place a very small amount of starch in a test tube and shake with 10 cc. of water. If you prefer, you may heat it and form a thin paste. Add a drop of iodine and shake. Note the color. If it is dark and very hard to distinguish the color, dilute with more water. This is the test for starch.

2. Test each of the bits of food by placing it in a test tube and adding a drop of iodine.

Observation.—Record the results of each test.

Conclusion.—What is the test for starch? Which foods contain starch?

Practical Application.—How can you find out what foods contain starch? Write your report in experiment form.

II. *The Test for Grape Sugar or Glucose.*

Materials.—Test tubes, test-tube rack and holder, Benedict's solution or equal parts of Fehling's solution A and B, Bunsen or alcohol burner, matches, and foods containing simple sugar, such as oranges, lemons, grapes, and other fresh fruits, cane sugar and dilute hydrochloric acid.

1. Dissolve a very small portion of grape sugar or use some corn syrup (glucose). Add 3–5 cc. of Benedict's or Fehling's solution. Heat slowly over the flame and note the color changes. This is the test for simple sugar.

2. Test each of the other foods for the presence of simple sugar.

3. Dissolve a few grains of cane sugar in water, add a drop of hydrochloric acid, and boil. Then add either Benedict's or Fehling's solution and note the test for simple sugar.

Observations.—Record your results.

Conclusion.—What is the test for simple sugar? What foods contain simple sugar? How can cane sugar be changed to simple sugar?

Practical Application.—How can you find out which foods contain simple sugar?

III. *The Test for Protein.*

Materials.—Test tubes, holder, rack, Bunsen or alcohol burner, matches, nitric acid, ammonium hydroxide, and foods containing protein, such as hard-boiled egg, cheese, lean meat, and lima beans.

1. Place a small piece of the white of a hard-boiled egg in a test tube. Add 5 cc. of water and 2 cc. of strong nitric acid. Heat gently over the flame. Be sure to shake the test tube to keep the egg white moving and prevent breaking the tube. Bring to the boiling point and note the color. Let it cool and then add a few drops of ammonium hydroxide. Note the color of the ring which forms on the top of the liquid.

2. Test the other foods in the same manner and note the results.

Observations.—Record your results.

Conclusion.—What is the test for proteins? Which foods contain them?

Practical Application.—How can you find out which foods contain protein?

IV. *The Test for Fats.*

Materials.—Test tubes, shallow dish, ether, white paper. *Do not use a flame.* Foods, such as butter, doughnuts, peanuts, and bacon.

1. Rub a piece of butter on white paper and note the grease spot.

2. Put a small piece of butter in a test tube and add 5 cc. of ether. (*This is inflammable. Keep away from an open flame.*) When most of the butter has dissolved, pour off the liquid into a shallow dish and let it evaporate. Then note whether there is a grease spot left. This is the test for fat.

3. Test the other foods and find out which ones contain fat.

Observation.—Record the results of your experiment.

Conclusion.—What is the test for fat? What foods contain fat?

Practical Application.—Why are peanuts and buttered popcorn usually sold in cellophane or waxed paper bags? How would you pack doughnuts?

V. *To Prove the Value of Milk.*—If you have white rats, choose a couple of the same size, sex, and age, preferably young rats about 21 days old.

Place in separate cages and give the same care with one exception:

To No. 1 give only milk to drink. This should be fresh daily. Do not give water, but otherwise give a variety of food to eat. To No. 2 give only strong coffee to drink, no other liquids. Give the same care and foods to each.

Every third day weigh each rat and keep a record of the weight. After a few weeks note any changes in size. Continue the experiment for several weeks until your teacher thinks it wise to change the diet.

Record your results. Make a graph of the gain in weight of each rat. What other physical differences soon become apparent?

VI. *Proving the Vitamins.*—If your school has white rats or guinea pigs, try to prove the value of each of the vitamins by giving one animal a balanced diet and a similar animal a diet lacking some particular vitamin.

VII. *Your Daily Diet.*—Look up a library reference for a Calorie chart of common foods. Make out a menu for yourself for three meals for one day and list the approximate number of Calories. How does this compare with your requirements as suggested on page 313?

VIII. *Vitamin Chart.*—Make a chart showing foods that are good sources of each of the minerals and vitamins. Plan a day's meals which will include all the necessary vitamins. Make each meal as inviting as you can.

REFERENCES

Asimov, *Chemicals of Life*. Abelard-Schuman.

Boyd-Orr, *The Wonderful World of Food, the Substance of Life*. Doubleday.

Crisp, *Be Healthy*. Lippincott.

DeKruif, *Hunger Fighters*. Harcourt, Brace.

Kilander, *Nutrition For Health*. McGraw-Hill.

Macy and Williams, *Hidden Hunger*. Ronald.

McCollum and Simmonds, *Newer Knowledge of Nutrition*. Macmillan.

McKey, *Know Your Vitamins*. Bookshelf Publishing.

Sense, *America's Nutrition Primer*. Barrows.

Sherman and Lanford, *Essentials of Nutrition*. Macmillan.

CHAPTER 22

The Digestive System

22.1 The Nature of Digestion

Man, like all other animals, is dependent upon plants for his food supply. Only green plants can manufacture carbohydrates (starch and sugar). Plants and animals can rearrange the elements in carbohydrates to form fats, add to them nitrogen and minerals to make proteins, and thus produce foods for other animals to assimilate.

These foods have to be simplified, made into a soluble form, and changed chemically before they can enter the body cells. This simplification is done in each animal by special organs, and the process is called **digestion.**

22.2 The Digestive Organs of Man

Man's digestive organs correspond to those already studied in the frog and mammal (Figs. 14-2 and 17-1). But in man each region is more complete, and the division of labor reaches a higher development. The parts of the digestive system are described under the following headings: the *mouth,* containing the teeth, tongue, and salivary glands; the *digestive,* or alimentary (al-ih-*men*-tuh-ree), *canal,* consisting of the throat or pharynx, esophagus, stomach, small and large intestines, rectum, and anus; and the *digestive glands,* such as the liver, pancreas, and gastric glands, which open into the digestive canal through ducts.

22.3 The Mouth

The mouth is lined with a soft membrane which is kept moist by the saliva. The roof of the mouth is called the **palate** (*pal*-it). The front part (*hard palate*) has plates of bone inside; the back part (*soft palate*) is a thin sheet of muscle covered by the *mucous* (*myoo-kus*) *lining* of the mouth. The soft palate separates the mouth from the nasal cavity. The palate, teeth, tongue, and lips work together to form words.

The **tongue** is a muscular organ which aids in swallowing. The upper surface has many small fleshy projections called *papillae.* Some of these are fairly large, and it is through them that we taste our food. Our power to taste sweet, sour, bitter, and salt, the four fundamental tastes in man, is due mainly to certain nerve cells (*taste buds*) located on these larger papillae. The papillae for these tastes are centered on different areas of the tongue.

Six **salivary** (*sal*-ih-vehr-ee) **glands,** three on each side, the *parotid* (puh-*rot*-id), *submaxillary* (sub-*mak*-sih-lehr-ee), and *sublingual* (sub-*ling*-wul) (Fig. 22-4), produce **saliva** (suh-*ly*-vuh) that moistens the food in the mouth and assists in digesting it. **Mucous glands** in the cheek help in swallowing by secreting **mucus** (*myoo*-kus), a lubricating substance.

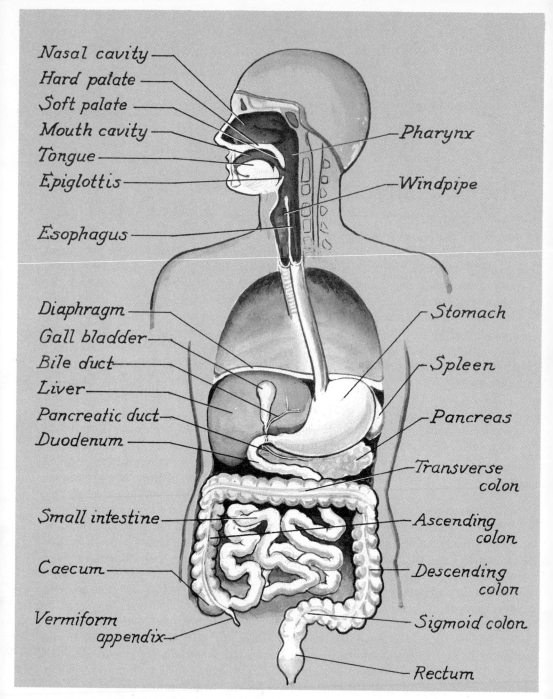

Nasal cavity

Hard palate

Soft palate

Mouth cavity

Tongue

Epiglottis

Esophagus

Pharynx

Windpipe

Diaphragm

Gall bladder

Bile duct

Liver

Pancreatic duct

Duodenum

Small intestine

Caecum

Vermiform appendix

Stomach

Spleen

Pancreas

Transverse colon

Ascending colon

Descending colon

Sigmoid colon

Rectum

FIGURE 22-1. *THE HUMAN DIGESTIVE SYSTEM*

Digestion takes place in the alimentary canal, aided by juices from the digestive glands. The epiglottis is a lid-like structure below the tongue which keeps food from entering the windpipe. The passage of food is possible because of the contractions of involuntary muscles in the stomach and intestines. How do digestive juices enter from the liver and pancreas?

22.4 The Teeth

Arranged in a semicircle around the center of the mouth cavity are the teeth. Each is especially adapted for a particular kind of work. In adults there are *thirty-two* teeth, sixteen in each jaw, belonging to four classes according to shape (Fig. 22-2).

The four front teeth on each jaw are **incisors** (in-*sy*-zers), which are used for cutting and biting, as in eating an apple. The four long pointed teeth, one on each side of the incisors on each jaw, are the **canine** teeth, used for tearing. Sometimes they are used for breaking the skin of some tough fruit. Next to the canine teeth, on each side of each jaw, are the **premolars,** two on each side top and bottom or eight in all. The premolars and the **molars,** which are the farthest back in the mouth, are used for grinding food. Some of the molars are called *wisdom teeth,* which usually grow in between the ages of seventeen to twenty-five. An adult who has not lost any teeth should have thirty-two. How many do you have? Can you name and locate each of your teeth?

Structure of a Tooth.—The three main regions of a tooth are the *crown,* the *neck,* and the *root* (Fig. 22-3). The inner cavity, or **pulp,** contains the nerves and blood vessels. It is surrounded by a bonelike layer called **dentine.** The *crown* of the tooth is covered by a layer of **enamel** which is harder than the dentine. The *root* is covered by a hard layer of **cementum** and is held firmly in the jaw by the **peridontal membrane.**

Care of the Teeth.—Teeth are hard, but that does not prevent them from decaying if neglected. When the teeth are not cleaned, a substance called *tartar* forms on them, which prevents the bacteria from being rubbed off and often pushes the gums back from the teeth.

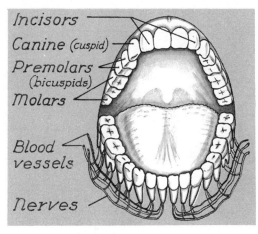

FIGURE 22-2. *ADULT TEETH*

Notice that there are four kinds of teeth. Each is shaped to perform different jobs. Incisors are for cutting, canines for tearing, premolars for tearing and grinding, and molars for grinding.

The activity of bacteria is hastened by the formation of acids from bits of food which remain between the teeth after eating. The activity of these bacteria results in toothache, bad breath, and the imperfect chewing of food. The teeth should be brushed morning and night to remove particles of food, particularly sugar, which ferments easily.

FIGURE 22-3. *HUMAN MOLAR*

Decay starts at tiny breaks in the enamel. It may continue through the bony layer of dentine and into the pulp, which contains nerves and blood vessels, thus causing toothache.

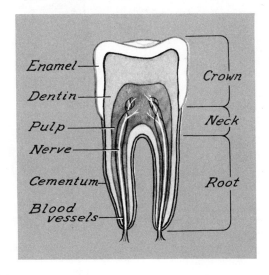

323

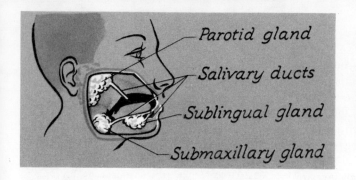

FIGURE 22-4. *SALIVARY GLANDS*

There are six salivary glands, three on each side, which secrete saliva containing the enzyme ptyalin. Ptyalin begins the digestive process by changing starch to maltose, a kind of sugar.

Brushing cannot make poor teeth good, but can protect good teeth. At least once a year you should visit a dentist to have cavities filled and prevent further decay. Some dentists use fluorine compounds on children's teeth.

Chewing.—No matter how many other good habits you have, you will never enjoy good health unless you chew your food well. Probably more bodily ailments come from hasty eating and the habit of washing down food than from any other cause. Few people chew their food enough, and no one chews his food too much.

Only by thorough chewing can we mix the saliva with our food. This secretion aids in digestion and in swallowing.

Saliva contains the enzyme **ptyalin** (*ty*-uh-lin), which changes starch into soluble sugars, thus starting the digestion of food before it reaches the stomach. The **enzymes** (*en*-zymz), or *ferments, are the chemical substances which digest the food.* All plants and animals digest their food by means of enzymes.

22.5 The Digestive Canal

The digestive, or *alimentary,* canal of man is a tube about thirty feet long, lined with tissue and containing two layers of muscles, one of which extends lengthwise and the other in ringlike bands. Different parts of it vary in size and shape, such as the stomach and the small intestine. The alimentary canal is

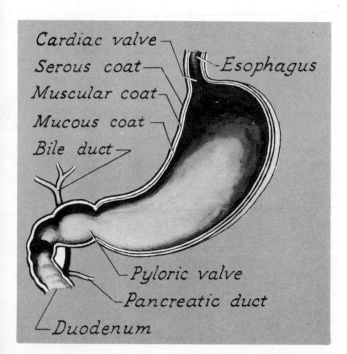

FIGURE 22-5. *STOMACH*

The stomach may change shape depending upon the amount of food within it. It has two valves, one called the *cardiac valve* which prevents food from reentering the esophagus; another called the *pyloric valve* which keeps the food in the stomach until the digestive juices have done their work.

one continuous tube, extending from the mouth to the end of the rectum (the anus).

The Throat.—Beyond the soft palate is the throat, called the **pharynx**. This is a funnel-shaped cavity, having two openings at its lower end, the front one leading to the windpipe, and the rear one to the esophagus. In the upper part of the pharynx, on each side, is the opening of a **Eustachian** (yoo-*stay*-kee-un) **tube** which passes to the middle ear. These tubes help to equalize the air pressure on the ear drum when going up or down a mountain or a high elevator shaft.

The Esophagus.—The esophagus, or gullet, is a nearly straight tube connecting the mouth with the stomach. It passes through the **diaphragm** (*dy*-uh-fram), a muscular partition separating the chest and abdominal cavities. It then enlarges, and becomes the stomach. As soon as one swallows, control of the food is lost, and further action is involuntary. Two sets of muscles, one extending lengthwise, the other around the esophagus, act together in forcing the food or water into the stomach. This explains why we can drink from a· brook when the head is much lower than the stomach.

The Stomach.—In man the stomach is the largest section of the digestive tube; it has a capacity of about three pints. It is usually pear-shaped (Fig. 22-5), but may vary in form. The lining contains gastric glands. At the point where the esophagus joins the stomach there is a muscular ring, the **cardiac valve,** which ordinarily prevents the food from passing again into the esophagus. In vomiting, this valve becomes relaxed. The opening at the larger and lower end of the stomach is guarded by the **pyloric** (py-*loh*-rik) **valve,** which serves to keep the food in the stomach until certain digestive changes have taken place.

The stomach walls contain three layers of smooth muscle: *longitudinal, circular,* and *oblique.* Action of these muscles gives a churning effect to the stomach.

The Intestine.—The intestine has two parts: a small, much-coiled tube about an inch in diameter and about twenty feet long called the **small intestine;** and a large section about five feet long and three inches in diameter, bent in a rough ∩ shape and called the **large intestine.** At the junction between these two regions projects a short sac, the **vermiform** (*ver*-mih-form) **appendix.** The disease called *appendicitis* (uh-pen-dih-*sy*-tis) affects this organ. The large intestine ends in the **rectum.** The opening of the rectum to the outside is the **anus** (*ay*-nus), which is controlled by a circular *sphincter muscle.*

The esophagus, stomach, and intestine are lined with a membrane similar to that in the mouth. This *mucous membrane* consists of epithelial tissue (Fig. 22-6) of closely packed cells. In the esophagus, the mucous membrane is smooth and moist, thus furnishing an easy passage for the food; in the stomach it lies in folds except when the stomach is full of food; and in the intestine, it has a velvetlike appearance due to projections called **villi** (*vil*-eye) (Fig. 22-6).

Glands.—The numerous glands of the stomach and intestine are located in the mucous membrane. Those which produce the digestive fluids are (1) millions of tiny **gastric glands** in the stomach lining which secrete *gastric fluid* containing hydrochloric acid; (2) the **pancreas** (*pan*-kree-us), which secretes *pancreatic fluid* by a duct into the small intestine; (3) the **liver,** the largest gland in the body, which secretes *bile* that is collected in the *gall bladder* and then emptied into the small intestine; and (4) numerous **intestinal glands** in

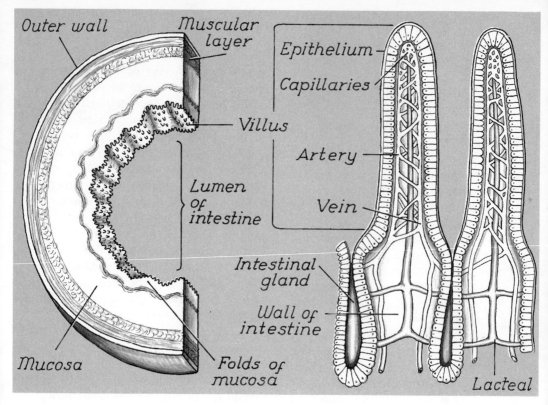

FIGURE 22-6. *THE LINING OF THE INTESTINE*
The diagram at the left shows the location of tiny villi on the intestinal wall. At right is an enlarged cross section of two villi. The blood vessels lie very near the thin walls of the villus enabling them to absorb digested materials from the intestine.

the small intestine secreting *intestinal fluid.*

22.6 The Process of Digestion

Digestion is carried on *mechanically* by the teeth and jaws, and *chemically* by several secretions that transform the food into solutions. It begins in the mouth, where the teeth break up the food and mix it with the *saliva,* which contains the enzyme *ptyalin* (Sec. 22.4). During this process, the carbohydrates are changed into soluble sugars. The fluids of the mouth are usually slightly *alkaline* (*al*-kuh-lyn, a chemical term, the opposite to sour or acid), but as soon as the food passes into the stomach it enters an *acid* (sour) medium, and the diges-

tive action of the saliva is stopped in a short time by the stomach fluid. The sugar and starch undergo no further digestive changes until they reach the intestine.

The *gastric glands* produce and pour out the *gastric juice* (a digestive fluid) into this acid medium of the stomach. The enzyme **pepsin** in this juice acts on the *proteins* and changes them to **peptones** and **proteoses**. The enzyme **rennin** (*ren*-in) acts on the *casein* (*kay*-see-in) of milk. The *hydrochloric acid,* which is also secreted by the gastric glands, dissolves minerals and kills bacteria.

In the stomach the heat of the body melts some of the fats into oils, but many of the fats used as food remain solid at

326

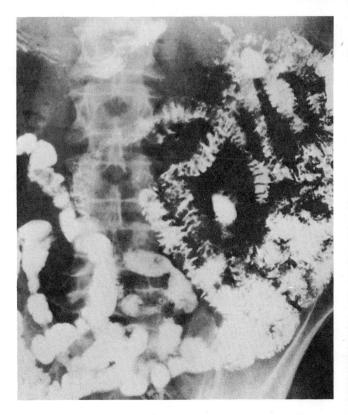

FIGURE 22-7. *X-RAY*

The digestive system can be observed by x-ray when the patient drinks an opaque liquid, usually a barium compound. In this picture, the coiled small intestine is at the left and the stomach at the right, with the spinal column visible in the center.

Courtesy Massachusetts
General Hospital

body temperature and are unchanged in the stomach.

Food usually stays in the stomach from one to five hours, depending on whether one is physically tired or emotionally disturbed or is sensitive to some special food. The muscles in the digestive tract keep the food moving along by means of an action known as **peristalsis** (pehr-ih-*stahl*-sis). But some food begins to pass into the **duodenum** (doo-oh-*dee-num*), the first part of the small intestine, within two minutes after entering the stomach.

As the partly digested food, or chyme, passes on into the small intestine, it undergoes further digestive changes in a medium that is now alkaline. Here the *pancreatic juice* causes at least three different changes. The enzyme **trypsin** (*trip*-sin) continues the breaking down of protein which began in the stomach into **peptids;** the enzyme **amylase** (*am*-

ih-lase) converts *starch* into *maltose;* and the enzyme **lipase** changes fats into fatty acids and glycerol. Bile from the liver emulsifies fats.

Other digestive changes take place in the intestines. The enzymes **maltase, sucrase,** and **lactase** change sugar to *glucose.* **Erepsin** (ee-*rep*-sin) changes peptids to *amino acids.* In addition to the action of the digestive glands, there is the work of bacteria in digestion. While the child is on a milk diet, certain bacteria become adapted to living in the intestine; later, when the diet is more varied, other forms of bacteria are added. The different kinds of bacteria are mostly restricted to the large intestine.

22.7   The Absorption of Food

After food has been completely digested in the small intestine, it must be absorbed before *assimilation* (Sec. 1.10)

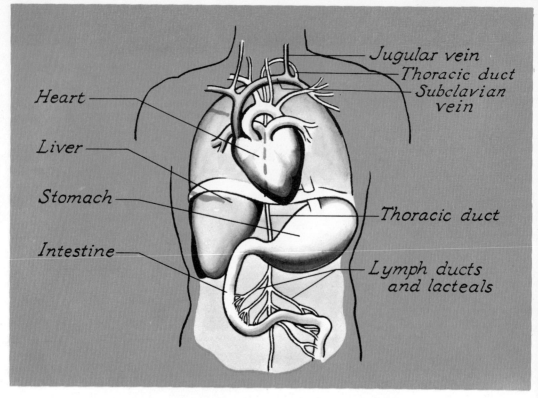

FIGURE 22-8. *PART OF THE LYMPHATIC SYSTEM*

The lymphatic system is necessary for the absorbtion of digestive fats. Unlike sugars and proteins, fats do not enter the blood directly, but first pass into the lymph capillaries or lacteals. The fluid is then moved by contraction of surrounding muscles, until it reaches the larger ducts and finally enters the blood stream by a vein near the heart.

is possible. **Absorption** *is the process of taking the digested foods into the blood.* Practically no food is absorbed in the mouth or esophagus, and but little in the stomach.

Some food is absorbed from the large intestine, but the small intestine is the main organ of absorption. Its great length and numerous *villi* and ridges are special adaptations for this particular work. The food is absorbed by tiny folds in the lining of the small intestine which affords more surface. The folds, villi, appear as a covering of minute hairs. The structure of these folds is shown in Figure 22-6. Water is absorbed chiefly from the large intestine.

The process of **diffusion** (Sec. 1.11) is the chief factor in the passing of the food into the blood vessels. It is assisted by the action of the living cells and the movements of the intestine.

The digested proteins and sugars pass directly into blood vessels which lead to the liver through the *portal vein.* In the liver this vein is divided into *capillaries* —minute branches that distribute the blood to the cells of the liver. As the blood thus passes among the liver cells, the larger part of the sugar is changed into *glycogen* (*gly*-kuh-j'n), an animal starch (Sec. 20.9), and stored temporarily in the liver cells. This stored-up starch, glycogen, is given out gradually

328

from the liver as sugar when it is needed by the blood; it thus yields energy to the body. It is also used to furnish energy to the contracting muscles. This work of the liver results in keeping a uniform amount of sugar in the blood. When more carbohydrates are eaten than the body needs, the excess is changed into fat for storage. Surplus proteins cannot be stored in the body as surplus energy foods can.

Fatty acids and glycerol pass into vessels of the villi, the **lacteals** (*lak*-tee-als), which are part of the *lymphatic system* (Sec. 23.11); these in turn open into larger ones. Eventually these vessels which carry **lymph** (*limf*), the fluid that surrounds the body cells, unite to form the *thoracic duct* which empties into the subclavian vein near the heart. The food is now in the blood stream and is carried to the individual cells of the body. Each cell takes the food which it needs, and by a series of changes as yet only partly known, makes the food into living protoplasm.

The indigestible part of the food continues to move through the small intestine into the large intestine, and on through the rectum. During this progress much moisture is absorbed, especially in the large intestine, which leaves the "undissolved" food harder and harder. The regular removal of the unused part of the food, **feces** (*fee*-seez), is of much importance in maintaining health, because the bacteria living in the digestive tract cause the waste material to decay, and the poisonous substances thus formed are injurious when absorbed into the blood.

Foods normally remain in the stomach from one to five hours, and in the small intestine about four hours; they may be from six to twenty-four hours in passing through the large intestine.

FACTS TO REMEMBER

The process of *digestion* is to simplify foods and make them soluble for absorption by body tissues.

The *digestive,* or *alimentary, canal* consists of the mouth, throat, esophagus, stomach, small intestine, and large intestine. A *mucous membrane* lines the entire canal. *Peristalsis* keeps the food moving through the digestive tract.

In the chemical phase of digestion, *enzymes* are secreted by *digestive glands* to break down the foods chemically. These glands are the salivary, gastric, liver, pancreas, and intestinal. Carbohydrates are converted to glucose, fats to fatty acids, and proteins to amino acids.

Digested food passes by *diffusion* through the *villi* of the small intestine into the blood stream and lymphatic system. Undigested food (*feces*) passes out of the body through the rectum.

WORDS TO REMEMBER

absorption	anus	casein
alimentary canal	assimilation	dentine
alkaline	bile	diaphragm
amino acids	canines	digestion
amylase	cardiac valve	digestive gland

duodenum	lymph	ptyalin
enamel	maltase	pulp
enzyme	maltose	pyloric valve
erepsin	molars	rectum
Eustachian tube	mucous membrane	rennin
feces	mucus	saliva
gall bladder	palate	salivary glands
gastric glands	pancreas	soft palate
glucose	papillae	stomach
glycogen	parotid	sublingual
hard palate	pepsin	submaxillary
incisors	peptids	sucrase
intestine	peptones	tartar
intestinal glands	peristalsis	taste buds
lactase	pharynx	trypsin
lacteals	premolars	vermiform appendix
lipase	proteoses	villi
liver		

QUESTIONS

1. Name in order the parts of the digestive canal of man.

2. Compare the digestive canals of the frog and man.

3. What is digestion? Absorption?

4. Locate the hard and soft palates. What do you think is the function of each?

5. How many kinds of taste do you have? Name them.

6. List the *four* kinds of teeth found in man. Which kind is most highly specialized in the rodents, like the rat; in carnivores, like the dog; and in ungulates, like the horse?

7. Explain how it is possible for man to eat such a wide variety of foods.

8. Describe the structure of a tooth.

9. Do you think small children need to care for their first teeth when they will soon lose most of them? Explain.

10. What enzyme is found in the mouth? What is its function? How is this related to the thorough chewing of food?

11. State the location and function of the two valves of the stomach.

12. Name as many adaptations of the small intestine as you can.

13. What is a gland? Name those which produce digestive fluids.

14. Describe the lining of the digestive tract. What glands are located in it?

15. What food is digested in the stomach? Name the enzyme which acts on it.

16. What happens to the food in the small intestine? Discuss the importance of the pancreatic juice and bile.

17. Which foods pass directly into the blood vessels that lead to the liver?

18. How is the larger part of the sugar stored?
19. Describe the absorption of fats.
20. What is the chief function of the large intestine?

COMPLETION TEST

As your teacher or classmate reads the following incomplete statements, with your book closed, write on a clean sheet of paper the word or phrase which correctly completes the statement.

1. Six glands in the mouth produce a fluid called _saliva_.
2. Fleshy projections on the tongue are called _papillae_.
3. In adults there are _32_ teeth.
4. The throat cavity is called the _pharynx_.
5. The _eustachian_ tube connects the throat with the middle ear.
6. Tiny projections which are found in the walls of the small intestine are called _villi_.
7. Most of the food is absorbed in the _small intestine_.
8. The _duodenum_ is the opening by which foods pass into the small intestine.
9. Animal starch in the liver is called _glycogen_.
10. Indigestible food material that is eaten passes into the _large intestine_.

PROJECTS

I. *How Does Saliva Act on Starch?*

Materials.—Test tubes, beaker, starch, iodine, Fehling's solution or Benedict's solution.

Method.—1. Test the starch for the presence of starch by adding iodine to a few grains.

2. Test the starch for the presence of grape sugar by heating with Fehling's or Benedict's solution. (There should be no sugar present.)

3. Collect some saliva in a test tube. Test one portion for starch and another portion for sugar. (There should be none of either.)

4. Place small amounts of starch in each of four test tubes. In two of the test tubes place 5 cc. of water. In the other two test tubes place 5 cc. each of saliva. Place all four test tubes in a beaker of water and keep at a temperature of 98° F. for about twenty minutes.

5. At the end of that time test each of the tubes for grape sugar by adding Fehling's or Benedict's solution, and heating.

Observations.—Record your results.

Conclusion.—What is the effect of saliva on starch?

Practical Application.—Why is it important to chew the food thoroughly?

II. *How Does Pepsin Act on Protein?*

Materials.—Pepsin, dilute hydrochloric acid, sodium hydroxide, white of egg (boiled), test tubes, and rack.

Method.—Cut the pieces of egg white very fine and place some in each of four test tubes. In the first tube place some pepsin solution and mix well.

In the second test tube place pepsin and a few drops of dilute sodium hydroxide solution.

In the third test tube add pepsin solution and one drop of dilute hydrochloric acid.

In the fourth test tube place pepsin solution and add several drops of dilute hydrochloric acid.

Place all four test tubes in a warm place and let stand for two days. Examine each very carefully. Where has digestion taken place?

Observation.—Record the result shown by each test tube.

Conclusion.—How does pepsin act on protein? What kind of solution is best?

Practical Application.—How does chewing the food thoroughly help the digestion of protein?

III. How Does Pancreatin Act on Food?

Method.—1. Follow the same procedure as for the action of saliva in Project I, but use pancreatin instead of saliva.

2. Follow the experiment for protein digestion in Project II, but use pancreatin instead of pepsin.

3. To show the effect of pancreatin on fat, use a small amount of pancreatin in an alkaline medium. You may use a few drops of dilute sodium hydroxide for this. Shake the fat solution and note the change.

Observations.—Record results and write each experiment separately.

IV. To Prove That We Do Not Taste Flavors.

1. Blindfold in turn several members of the class and have each hold his nose while a small amount of some highly flavored food is placed on the tongue. Such common foods as maple syrup, vanilla extract, marmalade, and jams are good for the test. Make a record of each test.

2. Remove the hand from the nose and again taste the same substances. The difference is due to the sense of smell.

3. Test other foods and try to determine where each of the four primary tastes is located.

V. Copy the following table and fill it in, comparing the digestive system of man with the digestive systems of the animals studied in previous units. This will help you to understand better the parts of the digestive system of man and the work that each part does.

Animal	One Cell	Many Cells	No Digestive Tube	Digestive Tube	No Well-defined Digestive Glands	Require Food?
Paramecium						
Frog						
Man						
etc.						

REFERENCES

Best and Taylor, *The Human Body and Its Functions*. Holt.

Best and Taylor, *The Living Body*. Holt.

Burton-Opitz, *An Elementary Manual of Physiology*. Saunders.

Carlson and Johnson, *The Machinery of the Body*. University of Chicago Press.

Clendening, *The Human Body*. Knopf.

Harvey, *Simple Lessons in Human Anatomy*. American Medical Association.

Kohn, *Your Digestive System*. Blakiston.

McCollum and Simmonds, *Newer Knowledge of Nutrition*. Macmillan.

Morrison, Cornett and Tether, *Human Physiology*. Holt.

Sense, *America's Nutrition Primer*. Barrow.

Sherman, *Chemistry of Food and Nutrition*. Macmillan.

Storer and Usinger, *General Zoology*. McGraw-Hill.

Tokay, *Fundamentals of Physiology*. Garden City.

Walker, *Human Physiology*. Pelican Books.

Woodhouse, *Dental Careers*. Funk and Wagnalls.

Your Teeth—How to Save Them. Public Affairs Pamphlet No. 147.

CHAPTER 23

The Circulatory System

23.1 Methods of Circulation in Our Bodies

The simple protozoans do not need specific structures to carry food to all parts of their bodies, and their waste matter is dumped into the surrounding water. The hydra, though composed of many cells, lacks anything resembling blood, heart, or arteries. These tiny animals never grow to large size or move continuously for a definite period as a fish does. But relatively large, active animals, such as earthworms, crayfish, and vertebrates, need more elaborate systems for carrying blood and lymph to every cell.

In our bodies, the **circulatory system** consists of the *heart* and *blood vessels*. It distributes the digested food to all parts of the body, carries oxygen to produce heat and energy, and carries off the wastes.

The blood continues to move from the heart to the other organs in an endless stream, requiring about 30 seconds to complete its circuit back to the heart.

William Harvey (page 680) described the heart as a muscular pump forcing blood to circulate through the body. In a similar way, oxygen keeps moving. It is passed into the blood from air which is taken in by the lungs since there is no general storehouse for oxygen within our bodies. There is a continuous formation of wastes removed by the kidneys.

While each process is described separately, think of them as depending on each other, one leading into another with no sharp line of distinction.

23.2 The Blood

Blood is a *fluid tissue* which circulates through the heart, arteries, capillaries, and veins, supplying nutritive material to every part of the body. It is made up of a fluid **plasma** (*plaz*-muh) which contains cells, or **corpuscles** (*kor*-pus-'ls), and **platelets** (*playt*-lets). The volume of blood in the average person is about six quarts.

The **red corpuscles** are very small discs which are indented on both sides.

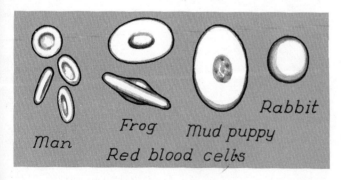

Man
Frog
Mud puppy
Rabbit
Red blood cells

FIGURE 23-1. *OXYGEN CARRIERS*

The red blood cell varies in size and shape in different animals. Mature red cells of mammals do not have nuclei.

334

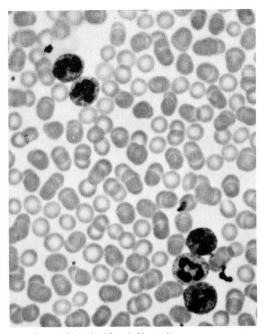

General Biological Supply House, Inc.

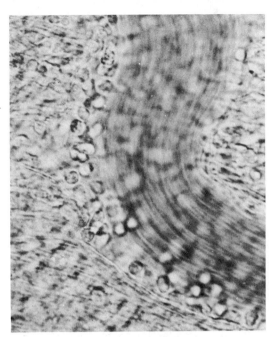

W. Barry Wood, Jr., Johns Hopkins Medical Institutions

FIGURE 23-2. *HUMAN BLOOD CELLS*

Human blood (*left*) contains red corpuscles and white corpuscles. White corpuscles are larger, fewer in number, and contain nuclei. The picture on the right is an injured blood vessel showing the white corpuscles sticking to the wall (small bodies on left side of vessel) where they have gathered to help destroy infection. The streak is caused by a flow of red cells.

They are colored with an iron compound, **hemoglobin** (*hee*-moh-gloh-bin). When a few of these corpuscles are examined through a microscope, they appear yellowish instead of red; but when a large number of them are seen in a mass, the red color shows. After the red cells are formed in the bone marrow, their nuclei gradually disappear. As a result, the mature red corpuscles, unlike all the other cells, have no nuclei.

Red corpuscles carry oxygen from the lungs to the cells of the body. As soon as oxygen from the air we breathe in enters the blood, it unites chemically with the hemoglobin in the red blood corpuscles to form oxyhemoglobin. Here it remains until it passes by diffusion from the blood into the cells. These cells take the oxygen and use it in the process of *oxidation*, which goes on continuously in every living cell. A good supply of red corpuscles is necessary if the cells of the body are to have a sufficient supply of oxygen.

At the same time that oxygen is received from the blood by the body cells, carbon dioxide is given off. *Diffusion,* (Sec. 1-11) explains the method of this transfer. The carbon dioxide forms a chemical compound in the red cells and is carried in this form to the lungs, where it is changed back to carbon dioxide gas and released.

The **white blood corpuscles,** larger and fewer in number than the red, are formed in bone marrow and lymph tissue. Ameba-like, they can change shape to pass through capillary walls and move about among the body cells. They are the scavengers of the blood. Some, called **phagocytes** (*fag*-uh-syts),

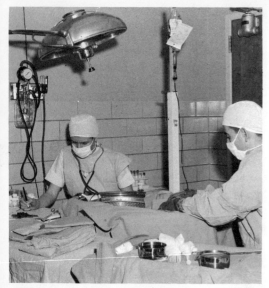

Courtesy The Children's Hospital, Boston

FIGURE 23-3. *RH BABY*

A newborn baby whose blood contains anti-Rh substances from the mother's blood can be given an entirely new blood supply by transfusion.

leave the blood vessels when necessary and collect at one place to aid the body in destroying disease germs. They have the power to engulf bacteria and digest them.

Blood platelets are small colorless bodies which aid in the clotting of the blood. They are even smaller than the corpuscles.

The blood **plasma** has its source in the liquids taken into the body. It is straw-colored and varies in composition from day to day, and from hour to hour. It contains digested foods going to the cells, and waste products on their way to the kidneys, lungs, and skin. It carries hormones secreted by the ductless glands (Sec. 26-1), antibodies which fight disease (Sec. 28-22), and fibrinogen which helps in blood clotting (Sec. 23.3).

The composition of the blood is constantly changing as it receives and distributes food, wastes, glandular secretions, oxygen, and other substances.

When there is considerable loss of blood, as in surgery, or **hemorrhage** (*hem*-er-ij) from other causes, such as accident, sudden illness, or injury, there may be a loss of large numbers of red blood cells. The body begins at once to replace this loss and under normal conditions is able to do so within a month or two. In severe cases a **blood transfusion** is given to the patient. This **whole blood** not only brings the much needed red cells but also the blood plasma in which they are carried.

It was not until scientists had discovered that there are four distinct types of human blood that transfusion was considered a safe procedure. Human beings inherit their blood types. The four **blood types** are called A, B, O, and AB. Each person's blood is one of these types. When a transfusion is made, the patient must be given blood of the proper type. The new blood must mix with the patient's own blood without clumping in masses. This is called *agglutination*.

Blood is also grouped according to whether or not it possesses the **Rh factor**, a protein substance, antigen, found in red corpuscles. This factor, which is also inherited, was so named because it was discovered in a study of rhesus monkeys. Persons with the same blood type, A, B, O, or AB, may differ in their Rh factor. A person who has the Rh factor is called "Rh-positive," and a person who does not have it is called "Rh-negative." About 87% of Caucasians are Rh-positive. The remaining 13% are Rh-negative.

The Rh factor is important in blood transfusions, and it is especially important in connection with childbirth. If the mother is Rh-negative and the father is Rh-positive, the health of their child may be damaged. When it is known in advance that this situation exists in the

336

parents' blood, doctors can often take preventive measures so that these people will have normal, healthy children. **Hapten,** a substance obtained from red cells, is helpful in preventing the destruction of red cells by the Rh factor.

With modern methods of refrigeration, whole blood may be preserved for a limited time in *blood banks.* Thus it is possible to ship blood to far distant disaster areas and battlefronts as well as to ship it to hospitals for local use. Many products are made from blood plasma. Some of these will keep indefinitely. Others will be of value only when used within a few hours. An effort is being made to encourage healthy adults from 18 to 60 years of age to donate blood at frequent intervals. Usually one pint is donated each time. In this way a supply can be maintained at suitable locations for use in emergencies.

Whole blood is used for excessive bleeding, for surgery, and for shock resulting from injuries, as it replaces both plasma and cells. *Plasma* is given for burns, since it contains 91% water and 9% solids which are mostly protein. In addition to the water and protein solids, plasma also contains some sugar, minerals, vitamins, hormones, enzymes, and proteins. **Plasma proteins** have been separated and are available for use in specific cases of need. These plasma proteins include: (1) **serum albumin** (al-*byoo*-min), used for shock and to replace the protein lost in kidney and liver diseases; (2) **gamma globulin** (*glob*-yoo-lin) which carries antibodies to prevent such diseases as measles; (3) **fibrinogen** (fy-*brin*-oh-jen) and **thrombin** which supply *fibrin foam,* a spongy material used by surgeons and put directly into a wound to help it clot, and *fibrin film,* which is used to cover delicate tissue such as brain tissue.

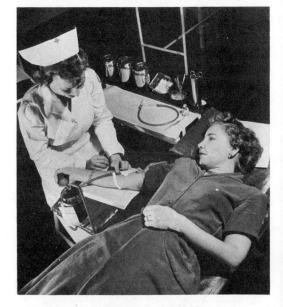

FIGURE 23-4. *BLOOD DONOR*

Since blood transfusions have come into common use, blood banks have been set up to stock blood for emergencies.

Plasma also carries *prothrombin,* an enzyme produced in the liver when vitamin K is present. At present there is no known substitute for whole blood which is entirely satisfactory.

23.3 The Clotting of Blood

When blood escapes from a broken blood vessel, it forms a clot. This is a peculiarity of blood, and if it were not for this property, animals would bleed to death from even a slight cut. The clot stops the flow of blood by sealing up the opening, and allows the wound to start healing.

Just what happens in the clotting of blood is not understood. At least three substances seem to be necessary for the formation of a clot. They are calcium salts, *fibrinogen,* and other compounds from a broken cell. When blood starts to escape from a cut, the platelets stick to the rough edges of the wound and begin to dissolve, releasing *thromboplastin* which unites with dissolved cal-

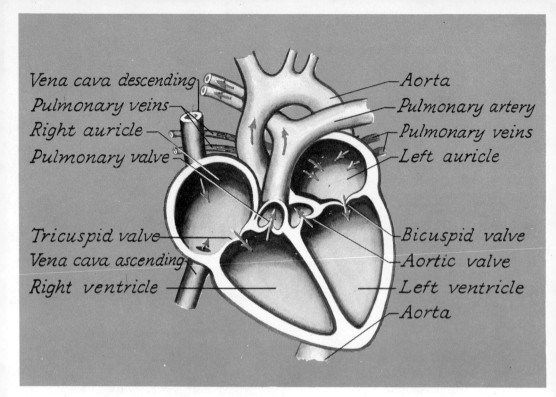

Figure 23-5. *THE HUMAN HEART*

    This cross section of the heart shows its four chambers. Which parts receive blood and which distribute it? Arrows indicate the direction of the blood flow, to the heart from the veins and away through the arteries. Note also the valves which control flow within the heart and regulate its passage into the aorta and pulmonary artery.

cium and a protein called **prothrombin.** The prothrombin which is produced with the help of vitamin K acts on the fibrinogen in the plasma and changes it to **fibrin threads** which form a trap for the corpuscles. As this net contracts, much of the serum is squeezed out, thus producing a firmer clot.

23.4 The Temperature of the Blood

    The normal temperature of the body of an adult is about 98.6° F, although there are a few healthy persons who regularly have a temperature below or above this average. This is known as **blood heat,** since it is maintained evenly throughout the body by the blood. This temperature may be lowered in the ears,

fingers, toes, and nose by exposure, and it may be raised all over by *fever;* when it is higher than 98.6°, the patient is said to have a fever. This is usually a sign that something has gone wrong somewhere in his body.

23.5 The Work of the Heart

    The heart consists of two **auricles** which receive blood from the veins, and two **ventricles** which force blood through the arteries. It is about the size of the fist and has strong muscular walls, continually pumping blood to all the cells of the body and back again. In a healthy person, the heart contracts about seventy times a minute. It is located in the *thoracic,* or chest, *cavity,* a little to the

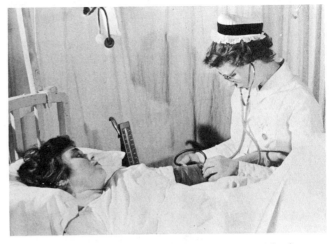

FIGURE 23-6. *CHECKING BLOOD PRESSURE*

The pressure of the blood against the walls of the arteries can be measured by a doctor with the help of a rubber bag around the arm and a mercury scale. Your blood pressure may vary from day to day because of fatigue, exertion, excitement, etc.

left side and between the lungs (Fig. 23-5). ("The work the heart does during the day is about equal to the energy expended by a man in climbing to the top of a mountain 3600 feet high. Assuming that the man weighs about 150 pounds, this would be equal to an amount of energy sufficient to lift 90 tons to a height of three feet. The work of the left side is greater than that of the right, since the former has to drive the blood all over the body, while the latter has only to force it to the lungs, which are near by. For this reason the muscle walls of the right ventricle are much thinner than those of the left ventricle."—CONN AND BUDDINGTON.)

Sometimes a fatty substance, cholesterol, collects on the lining of the arteries. If a small piece breaks away, it may plug up an artery in the heart muscle and cause a severe heart attack.

The Pulse.—Every time the heart beats (contracts), the blood is forced into the arteries in a wave which can be felt in the wrist or neck by placing the finger over an artery. This rhythmic wave is the **pulse.** By counting the number of waves in a minute, we determine the rate at which the heart beats. When a person runs or takes violent exercise, the pulse rate increases. A similar increase in the pulse rate occurs when a person becomes either angry or excited. An irregularity in the pulse or in the heartbeat may result when the heart valves between the auricles and ventricles do not completely close.

Closely associated with the pulse is the **blood pressure.** Blood pressure is the force with which the blood pushes against the walls of the arteries with every heartbeat. There are special appliances to measure this pressure. Too high or too low blood pressure is a danger sign. Very high blood pressure may break capillaries in the brain tissue, causing a cerebral hemorrhage.

23.6 The Circulation of the Blood

In order to follow the process of circulation, the meaning of three words must be clearly understood: *artery, vein,* and *capillary.* **Artery** is the name given to the *blood vessels which carry blood from the heart.* **Vein** is the term applied to the *vessels which return blood to the heart.* There are small structural differences between the veins and arteries in that the walls of the arteries are thicker, and there are no small *valves* as in the veins. These valves consist of small folds of tissue which lie closely pressed against the walls when the blood flows in one direction but form pockets and then fill with blood when backward pressure is

THE CIRCULATORY SYSTEM

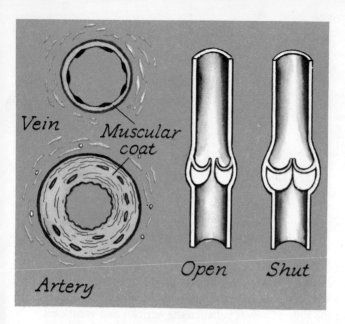

FIGURE 23-7. *STRUCTURE OF BLOOD VESSELS*

The cross section of the vein and artery (*left*) illustrates the difference in the muscular lining. The thick walls of the artery enable it to withstand the great pressure of inrushing blood from the heart. Valves in the vein (*right*) keep the blood from backtracking on its return to the heart.

exerted, thus keeping the flow of blood in one direction only. As the arteries divide into smaller and smaller branches, their walls, which consist of a thin, epithelial coat, allow food and oxygen to pass to the individual cells by diffusion. These tiny branches are called **capillaries** (Fig. 23-9).

23.7 Pulmonary Circulation

The *right ventricle,* after it receives the blood from the *right auricle* above, contracts and forces the blood into a *pulmonary* (lung) *artery* which forms two branches (Fig. 23-8). One of these goes to each lung, where it divides in the tissues of the lung into fine capillaries. These small capillaries, in close contact with the air sacs in the lung, supply the blood with oxygen and carry off its carbon dioxide. Finally the blood flows from these capillaries into the *pulmonary veins* which unite eventually and return the blood to the *left auricle.*

This is the **pulmonary circulation,** and by it the blood loses carbon dioxide and water and secures a fresh supply of oxygen. Its color changes from a bluish red to a bright red.

23.8 Systemic Circulation

From the *left auricle* the blood passes to the *left ventricle,* which pumps it through the **aorta** (ay-*or*-tuh), the largest of the arteries. The aorta branches out into smaller arteries which enter every organ in the body (Fig. 23-8). The *coronary arteries* supply the heart muscle itself. After the arteries enter the different organs, they divide into capillaries, which come into close contact with all the cells of the body, and supply them with dissolved oxygen and foods. The capillaries are so numerous that a piece of muscle with a cross section the size of a pinhead has about 800 of these capillaries.

Because of their great numbers, the capillaries can easily carry nourishment and oxygen to the tissues, and readily remove the waste. The capillaries carry the blood from the arteries toward the smaller veins, which unite to become larger much as a river system is built up by numerous branches. These veins carry the blood back to the right auricle through two main veins, the **venae cavae** (*vee*-nee *kay*-vee). This is the **systemic circulation,** during which the blood gives

NUTRITION IN MAN

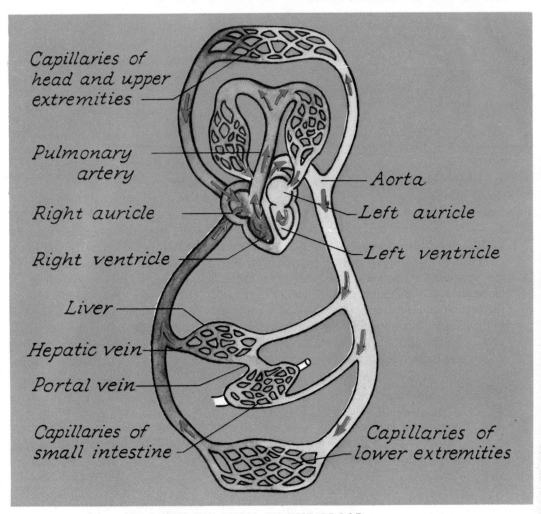

FIGURE 23-8. *CIRCULATION OF THE BLOOD*

This diagram represents circulation, both pulmonary and systemic, in the human body. Can you tell what happens to the blood as it circulates through the lungs, and describe its course from that point on?

Labels on figure:
- Capillaries of head and upper extremities
- Pulmonary artery
- Right auricle
- Right ventricle
- Liver
- Hepatic vein
- Portal vein
- Capillaries of small intestine
- Aorta
- Left auricle
- Left ventricle
- Capillaries of lower extremities

up to the cells much of its supply of oxygen and food value.

23.9 Portal Circulation

The **portal circulation** is that part of the systemic circulation which carries blood from the digestive organs to the liver. After passing through the liver, the blood is carried back to the heart. Digested foods are picked up from the digestive organs and much of the carbohydrate load is left in the liver, where it is stored as glycogen. At the same time other soluble substances may be picked up in the liver.

Thus the composition of the blood changes as it passes through the various organs of the body, such as the skin, muscles, and stomach. The blood in the capillaries supplies the substance necessary for the secretions of the glands; in the small intestine the capillaries absorb the elements of digested food; in the lungs they take up oxygen and give off

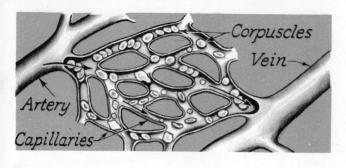

The microscopically small capillaries which connect arteries and veins form a network over the entire body. Their walls are only a single cell thick, so that food may pass out to cells, and waste matter be carried away.

carbon dioxide; and in the kidneys they throw off the waste products they have collected.

23.10   Renal Circulation

The **renal circulation** is that part of the systemic circulation which carries blood through the kidneys. A branch of the aorta, the *renal artery,* carries blood to the kidneys where various waste products are removed from it, and the *renal vein* brings blood back to the vena cava.

23.11   Lymph

As the blood flows through the capillaries, part of the plasma passes through the thin walls into the spaces between the cells and bathes the cells. This fluid which escapes from the capillaries is called **lymph** (*limf*). It is composed of digested food, water, and other substances. The cells use the food which they need and put back into the lymph the wastes which they have formed in the process of growth and repair. The

FIGURE 23-10. *PART OF THE LYMPHATIC SYSTEM*

Movement of lymph through the lymphatic ducts is accomplished by the contraction of the surrounding muscles. Lymph nodes, accumulations of lymphatic tissue, remove much toxic matter and bacteria from the blood.

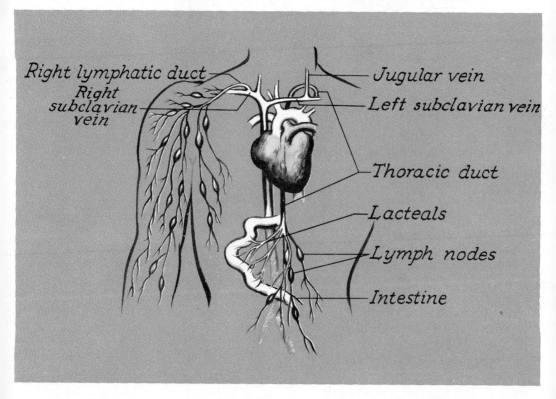

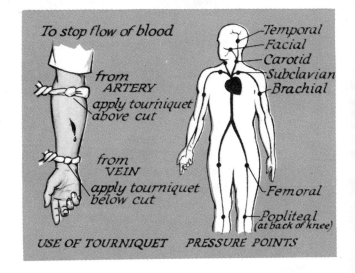

FIGURE 23-11. *PRESSURE POINTS*

A tourniquet may be used in an emergency to control bleeding. Its proper placement is shown at left. Hand pressure may be applied near pressure points (*right*). Why might the use of a tourniquet be dangerous in the hands of amateurs?

spaces between the cells form **lymph tubes.** They are small and irregular in shape, but form a mesh which joins to make larger vessels. Enlargements of these tubes form **lymph nodes** where white cells destroy bacteria. The lymph is collected into the large *thoracic duct* and the right lymphatic duct which open into the *subclavian veins* near the neck.

The **lymphatic circulation** differs from that of the blood in several ways. (1) There is no special organ for forcing the lymph along. Its circulation depends upon the movement of muscles. (2) The lymphatic nodes are places where bacteria in the lymph are destroyed by white corpuscles. (3) The lymph contains no red corpuscles. (4) The lymph does not travel its complete course in closed vessels as does the blood.

23.12 Cuts

Since blood vessels cross every part of the body inside the skin, we cannot injure any part without breaking some of them. A small cut causes the blood to flow only from capillaries, and it flows slowly and in small quantities. Pressure applied directly over the wound should be enough to stop the bleeding. When a vein is cut, the blood is dark in

color, and flows in larger quantities, but steadily. A severed artery sends out bright red blood in waves corresponding to the beats of the heart. To stop the flow of blood from a vein, compress the vein beyond the cut; to stop the flow from an artery, compress the artery between the cut and the heart.

A tourniquet should be used only for severe, life-threatening bleeding that cannot be stopped by other means. Once in place, the tourniquet should be released only by a physician. Continued pressure for more than two hours can cause severe damage or even death.

Hand pressure may be applied at parts

FIGURE 23-12. *A BLOOD CLOT*

Loss of blood is prevented by clotting. When blood is exposed to air, fibrin fibers are formed which trap the cells and prevent further flow.

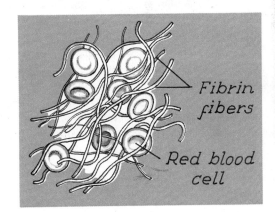

343

of the body where large blood vessels are near the surface. These are known as *pressure points* and are indicated on Figure 23-11. Study this figure carefully and try to locate them on yourself.

23.13 Exercise and Circulation

The purpose of a circulatory system is to supply every cell in the body with food and to carry away the waste. The more active the process of circulation, the better. The heart beats more rapidly, the lungs work harder, and the body becomes warm after a few minutes of vigorous exercise. These changes help to build up the body and remove the wastes.

23.14 Fainting

Fainting is due to an insufficient supply of blood in the brain. This lack of blood may arise from several causes, but the most common is some disturbance of the digestive processes, which causes the heart to beat too slowly. A fainting person should be placed flat on his back, if possible, with his head slightly lower than the rest of his body, and should be given plenty of fresh air. Cold water on the face or a bottle of ammonia held to the nostrils is often helpful in restoring consciousness.

23.15 Anemia

A reduction in the number of red corpuscles or the quantity of hemoglobin results in a condition known as **anemia**. A person may lose blood during surgery or through a cut or wound in an accident. Blood cells may also be destroyed during a disease or infection. There may be a lack of iron in the diet or a condition of the bone marrow that prevents red blood cells from forming.

23.16 Atomic Radiation

Atomic radiation changes molecules and atoms in living cells into electrically charged particles called *ions*. These ions may react in unpredictable ways in the body as a result of the radiation.

In addition to skin burns, radiation also causes damage to blood vessels and prevents the blood from clotting. In serious cases the blood cells are destroyed and new ones are unable to form. The proteins in the blood are reduced and digestion is disturbed. In severe cases, or acute *radiation sickness,* there is fever and bleeding. Radiation burns affect many parts of the body, causing redness, swelling, and large blisters. Because of the effect on the blood cells, atomic radiation can cause intense suffering and death.

FACTS TO REMEMBER

The function of the *circulatory system* is to carry oxygen and digested food to all parts of the body and to remove wastes. The organs of blood circulation are the heart and blood vessels, which consist of arteries, veins, and capillaries.

Blood is a fluid tissue, composed of a liquid plasma and solid substances, the corpuscles and platelets. The *red corpuscles* contain *hemoglobin,* which unites with oxygen and carries it to the cells. The *white corpuscles* aid the body in fighting infection. *Platelets* are believed to help in the clotting of blood. *Plasma* consists of water, plasma proteins, digested food, cell wastes, and any other substances carried by the blood.

For purposes of *transfusions,* there are four blood types: A, B, O, and AB. These types are also grouped with the *Rh factor* in a person's blood.

Blood forms a *clot* when the platelets at the site of a wound disintegrate, releasing a substance which reacts with calcium and certain blood proteins to form a *fibrin net*.

The *heart* consists of two auricles which receive blood from the veins, and two ventricles which pump the blood into the arteries. The *pulmonary circulation* carries blood to the lungs, where it picks up oxygen. The *systemic circulation* distributes blood to all parts of the body. The *portal circulation* carries digested food to the liver, where the carbohydrates are stored as glycogen. The *renal circulation* carries blood to the kidneys, where liquid wastes are removed. The *lymphatic circulation* consists of lymph vessels and lymph which bathes all the cells in fluid.

Fainting is a result of an insufficient supply of blood to the brain. *Anemia* is caused by a reduction of red blood corpuscles. *Atomic radiation* destroys the blood cells and prevents new ones from being formed. Heart valve damage may result from bacterial infections.

WORDS TO REMEMBER

anemia	fibrinogen	pulmonary circulation
aorta	fibrin threads	pulse
artery	gamma globulin	radiation
auricles	hapten	red corpuscles
blood	hemoglobin	renal circulation
blood bank	hemorrhage	Rh factor
blood heat	ions	serum albumin
blood pressure	lymph	systemic circulation
blood transfusion	lymphatic circulation	thrombin
blood type	lymph nodes	tourniquet
capillary	phagocytes	valve
circulatory system	plasma	vein
fainting	plasma proteins	venae cavae
fever	platelets	ventricles
fibrin film	portal circulation	white corpuscles
fibrin foam	prothrombin	whole blood

QUESTIONS

1. What is blood? Of what is it made?
2. Describe the red corpuscles. What is their function?
3. What is the function of the white corpuscles? The platelets?
4. Describe the formation of a blood clot.
5. What is the normal body temperature of an adult?
6. What is meant by pulse? Blood pressure?
7. Define: artery, vein, capillary, lymph, plasma.
8. Name four important blood types.
9. Discuss the changes which take place in the blood as it passes through the lungs.

10. What makes it possible for the blood to reach every part of the body?

11. Describe the portal circulation.

12. List *three* ways in which the lymphatic circulation differs from the blood circulation.

13. What is the effect of exercise on circulation?

14. What condition may result from an insufficient supply of blood to the brain? What treatment should be given?

COMPLETION TEST

As your teacher or classmate reads the following incomplete statements, with your book closed, write on a clean sheet of paper the word or phrase which correctly completes the statement.

1. The oxygen-carrying substance in the red corpuscles is called _____.
2. The _____ corpuscles are able to change shape.
3. The heart beats about _____ times per minute.
4. Vitamin _____ helps in clotting the blood.
5. The heart is located in the _____ cavity.
6. The _____ vein takes blood from the lungs to the heart.
7. The largest artery in the body is the _____.
8. Valves are found in the _____.
9. _____ bathes all the body cells.
10. For a cut _____, pressure should be applied between the cut and the heart.

PROJECTS

I. *To Show the Effect of Exercise on Pulse Rate.*

Materials.—Watch with second hand.

Method.—1. Work with another student. Find his pulse at the wrist and count the number of times it beats a minute. Take three trials.

2. Have your partner take some exercise. If you are at school, he may be able to go quickly down two or three flights of stairs and return or he may bend over and touch his toes ten times. Count his pulse rate after exercise.

Observations.—Record your results in a table similar to the following.

Pulse Rate		
Trial	At Rest	After Exercise
1		
2		
3		
Average		

Conclusion.—What is the effect of exercise on pulse rate?

Practical Application.—Why does the body need to have the blood circulate faster during exercise?

II. *Location of Pressure Points.*

Method.—1. In your library find the Red Cross First Aid textbook and also refer to Figure 23-11. Locate the following pressure points on yourself and on another person:

    a. Temporal—against the temple.

    b. Facial—against the lower jaw.

    c. Carotid—against the bones of the neck.

    d. Subclavian—against the first rib.

    e. Brachial—against the humerus in the upper arm.

    f. Femoral—in the groin, against the pelvis.

2. Using Figures 23-5 and 23-8 in the text as references, make a drawing of the main blood vessels and label the pressure points.

3. When would you apply pressure? How long should it be maintained at a time?

III. *The Use of a Tourniquet.*—This consists of a cloth or rubber band at least 1½ to 2 inches wide. It is placed above the cut if an artery is severed.

Study the Red Cross First Aid textbook and practice applying a tourniquet on an arm and a leg. Once the tourniquet is applied, it must be inspected by a physician within an hour. He will release it to let blood flow if the clot has not formed by then. This will prevent the action of harmful bacteria in the wound and a condition known as *gangrene*. Remember a tourniquet has a definite use, namely, to stop the flow of blood from a severe wound. It is, however, a *very dangerous bandage to apply*, since it requires constant care to prevent serious consequences.

IV. *Study of the Corpuscles.*—Sterilize a blood lance with alcohol. Wash your hands and scrub them thoroughly. With a piece of cotton dipped in alcohol, clean your finger or thumb. Release the spring of the lance and collect a drop of blood on a clean glass slide. Place a cover glass over it and examine it under the microscope. Put a drop of iodine on your finger and let it dry.

1. Find the tiny red corpuscles and try to determine their shape.

2. Locate some white corpuscles if you can.

3. Notice that the solution does not appear bright red when seen under a microscope in small amounts.

4. Write your observations and try to draw what you see.

V. *Comparison of Circulatory Systems.*—Using reference books, write a comparison of the circulatory systems of the fish, frog, turtle, bird, and mammal. Illustrate with colored sketches or diagrams if you can.

VI. *The Work of Malpighi.*—Find out all you can of the work of Marcello Malpighi (page 683) on capillary circulation. Why did William Harvey (page 680) not find the capillaries?

VII. *Study of Hemophilia.*—Look up the record of the royal families of Spain and Russia and find out all you can about hemophilia, which is inherited. Why are persons with hemophilia called "bleeders"?

REFERENCES

Amberson and Smith, *Outline of Physiology.* Williams and Wilkins.
Blakeslee, *Blood's Magic for All.* Public Affairs Pamphlet No. 145.
Burton-Opitz, *An Elementary Manual of Physiology.* Saunders.
Fishbein, *An Hour of Health.* Lippincott.
Glynn, *The Story of Blood.* A. A. Wyn.
Greisheimer, *Physiology and Anatomy.* Lippincott.
Know Your Heart. Public Affairs Pamphlet No. 137.
Schneider, *Lifeline, The Story of Your Circulatory System.* Harcourt, Brace.
The Story of Blood. American Red Cross.
Williams, *Healthful Living.* Macmillan.
Your Heart. Metropolitan Life Insurance Co.

CHAPTER 24

Respiration and Excretion

24.1 Respiration

The process of taking oxygen into the cells, releasing energy, and removing carbon dioxide is called **respiration.** Simple animals, like the ameba and hydra, take oxygen directly into the cells from the water in which air is dissolved. Higher animals need specialized breathing organs to bring oxygen into the body, where it can be carried by the blood to the cells. For this purpose the fish has gills, the earthworm a thin skin, and reptiles, birds, and mammals have lungs, which are very highly developed organs.

24.2 Breathing Organs of Man

Man is able to take air in and out of the lungs through the **respiratory system.** The air enters the nose and passes through the throat into the windpipe, or **trachea** (*tray*-kee-uh). The opening into the windpipe is covered by the **epiglottis** (ep-ih-*glot*-iss), which is raised during breathing and closed when food is swallowed. The windpipe leads into the *voice box,* or **larynx** (*lair*-inks),

FIGURE 24-1. *THE LUNGS*

Air travels down the trachea, through the bronchi, and into the lungs, the major organs of respiration, where the blood receives fresh oxygen. Note the large vein and artery which travel between the heart and lungs.

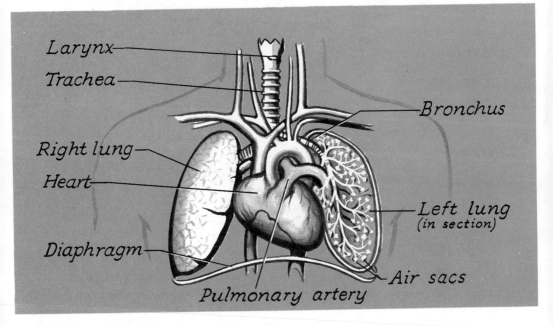

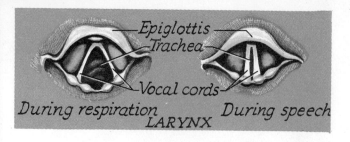

Epiglottis
Trachea
Vocal cords
During respiration   During speech
LARYNX

FIGURE 24-2. *LARYNX*

The larynx or voice box contains the vocal cords, which are put in vibration by a stream of air during speech.

which is just below the opening into the windpipe. The thyroid cartilage which protrudes in front is often called "Adam's apple." The larynx is formed by several large pieces of cartilage lined with a mucous membrane. Inside it are two folds of elastic tissue called the *vocal cords*. The windpipe divides into two branches, one entering each lung. Each branch is called a **bronchus** (*bronkus*). Air is carried to the lungs through the windpipe and bronchi, which are kept open by many stiff cartilage rings.

As each bronchus enters the lung, it divides into branches which in turn branch out again and again, until the entire lung is penetrated by these passages. Each branch ends in a small pouchlike sac called an *air sac* or **alveolus** (al-*vee*-oh-lus). The walls of the air sacs are thin, and the sacs themselves are surrounded by tiny branches of the blood vessels. These thin walls of the lungs and blood vessels are adapted to the passage of oxygen into the blood and to getting rid of wastes, especially carbon dioxide and water.

24.3   How We Breathe

The lungs are elastic and covered with a *pleural membrane*. **Inspiration** is the term applied to the taking of air into the lungs, and **expiration** to the forcing out of air. The full capacity of adult lungs is about 4000 cc. of air. During inspiration the muscles of the chest do

FIGURE 24-3. *ACTION OF THE DIAPHRAGM IN RESPIRATION*

Air is drawn into the body through the trachea. During inspiration, the chest cavity expands because the diaphragm flattens and the ribs move up and out. Why is breathing more rapid during vigorous exercise?

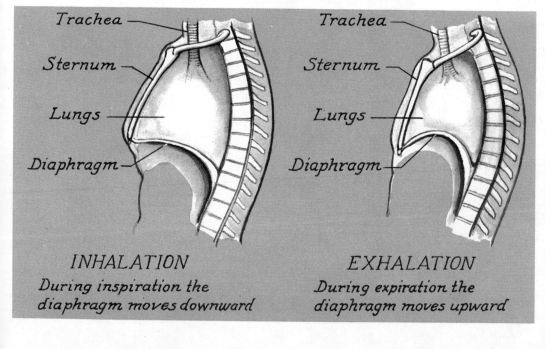

Trachea
Sternum
Lungs
Diaphragm

INHALATION
During inspiration the diaphragm moves downward

Trachea
Sternum
Lungs
Diaphragm

EXHALATION
During expiration the diaphragm moves upward

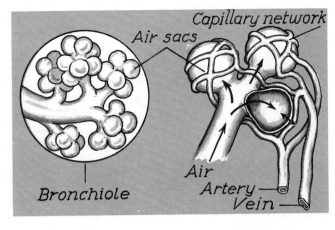

FIGURE 24-4. *EXCHANGE OF GASES*

Bronchioles are composed of many tiny air sacs. Capillaries cling to the thin walls of each sac, allowing molecules of oxygen and carbon dioxide to be exchanged.

considerable work: the cartilages attached to the ribs must be bent, the walls of the abdomen stretched, and the muscular diaphragm pushed down. This contraction of the respiratory muscles increases the volume of the chest cavity, creating a lowered air pressure in the lungs which causes an inrush of air. About 500 cc. of air is taken in by each inspiration during normal breathing.

As the respiratory muscles relax, the elasticity of the cartilages, the increased pressure of the abdomen, and the upward movement of the diaphragm force the air out. About 500 cc. of *tidal air* thus pass out, leaving, in an adult, about 3500 cc. of *complemental air* still in the lungs. We can remove the larger part of this air from the lungs and replace it with fresh air by breathing deeply a few times. That part of the complemental air which is never taken out of the lungs at any one breath is called *residual air*.

If you wished to hold your breath, you could not do so for much more than a minute. This is a protection of the body to keep a steady supply of air moving to the lungs. While you are holding your breath, the body continues to carry on its normal activities, with oxidation taking place in the cells and carbon dioxide being formed. As you keep holding your breath, the carbon dioxide in the blood increases in amount.

The excess carbon dioxide causes a message to be sent to the breathing center of the brain, the *medulla,* and you gasp for fresh air.

The natural rate of breathing is about eighteen times a minute, but the rate is higher in persons with a small lung capacity. Exercise increases the rate of breathing. (Explain why outdoor exercise is better for us than indoor exercise.)

All the air passages are lined with cells bearing numerous *cilia* (Fig. 4-5), which are constantly in motion. Their work is to carry toward the mouth the particles of dust and other foreign material brought in by the air. This foreign matter is removed when we cough or clear our throats. (Why is clean air better for us than foul air?) Because the nasal passages are lined with cilia, and a warm, moist membrane, it is healthier to breathe through the nose.

The purpose of breathing is to pull air into the lungs, so that oxygen may be taken from it and used in the body; and to get rid of air laden with carbon dioxide. Both these processes take place by means of capillaries in the walls of the air sacs. Through them, oxygen is taken in from the fresh air we inhale, and absorbed into the blood. In return, carbon dioxide is given off into the air we exhale.

RESPIRATION AND EXCRETION

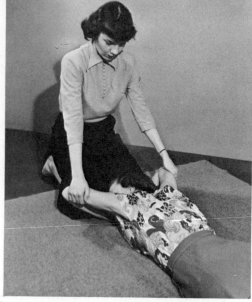

FIGURE 24-5. *ARTIFICIAL RESPIRATION*

These pictures illustrate the back pressure-arm lift method which is accepted as standard by the American Red Cross. Artificial respiration is sometimes necessary when water or gas has been taken into the lungs. Resuscitation of a victim has been known to take as long as 8 hours.

24.4 Exchange of Gases

Oxygen from the air passes through the thin walls of the air sacs into the blood. There it combines with the hemoglobin of the red corpuscles and forms **oxyhemoglobin,** a bright-red compound seen in arterial bleeding. As the blood circulates, the oxygen is released and passes through the capillary walls to the cells. Carbon dioxide diffuses into the lymph and then the capillaries. Some unites with hemoglobin and the rest dissolves in the plasma. When it reaches the lungs, it is set free.

24.5 Systematic Exercise

If we keep our bodies in correct posture, little need be said about breathing exercises. It is desirable to be able to breathe deeply and to have a large chest to give the heart more room in which to do its work. Lazy habits of breathing tend to weaken the muscles of inspiration, with the result that too small a part of the lungs is used.

The normal movements in breathing permit the ribs to be lifted as air is drawn into the lungs. Wearing tight clothing around the chest interferes with these normal movements and makes it hard to get the required amount of oxygen into the lungs. Unless loose clothing is worn during exercise, the muscles used in respiration are not properly benefited.

24.6 Suffocation and Artificial Breathing

When a person stops breathing, the lack of oxygen will cause permanent brain damage within minutes unless air is rhythmically forced into the lungs. Some causes of suffocation are choking, drowning, electric shock, drugs, heart attack, gas, or an air-tight space.

Persons who have suffocated can often be revived by artificially moving the muscles of the chest so as to imitate as closely as possible the normal breathing movements. The following methods of artificial respiration are approved by the American National Red Cross.

For the *mouth-to-mouth rescue method,* these procedures should be followed:

1. Place the victim on his back and clear the air passages.

2. Tilt his head back and move the jaw forward to keep the tongue away from the back of the throat.

3. Keeping this position, place your open mouth airtight over his mouth and pinch his nostrils to avert air leakage.

4. Blow into the victim's mouth until you see the chest rise; then remove your mouth and listen for the returning air.

5. Repeat breathing, taking your mouth off after each breath. Continue at 12 breaths a minute for an adult and 20 for a child. Continue until breathing starts or a physician directs otherwise.

Follow these procedures for the *back pressure-arm lift method:*

Place the victim face down. Bend his elbows and place his hands one upon the other. Turn his face to one side, placing his cheek upon his hands.

Kneel at the victim's head, close to his forearms. Place your hands upon the flat of the victim's back so that the heels of your hands are just below a point running between his armpits. With your thumb tips just touching, spread your fingers down and outward.

1. Rock forward until your arms are about vertical and allow the weight of your body to exert slow, steady, even pressure down on your hands. This forces air from his lungs. Keep your elbows straight and exert pressure almost directly downward on his back.

2. Release the pressure, avoiding a final thrust, and begin to rock slowly backward. Slide your hands up to a point just above his elbows.

3. Draw his arms up and toward you. Apply just enough lift to feel resistance and tension at the victim's shoulders. Do not bend your elbows and as you rock backward his arms will be drawn toward you.

4. Drop the victim's arms to the ground. The arm lift expands the chest.

Repeat the cycle 12-15 times a minute at a *steady* rate.

24.7 Ventilation

Temperature, moisture, and the oxygen-carbon dioxide content of the air are very important in maintaining health. Movement of air speeds up evaporation of perspiration on the skin. Moisture in the air keeps the membranes of the nose and throat from becoming too dry. When this happens, infections such as colds may lower body resistance to disease. Gases from cooking, furnaces, and automobile engines may contain enough carbon monoxide to be dangerous by uniting with the hemoglobin of the blood. With proper ventilation, the body is able to receive enough fresh air to prevent this.

24.8 Oxygen at High Altitudes

Oxygen is heavier than air, and is present in large enough amounts near the earth's surface for man to breathe normally. As mountain climbers go higher, the air pressure decreases, and the necessary oxygen supply is harder to get at each breath. People living on the mountains of Peru in South America have become used to a small oxygen supply and adapt themselves to it, but travelers have difficulty doing so for a few days. The amount of oxygen above

Official U.S. Navy Photo

FIGURE 24-6. *DIVING OUTFIT*

A diver prepares for a salvage operation dressed in a pressurized suit and helmet with air line.

ten thousand feet, however, is too low for human survival. When airplane pilots fly higher than this level, they either wear oxygen masks or use pressurized cabins or resort to both.

24.9 Sea Diving

When divers plan to remain under water for long periods of time, they must wear pressurized diving suits and carry a supply of oxygen. This is not pure oxygen, but also contains some carbon dioxide to stimulate breathing. Man is utterly dependent upon an adequate supply of oxygen to maintain life.

24.10 Respiratory Diseases

Nearly everyone has had some respiratory diseases and is concerned with their prevention. Colds, catarrh, bronchitis, influenza, pneumonia, and tuberculosis are infections of the respiratory tract. Many serums and antihistamines are being tried with varying amounts of success. Different strains of filtrable viruses may cause these infections.

An *allergy,* which is a sensitivity to certain substances, may inflame membranes of the nostrils and sinuses, causing headaches and sneezing. Hay fever is usually produced by pollen grains irritating the mucous membranes. Dust particles from quarries and mines may cause *silicosis* (sil-ih-*koh*-sis), a lung condition that may lead to tuberculosis.

24.11 Tonsils and Adenoids

The *tonsils* at the back of the throat help to remove bacteria as the blood flows through them. When there are too many bacteria, the tonsils become infected and often must be removed.

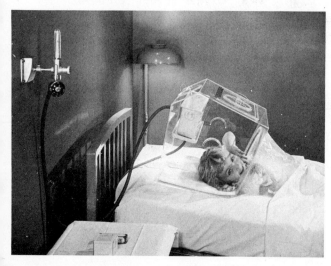

FIGURE 24-7. *OXYGEN TENT*

When anoxia, or lack of oxygen, results from such diseases as pneumonia, heart ailments, etc., the oxygen tent is a useful device to supply the patient with more oxygen than is normally found in air. Modern tents are transparent, so that the patient will feel less confined.

Linde Air Products Co.

Adenoids (*ad*-in-oids) are also growths of tissue located in the back of the throat. When these become infected or enlarged, they partly block the nasal passages and force a child to breathe through the mouth. Sometimes these have to be removed or reduced in size.

It is essential that good health be sought through normal and rational living. Fresh air, adequate rest, proper food, and systematic exercise are vital, especially for boys and girls.

24.12   Oxidation in the Cells

Oxygen unites with the carbohydrates and fats in all cells, producing heat and releasing energy. A muscle cell releases energy in the form of muscular contractions; a nerve cell releases energy as nerve activity or chemical change. Resultant wastes from muscle cells and fatigue toxins from nerve reactions must then be removed.

24.13   Assimilation

Proteins are brought to the cells in the form of *amino acids,* which are used to build and repair the protoplasm. They are carried by the blood plasma, and as it circulates slowly through the capillaries, the materials needed for the growth and repair of the cells pass by diffusion through the thin walls of the capillaries into the lymph surrounding the cells. Each cell is thus able to take in whatever it needs to build and repair its protoplasm. This process of building and repair is called **assimilation.**

The cells of the body are being constantly worn out: (1) whenever the muscles are used; (2) when objects come in contact with the epidermis; (3) when food passes along the alimentary canal. Nerve cells wear out with constant use and need to be rebuilt.

When the body is burned, cut, or

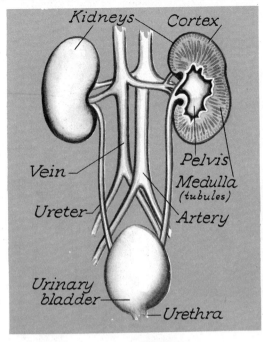

FIGURE 24-8. *THE KIDNEY SYSTEM*

The kidneys are one of the chief excretory organs. Blood is carried to the kidneys by the *renal artery.* As the blood passes through the *glomerulus,* the mass of capillaries at the top of the kidney tubules, waste matter is withdrawn from the blood. It is conducted to the bladder by two tubes, the *ureters.*

otherwise injured, new cells must be formed. In order to develop normally, children need to produce many new cells. The amino acids are needed for growth as well as replacement. The wastes from amino acids during growth are changed into urea, mostly in the liver, before being released into the capillaries. Minerals are also necessary to build bones and teeth and to grow hair and nails.

24.14   Excretion

The removal of waste substances from the body is known as **excretion.** The kidneys, sweat glands, and lungs are the chief excretory organs, but the greater part of the elimination of waste substances is done by the kidneys.

RESPIRATION AND EXCRETION

355

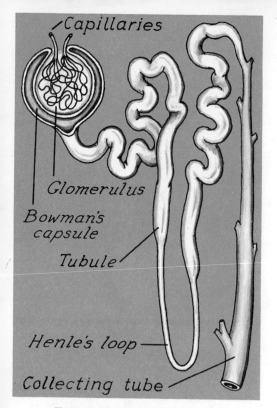

Capillaries

Glomerulus

Bowman's
capsule

Tubule

Henle's loop

Collecting tube

FIGURE 24-9. *KIDNEY
GLOMERULUS*

There are over one million glomeruli in a single human kidney. As blood flows through a glomerulus, fluid filters out and passes to the tubule. Water and needed salts are reabsorbed; wastes are passed into the collecting tube.

24.15 The Kidneys

The kidney system consists of a pair of *kidneys,* two *ureters,* the *bladder,* and the *urethra.* The kidneys are dark-red, bean-shaped organs located at the back of the abdominal cavity, one on each side of the spinal column. Each of the kidneys is about four inches long, two and a half inches wide, and an inch thick (Fig. 24-8).

On the outside of the kidneys is the **cortex** for protection. The inner layer, the **medulla** (meh-*duhl*-uh), is composed of millions of tiny *tubules,* which remove wastes from the blood. The tubule is the structural unit of the kidney

and is similar to a sweat gland. It is a long, thin-walled tube bent inward at the medulla to form a thin-walled cup (Fig. 24-9) with a thick mass of capillaries, the **glomerulus** (gloh-*mer*-yoo-lus). As the blood passes through a glomerulus, the wastes are removed by diffusion and collected in the tubules where the cells remove useful substances such as glucose and mineral salts. This process is *resorption,* since the materials return to the blood. The small remainder of wastes and the water are carried to the **pelvis** of the kidney, a hollow region near the center.

These wastes, the **urine,** are then carried by the **ureters** (yoo-*ree*-ters) to the **bladder,** from which they are excreted through the **urethra** (yoo-*ree*-thruh). The urine is about 95 per cent water and 5 per cent wastes containing nitrogen and salt.

The functions of the two kidneys are (1) to remove the waste materials, (2) to help regulate the balance between the salt and water in the body, (3) to help control the formation of red blood cells in the bone marrow, (4) to help with the transformation of fats and proteins in the body, and (5) to help regulate the blood pressure.

24.16 The Lungs as Organs of Excretion

The carbon dioxide gas formed as a waste product of the cells is removed from the blood into the air sacs and passed out through the lungs. In addition to this, all exhaled air contains water vapor. Thus water is excreted from the lungs, as well as from the skin and from the kidneys.

24.17 The Sweat Glands of the Skin

As you will recall from Section 19.5, the sweat glands are very important in

356

removing nitrogenous wastes and mineral salts from the blood. Again it is important to remember to drink plenty of water, since it carries away dissolved wastes and is excreted in large amounts through the pores.

24.18 The Intestine

The excretion wastes from the intestine include several digestive secretions which are not absorbed after they have caused the different digestive changes. The *bile pigments* may be especially mentioned as excretions that pass from the body through the intestine. The indigestible part of the food which is not taken up by the blood also passes out through the large intestine as *feces*. This process is called **elimination.**

24.19 The Necessity of Excretion

Unless the several organs of excretion do their work properly, the wastes of the body accumulate. These wastes are poisonous, and harmful results follow if they are allowed to remain in the system. A skin which is not healthy cannot be expected to hold healthy nerve endings or to do its work as it should. Overeating or eating too much meat places an extra burden on the kidneys, because the body absorbs only as much nutriment as is needed and such excess as can be stored as fat. The rest has to be removed, thus increasing the work of the kidneys. Regularity and moderation in eating, as in all habits, are two excellent rules to follow. The removal of wastes from the body is greatly influenced by the amount of water that is taken daily. There are few people who drink enough water for these requirements and very few people who ever drink more than is necessary.

FACTS TO REMEMBER

The function of the *respiratory system* is to supply the cells with oxygen and remove the carbon dioxide. In the *lungs,* oxygen passes by osmosis from the *alveoli* into the surrounding capillaries, and is carried by the blood to all cells of the body. Carbon dioxide is removed in a similar manner. The process of *breathing* enables us to take air into the lungs and expel the carbon dioxide. In the cells, some foods are *oxidized* to produce heat and energy, and other foods are *assimilated* to build and repair tissue.

Artificial respiration can be used to revive people who have suffocated from lack of oxygen. Proper *ventilation* and *systematic exercise* are also important in supplying our bodies with the necessary amount of oxygen and to prevent respiratory diseases.

The function of the *excretory system* is to remove waste materials from the body. The organs of excretion are the kidneys, sweat glands, large intestine, and lungs. Blood is filtered through the *kidney tubules,* and the *urine* is carried from the kidneys through the *ureters* and stored in the *bladder* until it is removed from the body through the *urethra.* The tubules of the kidneys and the *sweat glands* of the skin have similar structure and function. The *lungs* remove water vapor, and the *large intestine* eliminates the remaining undigested food and intestinal secretions as feces.

WORDS TO REMEMBER

adenoids
allergy
alveolus
artificial respiration
assimilation
bladder
breathing
bronchus
complemental air
cortex
elimination

epiglottis
excretion
expiration
glomerulus
inspiration
kidney
larynx
medulla
oxyhemoglobin
pelvis
residual air

respiration
respiratory disease
suffocate
tidal air
tonsils
trachea
tubule
ureter
urethra
urine
ventilation

QUESTIONS

1. Name the breathing organs in man.
2. How are the air sacs adapted for the exchange of gases?
3. Explain how we breathe.
4. Explain artificial respiration.
5. Explain the difference between tidal air and complemental air. What is residual air?
6. What is the effect of systematic exercise on the organs which perform breathing?
7. Mention as many causes of suffocation as you can.
8. Explain how gases are exchanged in the lungs.
9. What is assimilation? Why is it necessary?
10. Compare the function of the kidneys with the function of the sweat glands.
11. Name two other organs of excretion and the wastes given off by each.
12. Distinguish between excretion and elimination.

COMPLETION TEST

As your teacher or classmate reads the following incomplete statements, with your book closed, write on a clean sheet of paper the word or phrase which correctly completes the statement.

1. The process of taking oxygen into the cells and giving off carbon dioxide is called _____.
2. The opening into the windpipe is covered by the _____.
3. The voice box is called the _____.
4. Taking air into the lungs is called _____.
5. During _____ the diaphragm moves upward.
6. The natural rate of breathing is about _____ times per minute.
7. The treatment for any form of suffocation is usually _____ _____.
8. The union of oxygen with food material is called _____.
9. Wastes excreted by the kidneys are nitrogenous wastes and _____.
10. A person should drink at least _____ glasses of water a day.

NUTRITION IN MAN

PROJECTS

I. *The Effect of Exercise upon the Rate of Breathing.*

Method.—1. Work with another student. Place your hand upon his chest and count the number of times he breathes a minute. Inspiration and expiration count as one breath. In the meantime have him read something to himself to keep his mind away from his breathing. Otherwise, he may not breathe regularly. Take three trials.

2. Have him take some exercise until he is out of breath. Then count the number of breaths per minute. Take three trials in all, having him exercise each time.

Observation.—Record and average your observations in a table.

Conclusion.—What is the effect of exercise on the breathing rate?

Application.—Why does the body need more oxygen during exercise?

II. *Artificial Respiration.*—Learn the back pressure-arm lift method of artificial respiration from a doctor or a Red Cross first-aid instructor. Practice until you have mastered the correct method and can keep even rhythm at a rate of twelve to fifteen times a minute.

1. When should artificial respiration be given?
2. How long should it be continued?
3. What should be done to lessen shock during the process?
4. What after treatment should be given?

III. *Find Out All You Can about Silicosis.*—What is being done to prevent it? What is the danger of it?

IV. *To Show That Lungs Excrete Carbon Dioxide.*

Materials.—Limewater, test tubes, glass tubes.

Method.—Pour a small amount of limewater into two test tubes. Cover one tube and let it stand for twenty minutes. Blow slowly through a glass tube into the second test tube. Watch for any change in color. You will recall that the test for carbon dioxide gas is to force it into limewater until a white color appears.

Observation.—Record the appearance of the limewater in each test tube. Why are two test tubes of limewater used in this experiment?

Conclusion.—Do the lungs excrete carbon dioxide? Your proof?

Practical Application.—Why is it important to breathe deeply?

V. *Comparison of Excretory Systems.*—Make a comparative study of excretion of liquid wastes in paramecium, the earthworm, the crayfish, frog, and man. Illustrate your report with diagrams.

REFERENCES

Haupt, *Fundamentals of Biology.* McGraw-Hill.

Hunter, *Problems in Biology.* American Book.

Kimber, Gray, Stackpole, *Textbook of Anatomy and Physiology.* Macmillan.

Newell, Martin, *The Human Body.* Holt.

Pomerantz, *Your Respiratory System.* Blakiston.

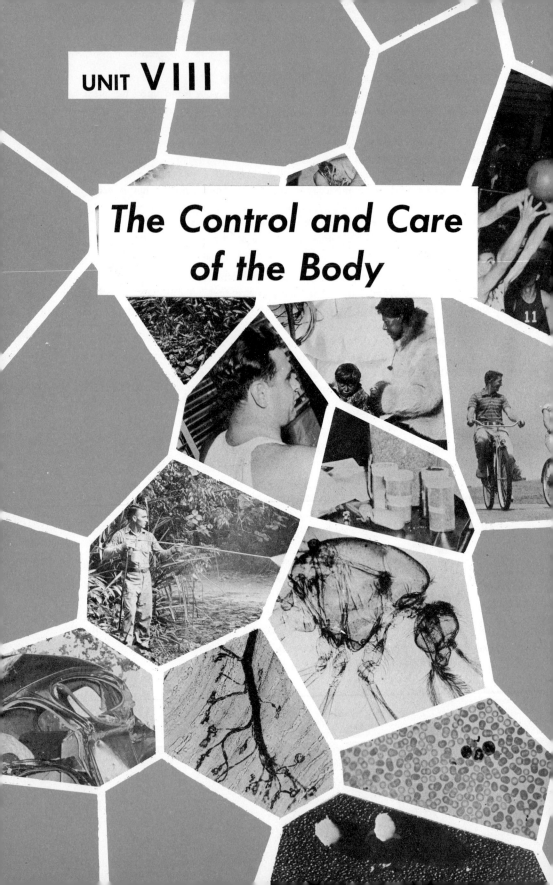

The Control and Care of the Body

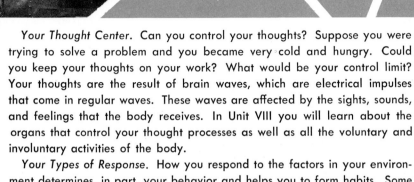

Your Thought Center. Can you control your thoughts? Suppose you were trying to solve a problem and you became very cold and hungry. Could you keep your thoughts on your work? What would be your control limit? Your thoughts are the result of brain waves, which are electrical impulses that come in regular waves. These waves are affected by the sights, sounds, and feelings that the body receives. In Unit VIII you will learn about the organs that control your thought processes as well as all the voluntary and involuntary activities of the body.

Your Types of Response. How you respond to the factors in your environment determines, in part, your behavior and helps you to form habits. Some responses are automatic, like jumping at a sudden sound or blinking in bright light. Others have to be learned, like tying your shoe, skating, or riding horseback. What kinds of habits have you formed? Is your handwriting good? Are you careful in crossing streets? Are you courteous?

Some responses require thought, such as learning new things and understanding what you read. When you learn in Unit VIII that there are harmful effects in the use of alcohol and tobacco and you decide not to use any of them, this will show in your behavior and also result in good health. Do you really have good control of your thoughts? Can you show response on a high level?

Your Glands and Your Behavior. Some glands help give extra strength during emergencies. Others make you grow tall or remain short. Some glands prevent conditions such as diabetes or lack of muscular control. In Unit VIII you will discover the importance of these ductless glands in regulating your growth and keeping you strong. The chemicals produced by these glands can make you feel energetic and ready to study or just tired and not interested in your work. In Unit VIII you will have an opportunity not only to think about your own behavior but also to learn how your own glands work. You will learn how life begins from a single cell and how it develops through the life cycle of man.

CHAPTER 25

The Nervous System

25.1 The Brain, Control Center of the Body

One of the first systems to be developed in animals is the **nervous system.** This is the system which enables them to find food, to fight enemies, and to guard against danger.

The simplest animals, as ameba, do not have brains but respond with their whole bodies. Paramecium has to coordinate the action of the cilia so that they stroke together, or else it could not move in response to danger or food stimuli. Tiny strands of protoplasm between the nucleus and the cilia make this possible.

Animals like the jellyfish have a *nerve net* instead of a central system. This means that every tentacle has to learn by itself. If you had this kind of a system, each separate finger would have to learn that the stove was hot. With a *central nervous system,* one burned finger sends the message to the brain, and your thought brain tells you that the hot stove would burn any part of the body and that you had better keep away from it.

Animals like the earthworm and those more highly developed have nerve centers, the main ones being called the *brain.* Vertebrates have the most highly developed brains. Fish, frogs, and reptiles show increasing complexity. Since they are warm blooded, birds and mammals need well-developed nervous systems to help protect them in their more active lives.

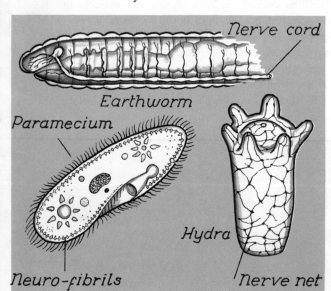

Nerve cord

Earthworm

Paramecium

Hydra

Neuro-fibrils

nerve net

FIGURE 25-1. *SIMPLE NERVOUS SYSTEMS*

Even the single celled paramecium has a system of coordination. Neurofibrils regulate its cilia. Compare this to the systems of the hydra and earthworm.

362

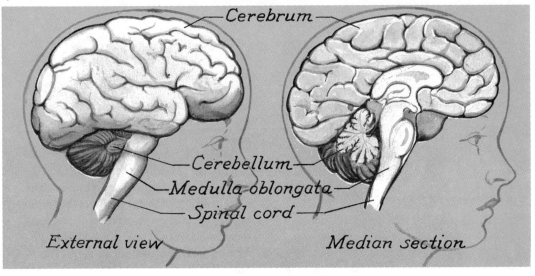

FIGURE 25-2. *CENTRAL NERVOUS SYSTEM*
The central nervous system consists of the brain and spinal cord. The brain has three major parts: the cerebrum controls thought and voluntary actions; the cerebellum coordinates the muscles and makes balance possible; and the medulla controls vital automatic activities of the body.

In man, the **central nervous system** consists of the *brain* and *spinal cord*. The brain is the control center of the body; it receives messages from all parts of the body and sends out the orders causing movement and other responses.

Living brains produce electrical impulses. These impulses come in regular, or rhythmic, waves. Each nerve cell has a small positive charge on the surface and a negative charge inside. As the impulse passes each point along a nerve fiber it becomes neutral for an instant. Then the area builds up an electrical charge. This results in brain waves which vary with activity. Brain waves have been picked up as sound waves. Each individual has a different brain wave pattern. The normal reactions to various *stimuli* are similar. Unusual sights or sounds that provoke anxiety or fear affect the responses in the brain and set up physical reactions which are beyond the control of the will. It is on the basis of some of these reactions that lie detectors are used.

25.2 · Organization of the Brain

There are three main parts of the brain: (1) the **cerebrum** (*seh*-ruh-brum) which controls our thoughts and actions; (2) the **cerebellum** (seh-ruh-*bel*-lum), which controls balance and voluntary muscles; and (3) the **medulla oblongata** (meh-*duhl*-uh oblong-*gay*-tuh), which controls the involuntary muscles and automatic internal organs.

The *cerebrum* of man shows the highest development of any animal. The outer *cortex* has deep convolutions which increase the surface area. The cerebrum contains *gray matter,* nerve cells without sheaths, and *white matter,* fibers with sheaths. Different areas control specific activities but are connected through association fibers. When a child is born, his cerebrum consists of scattered nerve cells. As the child develops, he forms associations and makes a network of pathways among the brain cells. Thus experiences are recorded, memory develops, and man is able to learn.

Your ability to learn depends upon

THE NERVOUS SYSTEM

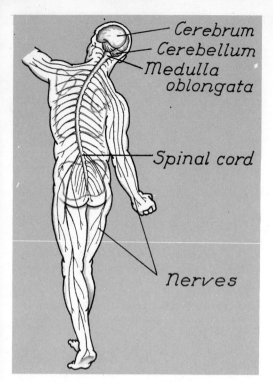

FIGURE 25-3. *NERVOUS SYSTEM*

The nervous system reaches all parts and regulates all functions of the human body. Some major nerves are shown here as they branch from the spinal cord.

how well the outer surface (**cortex**) of the cerebrum is able to register the impressions of things you see, hear, and

feel; the kind of connections that the *association fibers* can make; and the relationship to your past experience. The more impressions you make through learning experiences and the more active you keep the association fibers, the better you will be able to think.

The cerebrum has twelve pairs of cranial nerves which send messages directly for immediate interpretation. The eyes can only transfer light waves to the brain, but unless the cerebrum interprets them, we are not aware of what we see. The ears carry sound waves to the brain, but without the cerebrum we should not understand what we hear.

The *cerebellum* aids balance and regulates the action of voluntary muscles, such as those of the arms and legs. As a child, you had to learn to walk. Your cerebrum, or thought brain, helped to direct your feet; your cerebellum gave you balance until walking became automatic. So it is with writing; the cerebellum controls the muscles used in the actual motions of writing, leaving the cerebrum free to think about what to write.

The *medulla oblongata* controls the vital body processes and regulates the

FIGURE 25-4. *SPEEDY REACTION*

A stimulus received when the boy's hand touches the flame activates a motor neuron without entering the brain (*left*), causing him to remove his hand. When the stimulus later reaches his brain, he feels pain.

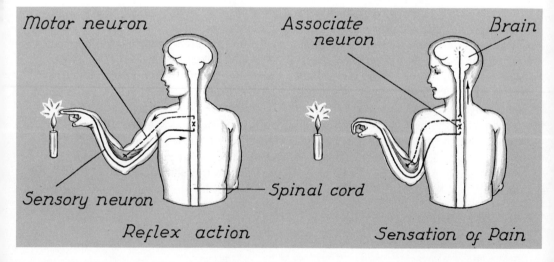

involuntary muscles and the action of the internal organs, such as the heartbeat and respiration. It also controls the reflexes of coughing and sneezing.

25.3 The Spinal Cord, the Main Trunk Line

The spinal cord is a long rod of nervous tissue protected by the backbone and extending the whole length of the back. It connects the brain with other parts of the body by sending out thirty-one pairs of nerves. Each nerve branches off from one side of the spinal cord at a ganglion. The dorsal strand brings messages *from* the body and the ventral strand carries impulses *to* the body.

Some sensations do not have to go to the brain to get a reaction, but only to the spinal cord and back. For instance, if you touch a hot radiator, you immediately withdraw your hand; the message that the radiator was too hot had only to go to the spinal cord and back to your hand. The whole thing was done in a flash.

When a message is traveling along a nerve, there is a flow of electric current which can be measured. This current can travel more than 300 feet a second. The speed of this current helps in emergencies by enabling a person to move quickly.

The spinal cord also transmits messages to and from the brain. For example, after you have jerked your hand away from a hot radiator, another message goes to the brain and you are aware of pain.

25.4 Nerves

Nerves consist of connected bundles of **nerve fibers,** like large cables, with some fibers leading to the brain and some away from it. The nerves which lead directly from the brain are known

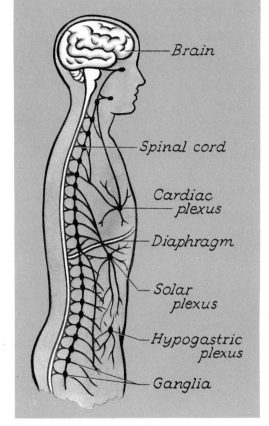

FIGURE 25-5. *AUTONOMIC NERVOUS SYSTEM*

The autonomic system regulates gland action and involuntary muscles. It consists of *ganglia* connected to the spinal cord. A mass of ganglia is a *plexus*.

as **cranial nerves;** those leading from the spinal cord are **spinal nerves.** The nerves which connect the brain and spinal cord with all parts of the body are covered with a thick, fatty, protective sheath [*medullary* (*med*-yoo-lair-ee) *sheath*] which is called **white matter.** In contrast with this white matter is the **gray matter** found in all nerves, which helps transmit the impulses. In the brain, the gray matter acts as a kind of central switchboard accepting impulses coming in on the sensory nerves and sending those going out on the motor nerves.

25.5 The Peripheral Nervous System

In order to control every part of the body, definite nerve pathways have been established. Our nerves are the communication lines of our human telephone system. The nerves which bring impulses inward to the brain and spinal cord are called **sensory,** or **afferent** (*af*-er-ent), **nerves.** Those nerves which carry impulses outward from the brain and spinal cord are called **motor,** or **efferent** (*ef*-er-ent), **nerves.** Together they form the **peripheral** (peh-*rif*-er-al) **nervous system.**

25.6 The Autonomic Nervous System

The nervous system is divided into three main parts, two of which you are already familiar with—the *central nervous system,* consisting of the brain and spinal cord, and the *peripheral nervous system,* which includes the nerves going from the spinal cord to all parts of the body. The third system is the **autonomic** (aw-tuh-*nom*-ik) **nervous system.**

This autonomic nervous system consists of two chains of nerve clusters called **ganglia,** which are connected by pairs of nerves to the spinal cord. These ganglia, which are composed of cell bodies of nerve cells, control the action of glands and of many involuntary muscles, such as those that regulate the size of the pupil of the eye or the rate of the heartbeat. They also control *peristalsis* (the muscular action which keeps food moving along the alimentary canal) and the secretions of the ductless glands.

Some ganglia are grouped together to form large masses. Each of these masses is called a **plexus** (*plek*-sus). The *cardiac plexus* near the region of the heart, the *solar plexus* by the pit of the stomach, and the *hypogastric plexus* in the abdominal region are the best known. Injury to these stops the action of the internal organs they control and seriously affects the body, often causing death.

The autonomic system is indirectly under the control of the *medulla.* Together they control all the involuntary muscles which are necessary to the maintenance of life.

25.7 The Neuron, a Single Unit

All parts of man's nervous system are made of **neurons** (*noo*-rons) (Fig. 25-6). These are highly specialized cells which carry the nervous impulses. A neuron consists of (1) a **cell body** containing a nucleus and cytoplasm, which regulates cell activities; (2) short branching **dendrites** (*den*-dryts), which receive stimuli; and (3) an **axon** (*ak*-son), a long fiber with terminal branches, which relays the stimuli to the next neuron. The cell bodies of nerve cells are only in the gray matter of the brain, in the plexuses, and in the ganglia of the spinal cord.

There are three kinds of neurons: (1) the *sensory,* or *afferent,* (2) the *associative,* in the switchboard of the brain, and (3) the *motor,* or *efferent.* Sensory neurons receive stimuli and pass them to the

FIGURE 25-6. *A NEURON*

The branching dendrites conduct impulses toward the cell while the axon conducts impulses away from it.

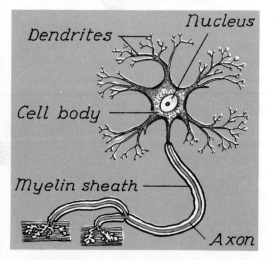

Dendrites

Nucleus

Cell body

Myelin sheath

Axon

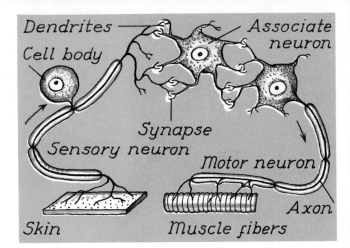

FIGURE 25-7. *REFLEX ARC*

These three neurons form a reflex arc. They do not connect directly with each other but pass impulses across the synapses by chemical means. Trace the path of the impulse.

brain, which interprets them and sends them on by motor neurons to a muscle or gland.

25.8 Synapses, the Connecting Links

As a child grows and develops, the scattered neurons in his brain and spinal cord come into closer functional contact with each other. These contacts are called **synapses** (sih-*nap*-sees), and are the points where the nervous impulses pass from one neuron to another (Fig. 25-7). The neurons do not connect directly, but a substance called *acetylcholine* (uh-set-il-*koh*-leen) forms at the ends of the axons to make functional contact. When acetylcholine reaches the muscles, it relaxes them. Messages coming from the sympathetic ganglia cause the nerve endings to discharge another substance thought to be *adrenaline* (ad-*ren*-uh-lin). When this substance reaches the muscles, it causes them to contract.

The ease with which impulses pass is increased by: (1) the frequency of the transmission over the same pathway, (2) the secretion of sufficient acetylcholine, and (3) the absence of fatigue toxins, wastes that accumulate from too great activity.

An impulse cannot travel from one sensory nerve to another. It must first be received by the dendrite of a motor or an associative neuron.

25.9 Sensation

The state resulting from the neurons' receiving impulses and responding to them is known as **sensation.** Although we are not aware of it, when we feel cold or warm, frightened or angry, thousands of tiny nerve cells in our bodies receive stimuli and cause us to respond to the situation. Man not only has an autonomic system to control his internal organs, and a system of nerves to carry impulses, but also a brain, which receives impulses and interprets sensations, thus enabling him to think and to adapt himself to his environment.

25.10 The Sense Organs

Most animals have special organs to respond to definite stimuli. Euglena has a sensitive eye spot to direct it toward the best light conditions for food manufacture. Insects use their antennae for smell and touch, and they also have eyes for seeing and simple ears to receive the stimuli of certain vibrations which may come to them. The sense organs of man are (1) the *nose,* (2) the *tongue,* (3) the *skin,* (4) the *eyes,* and (5) the *ears.*

THE NERVOUS SYSTEM

367

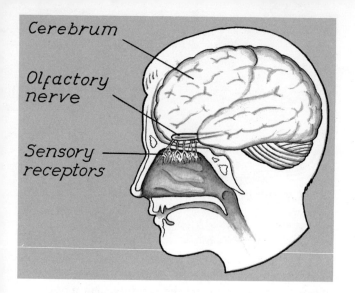

Cerebrum

Olfactory nerve

Sensory receptors

FIGURE 25-8. *SENSE OF SMELL*

The sensory receptors in the nasal cavity and the taste buds are stimulated by chemicals in solution. The sensations of taste and smell are often confused because when one eats food, the chemicals that contact the taste buds often give off vapors which enter the nose.

25.11   The Sense of Smell

When the ends of the *olfactory* (ol-*fak*-tuh-ree) *nerve* in the upper part of the nasal cavity are stimulated by certain chemical substances, impulses are created and carried directly along the olfactory nerve to the olfactory lobe of the brain, where they may be interpreted and sent back as orders or warnings. When we smell smoke, we are immediately warned that something is burning. We move quickly to put out the flame, or to get as far away from the flames as is possible. Animals depend almost wholly upon their sense of smell to detect their enemies or attract their mates.

25.12   The Sense of Taste

The tongue, in both man and animals, is the organ of taste, and on it are many little rough-feeling elevations called *papillae.* The papillae at the back, sides, and front of the tongue contain the main *taste buds,* which in turn hold the endings of the nerves that carry the impulses to the taste center in the brain. When the impulse reaches this taste center, the substance in the mouth is identified as *sweet, sour, salty,* or *bitter.* Taste is a response to a chemical stimulus and may add greatly to the enjoyment of life. Very sweet or highly seasoned foods lessen our power to enjoy them.

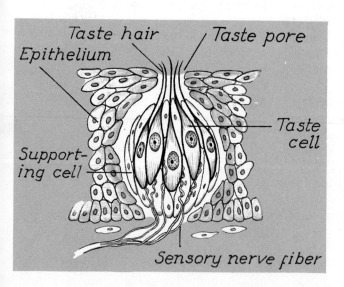

Taste hair
Epithelium
Taste pore

Taste cell

Supporting cell

Sensory nerve fiber

FIGURE 25-9. *TASTE BUD*

Taste buds are found on the tongue. They are composed of taste cells and supporting cells. Each taste cell has nerve fibers connected to it to transmit the stimuli.

368

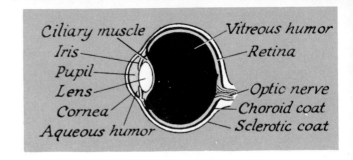

FIGURE 25-10. *THE EYE*

Light waves pass through the cornea and aqueous humor and, passing through the vitreous humor, are focused by the lens on the retina. An image is transmitted by the optic nerve to the brain, and man "sees."

25.13 The Sense of Touch

Touch is the sense which gives to man his most thorough knowledge of things in the world about him. There are nerve endings in the body's entire covering of skin which are sensitive to stimuli such as *touch, heat, cold, pressure,* and *pain.* However, each nerve ending responds to only one kind of stimulus. When a nerve ending receives a stimulus, it sends an impulse along the sensory nerve to the spinal cord and finally to the brain. As soon as the message is interpreted, we become aware of the situation and decide what is best to do about it. The nerve endings for touch are closer together on the finger tips than on the back, making our fingers much more sensitive. Try to find some of the nerve endings for cold, heat, and pressure. People vary greatly in their sensitivity to these stimuli.

25.14 The Sense of Sight

Man is able to see an object by means of a portion of the eye called the *lens,* which receives light rays and focuses them on the **retina** (*ret*-ih-nuh), a structure at the back of the eye containing cells especially sensitive to light.

The eye itself is covered with three layers of tissue: (1) the **sclerotic** (skleh-*rot*-ik) **coat,** which protects the eyeball; (2) the **choroid** (*koh*-roid) **coat,** a layer of tissue filled with blood vessels and pigment. which nourishes the eye; and (3) a thin, almost transparent layer of nerve cells called the *retina,* containing **rods** and **cones,** which receive the light rays. At the point where the eye becomes colored, the sclerotic coat becomes transparent and is known as the **cornea** (*kor*-nee-uh). Beneath the cornea is the part of the choroid coat which forms the **iris** (*eye*-riss), or colored portion of the eye, in the center of which is the **pupil.** It also contains the **ciliary** (*sil*-ee-ay-ree) **muscles** which keep the lens of the eye in focus. Between the iris and the cornea is a space filled with a liquid known as the **aqueous** (*ay*-kwee-us) **humor.** Just back of the iris is a most important part of the eye called the *lens,* the organ which catches and bends the light rays so that they may be clearly focused on the light sensitive cells of the *retina.*

The lens and iris together form a sort of partition between the aqueous chamber and the back part of the eye. The large space behind the lens is filled with a transparent, jellylike fluid known as the **vitreous** (*vit*-ree-us) **humor.** The next and most important layer of the eye is the retina, for it contains the delicate nerve cells which enable us to see. When light rays fall upon the rods and cones, the impulse is sent along the *optic nerve* to the visual center of the brain. The optic nerve is able to send impulses, but cannot receive them directly; therefore, at the point where the optic nerve leaves the eye, no impulses are received, and that spot is called a "blind spot."

How We See.—Light rays traveling in straight lines pass through (1) the

FIGURE 25-11. *THE BLIND SPOT*

To demonstrate the blind spot hold the page about a foot from the right eye, keeping the left eye closed. Now look at the cross and move the page forward and back until the black circle can no longer be seen. This will occur when the rays from the black circle fall on the place where the optic nerve enters the retina, the blind spot.

transparent cornea, (2) the aqueous humor, and (3) the pupil, finally reaching the lens. In passing through the lens, they are bent until they all meet at one point, the focus, which falls on the retina. The light rays, as they fall on the retina, really form a tiny image. The sensitive nerves of the retina are affected by the light rays, and send impulses along the optic nerve to the visual center in the cerebrum, where the impulses are finally interpreted as pictures of the objects at which we are looking.

The cells of the retina which receive impulses from light rays are the *rods* and *cones*. The cones are sensitive to bright light and color. The rods produce a substance called *visual purple* which helps them respond in reduced light, such as at night or in a darkened movie theater. Many animals can see better at night than man because they have more rods in the retina of their eyes.

The Eye Muscles.—The muscles of the eye play a very great part in helping us to see properly. The muscles at the

FIGURE 25-12. *LIGHT CONTROL*

The muscles of the iris, the colored portion of the eye, control the amount of light entering the eye. In bright light, the iris expands, causing the pupil, its black center, to decrease in size (*left*). In dimmer light, the pupil enlarges, allowing more light to enter (*right*).

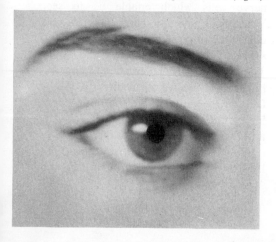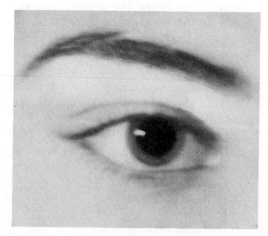

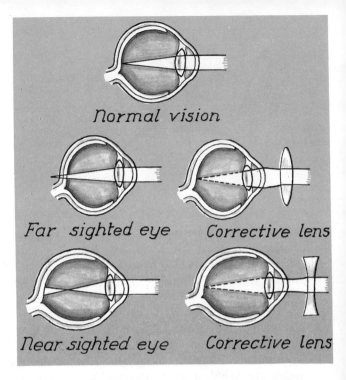

FIGURE 25-13. *NORMAL AND ABNORMAL EYES*

In the normal eye, light rays are focused directly on the retina. The eyeball of the farsighted eye is shortened, causing light rays to focus behind the retina. A corrective convex lens is used to change the focus. In the nearsighted eye, the eyeball is too long and light rays are focused in front of the retina. This condition can be corrected by a concave lens which then focuses light on the retina.

Normal vision

Far sighted eye

Corrective lens

Near sighted eye

Corrective lens

back of the eye can turn it in order to receive more light rays from the object in view. The muscles of the lens, *ciliary muscles,* may relax or tighten in order to make the lens thinner for a distant object, or thicker for one close at hand. The muscles of the iris may nearly close the pupil, if the object is in the bright sunlight, or open the pupil, if it is growing dark. The muscles of the eyelids cause the lids to open and close frequently to keep the eyes moist and clean.

The Use of Glasses.—There are three common eye defects which are usually corrected by glasses. They are (1) *farsightedness,* (2) *nearsightedness,* and (3) *astigmatism* (uh-*stig*-muh-tizm). If the eyeball is too short from front to back, or the lens is too flat, the condition is known as **farsightedness.** This means that a person so afflicted can see distant objects clearly, but near objects are indistinct because their image is focused behind the retina, as shown in Figure 25-13. Such people need glasses with

convex lenses. On the other hand, when the eyeball is too long from front to back, or the lens is too curved, **nearsightedness** occurs, and the object is indistinct because its image is focused in front of the retina (Fig. 25-13). Glasses with concave lenses are necessary in order to bring the object into proper focus.

Astigmatism is due to the improper curvature or uneven shape of the lens or cornea. People with this defect see only parts of a picture clearly until glasses with the proper curves are worn.

Ophthalmologists are physicians who treat eye defects and diseases. *Optometrists* test eyesight and prescribe glasses. *Opticians* grind the lenses.

Care of the Eyes.—When you are reading, sewing, or doing anything for which you must use your eyes steadily, be careful about the source and position of the light. It should be steady, of sufficient strength, and at the proper angle to prevent tiring your eyes or causing a glare on the page.

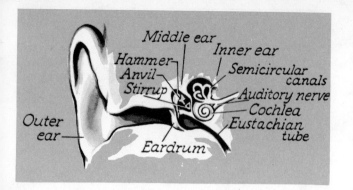

FIGURE 25-14. *STRUCTURE OF THE EAR*

The cochlea is lined with nerve endings which pass the sound stimuli along to the brain by way of the auditory nerve. How are these stimuli sent to the cochlea? Why do your ears "pop" when you travel from a low to a high altitude?

25.15   Sense of Hearing

The human ear has three divisions: (1) the *outer ear,* which helps to direct the air vibrations inward; (2) the *middle ear,* which strengthens the vibrations; and (3) the *inner ear,* which receives the stimuli and sends the resulting impulses to the brain. The outer ear is visible and is familiar to us all. Just inside the visible part of the ear is a tube, the **auditory canal,** leading to the membrane of the middle ear, which is known as the **tympanic** (tim-*pan*-ik) **membrane,** or more commonly, the *eardrum.* In this tube are found many fine hairs, and also glands which secrete the yellowish material called "wax." The hairs and wax protect the middle and inner ears by keeping out foreign particles.

The middle ear contains three ear bones known as the **hammer, anvil,** and **stirrup,** because of their shape. These bones form a sort of chain, extending from the eardrum through the cavity of the middle ear to the partition which shuts off the inner ear from the other cavities. In order that the air in the middle ear may be at the same pressure as that on the outside, there is an opening in its wall which leads to the back part of the mouth. This opening leads into the **Eustachian** (yoo-*stay*-kee-un) **tube.** When we swallow or yawn, this end of the tube opens, equalizing the pressure on both sides of the eardrum.

Unlike the outer and middle ears, the inner is not filled with air, but with liquid. The sound waves pass through the outer and middle ears to the liquid, which begins to vibrate. The nerve endings which line the spiral **cochlea** (*kok*-lee-uh) then receive the stimuli from the vibrating liquid, and send the resulting impulses along the *auditory nerve* to the brain.

The inner ear also contains three arches at right angles to each other, in three different planes, called **semicircular canals.** These canals are filled with a watery liquid which moves as the head changes position. The nerve endings lining the walls of these canals extend to the cerebellum, meeting the nerves which control our muscles and enable us to keep our balance. Any motion, like whirling, that causes a disturbance of the liquid in these canals may cause dizziness and often sickness.

How We Hear.—Sound vibrations reach the outer ear, enter the ear canal, and beat against the eardrum. This membrane then begins to vibrate and sets in motion the hammer, which in turn strikes the anvil. This causes the stirrup to beat against the membrane of the inner ear. The vibrations are thus transferred to the liquid of the cochlea, where the nerve endings in the walls receive and transmit the impulses along the *auditory nerve* to the cerebrum of the brain. Here they are finally interpreted.

Care of the Ears.—Next to our eyes the ears are our best sense organs, and we should take care of them. Let the ear alone except to keep it clean. The wax in it normally moves outward and a cloth on the end of the finger will keep the ear sufficiently clean. Heed the old saying, "Never pick your ear except with your elbow." Digging the ear with toothpicks, hairpins, or anything sharp is dangerous. If your ears hurt, or you do not hear well, go at once to an ear specialist.

Most ear trouble comes from infection in the middle ear. If you have a cold and blow your nose hard, especially if you close one nostril, you may force germ-laden mucus into the Eustachian tube. Here the germs grow rapidly, causing congestion and inflammation.

The chief causes of deafness are infections of the middle ear and injuries to the eardrum. Never strike a person on the ear.

25.16 Behavior

The response of an organism to the factors in its environment is known as **behavior.** Sensory nerves from the various sense organs carry messages to the brain, which interprets them and sends out orders by the motor nerves.

The simplest response of man involving the nervous system is the *reflex act.* A higher, learned response is a *habit,* and a response that requires thinking is a *voluntary act.* Each results in a certain type of behavior.

25.17 Reflex Action

Man inherits a few fixed patterns of response which are chiefly for protection, such as jumping at a sudden sound, blinking in a dust storm, or withdrawing

Courtesy Audivox, Inc.

FIGURE 25-15. *INVISIBLE AID*

Hearing aid design has improved greatly in recent years. This aid is almost completely contained in the glasses frame. Only the tiny tube, which conveys the sound to the ear, is visible.

rapidly from a pain or danger stimulus. When such an action occurs, the response to the stimulus comes directly from the spinal cord, without going to the brain. Later a message is sent to the brain and the person then becomes aware of the sound or pain or storm. **Reflex** (*ree*-fleks) **action,** then, *is more rapid than action which depends on thinking.*

The path over which a reflex act travels is called a **reflex arc.** It involves (1) the sensory nerve endings in the skin or other organ, which carries the impulse to (2) an associative cell in the spinal cord. This transmits the impulse to the (3) motor nerve which carries it to the muscle.

25.18 Conditioned Reflexes

The simplest types of acquired, or learned, reflexes are known as **conditioned reflexes.** They are performed in

FIGURE 25-16. *LEARNED RESPONSE*

The series of simple motions necessary for driving a car are learned through practice. An experienced driver is then free to concentrate on traffic signals and other automobiles.

Hays from Monkmeyer

response to a *secondary* stimulus, not an original one. Your dog shows a reflex act when saliva drips from his jaws upon the sight of food. Normally the dog would seize the food. If you can make him understand that he will get food only when *you* give it to him, he will soon react to the sight of you just as he previously did to the sight of the food. He will be conditioned to respond to a secondary stimulus (you) rather than the original one (food).

Conditioned reflexes are not inherited; they are a very simple form of learning. Ivan Pavlov, a Russian physiologist, did many pioneer experiments in this field to demonstrate how animals and man acquire conditioned reflexes.

25.19   Habit

Acquired reflexes of a higher level, requiring more thought and practice to establish them, are called **habits**. They are sometimes considered to be a chain of reflex arcs which have become established in a fixed series.

If you wish to be able to dance well, you must first *learn* the kinds of steps to take and how to keep in time to the music. Then you must *practice* them until they become automatic. During the learning process, nerve connections are made in the cerebrum, because you are thinking about what you are doing. However, once you have learned, the cerebellum controlling the voluntary muscles keeps the actions in the proper series, leaving the thought-brain free. Thus you may engage in pleasant conversation while dancing, or you may simply enjoy the music without thinking about the steps.

25.20   Voluntary Acts

Voluntary acts require thinking and involve associations of the highest level. We are constantly called upon to make decisions of all kinds. When we are born, most of the brain neurons have no definite connections. As we grow and develop, however, we begin to learn, make choices, and store facts in our memory. As we make these thought associations, we establish series of reflex arcs, develop habits, and form learning patterns so that in later years we can remember places or people when the proper stimuli start our train of thought.

25.21   How Steady Are Your Nerves?

Try to hold your hand perfectly still. You will find it a difficult task. When you are rested and when your nervous system is in good order, you will be able to do much better than when you are tired. Just as muscles need rest and relaxation, the brain and nerve cells need to be repaired and kept free of waste products. This is best accomplished during sleep. Growing boys and girls need nine or ten hours of sleep each night in order to repair worn-out tissue and build new cells for growth. If you are getting enough sleep, you should feel rested and ready for activity every morning. Young boys and girls sometimes fall into the bad habit of not getting enough sleep. Biology students, however, are aware of the serious consequences of this habit. Are you getting enough sleep?

FACTS TO REMEMBER

The function of the *nervous system* is to coordinate all activities of the body. There are three main parts of man's nervous system: (1) the central nervous system, (2) the peripheral nervous system, and (3) the autonomic nervous system.

The *central nervous system* includes the spinal cord and the brain, which consists of the cerebrum, cerebellum, and medulla oblongata. The *peripheral nervous system* consists of the afferent and efferent nerves which carry impulses from all parts of the body to and from the brain and spinal cord. The *autonomic nervous system* controls many of the involuntary activities of the body.

The *neuron* is the unit of structure of a nerve fiber. It consists of a cell body, dendrites, and an axon. There are three types of neurons: (1) sensory (afferent), (2) motor (efferent), and (3) associative. A *synapse* is the space between the axon of one neuron and the dendrites of the next. A *nerve impulse,* which travels as an electric current along a nerve, crosses a synapse by a chemical reaction.

Man responds to his environment by stimuli received through the *sense organs*. The sense of smell is perceived through the *nose,* and is transmitted to the brain by the olfactory nerve. The sense of taste comes through the nerve endings in the taste buds located in the papillae in the *tongue*. Nerve endings in the *skin* enable us to feel heat, cold, touch, pressure, and pain. The lens of the *eye* focuses light rays on the retina, where rods and cones receive the impulses and transmit them to the brain along the optic nerve. Sound vibrations are carried through the outer and middle *ear* to the nerve endings on the cochlea in the inner ear, where the impulses pass on to the brain along the auditory nerve. The inner ear also contains the *semicircular canals,* in which are found the nerve endings for equilibrium.

The *behavior* of a person is determined by reflex action, conditioned reflexes, habits, and voluntary acts.

WORDS TO REMEMBER

acetylcholine	anvil	astigmatism
adrenaline	aqueous humor	auditory canal
afferent neuron	associative neuron	auditory nerve

autonomic nervous
   system
axon
behavior
blind spot
brain
cardiac plexus
cell body
central nervous
   system
cerebellum
cerebrum
choroid coat
ciliary muscles
cochlea
conditioned reflex
cones
cornea
cortex
cranial nerves
dendrite
efferent neuron
Eustachian tube

farsightedness
ganglia
gray matter
habit
hammer
hypogastric plexus
inner ear
iris
lens
medulla oblongata
medullary sheath
middle ear
motor neuron
nearsightedness
nerve fiber
nerve impulse
nerve net
nervous system
neuron
olfactory nerve
optic nerve
outer ear

peripheral nervous
   system
plexus
pupil
reflex action
reflex arc
retina
rods
sclerotic coat
semicircular canals
sensation
sensory neuron
solar plexus
spinal cord
spinal nerves
stimulus
stirrup
synapse
tympanic membrane
visual purple
vitreous humor
voluntary act
white matter

QUESTIONS

1. Name three parts of a neuron and give their functions.
2. Explain how impulses travel from one neuron to the next.
3. Name and locate the two parts of the central nervous system.
4. Of what does the peripheral nervous system consist?
5. What is the function of the autonomic nervous system?
6. List four kinds of stimuli which affect the skin. Give an example of one from your own experience and tell how each has affected you at some time.
7. What is the purpose of the lens of the eye? How can it be adjusted for objects of varying distances?
8. What is the name of the colored portion of the eye? What is its function?
9. How do the ear bones help in hearing?
10. Where is the Eustachian tube? What is its use?
11. To what kind of stimuli does the olfactory nerve respond? Where are its nerve endings located?
12. List in order the parts of a reflex arc.
13. Name four reflex acts and tell how they are helpful to the body.
14. How do voluntary acts differ from habits? Give two examples of each.

       THE CONTROL AND CARE OF THE BODY

15. Explain how you could form the habit of reading a newspaper every day by following these rules: desire, application, repetition, and satisfaction.

16. If you have a dog or any pet, watch it carefully and record the results of the following observations:

    a. One reflex act.

    b. One conditioned reflex.

    c. One habit it has formed.

    d. How it rests and when.

    e. To what kinds of stimuli it responds.

COMPLETION TEST

As your teacher or classmate reads the following incomplete statements, with your book closed, write on a clean sheet of paper the word or phrase which correctly completes the statement.

1. Light waves are focused on the _____ by the lens.

2. The _____ nerve carries sound vibrations to the brain.

3. The tympanic membrane is more commonly called the _____ _____.

4. The semicircular canals are filled with a liquid which helps the body maintain its _____.

5. The tough outer covering in the front of the eye is called the _____.

6. The taste buds on the tongue are called _____.

7. _____ nerves carry messages to the brain.

8. _____ nerves carry messages to the muscles.

9. The _____ nervous system controls the action of involuntary muscles.

10. A group of neurons forms a _____.

PROJECTS

I. *Taste and Smell.*—1. Select ten substances with characteristic odors, such as an onion, orange, fish, or peanut. Place them in small corked bottles. Blindfold your companion and be sure he holds his nose so that he cannot smell. Let him taste each substance separately and describe it to you. Record each description carefully. Make two trials.

2. Keep him blindfolded, but do not hold his nose. This time let him smell each substance and describe it. Make two trials.

3. Compare the descriptions of the taste and smell of each substance as he gives it to you. How do they differ? Can you draw any conclusion about a person's relative ability to taste and smell? Do you think a cold in the nose makes any difference in the enjoyment of food? Why?

II. *Conditioning a Reflex.*—1. Choose a goldfish, bird, white rat, dog, or any animal which you may have. Devise an experiment which will make him respond to a stimulus other than the original. For example, if you wish to condition a goldfish, flash a light at one side of the aquarium when you place the food in the feeding ring. Note the length of time before the fish responds to food. Continue this for several days until the average length of time does not vary greatly.

2. Then flash the light and do not give the food at the same time. Does the fish respond? Reward it by feeding it. Repeat this for several days and at different times each day. Does the fish respond to the light? Has it been conditioned to the light instead of the food? How do you know?

3. If you wish to find out if the fish will lose this condition, flash the light each day, but do not give the food. How long does the fish continue to respond to the light?

III. *Forming a Habit.*—1. Decide on some habit you wish to form. Perhaps you may resolve to brush your shoes every morning.

2. Collect the necessary equipment and find a suitable place in which to keep it. Set aside a particular time of day for brushing your shoes and do it at that time. Make a record each day that you do this.

3. Do not let anything interfere with this task.

4. Do you feel a kind of satisfaction when you are complimented on your good grooming?

5. After a time you will brush your shoes as regularly as you wash your face. How many days did it take before the habit was established? Did you think about it at first? What part of the brain is working chiefly after the habit is established? Can you now think about something else when you are brushing your shoes?

IV. *Do Animals Vary in Learning Ability?*—If you have some white rats, select those of the same age for the test. Other animals may be used.

Construct a maze of cardboard or wood. Place some food at the end of the only through route. Test each rat separately, keeping a record of the time it takes to reach the food.

Repeat the lesson each day until there is little variation in the time it takes each rat.

Construct a graph or chart, showing the speed of learning. Did each rat reach its food in the same length of time? Explain. How many times did each rat make the same mistake? How did this affect its learning time?

Write a complete account of your work.

V. *Training Animals.*—Using reference books and your own observation write a detailed account of how the following animals are taught to do tricks. Give specific examples.

1. dogs	5. seals
2. elephants	6. bears
3. horses	7. monkeys
4. lions	

REFERENCES

Cannon, *The Wisdom of the Body.* Norton.
Cobb, *Health for Body and Mind.* Appleton-Century.
Dorsey, *Why We Behave Like Human Beings.* Blue Ribbon Books.
Fink, *Release from Nervous Tension.* Simon and Schuster.

Frolov, *Pavlov and His School*. Oxford.

Herrick, *The Thinking Machine*. University of Chicago.

Jackson, *Outwitting Our Nerves*. Garden City.

Montagne, *Nervous Stomach Trouble*. Blue Ribbon Books.

Morgan and Gilliland, *Introduction to Psychology*. Macmillan.

Pierce and David, *Man's World of Sound*. Doubleday.

Rice, *Living*. Scott, Foresman.

Shaffer, *The Psychology of Adjustment*. Houghton Mifflin.

Sutton and Vane, *The Story of Eyes*. Viking Press.

Wells, Huxley, and Wells, *The Science of Life*. Doubleday, Doran.

Wiggam, *Exploring Your Mind with the Psychologists*. Blue Ribbon Books.

Woodworth, *Psychology*. Holt.

CHAPTER 26

The Endocrine System

26.1 Chemical Messengers

The human body is a living chemical laboratory. Each cell is composed of chemical substances grouped together to form protoplasm. Throughout life, food and oxygen are taken into the body and used to furnish heat and energy, to build new cells and repair old ones. Each portion of the body has its own work to do and seems to care for itself.

In reality, however, every cell is dependent upon the activity of other cells in the body. Some of these are specialized into gland cells, which produce chemical substances called **hormones** (*hor*-mohns). These travel through the blood stream and help to regulate the activities of various organs.

26.2 Glands of the Body

A **gland** *is a cell or group of cells which manufactures and secretes a chemical substance needed by the body.* Some glands, such as the salivary and sweat glands, pour out their secretions through ducts or tubes. Others, such as the thyroid and adrenal glands, have no ducts; their secretions are absorbed directly into the blood stream.

The substances produced by glands are called **secretions**. Thus saliva is the secretion of the salivary gland, and perspiration, of the sweat gland. The chemical substances in these secretions have special names, according to the work they do. The secretions of digestive glands contain *enzymes,* and those of the **endocrine** (*en*-doh-kryne) or **ductless glands** have *hormones.* When these are produced in the right amounts the body remains healthy, and the organs work in harmony.

26.3 The Pituitary Gland

For a long time it was known that giants and dwarfs existed. They seemed to be well proportioned but very different in size from the ordinary person. Finally, it was found that a small gland on the floor of the brain plays an impor-

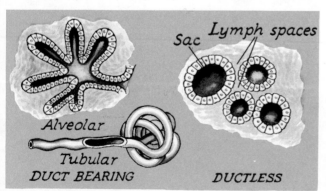

FIGURE 26-1. *GLANDS OF THE BODY*

The form of duct-bearing glands is either *alveolar,* made up of small sacs, or *tubular.* Ductless glands pour their secretions directly into the blood stream by osmosis.

380

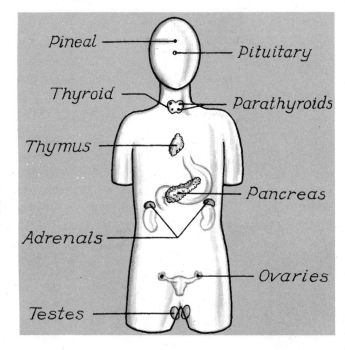

FIGURE 26-2. *THE DUCTLESS GLANDS*

This diagram shows the location of the endocrine glands in the human body. The secretions of endocrine glands are called hormones. These are released directly into the blood and have important roles in the development and function of the body.

tant part in the body's growth and development.

The **pituitary** (pih-*tyoo*-ih-ter-ee) **gland** consists of two main lobes: the *anterior* (front) and the *posterior* (back). The **anterior lobe** produces the **somatotropic** (soh-mat-oh-*troh*-pik) hormone, which regulates skeletal growth. When too much of this hormone is secreted during the growing years, a person may become unusually tall, reaching heights of seven to nine feet. This condition is called *giantism*. However, if not enough somatotropic hormone is secreted, the person becomes a pituitary dwarf, or *midget*, well-proportioned but small. Oversecretion of this hormone in adults causes *acromegaly* (ak-ruh-*meg*-uh-lee), which is a condition of enlarged bones of the head, hands, and feet.

The **gonadotropic** (guh-nad-oh-*troh*-pik) hormone is another secretion of the anterior lobe of the pituitary gland. This hormone affects the development and secretions of the reproductive or-gans, and aids in the body changes which occur during *adolescence*.

The anterior lobe of the pituitary gland also produces *prolactin,* which stimulates the production of milk in mother animals; the *thyrotropic* hormone, which affects the activity of the thyroid gland; the *parathyrotropic* hormone, which helps regulate the parathyroid glands; and *ACTH* (*adreno-cortico-tropic-hormone*), which stimulates the outer part, or cortex, of the adrenal glands (Sec. 26.9).

The **posterior lobe** of the pituitary gland produces a hormone, **pitressin** (pih-*tress*-in), which seems to affect the blood pressure and water content of the body. This lobe also produces **pitocin** (pih-*toh*-sin), which regulates the muscles of some internal organs.

26.4   The Pineal (*pin*-ee-ul) Body

This tiny organ is located in the head on the dorsal surface of the mid-brain. For many years after its discovery it was thought to be an endocrine gland whose function was unknown. However, it is now thought by many scientists to be the vestigial remains of a third eye which is found in some very primitive vertebrates.

26.5 The Thyroid Gland

Perhaps the most familiar of all the ductless glands is the thyroid, located in the neck. There are two lobes, one on either side of the trachea, connected by a thin strip of tissue.

The hormone **thyroxin** (thy-*roks*-in) controls the *rate* of metabolism and the oxidation of food. This indirectly affects the heart and blood vessels, the nervous system, and other body activities. It also affects growth. The hormone thyroxin is partly made of *iodine*. A lack of iodine can cause the thyroid gland to enlarge, causing a swelling in the throat region. This condition is known as *simple goiter*. In areas where there is very little iodine in the soil, iodized salt is widely used to supply this lack.

Children and infants lacking thyroxin do not grow as they should. The face becomes fat and puffy, the abdomen protrudes, and mental growth is retarded. Children affected by such a condition are said to be suffering from *cretinism* (*kree*-tin-izm). They may become thyroid dwarfs with stunted bodies, short, thick limbs, and head greatly enlarged. Cretinism may be corrected with thyroid extract if the treatment is begun early enough.

When the thyroid glands of adults become less active than normal, the rate of oxidation decreases and the activity of the nervous system slows down. The heart action is slower and sometimes the heart enlarges. This condition is called *hypothyroidism* (hy-poh-*thy*-roid-izm).

When adults suffer from a serious lack of thyroxin the condition is called *myxe-*

Ewing Galloway

FIGURE 26-3. *THE LONG AND THE SHORT OF IT*

A malfunctioning of the pituitary gland in childhood resulted in the abnormal size of these circus performers.

FIGURE 26-4. *THYROID AND PARATHYROID GLANDS*

These ductless glands are located between the trachea and the esophagus.

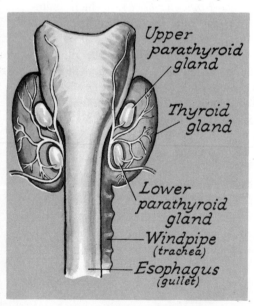

Upper parathyroid gland

Thyroid gland

Lower parathyroid gland

Windpipe (trachea)

Esophagus (gullet)

382

dema (mik-seh-*dee*-muh). The person becomes weak, but gains in weight. The skin is dry and scaly, the hair turns white and falls, and the mind is dull. Such cases show rapid recovery when the proper amounts of thyroxin are administered.

When the thyroid gland is overactive, it causes a person to be restless, excitable, and nervous. He has a rapid heart beat, is usually thin, and sometimes develops a tremor in his hands. It may also cause a type of goiter which results in making the eyes bulge. This condition, known as *hyperthyroidism,* is harder to treat than lack of thyroxin, because it often requires an operation either to remove a portion of the gland or to constrict some of the blood vessels leading to it.

26.6 The Parathyroid Glands

Back of the thyroid gland and attached to it lie two pairs of glands called **parathyroids** (pair-uh-*thy*-roids). They secrete **parathormone** (pair-uh-*thor*-mohn), which regulates the amount of calcium and phosphorus in the blood and maintains a normal supply in the bones and teeth. When they do not function properly, calcium is sometimes removed from the bones and deposited in the joints, where it causes pain. The action of the parathyroid hormone is related to the use of Vitamin D in the body.

The parathyroid gland also aids in muscular control and normal nervous activity. When calcium is lacking, the muscles may go into spasms or "cramps." This is known as *tetany* (*tet*-uh-nee). Sometimes children lacking calcium have convulsions.

26.7 The Thymus Gland

The thymus gland lies at the base of the neck below the thyroid gland. Once

Courtesy Dr. F. Maloof, Massachusetts General Hospital

Figure 26-5. *THYROID DISEASE*

Radioactive iodine, swallowed by a patient, may be used in the diagnosis of thyroid conditions by tracing its path with a counter. It may also be used to treat an overactive thyroid.

thought to be an endocrine gland of unknown function, it gradually decreases in size from childhood until it nearly disappears in adults. Recent experiments by Drs. Metcalf and Neil indicate that the thymus is a source of *leucocytes,* or white blood cells important in the production of antibodies. Oversecretion of the thymus may cause excessive growth of the tonsils and spleen. To counteract this, X-rays are sometimes used.

26.8 The Pancreas, Gland of Double Duty

The pancreas, located at the junction of the stomach and small intestine, is both a duct and ductless gland, thus performing a double function. In its function as a duct gland it contains cells which secrete enzymes for the digestion of proteins, fats, and starch. These are

THE ENDOCRINE SYSTEM

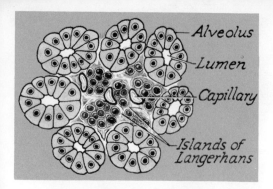

FIGURE 26-6. *PANCREAS SECTION*

The pancreas is both a duct and duct-less gland. The alveoli contain cells which secrete enzymes through the pancreatic duct; the Islands of Langerhans secrete insulin directly into the blood.

carried by the pancreatic duct to the small intestine. Thus the pancreas is a duct gland.

The pancreas also has small groups of specialized cells called the **Islands of Langerhans** (*lahng*-er-hahns). They produce **insulin** (*in*-soo-lin), which is taken directly into the blood by diffusion.

FIGURE 26-7. *EMERGENCY*

In times of stress, extra epinephrine is poured into the blood, enabling the body to make the required effort.

Philip Gendreau

Insulin regulates the amount of sugar in the blood by acting upon the liver and muscles to control the amount of glycogen or animal starch released.

When the pancreas does not supply enough insulin, *diabetes* results. Sugar, instead of being stored and gradually released by the liver and muscles, accumulates in the blood in excessive amounts. This the body tries to eliminate through the kidneys, with the result that sugar is found in the urine.

In 1924, Dr. Frederick G. Banting, a Canadian scientist, prepared insulin from animals. This is given by injection to persons suffering from diabetes. It is not a cure, but a treatment which, when followed regularly, supplies the body with the missing hormone.

26.9 The Adrenal Glands for Emergency

When we are frightened, angry, or in grave danger, the **adrenal** (ad-*ree*-n'l) **glands** are activated. These glands are located above the kidneys. They consist of two parts: the **cortex** on the outside and the **medulla** within. During excitement **epinephrine** (eh-pee-*neh*-freen), or *adrenaline,* from the adrenal medulla, is poured into the blood in increased amounts. This stimulates the sympathetic nervous system and makes the liver change some of its stored animal starch, or *glycogen,* back into sugar, which the blood carries to the muscles.

Epinephrine causes the blood to clot more readily, so that small wounds bleed less freely. For this reason it is used in operations. It also lessens shock and stimulates heart action.

The adrenal cortex produces a hormone called **cortin** (*kor*-tin). Deficiency of cortin results in fatigue and lethargy. Cortin helps to prevent *Addison's disease,* a condition in which the skin darkens, extreme weakness develops, and digestive disturbances arise.

When the adrenal cortex is stimulated by *ACTH* (Sec. 26.3) from the pituitary gland, it secretes *cortisone* (*kor*-tih-sohn), a hormone that controls part of the metabolism of carbohydrates, fats, and protein, and helps to control the production of some white corpuscles. It is of some benefit in arthritis, asthma, and other allergies, but it is given under the supervision of a doctor because it may cause harmful side effects.

26.10   The Reproductive Organs

These are also glands, both duct and ductless. Both the **testes** of the male and **ovaries** of the female produce several hormones. **Estrogen** (*es*-troh-jen) from the ovary produces female secondary sex characteristics. The male hormone, **androgen** (*an*-droh-jen) from the testis, and **testosterone** (tess-*toss*-ter-ohn), an artificial androgen, produce secondary male sex characteristics.

During adolescence when these hormones become active, the body assumes different proportions and different characteristics. The boy's voice deepens and hair grows on his face, so that he needs to shave. A girl's voice has a different quality; she grows taller and rounder. These traits in boys and girls are called *secondary sex characteristics*. Children become more emotional during adolescence, likes and dislikes vary, and small happenings assume enormous importance. The whole outlook on life changes as the hormones from the reproductive glands develop.

26.11   Ductless Glands of the Small Intestine

Some cells of the small intestine manfacture the hormone **secretin** (seh-*kree*-tin). Its function is to stimulate the liver and pancreas into pouring their digestive juices into the small intestine when food is there to be digested.

26.12   The Endocrine System

The endocrine or ductless glands form a system of organs within our bodies just as do the parts of the digestive, respiratory, and nervous systems. When we make a microscopic study of the endocrine organs, we find certain cells which take from the blood the raw materials needed to manufacture their specific products; for example, some thyroid cells produce thyroxin, some adrenal cells, epinephrine.

Each gland combines these products, the hormones, which are frequently termed the *chemical regulators*. All such combined hormones are returned directly from the gland into the blood stream from which the cells take the raw products. Each of these endocrine products has a specific effect on different parts of our body.

We have really made only a beginning in the scientific study of the endocrine system, and we anticipate that a great deal more will be discovered in the next few years.

FACTS TO REMEMBER

The function of the *endocrine* or *ductless glands* is to secrete *hormones* which help regulate the various body activities, including the regulation of the ductless glands themselves. These secretions are absorbed directly into the blood stream.

The *glands* of the endocrine system include: the pitiutary, the thyroid, the parathyroids, the pancreas, the adrenals, the ovaries and testes, and certain cells of the small intestine.

WORDS TO REMEMBER

acromegaly
ACTH
Addison's disease
adolescence
adrenaline
adrenals
androgen
anterior lobe
chemical regulators
cortex
cortin
cortisone
cretinism
diabetes
ductless gland
endocrine gland
epinephrine
estrogen

giantism
gland
goiter
gonadotropic hormone
hormone
hyperthyroidism
hypothyroidism
insulin
Islands of Langerhans
medulla
midget
myxedema
ovaries
pancreas
parathormone
parathyroid
parathyrotropic
   hormone

pineal body
pitocin
pitressin
pituitary
posterior lobe
prolactin
secondary sex
   characteristics
secretin
secretion
somatotropic hormone
testes
testosterone
tetany
thymus
thyroid
thyrotropic hormone
thyroxin

QUESTIONS

1. What are hormones? Why are they often called "chemical messengers"?
2. Name two kinds of glands in the body. Give examples.
3. Explain how the pancreas can be both a duct and a ductless gland.
4. What is a secretion? An enzyme? A hormone? Name several hormones.
5. Describe the pituitary gland and tell why it is considered so important.
6. What causes myxedema? Cretinism? Goiter? Describe each condition.
7. Name and locate a gland of early growth which is very small in adults.
8. How do you think the adrenal glands could help a baseball player in an exciting game?
9. What causes marked bodily changes during adolescence?
10. Describe the parathyroid glands. Of what importance are they?

COMPLETION TEST

As your teacher or classmate reads the following incomplete statements, with your book closed, write on a clean sheet of paper the word or phrase which correctly completes the statement.

1. The _____ is a ductless gland located in the head.
2. The _____ glands are found on the top of the kidneys.
3. Glands of the small intestine produce the hormone _____.
4. The _____ regulates the amount of sugar in the blood.
5. The _____ regulates the amount of calcium in the blood.
6. An oversecretion of the hormone _____ often causes a person to become a giant.
7. _____ is a hormone produced by the adrenal cortex.
8. Secondary sex characteristics are produced by hormones from the _____ glands.
9. Endocrine glands are commonly called _____ glands.
10. The adrenal glands consist of two parts, the _____ and _____.

PROJECTS

I. *Experiment to Show the Effect of Thyroxin on the Development of Tadpoles.*—Obtain some thyroid extract and place a very small amount in the water in which the tadpoles are swimming, or mix a small amount with flour to form a paste and feed it to them. Keep one jar of tadpoles as a control and do not add any thyroxin. Observe both jars from day to day and record any changes which take place. Be sure to note the date each time you make a recording so that you will be able to make comparisons.

II. *Experiment to Show the Effect of Pituitrin on the Growth in Size of Tadpoles.*—Obtain some pituitrin and with your teacher's help inject a small amount into the muscle of the tails of the tadpoles used for the experiment. Keep all the tadpoles under the same laboratory conditions. Observe frequently and weigh and measure them each week. Do you note any change in growth? Keep an accurate record of your experiment.

III. *Endemic Goiter.*—By means of charts and diagrams and with the use of library books locate the so-called goiter belts of the world.
    a. Make a series of charts to show their location.
    b. Write a composition on the effect of such soil conditions on the health of the people.
    c. Include a description of "cretins."
    d. Find out whether or not you are living in the goiter belt and what, if anything, is being done about it.

IV. *Diabetes.*—*a.* Investigate the work of Banting.
    b. Describe some of his experiments on dogs.
    c. Find out some of the symptoms and the current method of treatment of diabetes.

V. *Human Oddities.*—Find information in the library on circus freaks.
    a. Read the life of Tom Thumb.
    b. Find out about the midget colony.
    c. Look up the record of giants.

REFERENCES

Bermen, *The Glands Regulating Personality*. Macmillan.

Carlson, *How to Develop Personal Power*. Harper.

Dietz, *Medical Magic*. Dodd, Mead.

Elwin, *Yourself, The Story of the Human Body*. Grosset and Dunlap

Gladstone, *Progress in Medicine*. Knopf.

Gray, *The Advancing Front of Medicine*. McGraw-Hill.

Hoskins, *The Tides of Life*. Norton.

Reidman, *Our Hormones and How They Work*. Abelard-Schuman.

Sure, *The Little Things of Life*. Appleton-Century.

Turner, *General Endocrinology*. Saunders.

Woodworth, *Psychology*. Holt.

CHAPTER 27

The Life Cycle of Man

27.1 The Beginning

From the period of earliest man up to the present, there have been but minor changes in the human body. Some of these are a more erect posture, a differently shaped head, and a more flexible thumb. No really new structures have been added throughout this long period.

While we know little about the origin of the race of man, we do have some definite facts about how each of us started our individual lives, that is, when a sperm cell united with an egg, or ovum. In this respect we resemble all the higher animals and even some plants. *All living things begin life as single cells.*

FIGURE 27-1. *CHROMOSOMES*

Chromosomes determine the characteristics of the organism. Every cell in the body of the organism contains the fixed number for that species.

General Biological Supply House

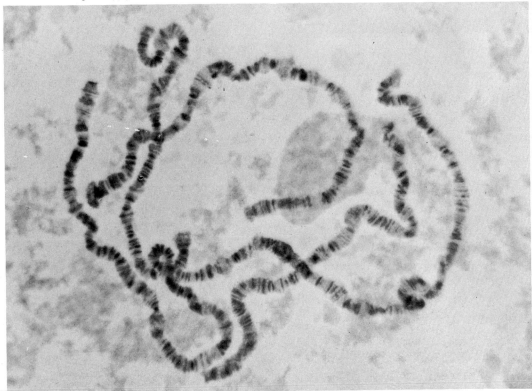

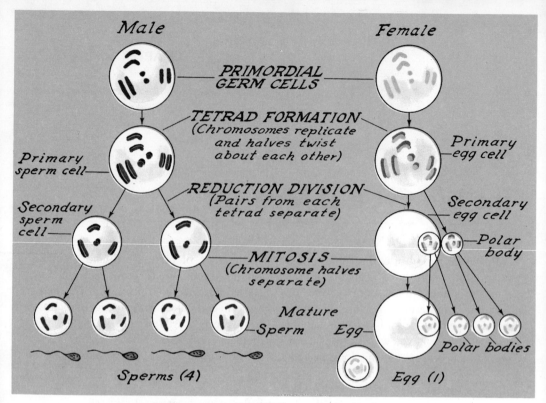

FIGURE 27-2. *MATURATION OF GERM CELLS*

When the primordial germ cells, male and female, produce mature sperm and egg cells, the primary cells divide by *reduction division,* one whole chromosome of each pair going to each of the two new cells (secondary cells). These cells then divide once more—this time by *mitosis.* Four sperms are produced, each containing half the usual number of chromosomes in the body cells. The primary egg cell produces only one mature egg, the other three cells becoming polar bodies. The original chromosome number is restored when egg and sperm unite.

This was stated as a part of the cell theory in Section 4.4.

27.2 The Germ Cells

A cell, as you already know, contains a nucleus in which are very minute structures known as *chromosomes.* Chromosomes carry **genes** (*jeens*), factors which pass on hereditary characteristics through a chemical process as yet not fully understood. When body cells divide, each chromosome splits lengthwise, so that equal amounts of each chromosome go to the new cells. This process is *mitosis* (Section 5.3).

During the years that the young animal is developing and growing to maturity, each of its reproductive cells, called **primordial** (pry-*mor*-dee-al) **germ cells,** is growing and dividing by mitosis as are the other cells. Beginning at the time of adolescence and continuing during the greater part of adult life, these germ cells mature singly in the case of the egg cell, or several at a time in the case of sperm cells.

These primordial germ cells, which are produced by the *ovary* of the female animal (the *egg cell*) and the *testis* of the male (the *sperm cell*), also contain

390

chromosomes. The genes carried by these chromosomes determine the characteristics which may be passed from parent to offspring.

27.3 Maturation

Maturation (mat-cher-*ay*-shun) is the name given to the maturing of the primordial germ cells bearing the **diploid** (*dip*-loyd) **number** of chromosomes. This is the number of chromosomes that is characteristic of the species. A careful study of Figure 27-2 will show how during this maturation period the chromosome material of the germ cell divides by a process called *reduction division* or **meiosis** (my-*oh*-sis). During reduction division the chromosomes in each pair *do not split* as in regular mitotic cell division (Fig. 5-1), but *one whole chromosome of each pair* is drawn to each pole, so that when the cell divides each daughter cell has one half the original number, the **haploid** (*hap*-loyd) **number,** of chromosomes. In the human body the egg cell of the female contains twenty-three chromosomes, and the sperm cell of the male, twenty-three. This is the human haploid number. If the primary egg and sperm cells divided by mitosis, like other body cells, the mature sperm and egg would each have forty-six chromosomes, the human diploid number, and the new generation formed from the union of these two cells would have double the proper number of chromosomes.

Each of these daughter cells then undergoes another division by mitosis. Every primordial sperm cell produces four functional cells, while the primordial egg cell produces one functional cell and three non-functional cells called *polar bodies*. In order to have yolk material to nourish the embryo, this one functional cell retains most of the yolk

and becomes the egg. The polar bodies, lacking yolk for nourishment, are small and disappear either by absorption or excretion. The single egg cell, which is called an **ovum,** is now mature and ready to be fertilized.

These sex-cells—the female egg cell and the male sperm cell—are called **gametes** (*gam*-eets), from the Greek verb meaning *to marry*. Each gamete is now capable of transmitting its load of chromosomes and genes to the next generation. It has one gene for each characteristic, depending on which chromosomes with genes it received during reduction division. The chromosomes which were cast off in the polar bodies are unable to transmit their characteristics. Thus if some desirable characteristics happen to be in the polar bodies. and not in the gametes, they will be lost as far as the new individual formed from that egg cell is concerned.

27.4 Fertilization

The union of the sperm cell with the egg cell is called **fertilization** and this process takes place within the bodies of mammals. The nucleus of the sperm cell enters the egg, leaving the *flagellum,* or tail, outside. As soon as one sperm cell has punctured the egg membrane a chemical change takes place by which the membrane becomes tough and impenetrable, preventing all of the other sperm cells from entering the egg. They usually die and are excreted. When the egg and sperm nuclei unite within the egg cell, each contributes twenty-three chromosomes, the haploid number, thus producing in the new cell forty-six chromosomes, the diploid number, and the number characteristic of man. Each parent cell thus contributes an equal number of genes. The fertilized egg is called a **zygote** (*zy*-goht).

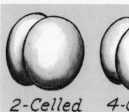

2-Celled   4-Celled   8-Celled   16-Celled   32-Celled

Endoderm

Ectoderm   Mesoderm   Endoderm

  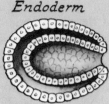  

64-Celled   Blastula   Gastrula   Germ layers
(section)   (section)   (section)

FIGURE 27-3. *STAGES IN CLEAVAGE*

Immediately after fertilization of the egg, cell divisions begin. The zygote divides, the resulting new cells divide, and so on until the blastula stage is reached. Then the cells begin to differentiate, and the germ layers are formed from which specific organs and systems will develop.

27.5 Cleavage

As soon as the egg is fertilized, a series of cell divisions takes place. This is known as **cleavage.** The zygote divides into two cells; these in turn divide, forming four cells. This process continues until each new cell formed is the size of the average cell in the body.

As more are produced they are crowded against each other until they form a hollow ball which is called the **blastula** (*blas*-tyoo-luh). The cells then begin to rearrange themselves to form the new **embryo** (*em*-bree-oh). One side of the ball dents in, forming an inner and an outer layer. This is the **gastrula** (*gas*-troo-luh) stage. The outer layer is called the *ectoderm,* and the inner layer is the *endoderm.* A third layer, the *mesoderm* (*mes*-oh-derm), forms between them. The three layers are called **germ layers,** and it is from these that all the organs and systems of the body originate.

The stages in the formation of the embryo, then, are as follows:

(1) cleavage divisions—2, 4, 8, 16, cell stages; solid-ball stage, etc.
(2) blastula—hollow-ball stage
(3) gastrula—indented-ball stage; formation of germ layers: ectoderm, mesoderm, endoderm
(4) organ formation

27.6 The Embryo

When fertilization takes place within the body, which is the case with all the higher animals, special organs are usually present in which the young animal is cared for until old enough to be set free. Shells and embryonic membranes are examples of these.

The cells of the *ectoderm* form the brain and spinal cord, and the skin and its projections, such as hair and nails. The *endoderm* goes to form the digestive and respiratory systems and such glands as liver and pancreas, while from the *mesoderm* the skeletal and circulatory systems are developed. The various systems are established, and each part of the body is partially formed during

392

the first few hours of life. The rest of the time before birth is chiefly for growth and strength.

It takes nine months for the human egg cell to grow a complete set of human organs. We are really nine months old when we are born. Some of these organs begin to work long before others. For example, the heart starts to pump blood to the growing organs several months before birth. Blood vessels *absorb* food from the mother, and thus energy for the growing child is always present.

27.7 Development

The fertilized ovum of man develops from the embryo to the infant and the boy or girl. During this growth process, each individual takes on a certain color of hair, eyes, and skin. These characteristics and the general proportions of the body indicate that the young child is to be somewhat like the father or mother in appearance or partly like some of his ancestors due to inherited genes.

For a period of time, through infancy, childhood, and adolescence, growth takes place at varying rates. The individual increases in stature, develops mentally, and learns to cope with the many factors of his environment.

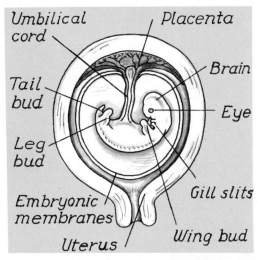

FIGURE 27-4. *HUMAN EMBRYO*

This diagram shows an embryo after about two months' development. The embryo's circulation is connected to its mother's through the umbilical cord and placenta, from which it receives nourishment. Legs and arms will develop from the leg and wing buds, while the tail and gill slits will disappear.

No one can predict which modifications of color, size, or temperament will appear in the child. One child has red hair and another black. One child grows tall and another short, and a similar variation holds true for all of the organs in our bodies.

The Law of Chance.—No one knows what determines which chromosomes

FIGURE 27-5. *FAMILY RESEMBLANCE*

The obvious family resemblance in this picture is due, of course, to the laws of heredity. Children usually resemble their parents and grandparents in inherited characteristics; but there is also a great deal of variation. Human heredity is very complex, and it is impossible to predict a child's traits before birth.

H. Armstrong Roberts

393

Hays from Monkmeyer

FIGURE 27-6. *INDIVIDUAL DIFFERENCES*

By means of aptitude tests, the psychologist evaluates an individual's skills for use in vocational counseling. The test pictured is for finger dexterity.

are sorted out to go into the new cells during reduction division. Therefore this sorting out is called the **law of chance.** Likewise, no one can predict which sperm cell will fertilize an egg cell. It is always the one which first penetrates the egg membrane. This also is due to the law of chance. If you inherited the chromosomes and genes for desirable characteristics, you are indeed fortunate. Man, with forty-six chromosomes, each with its load of genes, is thus capable of possessing and transmitting a great many characteristics. Those which you received were partly due to the law of chance.

27.8 Individuality and Learning

Although each of us has the same kinds of organs and cells, these organs and cells behave in ways that indicate there are differences in all of us. Growth takes place at different rates. Some have allergies and eye defects or musical talents and manual skills. Learning takes place at different rates. Some enjoy reading; others prefer mathematics. Thus from the very beginning each has different problems to solve. By the time we reach the age of twelve or fourteen years, certain cells become active for the first time and their activity results in manufacturing products that stimulate our bodies to grow rapidly and induce the other marked changes of adolescence.

By this period in our lives we have tried to gain control of our bodies and minds, and we begin to understand our capabilities and our limitations. During the time of education in high school and college each of us needs to set an objective or goal. As we aim to fit into our civilization, we shall find other problems to solve. One of the factors in our success will be the degree with which we understand our own individual biology and couple this understanding with high moral and ethical values.

When we have passed our examinations and have started on our chosen work, whether it be the making of a home or developing a profession or trade, new problems will demand attention. Their solution will be influenced by our biological equipment and our ability to achieve physical, social, and emotional maturity.

27.9 Eugenics

During adult life there are many important problems to consider, such as a career, home, family, children, educational needs, and religious and social groups. We must consider our own heredity and the possibility of passing desirable characteristics to our children. Should people with physical and mental

THE CONTROL AND CARE OF THE BODY

defects be allowed to marry? Is there a chance of producing a brilliant person if both parents are well educated and of unusual ability? Should there be marriage laws to help govern our choice? Perhaps some studies from the field of *eugenics* may help answer these questions.

Eugenics (yoo-*jen*-iks) is the study of the biological and social factors which may improve or impair the inherited physical and mental qualities of man. Man has known for a long time that he could improve his domestic animals and plants, and eugenics is an attempt to apply the same methods to human betterment. Sir Francis Galton, an English scientist, began investigations of family histories and established this branch of science in 1883. Then in 1904, Charles B. Davenport in America started a laboratory of research at Cold Spring Harbor on Long Island, New York.

Human inheritance is studied from case histories and family records. Many of these are incomplete. Very few people have pure unmixed ancestry. Most people are of mixed races, and there may be more than one gene that determines a human character, such as the color of the skin, eye, and hair.

A person with special abilities, such as those for art, music, or crafts, needs special training in order to make the best use of his inherited traits. It would be useless for a color-blind man to train for a railroad engineer, since he would not be able to pass the safety test for signals. Instead, he might become a very skilled craftsman in a field where color was less important.

Just as man inherits his physical characteristics from some of his immediate ancestors, so he becomes influenced by the social customs of his group. The particular nervous system and other physical characteristics he has inherited will in part determine how he reacts to his environment and the extent to which he is able to develop his mental ability, emotional stability, and moral strength. The training of nerve responses and thought processes is very important. Some of the social factors which affect one's environment are parental influence, religious training, educational objectives, political policies, and economic pressures. Those individuals who use the best of their heredity and environment will be most likely to succeed in adult life.

27.10   Study of Family Histories

The histories of two notable defective families, the Jukes and Kallikaks, have been investigated. (These are not the real names of the families.)

The Jukes family history includes 709 descendants of Max Jukes, who was a shiftless backwoodsman. One half of the children died in infancy, and of those who lived, 310 were paupers and over 30 convicted criminals. The cost of maintaining and prosecuting these criminals has been several million dollars.

The Kallikak family shows in a striking fashion that mental deficiency when once started may persist for many generations. Of 481 descendants traced from a feeble-minded mother, 143 were feeble-minded and 291 were inferior in intellectual ability. In this same family there were 496 descendants from an intelligent mother and only two showed any indication of subnormal mentality, while the other 494 were successful citizens in their several communities. In these two tragic illustrations, mental deficiency made a poor parent and there was a long line of poverty, misery, sin, and crime.

However, in every great country of

FIGURE 27-7. *NATURALIST*

Charles Darwin, the formulator of the theory of evolution, is himself an example of the value of good heredity.

the world, we find a very long list of eminent men who are related by descent. In the Bach family there were 20 eminent musicians and over 40 less eminent. The Darwins became noted for their scientific ability two generations before the birth of Charles R. Darwin. Erasmus Darwin was an eminent man. He had a son Robert who was a distinguished physician. Robert was the father of Charles, who is regarded as one of the greatest men of science. The four sons of Charles Darwin all became prominent.

In America we have the famous family of Edwards. Richard Edwards was first married to Elizabeth Tuttle, a woman of great mental power; from this union resulted one of the most brilliant families recorded. Jonathan Edwards, the grandson of Richard Edwards and Elizabeth Tuttle, was a noted New England clergyman. In 1900, 1394 descendants of Richard Edwards and Elizabeth Tuttle were known. Among these there were 295 college graduates, 13 college presidents and many school principals, 60 physicians, 100 clergymen, 75 officers in the army and navy, more than 100 lawyers, 30 judges, and 80 holders of public office. Richard Edwards' second marriage was to Mary Talcott, a woman of average ability; this union resulted in an average line of descendants.

The contrast between the Jukes and

FIGURE 27-8. *YOUTH AND AGE*

Both the beginning and the end of life should be happy, busy times. The wisdom and experience of the old are as necessary to the community as the vigor and enthusiasm of the young.

the Kallikak families on the one hand, and those of Bach, Darwin, and Edwards on the other, indicates that good heredity is a priceless gift from parent to child. Of great value also is the thoughtful nurture of that heredity through adequate nutrition and physical care, sound education, stimulating home environment, and responsible civic attitudes.

If we have inherited strong bodies and keen minds, and have been well brought up, we should try to develop our skills and live up to our training. We too may pass on desirable characteristics and encourage sound attitudes in our children, in order that the next generation shall have men and women who will be able to advance human progress.

27.11 Decline

Just as there is joy and rejoicing when a child is born, so is there awe, reverence, and respect in the presence of a kindly, dignified old person. Physically, the body cells are unable to keep themselves in good repair. The body is literally wearing out. But this may still be a happy time of life, for the years of experience usually help older persons to use their judgment to guide and direct important activities of those about them.

As the body grows older and certain cells no longer work as well as they did in middle life, other biological problems make their appearance for the first time. No one can tell in advance which group of cells will begin to slow up first, but when this period is reached (and there is no fixed age limit set for its arrival), we have to adapt ourselves to the weaknesses of old age.

Finally one or more groups of cells fail entirely to do their tasks. The work which they have been doing through life is indispensable, and death follows. *Death* marks the biological end of all forms of life.

FACTS TO REMEMBER

The *primordial germ cells* contain chromosomes which carry *genes,* the determiners of hereditary characteristics. By *reduction division* (*meiosis*) in the reproductive cells, the forty-six chromosomes in man are reduced to twenty-three. Then, when a sperm and egg cell unite, they form a *zygote* which restores the original number of forty-six chromosomes. Following *fertilization,* the zygote undergoes *cleavage,* and the *germ layers* are formed.

During the period of *development,* the embryo begins to assume the characteristics it inherited from the parents. These characteristics are determined by the *law of chance.*

Each person acquires his own *individuality* as the body grows and matures. It remains only for the person to develop his characteristics to their greatest potentialities. The study of *eugenics* illustrates the importance of heredity in determining human accomplishments.

WORDS TO REMEMBER

blastula	cleavage	egg cell
chromosome	diploid number	embryo

eugenics   haploid number   ovum
fertilization   law of chance   polar bodies
gamete   maturation   primordial germ cells
gastrula   maturity   reduction division
gene   meiosis   sperm cell
germ layers   mitosis   zygote

QUESTIONS

1. What is maturation?
2. Why is the chromosome number reduced?
3. How many functional sperm cells are produced from each primordial germ cell? How many egg cells?
4. Define: fertilization, zygote.
5. Describe the process of cleavage.
6. Name at least one organ system which develops from each of the germ layers.
7. What part does the law of chance play in heredity?
8. Explain how the study of the Kallikak family illustrates the inheritance of unfavorable characteristics.
9. What kinds of abilities may be inherited?

COMPLETION TEST

As your teacher or classmate reads the following incomplete statements, with your book closed, write on a clean sheet of paper the word or phrase which best completes the statement.

1. The bearers of hereditary characteristics are the _____.
2. Each primordial egg cell produces one egg cell and _____ polar bodies.
3. A fertilized egg is called a _____.
4. The study of heredity is known as _____.
5. The middle germ layer is the _____.
6. There are _____ chromosomes in the body cells of man.
7. There are _____ chromosomes in the egg and sperm cells of man.
8. The sperm cell has a _____ for locomotion.

PROJECTS

I. Look up the history of the Darwin family. If possible, make a chart showing the relationship and contribution of each.

II. Find all you can about the marriage laws in your state. Are physically and mentally handicapped people allowed to marry?

III. *Maturation.*—Using plasticine make a series of models showing the stages of egg and sperm formation. Paint your models, using a different color for each chromosome in the primary germ cell. By the use of colors, trace each chromosome through all the stages of division until it becomes part of the gamete.

REFERENCES

Corner, *Attaining Womanhood*. Harper.

Cowdry, *Human Biology and Racial Welfare*. Paul B. Hoeber.

Dickerson, *Growing Into Manhood*. Association Press.

Goddard, *The Kallikak Family*. Macmillan.

Guyer, *Being Well Born*. Bobbs-Merrill.

Holmes, *Human Genetics and Its Social Import*. McGraw-Hill.

Huntington, Ellsworth, and Others, *Tomorrow's Children, The Goal of Eugenics*. Wiley.

Hurst, *Heredity and the Ascent of Man*. Macmillan.

Jewett, *The Next Generation*. Ginn.

Poponoe, *Applied Eugenics*. Macmillan.

Rice, *How Life Goes On and On*. American Medical Association.

Rice, *In Training*. American Medical Association.

Scheinfeld, *You and Heredity*. Stokes.

Scheinfeld, *The New You and Heredity*. Lippincott.

Schultz, *It's Time You Knew*. Lippincott.

Sears, *Life and Environment*. Bureau of Publications, Teachers College, Columbia University.

Strain, *Being Born*. Appleton-Century.

Strain, *Love at the Threshold*. Appleton-Century.

Walter, *Genetics*. Macmillan.

Wilson, *The Cell in Development and Heredity*. Macmillan.

CHAPTER 28

Dangers from Disease

28.1 Kinds of Disease

A *disease is a condition which impairs the normal functions of the parts of an organism.* There are many kinds of disease. Some are inherited and some are occupational. Others are of dietary or glandular origin, or caused by abnormal growth of tissues. Many are caused by bacteria, yeasts, molds, viruses, protozoa, worms, poisons, and foreign bodies imbedded in the body. Some diseases progress rapidly; others are slow-moving and become chronic. Some diseases are more common in childhood and some in advancing age. It is important to know about the various kinds of disease, how they can be prevented, or, if acquired, how they can be treated.

28.2 Inherited Diseases

When several members of one family are afflicted with the same kind of disease, this may be due to their living in the same unhealthy environment where the same diseases can spread.

But often in cases of this kind, the disease is hereditary. Feeble-mindedness, deaf-mutism, color blindness, and hemophilia are inherited. In these cases men and boys are afflicted more often than women and girls, although the latter transmit the traits to their sons.

Persons suffering from hemophilia are known as "bleeders" because, with them, even small wounds bleed excessively, often causing death. This disease was found in the royal families of Spain and Russia.

Diabetes, a disease resulting from failure of the Islands of Langerhans in the pancreas to produce insulin, seems to be of an hereditary nature. The weakness of these ductless glands may be passed on from one generation to the next.

28.3 Occupational Diseases

In some occupations where the workers use chemicals and drugs, their bodies gradually absorb enough of the poisons to cause illness. In match factories or any place where phosphorus is extensively used, the jawbones may become affected. This is due to fumes which enter dental cavities and expose the bone to invading microbes. Those who work with radium need to take special precautions, since the constant bombardment of these rays on the body tends to destroy living tissues. However, radium also destroys diseased tissues and is very valuable in the treatment of cancers, tumors, and chronic skin diseases.

In the manufacture of aniline dyes or in the use of arsenical pigments in coloring, the workers sometimes suffer chronic poisoning from arsenic. This poison is used in some flypapers. Since it is also the basis of many of the insect sprays used on fruit trees, we should wash fruit carefully before eating it.

Mercury poisoning sometimes results from inhalation of the vapor during the manufacture of thermometers. Dust from mines and quarries causes a condition of the lungs known as silicosis.

28.4 Tumors and Cancers

A *tumor* is a new formation of tissue, apparently independent of the normal body cells. It is unlike the other body cells in structure, and is of no use to the organism in which it forms. Little is known of the cause or origin of the tumor. It is like a parasite, for it grows and takes nourishment from the host. As it grows, it penetrates or pushes aside the surrounding tissue.

There are two kinds of tumor: (1) *malignant tumor,* commonly called **cancer,** in which little pieces break off and are carried around the body by the blood and lymph, and (2) *non-malignant* or *benign tumor,* which is usually encased in capsules and becomes dangerous only when it presses on surrounding organs.

Cancer is the condition in which cells grow and divide at an abnormally high rate. It ranks second in the causes of death but may be stopped if treated early enough. The symptoms are (1) a sore, especially about the tongue, mouth, or lips, that does not heal within ten days or two weeks, (2) a lump on any part of the body, especially if it is on the breast, lip, or tongue and if its size increases, (3) white splotches on the tongue that do not quickly clear, (4) bleeding or a colored discharge from a body opening, (5) sudden progressive change in size or color of a wart, mole, or birthmark, (6) persistent indigestion, particularly in persons past 35 years of age, (7) persistent hoarseness, unexplained coughing, or difficulty in swallowing, and (8)

401

General Electric

FIGURE 28-1. *RADIATION SUITS*

Employees of an atomic power laboratory are protected by plastic boots, rubber gloves, masks, and headgear.

FIGURE 28-2. *CANCER CELLS*

Cancer is an abnormally rapid and disorderly growth of cells. Here, the dark areas are skin carcinoma cells.

General Biological Supply House

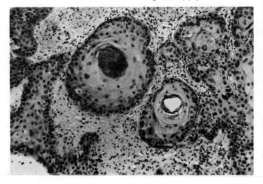

marked change in normal bowel habits.

Cancer recognized in its early stages can often be cured. The treatment may be (1) *surgery,* to remove the new growth of cells, (2) *X-rays,* to destroy the tissue, or (3) *radium,* to burn the underlying tissue and form a protective sheath.

Early diagnosis of cancer is essential. Immediate treatment may result in curing the cancer or at least delaying its progress. Some of the precancerous conditions are long continued irritation such as a wart or mole under a collar or belt, persistent sores, ulcers and unrepaired injuries from burns or childbirth. Prolonged or often-repeated exposure to radiation from X-rays, radium and "tagged atoms" (radioactive compounds used in research) may be followed by cancer. There may also be a hereditary factor in cancer. There is some evidence that certain forms of cancer may be caused by a virus.

Tests for the presence of cancer are made through (1) *biopsy,* examining sections of the tissue under the microscope, (2) the use of radioisotopes, (3) blood and urine tests and other means. It is very difficult to locate some kinds of cancer and this makes early diagnosis difficult. Regular check-ups, however, will aid diagnosis.

28.5   Dietary Diseases

In Section 21.5 we studied some of the dietary diseases. Those which are caused from the lack of vitamins include eye diseases, beriberi, pellagra, scurvy, rickets, and others. These dietary diseases lead to deformities, weaken the body, and make it less resistant to other diseases.

28.6   Glandular Diseases

Some of the diseases and abnormal conditions of the body are caused by the improper functioning of the ductless glands. Examples of these diseases are diabetes, cretinism, and unusual growth, such as seen in giants and dwarfs. Other diseases may affect the digestive glands. For example, gall stones in the gall bladder are caused by a diseased condition of the liver.

28.7   Organic Diseases

Some diseases of the kidneys, brain, and heart are due to faulty structures in the body organs. One of the leading causes of death today is *heart disease.* The heart is the first organ to start action before you are born and the only rest it has is between beats.

The blood vessels and kidneys are closely associated with the heart and have a direct effect upon its activity. They are often associated with diseases of the heart. High blood pressure may result from diseased kidneys. Hardening of the arteries may cause heart trouble. A blood clot in an artery or vein or in the heart may cause sudden death. In some cases the heart muscle or the valves may become affected. It is a necessary precaution to check the blood pressure frequently and to have a physician listen to the heart beat. In this way early diagnosis of some heart conditions may be made and preventive measures taken.

If you play basketball or football or take an active part in other sports, you have probably learned the importance of keeping health rules in order to maintain a healthy heart condition.

In *rheumatic fever,* streptococcus bacteria settle in the valves of the heart and interfere with their work. Conditions such as frequent nosebleeds, sore joints, or diseased tonsils, may call attention to the possibility of a rheumatic infection.

The treatment usually includes a great deal of rest in order to prevent more damage to the heart.

28.8 Diseases Caused by Plants and Animals

Some animals, such as the rattlesnake and Gila monster (Figs. 15-3 and 15-4), secrete poisons which may be fatal to anyone bitten by them. One of the most common mushrooms produces a similar poison which is not destroyed by cooking. If this particular mushroom is eaten, death is almost certain to follow. In both these cases the animal or plant is large enough to be seen, and should be easily recognized by any careful observer.

A large number of the plants and animals which cause disease, however, are microscopic. *Bacteria* and *molds* are some of the tiny plants causing disease, while *protozoa* and *worms* are representative of the small animals. Those causing disease are parasitic for at least a part of their lives. They either destroy certain cells or produce substances which act as specific poisons to the body.

28.9 Efforts to Prevent Disease

Long before the causes of disease were discovered, men were trying to relieve suffering. During the eighteenth century, smallpox was common everywhere. Many persons died and those who lived were badly disfigured. Doctors tried inoculation, but often the patient became violently ill and sometimes died. In 1796, Edward Jenner, having noticed that dairy-maids who had had cowpox seemed to be immune from smallpox, vaccinated an eight-year-old boy with serum taken from a cowpox blister. This proved successful and was the first vaccination of this kind. It soon became widely used in England, Russia,

The Bettmann Archive

FIGURE 28-3. *PIONEER*

Louis Pasteur, a great French scientist, discovered that bacteria cause disease and are responsible for food spoilage.

France, and America with such success that epidemics of smallpox are rare at the present time.

Jenner's amazing success in stopping smallpox paved the way for more studies into the cause, prevention, and cure of diseases.

28.10 Pasteur and the Germ Theory

From earliest times what he could not explain, primitive man called magic. He was superstitious and thought the gods sent disease as punishment to evildoers.

It was not until the nineteenth century that people began to look for the causes of disease. The invention of the microscope enabled scientists to improve methods of research. Louis Pasteur (page 684) was employed by the French Government to save the wine industry, for something was causing the fruit to spoil, and people were losing money. With his microscope and experimental methods Pasteur found the bacteria causing the trouble and devised the method of **pasteurization** (pass-ter-ih-zay-shun) now familiar to us in connection with milk.

About that time there were complaints that the silkworms were dying in large numbers. This was threatening the silk industry. Cattle and sheep were dying of a deadly disease called *anthrax*. People were going mad from the bites of rabid dogs. Again Pasteur was called on to help. With his microscope, he examined the fluids from the bodies of the silkworms and each time he found the same kind of *germ*. The fluids from the healthy worms did not contain them. Thus he concluded that those particular germs caused the disease.

Then Pasteur began in the same way to study anthrax that was killing the sheep. In this case he found a different kind of germ. From his researches he drew the conclusion that each disease was caused by a particular germ. This is known as the **germ theory** of disease.

28.11   Koch Proved His Postulates

While Pasteur was searching for microbes in France, Robert Koch (*kokh*) (page 681), who was about twenty years younger, began his career as a doctor in Germany. In his own country an epidemic of anthrax was raging among the cattle and sheep. He had heard of Pasteur's work and set about to isolate the dread disease germ. He was successful in making it grow in the laboratory on cooked food and finally on gelatine. Then he was able to study it more carefully, inoculate healthy animals with it, and make them immune by giving them a mild form of the particular disease.

Other problems soon presented themselves, and Koch began to study tuberculosis. It took him eight years to find the bacteria which were causing so many deaths among cattle as well as human beings. During this time he had improved his methods of studying and isolating germs. He was putting Pasteur's germ theory on a scientific basis where he could definitely prove it. His statements of procedure are known as **Koch's postulates.**

His postulates are: (1) find the disease-producing germ in the tissues of the diseased animal, (2) isolate it and grow it in a pure culture, (3) introduce it into healthy individuals so that they have a mild form of the same disease, and (4) isolate the same germ from the second individual.

To us, this explanation seems merely the expression of common sense, but to the people living at the time of Pasteur and Koch it was a wonderful discovery. This method is still used in studying disease today.

28.12   Malaria and Its Control

Now that the war on disease had begun, more scientists started investigations. The cause of many bacterial diseases was discovered, but in some parts of the world epidemics of enormous proportions continued to rage. Among these were *malaria* and *yellow fever*. Just how they were spread no one knew, but it was thought that something was attacking the red corpuscles.

It was Sir Ronald Ross, serving in the Medical Service in India, who seriously went to work on the problem of malaria. He had nearly been "eaten alive" by mosquitoes at some of his posts of duty. The suggestion that mosquitoes might carry malaria inspired him to work on the problem. This was difficult because the malarial parasite, which had already been discovered by Charles Laveran, is a protozoan and undergoes one stage in

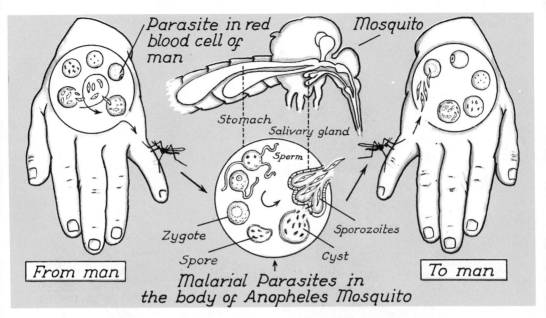

Parasite in red blood cell of man

Mosquito

From man

Stomach

Salivary gland

Sperm

Zygote

Spore

Sporozoites

Cyst

To man

Malarial Parasites in the body of Anopheles Mosquito

FIGURE 28-4. *LIFE CYCLE OF THE MALARIAL PARASITE*

The malarial parasite lives in the red blood cells of man where it multiplies asexually (*left*). When an Anopheles mosquito bites an infected man, it carries off some of the parasites. They develop sexually within the mosquito's stomach (*center*), enter its salivary glands, and may be passed on when another man is bitten (*right*).

the body of the female *Anopheles* mosquito (Fig. 28-4) and passes through another stage in the corpuscles of man.

Ross discovered two important things: (1) that there were parasites in the body of the mosquito, and (2) that a particular kind of mosquito spread the disease. Then he set to work to destroy the mosquitoes by (1) using screens on the houses, (2) covering garbage pails, and (3) draining the swamps where mosquitoes breed. *Quinine,* a drug made from cinchona bark, was formerly used to prevent and treat malaria. During World War II, *atabrin* was used to fight this disease. Since then *aralin, pentaquine,* and other drugs have been used but none is entirely satisfactory. Many new anti-malaria drugs are now being tested.

28.13 Yellow Fever Conquered by Man

While Ross was fighting malaria in his

country, brave men in America were also fighting great battles in an attempt to conquer yellow fever. Doctors Walter Reed and Jesse Lazear (luh-*zeer*) (page 682) were members of the Yellow Fever Commission sent to Cuba to search for the cause of the fever and a method of control (Fig. 12-9). They suspected that mosquitoes spread the disease, and they tried to prove this by experiments with people. Dr. Lazear allowed himself to be bitten by an Aëdes mosquito although he knew he might be in great danger. As a consequence he became very ill with yellow fever and died of the disease, a martyr to science.

When it was definitely proved that the Aëdes mosquito could transmit yellow fever after biting an infected person, William Gorgas undertook the extermination of this insect. He enforced rigid sanitary laws in Havana, and was then sent to Panama, where deaths from the disease threatened to halt the building

Courtesy Dr. J. Gross, Mass. General Hospital

FIGURE 28-5. *ELECTRON MICROSCOPE*

Streams of electrons, instead of light rays, are focused to magnify objects 25,000 times their own diameter.

of the Panama Canal. He again put in force his laws of health, insisting that swamps be drained and that all vessels of open water be screened. In thus destroying the breeding places of the Aëdes mosquitoes he also destroyed the Anopheles. Consequently both malaria and yellow fever were nearly eradicated from Panama.

28.14 Gaining Control of Disease

Another step in gaining control of disease was the use of *antiseptics* in surgery by Sir Joseph Lister (page 682). He also helped emphasize the fact that positive measures should be taken to destroy disease germs. This lead the way for Emil von Behring to perfect *antitoxin* for diphtheria and tetanus (lockjaw).

The *X-ray,* discovered by Roentgen in 1895, has been useful in finding out more about the body conditions. It can help in detecting broken bones and other body conditions.

The *electron microscope* can focus X-rays so that the internal structures of objects are made clearly visible. X-rays cannot be focused by optical lenses like ordinary light rays—they can only cast shadows of things they pass through. The electron microscope generates X-rays by an electron beam. This beam is focused by electronic lenses on a spot only a hundred-thousandth of an inch in diameter. X-rays coming from this tiny pinpoint cast sharp shadows which are picked up on photographic film or on a fluoroscope screen. Biologists are using this microscope in their study of very small living organisms. Dentists and doctors are able to study further such processes as tooth decay and hardening of the arteries. From such studies they can find out the nature of objects through which light cannot pass and which are too small to be seen by means of an ordinary microscope.

The discovery of *radium* by the Curies and their work on *radioactivity* were recognized in 1903. Radium is used to treat cancer. It has been found that *radioactive atoms* of different elements will go to a definite part of the body and locate there (Fig. 28-6). This is helpful in tracing the course of some diseases.

Radioactive atoms are often called *tagged atoms* or *radioisotopes.* They give off a constant stream of tiny particles, as does radium. Whenever a Geiger counter, an instrument used to

THE CONTROL AND CARE OF THE BODY

measure radioactivity, is put near a radio-isotope, the counter will tick violently. This makes it possible to trace various radioactive substances through different parts of the body.

Tagged carbon atoms are used in plant research. Radioactive iron and phosphorus atoms can be traced into the red blood cells. Radioactive calcium and phosphorus have been followed to the bone; radioactive gold has been traced to cancerous tissue; and radioactive iodine may be located in the thyroid gland.

28.15 Drugs and Molds That Combat Disease

Some bacteria that may get in our bodies and grow there produce harmful substances known as **toxins** (*tok*-sins). Toxins act on our bodies as poisons. Scientists have searched for a long time and are continuing to search for substances which are able to counteract the poisonous effect and also destroy the bacteria.

Paul Ehrlich, after many unsuccessful attempts, succeeded in producing *salvarsan,* an arsenic compound used in the treatment of syphilis. Other chemicals, the **sulfa drugs,** a group of dyes first used to fight infections by Domagk in 1932, are used in streptococcus infections such as scarlet fever, pneu-

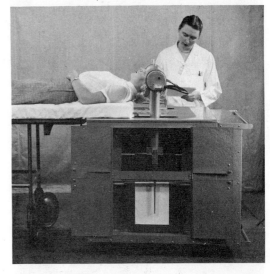

FIGURE 28-6. *USES OF RADIOACTIVITY*

Radioisotope tracers are here being used in brain tumor localization. In addition to diagnosis, certain radioisotopes may be used in the treatment of disease.

monia, tonsilitis, and some wound infections. These drugs may be made in the laboratory. They weaken germs and prevent them from multiplying.

Antibiotics (an-tih-by-*ot*-iks) are germ-destroying substances made by living organisms such as molds and bacteria. Dr. Alexander Fleming discovered *penicillin* in 1929 when he found some molds in his bacterial cultures that retarded the growth of the bacteria. Penicillin was first synthesized in 1946. It is effective in (1) the prevention of

FIGURE 28-7. *DETAIL OF PENICILLIUM MOLD*

Penicillium mold can be grown in liquid, which is then treated chemically and evaporated. The white solid remaining yields penicillin acid, which when changed to salts, is the form doctors use to combat many infections.

Courtesy E. R. Squibb & Sons, Inc.

407

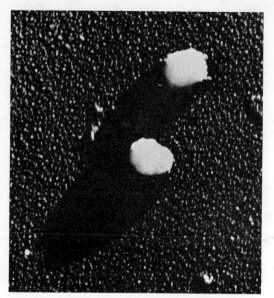

FIGURE 28-8. *SMALLPOX VIRUS*

Smallpox is caused by the smallest of organisms called a *filtrable virus*. Although viruses can be grown in the laboratory, they must be grown in living cells. Most virus diseases are spread by direct contact or droplet infection.

infection in wounds, (2) the promotion of healing in burns, (3) insuring skin grafts, (4) treatment of infections due to bacteria, either chronic in nature or of such severity as to render the prospect of death likely, such as meningitis and gangrene.

Streptomycin (strep-toh-*my*-sin), another antibiotic, was discovered by Dr. Selman Waksman (page 686) in 1944. It is produced by a filamentous mold, and combats certain infections that resist penicillin and the sulfa drugs. Tularemia, or "rabbit fever," some types of urinary tract, heart, and lung infections, certain forms of meningitis, and infections of the blood system have been treated successfully with this drug or with one of its associates such as *aureomycin, terramycin,* or *chloromycetin.* A similar antibiotic, *dihydrostreptomycin,* is now being used in the treatment of

tuberculosis along with a new drug, *PAS* (para-amino-salicylic acid). Chloromycetin is effective in the treatment of whooping cough and anthrax.

Other antibiotics include bacitracin, which is effective in mixed wound infections, and tetracycline, prepared in 1953, which has been used to fight other infections. Antibiotics are being fed to animals in order to improve their production by preventing infection and building up their bodies. More new drugs are continually being produced by the combined efforts of doctors, biologists, and chemists.

28.16   Causes of Disease

The organisms which cause disease include bacteria, viruses, rickettsiae, yeasts, molds, protozoa, parasitic worms, and others. The most common diseases are those caused by bacteria and viruses.

Bacteria (bak-*tihr*-ee-uh) are microscopic one-celled plant forms. They divide rapidly and increase in numbers under conditions of warmth, moisture, and a food supply. When bacteria grow they secrete poisonous substances called *toxins* which destroy cells. Bacteria which decompose foods produce poisonous *ptomaines* (*toh*-mayns). Bacteria cause such diseases as diphtheria, pneumonia, tuberculosis, typhoid fever, and lockjaw.

Viruses (*vy*-rus-es) are very small forms of matter which can only be seen under the electron microscope. When they are in living cells they can multiply and go through changes resembling those that take place in the chromosomes. Outside the body they are very much like nonliving protein molecules, but when viruses are in living tissue they feed on the cells and become able to grow and reproduce like living things. Scientists do not yet agree on whether

THE CONTROL AND CARE OF THE BODY

viruses are living or non-living forms. Some virus diseases are rabies, small-pox, poliomyelitis, mumps, measles, and colds. There is at least one form of virus pneumonia.

Rickettsiae (rik-*et*-see-eye) resemble bacteria, but they are much smaller. They cannot live outside of their host, and in this way resemble viruses. They were discovered by Dr. H. T. Ricketts who found them in spotted fever and typhus fever. They are carried by the body louse, rat flea, tick, and mite.

Protozoa cause such diseases as African sleeping sickness and malaria. *Worm* diseases are those caused by the tapeworm, hookworm, and trichina. *Fungi,* which are non-green plants, cause ringworm and athlete's foot. They also cause some ear and eye infections.

28.17   The Spread of Disease

Diseases may be spread in many ways. The organisms which cause them can come to us on food, in water, through the air, or by contact with diseased persons and others who are not ill, but who carry the germs. Insect and animal bites may also cause diseases. Since there are so many ways to become infected, we must follow health rules to protect ourselves and others. Carelessness may spread disease and cause epidemics.

Typhoid fever, and sometimes tuberculosis and diphtheria, are spread through food and milk. Flies are often responsible for carrying germs from places of infection to exposed food.

Tetanus, or lockjaw, is a real danger from cuts which do not bleed, especially if the wound is deep. This is because tetanus bacteria are *anaerobic* (an-ayr-oh-bik), which means that they can live without air. Other bacteria can also enter cuts and cause serious infection.

The germs of colds, pneumonia, measles, diphtheria, and sometimes tuberculosis can float in the air, and so are often breathed in by unsuspecting persons. These people may later develop the disease.

Diseases that are spread from one living thing to another are known as **communicable diseases.** Not only do flies, mosquitoes, ticks, cockroaches, bedbugs, and lice carry disease germs, but people themselves often spread disease. Neglect to wash the hands, failure to sterilize dishes, and unnecessary contact with those who are ill is certain to spread the germs that are present on objects touched or persons visited.

A few people are *carriers* of disease. They harbor certain kinds of disease germs in their bodies without themselves suffering from the disease. Unless they use special precautions, carriers become a serious menace to society. Usually, if known, carriers are required to register with the health officer, receive instruction as to necessary precautions, and at intervals report their whereabouts.

28.18   Destroying Disease Organisms

Bacteria and other microbes may be checked by (1) removing them, (2) killing them, or (3) preventing or slowing their growth. This can be done by the use of one or more of the following:

(1) *Disinfectants*—chemicals that kill or remove bacteria from objects.

(2) *Germicides*—substances that kill all microbes.

(3) *Antiseptics*—chemicals that check the growth of bacteria on the body.

(4) *Sterilization*—a method of killing all microbes usually with boiling water or steam.

(5) *Pasteurization*—a method of destroying some microbes without adversely affecting the chemical composition of the product.

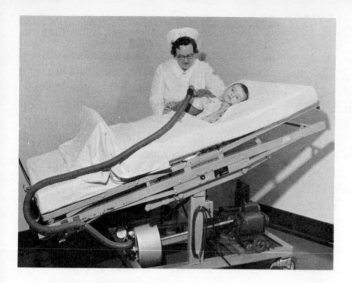

28.19 Poliomyelitis

This disease is caused by several filtrable viruses, and may take many different forms. It is thought that it may be contracted from the nose and throat discharges of infected persons. The incubation period, or time after the virus enters the body until the symptoms begin to appear, is usually from one to two weeks. The disease often begins with a slight fever and symptoms of a cold. Later, in some of the more severe forms, paralysis may develop. When the respiratory center is affected, an iron lung is used to aid breathing. When arm, leg, and other muscles are damaged, special heat and exercise treatments are given.

In 1953, mass inoculations of *Salk vaccine* were given to young school children in the hope of preventing "polio." This vaccine was prepared and given preliminary testing by Dr. Jonas Salk (page 684). The very weak or dead viruses are injected into the body to stimulate the production of antibodies and to develop an active immunity. When these test inoculations seemed to have good results, the vaccine was given to many more children and adults. Present evidence shows a great reduction in the number of new polio cases.

28.20 Prevention of Disease

The body has three lines of defense against disease: (1) the unbroken *skin* prevents the entrance of bacteria or viruses, (2) the *white corpuscles* attack those which get into the body, and (3) the *antibodies* in the blood counteract the toxins of those remaining. When the invasion is too great for the body to control, disease results.

28.21 Immunity

Another method of controlling disease is to establish *immunity* toward that disease. A person is immune to a biological disease if his body resists its germs so successfully that he does not develop the disease. In the case of scarlet fever, diphtheria, typhoid fever, and syphilis, tests show whether or not a person is immune. The *Dick test* is used for scarlet fever, the *Schick test* for diphtheria, the *Widal test* for typhoid fever, and the *Wassermann test* for syphilis.

Natural Immunity.—Many persons do not become sick when there is an epidemic of typhoid fever, measles, malaria, or the like. Such persons have inherited a **natural immunity** to those diseases. This resistance varies with age and the condition of the body. A person who

THE CONTROL AND CARE OF THE BODY

is ordinarily immune may become susceptible to a disease when he is exhausted by care or work.

Acquired Immunity.—Persons who recover from a disease then have an **acquired immunity** to that particular disease. This kind of immunity, acquired during one's lifetime, may be temporary or permanent. Immunity is acquired in two ways: (1) by an attack of a disease, since many germ diseases give immunity against another attack (not true of all diseases or for all persons), and (2) by immunization treatment.

28.22 Immunization

Two kinds of immunity can be acquired by treatment: (1) *active immunity* and (2) *passive immunity.*

Active immunity is acquired when the body produces its own **antibodies.** These are chemical substances which combat disease germs and their products. Active immunity is obtained by (1) having a disease and recovering from it by producing antibodies, such as with chicken pox and measles, and (2) when substances called *vaccines* (*vak*-seens) are injected into the blood. A *vaccine* is a preparation containing a weakened form of a virus or germ which stimulates the formation of antibodies but is not quite strong enough to cause the disease.

An **antigen** (*an*-tih-jen) is any substance that causes the human body to produce antibodies. In diseases such as typhoid fever, whooping cough, and poliomyelitis, immunity is produced by injecting the dead virus as an antigen.

Toxoids (*tok*-soyds) are bacterial extracts or poisonous substances which have been treated to be non-poisonous. In cases like diphtheria they produce immunity by stimulating the growth of antibodies in the blood stream.

Passive immunity is acquired by giv-

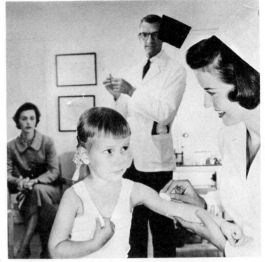

Courtesy Parke, Davis and Co.

FIGURE 28-10. *SCHICK TEST*

If the Schick test indicates that the child is susceptible to diphtheria, she can be immunized with toxoid.

ing injections of antibodies that have already been produced in the blood of other people or animals. Usually these antibodies are first developed in the body of an animal, and then *serum* is made from some of that animal's blood. The serum, which is the liquid part of the blood after it has been clotted, is injected into the person who is to be immunized. This is a protection from the disease when a person has already been exposed. It is only a temporary type of immunity, because it does not stimulate the production of new antibodies. Passive immunity is used to prevent scarlet fever, measles, and tetanus.

Each disease has its own specific virus or disease germ, and the cells must build up a separate immunity to each disease.

Inoculation against a disease greatly reduces the severity of the disease if it is acquired, but it does not absolutely prevent the disease. If a person gets too many germs in the inoculation, he may have a slight infection, but the chance of contagion is reduced.

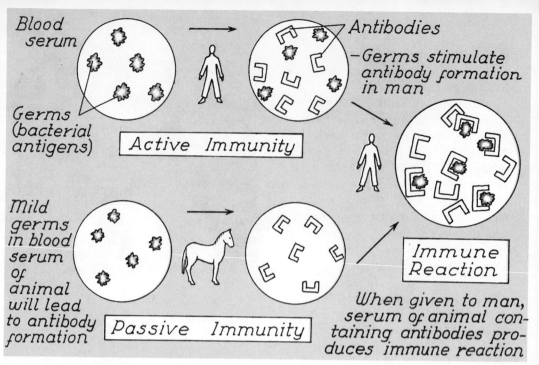

FIGURE 28-11. *IMMUNIZATION*

Vaccines and other preparations containing antigens stimulate the growth of antibodies when injected into the blood, and so produce an *active* immunity. *Passive* immunity is acquired by injecting serum containing antibodies already produced in another animal.

Much is being done to combat disease. A measles vaccine, developed by Dr. John Enders, was released in 1963. Records are being kept to show its effectiveness. Scientists are busy developing cures for other diseases too.

28.23 Progress in Medical Science

The development of surgical skills was held back many centuries because of a lack of knowledge of (1) the structure of the human body, (2) the methods of preventing great loss of blood during operations, (3) how to make a patient insensible to pain, and (4) how to prevent a wound from becoming infected. Scientists through centuries worked on these problems, among them Galen and Vesalius on anatomy, Paré on methods of stopping excess bleeding, and Wells

and Morton on the use of anaesthetics. Dr. Oliver Wendell Holmes recognized the dangers of blood poisoning, but it was Sir Joseph Lister who made modern surgery possible. In 1867 Lister announced his practical application of the germ theory to wounds. His method of sterilizing instruments and wounds has now been improved and universally adopted.

Although many men worked long and hard to advance the knowledge of science, it was the work of those with creative minds that enabled them to prove their theories and come to sound conclusions. In modern times there are vast numbers of research workers supported by grants of money from many organizations, and from government and industry, who are pushing forward to solve today's problems. Some of the scientists among these are Fleming, who discovered penicillin, Waksman, who worked on streptomycin, and Salk, who was successful in developing a polio vaccine. Pasteur, Koch, Lister, Lazear, Fleming, Waksman, and Salk were from different nations, yet all worked for the general good. The fight against disease and the effort to save lives is on behalf of all mankind. Through the efforts of the World Health Organization the work is being coordinated to help more people in more parts of the world.

FACTS TO REMEMBER

Diseases may be inherited or acquired in some occupation. They may be due to the abnormal growth of tissues. Diseases may be dietary, glandular, organic, or caused by such microorganisms as bacteria, viruses, rickettsiae, protozoa, molds, fungi, or worms.

Many men have contributed to our knowledge of disease. Jenner discovered vaccination for smallpox, Pasteur proposed the germ theory of disease and gave us pasteurization, Koch formulated his four postulates for investigating diseases, Ross discovered the cause of malaria, and Reed, Lazear, and Gorgas conquered yellow fever.

There have been many other notable contributions in gaining control over disease. Lister is remembered for antiseptic surgery, Roentgen for the X-ray, the Curies for the discovery of radium, and Salk for polio vaccine. The electron microscope, radioisotopes, antibiotics, sulfa drugs, have all advanced our knowledge of the cause and prevention of disease.

The *defenses* of the body against disease include the skin, the white corpuscles, and antibodies in the blood stream. Some people have a *natural immunity* to certain diseases, while others have an *acquired immunity,* which may be either active when the organism produces its own antibodies, or passive when antibodies are introduced from another organism.

WORDS TO REMEMBER

acquired immunity	disease carriers	ptomaines
active immunity	electron microscope	radioactive elements
anaerobic	germ	Rickettsiae
antibiotics	germ theory of disease	Schick test
antibodies	glandular disease	streptomycin
antigen	immunity	sulfa drugs
antiseptic surgery	inherited disease	toxin
antitoxin	inoculation	toxoid
bacteria	Koch's postulates	tumor
cancer	natural immunity	vaccination
communicable diseases	occupational disease	vaccine
Dick test	organic disease	virus
dietary disease	passive immunity	Widal test
disease	pasteurization	X-ray

QUESTIONS

1. Name at least one disease produced by each of the following: bacteria, virus, protozoa, worm, dietary deficiency.
2. What are some of the symptoms of cancer?
3. Why is it important to recognize cancer early?
4. What treatment is used for tumors and cancers?
5. What is meant by the germ theory of disease?
6. List Koch's postulates and explain how he used them in studying a particular disease, such as anthrax.
7. How was malaria brought under control?
8. In the fight against yellow fever, what active parts were taken by Reed, Lazear, and Gorgas?
9. Who was responsible for the first successful vaccination? Why is the vaccine made from cowpox rather than smallpox lesions?
10. Name two different kinds of immunization and explain how each kind is acquired.
11. Distinguish between natural and acquired immunity. How can acquired immunity be established?
12. Have you acquired immunity to any diseases? If so, list them. Do you consider this a protection? Why?
13. In what ways are infectious diseases spread? What can be done to prevent this?

COMPLETION TEST

As your teacher or classmate reads the following incomplete statements, with your book closed, write on a clean sheet of paper the word or phrase which best completes the statement.

1. Two diseases which are inherited are _____ and _____.
2. The Anopheles mosquito carries _____.
3. The Aëdes mosquito carries _____ _____.
4. The germs of _____ and _____ are carried by the housefly.
5. The germs of _____ and _____ are often spread through the careless handling of milk and water.
6. People who harbor disease germs in their bodies, without themselves suffering from the disease, are called _____.
7. Cancer is called a _____ tumor.
8. "Bleeders disease" is properly termed _____.
9. The toxin-antitoxin treatment for diphtheria was discovered by _____.
10. The common name for tetanus is _____.

PROJECTS

Investigate the lives and work of other great scientists, besides those mentioned in the text, who helped in the fight against disease. Make a careful study of at least five and write a summary of their contributions.

THE CONTROL AND CARE OF THE BODY

REFERENCES

Bolduan, *Public Health and Hygiene*. Saunders.

Chandler, *Famous Men of Medicine*. Dodd, Mead.

Epstein and Williams, *Miracles from Microbes*. Rutgers University Press.

Fishbein, *Common Ailments of Man*. Garden City.

Good News About Diabetes. Public Affairs Pamphlet No. 138.

Gray, *The Advancing Front of Medicine*. McGraw-Hill.

Haggard, *Science of Health and Disease*. Harper.

Health Hero, Biographies. Metropolitan Life Insurance Co.

How Shall We Pay for Health? Public Affairs Pamphlet.

Kopeloff, *Man versus Microbes*. Knopf.

Little, *What You Should Know About Tuberculosis*. National Tuberculosis Association.

Live Long and Like It. Public Affairs Pamphlet.

Meredith, *The Health of Youth*. Blakiston.

Ratcliff, *Yellow Magic*. Random House.

Rheumatic Fever. Public Affairs Pamphlet No. 126.

Sherbon, *The Family in Health and in Illness*. McGraw-Hill.

Silverman, *Magic In a Bottle*. Macmillan.

Sokoloff, *The Story of Penicillin*. Ziff-Davis.

Wood, *Health through Prevention and Control of Diseases*. World Book.

CHAPTER 29

Building Healthy Bodies and Minds

29.1 Radiant Health

The formula for good health has long been sought. Ponce de Leon searched for the "fountain of youth." Baseball players, actresses on stage and screen, and skilled musicians have hunted far and wide for the "magic" that would keep them young, strong, and vigorous.

If you feel energetic when you waken in the morning, and if you have a spring in your step and a song in your heart, you are well on your way to radiant health. With good health you will be able to:

1. Do the day's work confidently and enthusiastically.
2. Enjoy three well-balanced meals without digestive disturbances.
3. Sleep soundly eight hours a night.
4. Enjoy at least an hour of vigorous physical exercise daily without feeling tired.
5. Mingle with others without irritability, boredom, or self-consciousness.
6. Follow a hobby not connected with your regular work.

29.2 The Reasons for Good Health

A healthy body helps make a healthy mind. When you are not feeling well ordinary work seems difficult. Just at the time when you really want to play an important game, go to a special dance, take part in a play, or pass a test, it may happen that you do not feel well. With a serious illness, the thought of missing school and other activities, of remaining at home or in the hospital, or of carrying out limited amounts of work is even more disturbing. Yet when you feel well it is hard to realize this. With good health and a determination to

FIGURE 29-1. *THE ROAD TO RADIANT HEALTH*

By exercising in the open air, these young people are observing two important health rules. Daily observance of the basic health rules will pay handsome dividends throughout life.

Lew Merrim from Monkmeyer

416

do things well there is a chance for much happiness and success.

Good health comes to each of us in three ways: (1) we are born with good health, if our family tree is sturdy and strong; (2) we have good health care in our early years, if we have wise and far-seeing parents; and (3) we maintain good health, if we are wise enough to look after ourselves properly, when the responsibility for so doing becomes ours.

29.3 The Roads to Good Health

Good health has to be earned, often the hard way. We have to follow a set of rules that have been tried and found to work. And we have to follow them faithfully.

1. Have a medical checkup on your general health at least once a year.
2. Visit the dentist at least twice a year.
3. Keep your hands, body, and clothing clean to prevent infection.

Safety rules are important in order to be able to enjoy healthful living. Keep in mind some of the following points:

1. Avoid panic by controlling your emotions and trying to consider the situation clearly.
2. Prevent home accidents by removing combustible materials, keeping stairways clear, and checking electrical equipment to make sure it is working safely.
3. Prevent school accidents by not crowding in halls, around lockers, or near equipment.
4. Guard against automobile accidents while driving, riding, or walking.
5. Take care of *all* cuts, abrasions, and burns. Use the proper first-aid measures.

6. Avoid crowds and crowded places.
7. Do not take a pill for a headache or any drugs without the advice of a physician.

You may add to this list many other general health rules. The important thing is to remember to observe them.

29.4 Mental Health

Mental health is a feeling of satisfaction in life, a peace of mind, and an ability to deal with most situations. The person who possesses good mental health feels a confidence in himself that enables him to accept the usual emotions which come with his daily living. He has a sensible attitude toward other people. He feels that he has friends and is accepted in his social groups and loved by his family. In turn, he feels interest in others and responsibility towards them. Such people can meet the demands of life. They are willing to look ahead with long-range plans and still give proper attention to daily affairs. They expect to continue to grow in understanding and to improve their personalities.

Such sound mental health has been established in the family, school, and community, and within the individual himself. He has probably come from a home where he has been wisely loved and given a strong sense of acceptance and security. He has been surrounded by the kind of protection that has kept him safe from serious dangers and has helped him face the necessary pain and bewilderment which have come into his life. In dealing with him, his parents have granted him increasing independence to try out adventures and to take on more responsibilities for himself. The discipline in such a home has placed sensible limits on what he is allowed to do. He has known what those limitations

Hays from Monkmeyer

FIGURE 29-2. *STUDENT ADVISOR*

Some problems in adjustment can be resolved by consulting an experienced counselor in school, or through another agency.

were, why they were set up, and that there would be regularity in carrying them out. He has been shown that while he might feel annoyed or jealous, he would not be allowed to upset others or damage himself when he was experiencing those feelings. He has been given friendly guidance and has observed adults who have shown him by example how to get along with others. His parents have shared their religious faith with him, and the high moral tone of the home has given him a sense of the worth of the individual and a strong belief in important values.

During high school years, you become quite interested in your own personalities. You should try to learn something about how the personality grows, becoming mature, or becoming warped, failing to reach its best possibilities. At times, all of us show negative behavior and undesirable attitudes. By learning the causes of this conduct, and in many

cases, by changing yourself or your environment a little you can achieve greater mental health. When you feel upset it is important to talk it over with a wise and trusted friend. If this does not help enough, you should go to your pastor, guidance counselor, or someone trained to assist in personality growth. A modern attitude toward child guidance clinics and mental health centers should help the individual to be as ready and interested in receiving mental health aid as in going to a doctor when physically ill.

Among your friends and in your own classrooms it is important not to regard unusual people as peculiar, odd, or stupid, but to try to recognize some of the causes for personality differences. No kindly person today would avoid or laugh at a physically handicapped individual. Our attitudes toward those who are facing personality maladjustments need to be equally kind. Some of you may even wish to consider vocations that relate to personality adjustment and maladjustment such as child guidance or counselling.

Mental illness is a term that covers several forms of illness which affect the way a person thinks, feels, and behaves. The medical term for serious mental illness is *psychosis*. Less severe mental illness is known as *neurosis*. The term *insanity* has legal meaning only and refers to psychosis.

The nature of the illnesses can differ a great deal. Minor symptoms that go untreated and continue for a long while can build into something more serious. Excessive shyness, suspicion, moodiness, unhappiness, overdependency, seclusiveness, all indicate that an individual could use help. Mental illness seldom comes on rapidly. It may be caused by damage done to the nervous system, as

THE CONTROL AND CARE OF THE BODY

by brain injury, severe alcoholism, syphilis, and certain poisons, or by gradual body changes as in cerebral arteriosclerosis and advanced old age. A mental illness without a known physical cause, as paranoia and schizophrenia, is called a *functional psychosis*.

Some treatments for mental illness are carried on by regular visits to a doctor or clinic. Others may require hospital care. Most mental patients are quiet people; a few are overactive; but only a very small percentage are dangerous. Early recognition and treatment is very important. New and improved methods include occupational therapy, counselling, hydrotherapy, shock treatment, and psychiatric care. There is a great deal of hope that mentally ill patients who receive adequate treatment will fully recover.

In many communities there is serious neglect in providing preventive services and treatment for building mental health. The need is tragic. In 1958 at least one American in every 16 was suffering from a mental or emotional disorder. Nearly half of our hospital beds are filled with those who are mentally ill. Each community should provide adequate medical facilities, including mental health clinics. The school system should be equipped to aid pupils to plan wisely and to solve problems that arise in relationships with family and school. Recreational facilities should allow adults and young people a sound outlet for creative interests. Housing should adequately provide for conditions that make good family living possible. Work opportunities should provide jobs that bring security. Churches should offer opportunities for worship and moral leadership. Delinquency and crime problems should be adequately met. Counselling services should be provided that include marriage counsel-

ling, vocational advice, child guidance, and help for the chronic alcoholic. Mental health is a goal to be worked toward by the individual and the community. Much progress will be made when citizens take advantage of the services offered.

29.5   Public Health

Individual health measures are not sufficient to prevent the spread of disease. For this reason a *board of health* has been established in each community. When anyone is suffering from a communicable disease, or has been exposed to the germs of any such disease, the board of health may place him under *quarantine*. The nature of the quarantine depends on the specific disease and the laws of the town or state in which the person lives.

The board of health also gathers information on the diseases of the community in addition to taking measures to *prevent epidemics*. One very important function is educational. People should know: (1) that each germ disease is due to a specific germ, plant, or animal, living within the human body; (2) that most germ diseases are preventable; (3) that keeping our bodies clean, eating clean, well-cooked food, and taking plenty of exercise will accomplish more toward preventing germ diseases than many more elaborate measures that could be devised.

A second very important function is to prevent epidemics when communicable diseases break out in the community. This involves the prompt quarantine of the first cases and the immediate putting into operation of board of health regulations for communicable diseases.

In case of severe epidemics, in addition to the quarantine of individuals in a dwelling, all the inhabitants of a city or

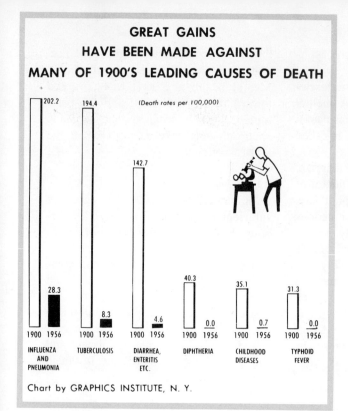

GREAT GAINS
HAVE BEEN MADE AGAINST
MANY OF 1900'S LEADING CAUSES OF DEATH

(Death rates per 100,000)

202.2 194.4 142.7 28.3 8.3 4.6 40.3 0.0 35.1 0.7 31.3 0.0

1900 1956 1900 1956 1900 1956 1900 1956 1900 1956 1900 1956

INFLUENZA AND PNEUMONIA | TUBERCULOSIS | DIARRHEA, ENTERITIS ETC. | DIPHTHERIA | CHILDHOOD DISEASES | TYPHOID FEVER

Chart by GRAPHICS INSTITUTE, N. Y.

FIGURE 29-3. *PROGRESS*

Since 1900, great progress has been made in the prevention and treatment of many serious diseases. In some cases, early diagnosis is the most important factor in controlling the disease; in addition modern research has produced revolutionary new drugs and other effective methods of treatment.

state may be quarantined. The transportation of stock from one state to another may be prohibited if a serious communicable disease exists in cattle or sheep.

Immigrants suffering from certain diseases are prohibited from landing in the United States. This means that there are national as well as state and city quarantine laws. The present quarantine laws are the most effective protective measures known against the spread of disease, and are the product of a high degree of civilization.

State and local boards of health safeguard community water and milk supplies. They establish control of the food supply and check on the sanitation of food establishments and cleanliness of food handlers. These boards inspect factories, check on housing conditions, and concern themselves with child labor

practices relating to health. They cooperate with street cleaning departments, fire departments, and other civic organizations. They also check on factories and housing in order to maintain healthful working and living conditions.

At least one city health department has been providing *multiple screening* tests for the public. These are series of checks such as height and weight measurement, X-ray, electro-cardiogram, blood and urine analyses, and eye and ear tests. These and many other tests are given free of charge, and the results sent both to the person taking the test and to the physician he designates. This plan serves two purposes. Firstly it lets the person know in general what his health condition is and allows him to seek help immediately if needed. Also, the use of multiple screening tests is a good method for public health depart-

420

FIGURE 29-4. *DISASTER EXPERTS*

In times of emergency, the Red Cross sends trained volunteers for such spectacular rescues as this one. Other activities of the Red Cross include an ambulance service and the maintenance of a blood bank.

Courtesy American Red Cross

ments to detect those diseases which might become public menaces if left untreated. Following these tests, a series of free clinics is held for those persons needing further health aid.

29.6 National and International Public Health Activities

The problem of maintaining pure water and food is often more than one state can manage. Therefore control of some of these activities has been taken over by the United States Public Health Service, a department of the national government. Much research is carried on by the National Institute of Health located at Bethesda, Maryland. In the same way, one nation cannot regulate conditions when a world-wide distribution of a disease exists. For example, malaria and yellow fever exist in all parts of the tropics. Cholera and typhus fever are confined mostly to the Eastern Hemisphere, while hookworm belts the world in an area extending about 33 degrees on each side of the equator. Such conditions call for international cooperation, and the World Health Organization, under the supervision of the United Nations, has been established for just this purpose.

There are many private organizations which also contribute to the well-being of mankind throughout the world. The best-known of these is the Rockefeller Foundation, which spends vast sums on public health and medical education, not only in the United States, but also in Canada, England, and China.

A very important public organization is the Red Cross, an international and national society of volunteers and professional workers. The Red Cross holds itself in readiness to offer the best trained volunteer assistance to provide basic needs. Food, clothing, shelter, and communications with family members and loved ones are given. These services are offered in times of great disasters, such as earthquake, fire, floods, tornadoes, droughts, war, and other serious and unusual conditions.

29.7 Man, an Exception

In this section on the biology of man, we have often noted man's similarities to animals and, in many instances, to plants. But there is one respect in which man is in a class by himself: he is the only living thing that finds drugs and tobacco a problem.

The problem is not new. Excavations show that man drank alcoholic beverages several thousand years B.C.; the history

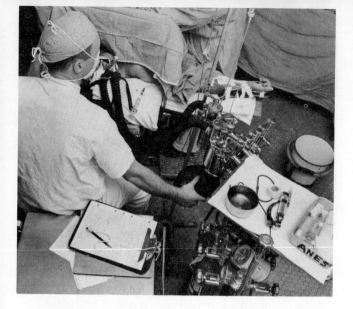

Figure 29-5. *ANAESTHESIA*

The development of anaes-
thetics has enabled great advances in surgery. Here the an-
aesthetist administers a mixture
of nitrous oxide and oxygen to
a patient during an abdominal
operation. He controls breathing
by squeezing the rubber bag.

Paul Weller

of morphine and cocaine antedates modern civilization; natives used tobacco
long before Columbus. But non-medic-
inal drugs and tobacco are in no way necessary to our health and happiness. If
we are as independent as we pretend to
be, they need not be a problem.

No one can make a really accurate
statement of the total number of persons
addicted to drugs. The chief trouble in
using drugs is the difficulty addicts have
in taking them in moderation. The disastrous results reach out into the economic, social, political, and spiritual
phases of human existence. The evidence growing out of this long experience is conclusively against their use.
This is one of the problems that man
has not solved. Science and medicine
are trying to help him.

29.8 Habit-Forming Drugs

*Drugs are special preparations used
to relieve pain or to increase or slow
down the activity of certain cells.* Most
drugs, when taken in doses greater than
the usual amount prescribed by a physician, may cause death. It is customary

to use such terms as *poison, anaesthetic*
(an-us-*thet*-ik), and *narcotic* (nahr-*kot*-
ik) to describe these drugs. Some substances, like opium, have the nature of
all three.

A **poison** is a substance which when
taken into the body tends to cause death
or serious injury to health. Opium, carbolic acid, and mercury are poisons, and
when taken in sufficient quantities, cause
death.

An **anaesthetic** is a substance that
causes a partial or complete loss of sensation or feeling. *General anaesthetics,*
like sodium pentothal and ether or
chloroform, given by a trained person,
cause a temporary loss of consciousness.
Unless anaesthetics are administered
properly, they may cause death. *Local
anaesthetics* like novocain are injected
into the body. Under a local anaesthetic
the patient remains conscious, but loses
sensation in the area injected.

A **narcotic** is a substance which causes
dullness or stupor, and even a temporary
relief from pain. The narcotics often
have a temporary quieting effect which
is sometimes associated with a pleasur-

able feeling. The common narcotics are opium, morphine, cocaine, codeine, laudanum, heroin, chloral hydrate, alcohol, nicotine, and various patent preparations. These are the chief habit-forming drugs.

Often preparations are taken by persons ignorant of the fact that they contain these harmful drugs. No reputable doctor will give any of these narcotics except for severe pain. No person except a physician has a right to prescribe drugs, and he only after a knowledge of the patient's symptoms. Many of these preparations affect the heart and blood, and few of them have any beneficial effect, except in the temporary relief from pain.

Many people take some of these narcotics under a physician's directions without becoming drug users. But those who continue their use find that the dose first taken no longer produces the same sensations. The morphine taker is a good example. Through the habitual use of morphine, he becomes less and less susceptible to its immediate effects, and has constantly to increase his regular dose in order to obtain the effect he desires. This is the most insidious feature of the drug habit. The fact that the victim must take larger and larger doses as he becomes used to the drug means that the harm done his body becomes greater and greater. His general health becomes impaired, and he loses weight. If he keeps increasing his dosage, his nervous system becomes so badly injured that he dies.

29.9 Opium

On July 13, 1933, a new world-wide opium pact went into effect. This was known as the League of Nations Convention for Limitation of Manufacture of Narcotic Drugs. This agreement marked a great step forward in the efforts of man to control narcotics. In order to put these new regulations into practice, the opium-growing nations had to place human welfare ahead of economic gain. This had never been done before.

We should take pride in the long and continued efforts of the United States to regulate the production of opium and suppress the opium traffic. The United States was the first nation to sign the new convention. It took twenty years to bring about this pact, for it was in 1912 that the first International Conference on the Regulation of Opium was held at the Hague.

Few of you who study biology are likely to become addicted to the use of opium, morphine, cocaine, marijuana, or similar habit-forming drugs. However, you should know that one notable authority says that the use of habit-forming drugs for thirty days is long enough to establish the habit in most people. Since the risk of addiction is so great, it would be very dangerous to try drugs in any form just for the sake of a new experience.

The drug addict cannot be trusted. Our modern civilization depends upon reliable people who are able to carry out their particular tasks. At the thought of turning these tasks over to drug addicts, we appreciate the seriousness of acquiring a habit that destroys trustworthiness.

29.10 Patent Medicine

There are many medicinal preparations that contain varying amounts of habit-forming drugs. These are usually spoken of as "patent" medicines and are put up and sold under special registered names. Many of these preparations contain opium or some of its derivatives. Pain-killers, cough cures, sleeping pills,

FIGURE 29-6. *NARCOTICS TAKEN IN RAID*

The large box contains marijuana weed used to make cigarettes (in hand, *right*). Heroin is wrapped in tinfoil, held by both men. In foreground are devices for preparing and injecting heroin.

infant reliefs, and other "medicines" may contain narcotic drugs.

Since the Federal Food, Drug, and Cosmetic Act was passed, the amount of narcotic in patent medicines must be stated on the label. In this way the United States Government tries to prevent the sale of habit-forming preparations to those ignorant of their composition and unaware of their nature.

Many people use these patent medicines rather than consult a doctor. The continued use of them in chronic conditions may lead to addiction and endanger your health. The Wheeler-Lea Act, which makes it unlawful to issue untrue statements or false claims in advertising a product, has helped to keep some of the worthless ones off the market.

29.11 Alcohol

The alcohol habit grows similarly to the narcotic habit. Although alcohol apparently is not as habit-forming as opium or morphine, its effect is different in degree rather than in kind. When it is taken in sufficiently large amounts, death results. When taken in sufficient amounts to produce stupor or temporary loss of control of the body, a definite narcotic condition results, and the individual cannot carry on his usual activities.

It has recently been found that most alcoholics have a vitamin deficiency. This may be due to an improper diet to which the addict is accustomed or to the fact that there is a decided increase in total metabolism during the alcoholic state. Consequently he suffers especially from the lack of the B vitamins.

Many people can drink a certain amount of alcoholic beverages and still retain control of their faculties. But no two persons exhibit the same reaction to alcohol. Because one individual can retain control of himself after drinking a certain amount, it is no indication that another can. Man's individuality has prevented science from finding many definite measures of the effect of alcohol on the human system.

In this connection another important condition enters the problem. If one drinks when the stomach is empty and consumes the liquor rapidly, the reaction is much more pronounced than when alcohol is taken slowly or at meals. The reason for this is that alcohol is absorbed directly into the blood without undergoing digestive changes and thus a larger amount of alcohol is quickly brought to act on the cells of the brain. These two facts, first, individual differences in the tolerance of alcohol, and secondly, the rate at which alcohol is introduced into the body, explain one phase of the effect of alcohol on man.

There are three stages that can be recognized in the absorption of alcohol:

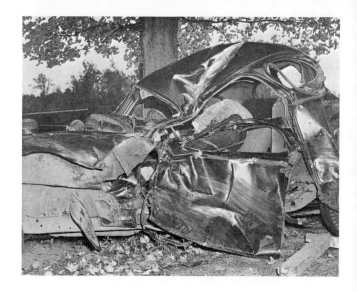

FIGURE 29-7. *A TRAGIC ACCIDENT*

Alcohol attacks the higher brain centers which control coordination. The inability to respond immediately and accurately may result in a fatal mistake like this one.

Philip Gendreau

first, the excitation stage due to the removal of the controlling influence of the brain; secondly, the period of non-coordination in which physical and mental balance are upset; and thirdly, the stage of stupor in which only strong stimuli bring about a response.

There is general agreement that alcohol is more detrimental to the nervous system and brain than to any or all other organs in the body. The nervous organs and brain contain a greater proportion of a fat known as *lipoid* (*lip*-oid). Any substance which dissolves lipoid, as alcohol does, is an anaesthetic. Alcohol causes *cirrhosis,* degeneration of the liver, and *gastritis,* inflammation of the stomach lining.

A large and growing number of physicians are of the opinion, based on experience, that alcohol is rarely useful or necessary as a medicine in the cure of disease. On the contrary, alcohol is known to decrease the power of the body to withstand disease, and it does not assist in destroying the poisons which arise in the case of bacterial diseases.

Alcohol and Oxidation.—Alcohol is absorbed directly into the bloodstream from the digestive tract without under-going digestive alteration. This peculiarity of alcohol permits rapid absorption into the blood, and thus affords a readily available source of heat.

After the alcohol is taken into the blood, it is distributed about the body and is oxidized. But, unlike foodstuffs, it cannot be stored in the tissues for future use, but remains in the blood until it is oxidized or excreted.

No matter how much alcohol there is in the blood, only a certain amount may be oxidized at a time. When there is too much alcohol in the blood, it limits its own oxidation, and this may prevent the oxidation of food material. In other words, the presence of too much alcohol in the blood obstructs the normal processes of oxidation.

Alcohol and Efficiency.—Modern experiments with their precise measurements of human reactions can detect losses of efficiency from quantities of alcohol that used to be considered harmless. It had been thought that one could not take enough, to affect his work, of so weak a drink as a beverage containing only 2.75% alcohol, but experiments have proved the contrary.

Experiments were conducted to show

that alcohol lowers efficiency in skilled acts. Small amounts of alcohol taken with food did not decrease typing speed appreciably, but the errors increased decidedly. When alcohol was taken without food, the typing errors increased more than 100%. This shows that the coordination was affected. The higher brain centers which regulate selfjudgment and self-control are the first to be weakened by the effect of even small amounts of alcohol. Memory is also impaired.

Alcohol next affects the speech and other senses until finally the muscles, respiration, and heart and circulation control are out of balance. The person loses consciousness and in extreme cases death may result.

Alcohol and Disease.—Those who drink alcohol are usually predisposed to disease, since their body resistance is lowered. The lack of vitamin B frequently becomes serious. Inflammation of the liver and poor digestion often result. This lowers the resistance of the body to bacterial infection. Frequently nervous disorders result, followed by various forms of mental illness. Often lack of common sense and a reckless attitude may lead to crime. Persons under the influence of alcohol frequently do not use good judgment and commit acts of violence.

Alcohol and Youth Activities.—Since school athletes need to be in the best of health for keen competition, training regulations forbid the use of alcohol. It is also very dangerous to drive a car after indulging in alcohol. If tempted, remember this warning:

"If you take a drink, don't drive.
If you have to drive, don't drink."

The effects of alcohol may last several hours, with the following effects: (1) slow reaction of eyes, hands and feet to signals, (2) inability to concentrate and wandering attention, (3) less dependable muscular response, and (4) recklessness due to impaired judgment.

Dr. Haven Emerson, former Health Commissioner of New York City, gives the following summary of alcohol:

1. Alcohol is a depressant, habit-forming drug.
2. Alcohol is a protoplasmic poison.
3. Alcohol reduces resistance to disease.
4. Alcohol increases liability to accident, and delays recovery.
5. Alcohol reduces endurance, accuracy, and rapidity of muscular action of all kinds, even when used in such small amounts as to show effects inappreciable to the user.

The Alcohol Habit.—Some people drink just to be sociable. Others feel a personal weakness or inferiority and think alcohol will stimulate them and make them strong. Far too many people think that a drink of alcohol will help them solve or forget their problems. Unfortunately, drinking to be sociable, to feel strong, or to forget life's problems, can ultimately become a habit.

After the first drink to find out what it is like, or because someone teases him into it, a person does not hesitate quite so much in taking another drink. Eventually, the drinks may become more frequent until the habit is fixed. It is difficult for a person to break such a habit unless he is helped by a doctor or he becomes a member of an organization known as "Alcoholics Anonymous." This group consists of people who were once confirmed alcoholics. Aware of the devastating personal and social consequences

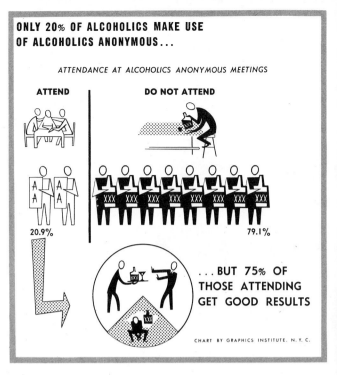

FIGURE 29-8. *ALCOHOLICS ANONYMOUS*

Alcoholics Anonymous is an organization composed of many people interested in a common problem. The members gather together to help themselves and others to recover from alcoholism.

of the alcohol habit, they try to help others who have become addicted.

Alcohol and Society.—In some families and countries and in some religious groups the use of alcohol is forbidden. In others, it is used in very moderate amounts. In almost all countries drunkenness is not respected and is not legal.

Alcoholism is a contributing factor in broken homes, auto accidents, and juvenile and adult crimes. Formerly, courts dealt with the drunken person as a criminal. Today, enlightened courts more frequently regard him as an individual who is physically and mentally ill. Many states have rehabilitation centers for alcoholics. Yale University is doing extensive research on the cause, result, and cure of alcoholism. The chances of becoming an alcoholic vary with individuals. There is always the possibility that one can not be an occasional or moderate drinker, but will become an alcoholic. For such a person, total abstinence is a necessity. The young person should not start to drink without being aware of the danger that he himself might become an alcoholic.

29.12 Tobacco

When Columbus discovered our land, he also discovered tobacco. He saw the natives place the short branches of a Y-shaped hollow stick in their nostrils and the stem in the smoke of burning tobacco. The smoke was inhaled directly into the nostrils. It was not until 1558 that tobacco was introduced into Europe. The French ambassador at Lisbon, Jean Nicot, in 1561, was much taken with the new plaything. It is from his name that the term *nicotine* comes.

If you care to look up the economic phases of smoking, you will be amazed at the amount spent annually for tobacco. Each year the American people spend several times as much for tobacco as they do for education. And for this expense they have only lowered vitality and damage done by careless smokers.

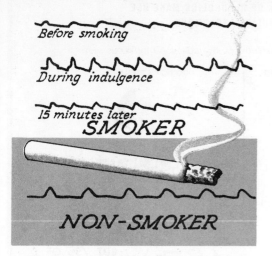

Before smoking

During indulgence

15 minutes later
SMOKER

NON-SMOKER

FIGURE 29-9. *SMOKING AFFECTS THE HEARTBEAT*

Compare the heart action of a smoker and a non-smoker. Each peak represents a single heart beat. The height of the peak indicates the strength of the beat.

There has always been a sharp difference of opinion over the effects of tobacco. It is harmful to those who have a low tolerance to nicotine and to those who smoke to excess. It is more injurious to those who inhale than to those who do not. In many ways the tobacco and alcohol problems are similar. The medical profession and practically everyone else agrees that children and young people should not use either tobacco or alcohol.

Tobacco and Eyes.—Various investigations on the influence smoking has on the eye prove conclusively that the poisonous effects are more marked and serious than earlier studies revealed. Inflammation is sometimes produced, which seems to act on certain nerve fibers of the optic nerve. This causes a defect in the central field of vision first for green, then for red, and finally for blue and white. There is also an alteration in the size of the "blind spot" in some smokers. When these symptoms appear, they can be relieved only by completely ceasing to use tobacco. If the person who is subject to tobacco toxemia does not abstain, permanent blindness may follow.

Tobacco and the Heart.—"Training starts to-morrow; no more smoking," is one of the athletic coach's orders at the beginning of each season. He knows that boys who smoke are more easily winded than boys who do not, and that these latter are stronger, larger, and steadier. The cigarette habit is undermining the health of thousands of boys and girls in America today. The charts on "smoker's heart" prove this point.

The accompanying illustration on the rate of the heartbeat and the strength of the pulse, adapted from charts by Professor McKeever of Kansas University, shows what happens when we smoke. The heart of the habitual cigarette smoker is weak, except for the few minutes during which he is indulging in the habit; the pulsations at this time are unduly excited.

Figure 29-9 shows three records of a young man nineteen years old who began smoking cigarettes at the age of fifteen and who inhaled the fumes. The three records were taken without removing or readjusting the instrument, as follows: No. I immediately before smoking, No. II during the indulgence in the habit, and No. III fifteen minutes later, after the effect of the narcotic had become apparent. No. IV shows the heart pulsations of a normal young man of the same age and temperament.

Says Professor McKeever:

"From the foregoing evidence we are led to the conclusion that in the case of boys and youths, cigarette smoking is very deleterious to the physical and mental well-being. Moreover, my investigations indicate that it makes very little difference in the effects whether the victime uses pipe or cigarettes, provided he inhales the fumes; and with few exceptions smokers of cigarettes are inhalers.

"The ordinary case exhibits about the following type of conduct: (1) While the craving is at its height, the victim manifests much uneasiness and often much excitation. (2) During the indulgence the cheek is alternately flushed and blanched, the respiration considerably increased, and the hands tremble. (3) About twenty minutes after smoking the muscles become relaxed, the respiration slow and shallow, the skin on the face dry and sallow, and there is an apparent feeling of unconcern about everything."

When cigarettes are burned, certain poisons are produced which may cause serious effects on persons who inhale tobacco smoke in this form. These poisons are absorbed in small quantities by the mucous membrane which lines the nasal passages and in larger quantities when the smoke is inhaled into the lungs. It makes little difference whether the smoke comes from cigarettes, cigars, or pipes. All kinds are harmful, especially when inhaled.

Nicotine and Health. — Because so many people have been forming the smoking habit, there has been a great deal of publicity about the harmful effects of nicotine on the nervous system and general health of the body. These adverse reports on smoking began to cause concern to the tobacco companies who wanted to sell their products. They started to investigate the nicotine prob-

Philip Gendreau

FIGURE 29-10. *NO SMOKING*

Athletes abstain from smoking because it affects the heart and cuts down on their "wind"—that is, the rate at which oxygen is transferred to the blood.

lem, and research workers studied the preparation of tobacco. They have been able to reduce the nicotine content in cigarettes from 3 per cent in 1915 to 2 per cent in 1955, and are still trying to make it less. Cigarette smoking is a probable cause of lung cancer, as indicated by research studies. It also results in digestive disorders.

Although some of the harmful effects of tobacco are being removed, there is still the danger of a slow poison seeping into the system. This is not necessary. Instead of a cigarette, choose some delicious food, and you will be healthier and happier.

FACTS TO REMEMBER

Good health is a priceless possession that you cannot afford to lose. By following a few simple rules, you can attain health of body and health of mind.

The health of a community is protected by the local board of health. In addition, national and international organizations, both public and private, have been formed to promote healthful living and freedom from disease throughout the world.

The *habitual* use of drugs, alcohol, and tobacco can have very serious effects on the general health of the body. *Narcotics* and *alcohol* are not only injurious to organs of the body, but they can also destroy a person's appearance, character, and mental alertness. Although *tobacco* is less serious in its effects, continual use of it can impair the proper functioning of the heart and the respiratory and nervous systems.

WORDS TO REMEMBER

addict	lipoid	nicotine
alcohol	local anaesthetic	opium
anaesthetic	multiple screening	patent medicine
drug	tests	poison
epidemic	narcotic	quarantine
general anaesthetic		

QUESTIONS

1. Give a definition of each of the following: poison, anaesthetic, drug, narcotic.
2. Name several drugs. Of what use are they in medicine? Why is it so dangerous to use them?
3. State five reasons why people should not drink alcohol.
4. What do you think of the use of "patent" medicines?
5. State three bad physical effects of smoking.
6. Why is there increased attention to mental health? What causes mental breakdowns?
7. Name five measures to help maintain good mental health.

COMPLETION TEST

As your teacher or classmate reads the following incomplete statements, with your book closed, write on a clean sheet of paper the word or phrase which correctly completes the statement.

1. An anaesthetic commonly administered is _____.
2. Alcoholics usually suffer from the lack of vitamin _____.
3. When Columbus discovered our land, he also discovered _____.
4. Cigarettes have a particularly bad effect on the _____.
5. _____ dissolves the lipoid in the nerve cells.
6. Alcohol can be absorbed directly into the blood without being _____.
7. Opium is classed as a _____.
8. "Patent" medicines used to contain relatively large amounts of _____.
9. Alcohol is absorbed more rapidly when the stomach is _____.
10. During smoking, the heart beats _____.

430   THE CONTROL AND CARE OF THE BODY

PROJECTS

I. *Keeping a Personal Health Record.*—Make a list of health rules which you consider important for a boy or girl of your age. Submit it to your teacher for criticism. If possible, discuss each one in detail. Make a revised list on a chart which can be posted in your room. Arrange spaces for daily checking. Keep your record at least for a month and as long as your teacher suggests.

If during this time you are forced to stay out of school because of illness, or if you suffer from minor health ailments, you should again carefully check with your doctor, the school nurse, and your teacher. For a project, you should have a complete health score for at least a month.

II. *Health in Your Home.*—Make a list of the health measures that are already being taken in your home, such as—
1. safe source of water supply.
2. drainage system and sewage disposal.
3. milk containers—handling and storage.
4. storage of food—raw and cooked.
5. ventilation.
6. heating system.
7. method of washing dishes.
8. cleanliness of clothing.

Make an additional list of the way you can help to improve these conditions.

III. *Health in Your Community.*—Find out all you can about the Board of Health or the Health Officer. What sanitary laws, if any, are enforced?

Visit or obtain information about the welfare work, Red Cross, and other agencies which are promoting health programs.

IV. *To Show the Toxic Effect of Tobacco.*—If there are small, green plant lice or other insects attacking your house plants, choose two similar plants for the experiment.

1. Place a small amount of tobacco in a metal dish and light it. Arrange it near the plant in such a way that the smoke circulates among the leaves. You may cover the plant lightly to help keep the smoke in. After a half hour remove the covering and look at the plant. Did the smoke have any effect on the insects? Write a careful report, giving a good explanation.

2. Boil a large handful of tobacco in a small amount of water to form a strong solution. Place in a spray gun and spray the small insects on the shrubs in your garden. Do you think there is anything in tobacco which could affect them? What proof do you have of this? What kind of control could you use for this experiment? Why is a control necessary? Record your experiment.

V. *To Show the Effect of Alcohol on Protoplasm.*—Place some protozoa from a good culture on a microscopic slide and observe. With a pipette place a drop of alcohol on the edge of the cover glass. Watch carefully and note whether alcohol has an effect on protozoa. Do they slow down? Are they killed suddenly? Or, has alcohol no effect? Make at least three trials and record your results.

VI. *Marijuana.*—In reference books find out all you can about marijuana, a drug made from a common plant, that has been put into cigarettes. Write your own comments as to whether you think there is real danger from this source.

VII. *Patent Medicines.*—Collect as many labels as you can from bottles or boxes containing patent medicines. Arrange them in some logical order and paste them in a scrap book. Write a brief summary, showing the relative amounts of alcohol and drugs which they contain.

REFERENCES

Alcoholism Is a Sickness. Public Affairs Pamphlet No. 118.

Billings, *Physiological Aspects of the Liquor Problem.* Houghton Mifflin.

Cutten, *The Psychology of Alcoholism.* Senate Report No. 1125, 72nd Congress.

Emerson, *Alcohol and Man.* Macmillan.

Fink, *Release from Nervous Tension.* Simon and Schuster.

Ford, *Man Takes a Drink.* Kenedy.

Fulop, Miller, and Rene, *Triumph Over Pain.* Bobbs-Merrill.

Haggard, *Devils, Drugs, and Doctors.* Harper.

Haggard and Jellinek, *Alcohol Explored.* Doubleday.

Jenkins and Neuman, *How to Live with Parents.* Science Research Associates.

Johns, *Psychology in Everyday Living.* Harper.

McCarthy, *Facts About Alcohol.* Science Research Associates.

Mendenhall, *Tobacco.* Harvard Health Talks.

Menninger, *Making and Keeping Friends.* Science Research Associates.

Menninger, *Understand Yourself.* Science Research Associates.

National Forum, *The Alcohol Problem.* The Nation Forum.

Rathbone, *Tobacco, Alcohol, and Narcotics.* Oxford.

Remmers and Hackett, *What Are Your Problems?* Science Research Associates.

Schacter, *Getting Along with Others.* Science Research Associates.

Smith, *Drugs You Use.* Revere.

Spalding and Montague, *Alcohol and Human Affairs.* World Book.

Starling, *The Action of Alcohol on Man.* Longmans, Green.

Steinhaus and Grundeman, *Tobacco and Health.* Association Press.

Stubbs and Bligh, *Sixty Centuries of Health and Physick.* Paul B. Hoeber.

Toward Mental Health. Public Affairs Pamphlet No. 120.

Ullman, *Getting Along with Brothers and Sisters.* Science Research Associates.

Vogel and Vogel, *Facts About Narcotics.* Science Research Associates.

COMPREHENSIVE TEST ON PART THREE

Write the answers on this test on a clean sheet of composition paper as your teacher directs. *Do not mark your book.*

I. Complete the following statements by writing a word or phrase in the space provided.
    a. The thought brain is called the _____.
    b. The _____ controls the voluntary muscles.
    c. A group of nerve cells is called a _____.
    d. A single nerve cell is called a _____.
    e. The simplest form of nervous activity in man is called a _____.
    f. A _____ nerve carries messages away from the brain.
    g. A _____ nerve brings messages to the brain.
    h. The _____ of the eye brings the light rays to a focus.
    i. The _____ nerve carries messages from the eye to the brain.
    j. The _____ nerve carries messages from the ear to the brain.

II. Write in the parenthesis at the right of Column B the number of the expression in Column A which most closely corresponds.

Column A	Column B	
1. parathyroid	secretin	( )
2. pancreas	cortin	( )
3. thyroid	parathormone	( )
4. adrenal medulla	sex hormones	( )
5. thymus	epinephrine	( )
6. anterior pituitary	insulin	( )
7. pineal body	pituitrin	( )
8. reproductive glands	near breast bone	( )
9. intestinal glands	thyroxin	( )
10. posterior pituitary	roof of brain	( )
11. adrenal cortex		

III. Write the number of the word or expression which best completes the statement in the space provided at the right.
    a. The number of chromosomes is reduced during the process called
        (1) fertilization (2) maturation (3) mitosis (4) cleavage. _____
    b. Polar bodies are formed during the development of the
        (1) sperm cell (2) egg cell (3) zygote. _____
    c. Cleavage takes place immediately after
        (1) maturation (2) formation of the embryo (3) fertilization. _____
    d. The digestive system is formed from the
        (1) ectoderm (2) mesoderm (3) endoderm. _____
    e. Reduction division occurs during maturation
        (1) only once (2) many times (3) three times. _____

f. The union of the egg and sperm cell is called
      (1) maturation   (2) cleavage   (3) fertilization.   _____
g. Tuberculosis is caused by
      (1) bacteria   (2) protozoa   (3) filtrable virus.   _____
h. Immunity to smallpox may be acquired by
      (1) inoculation   (2) vaccination   (3) sterilization.   _____
i. The germ theory of disease was proposed by
      (1) Koch   (2) Lister   (3) Pasteur.   _____
j. Malaria is carried by the
      (1) Anopheles mosquito   (2) Culex mosquito   (3) Aëdes
      mosquito.   _____

IV. Some of the following statements are true and some are false. If the statement is true, write the word *true* on the line at the right of the statement. If the statement is false, write on the line at the right a word which could be substituted to make the statement true.

a. Alcohol dissolves the lipoid in nerve cells.   _____
b. Pneumonia can be inherited.   _____
c. Immunity is susceptibility to disease.   _____
d. Jenner found salvarsan, which is used in the treatment of syphilis.   _____
e. Toxin-antitoxin is used to prevent diphtheria.   _____
f. The Pasteur treatment is used to prevent tetanus or lockjaw.   _____
g. A narcotic stimulates the heart action.   _____
h. Cigarettes are especially harmful to the ears.   _____
i. Alcohol is one of the chief causes of insanity.   _____
j. Cancer is thought to be a communicable disease.   _____

V. In each of the following groups of words or phrases one expression does not belong in the group. Write that expression in the space provided at the right.

a. tuberculosis, diphtheria, typhoid fever, pneumonia, yellow fever   _____
b. malaria, sleeping sickness, yellow fever, lockjaw   _____
c. chloroform, nicotine, opium, epinephrine, cocaine   _____
d. auditory nerve, optic nerve, tympanum, cochlea, semicircular canals   _____
e. axon, dendrite, cell body, cilia   _____
f. inoculation, pasteurization, sterilization, fumigation   _____
g. secretin, pituitrin, ptyalin, insulin, epinephrine   _____
h. astigmatism, rheumatism, nearsighted, farsighted   _____
i. blastula, gastrula, fistula, cleavage, germ layers   _____
j. cerebrum, cerebellum, sclerotic coat, spinal cord, medulla oblongata   _____

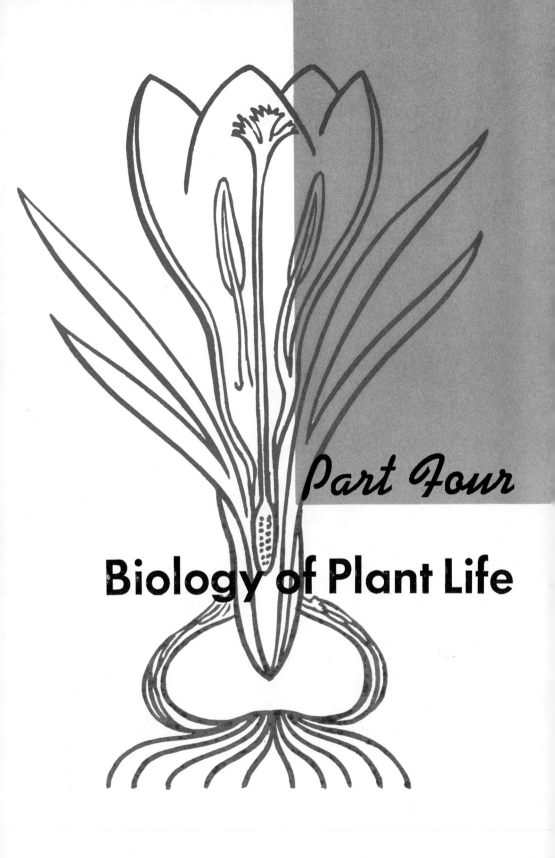

Part Four

Biology of Plant Life

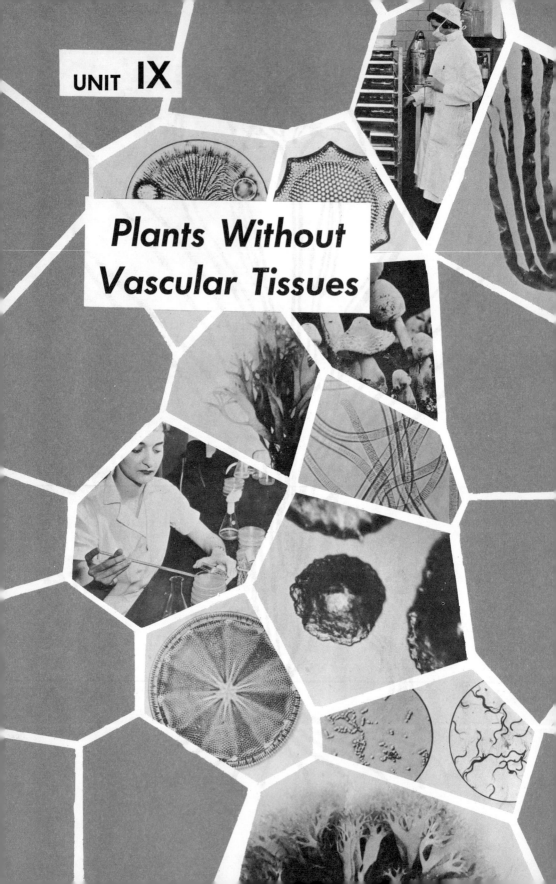

UNIT IX

Plants Without Vascular Tissues

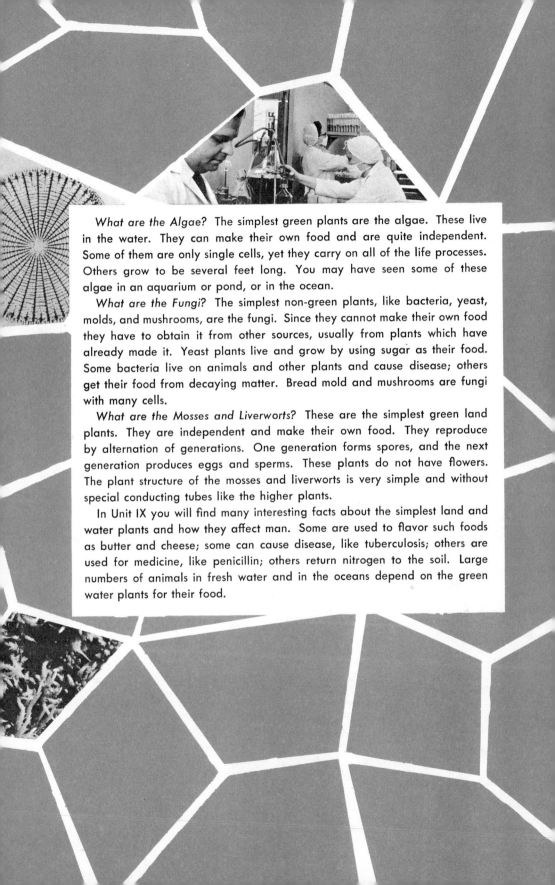

What are the Algae? The simplest green plants are the algae. These live in the water. They can make their own food and are quite independent. Some of them are only single cells, yet they carry on all of the life processes. Others grow to be several feet long. You may have seen some of these algae in an aquarium or pond, or in the ocean.

What are the Fungi? The simplest non-green plants, like bacteria, yeast, molds, and mushrooms, are the fungi. Since they cannot make their own food they have to obtain it from other sources, usually from plants which have already made it. Yeast plants live and grow by using sugar as their food. Some bacteria live on animals and other plants and cause disease; others get their food from decaying matter. Bread mold and mushrooms are fungi with many cells.

What are the Mosses and Liverworts? These are the simplest green land plants. They are independent and make their own food. They reproduce by alternation of generations. One generation forms spores, and the next generation produces eggs and sperms. These plants do not have flowers. The plant structure of the mosses and liverworts is very simple and without special conducting tubes like the higher plants.

In Unit IX you will find many interesting facts about the simplest land and water plants and how they affect man. Some are used to flavor such foods as butter and cheese; some can cause disease, like tuberculosis; others are used for medicine, like penicillin; others return nitrogen to the soil. Large numbers of animals in fresh water and in the oceans depend on the green water plants for their food.

CHAPTER 30

The Algae

30.1 Introduction to the Study of Plants

Plants, like animals, are made of cells, carry on the same life functions, and adapt themselves to various kinds of environments. Plants are so common that we do not realize how important they are to us.

Usually we think of a living plant as one having green leaves to manufacture food, roots to hold it in the soil and absorb water, and sturdy stems to support the leaves and carry the sap. We are familiar with the evergreens which produce seeds in cones, but we especially enjoy plants which have bright-colored flowers that later produce the seeds and fruit.

Not all plants, however, are large, have green leaves, and produce food for man and animals. In this richly varied world there are large plants, like trees, some of which are the largest living things, and small plants, thousands of which can live in a small drop of liquid. There are plants that are green and those that lack color; helpful plants that man cultivates and harmful ones that he tries to get rid of; plants that live only in water and those that live only on land; plants that produce flowers and fruit and others that do not; plants that live for hundreds of years and plants that live for only a few hours; plants that like abundance of sunshine and those that prefer dim light.

There are so many different kinds of plants, and they live in such a variety of ways, that we cannot study them all, but must select a few to give us a general

FIGURE 30-1. *SEAWEED*

Algae are the simplest form of plant life which manufactures its own food. They may be one-celled or many-celled forms. The seaweed pictured here is a brown algae found in salt water.

U.S. Dept. of the Interior

438

idea of the biology of plant life. This special study is known as **botany**.

The smallest and simplest plants have no stems, roots, or leaves. These plants produce no flowers, fruits, or seeds. They also lack **vascular tissue**, which is a tubelike system in higher plants for conducting liquids. Some plants are green and make their own food, but many are dependent upon other organisms for food. Many are so small that they can be seen only with a microscope.

30.2 Characteristics of the Algae

Algae (*al*-jee) are the simplest plants which have chlorophyll and can make their own food. They are grouped according to (1) cell pigmentation, (2) nature of the reserve foods which they make and store, and (3) structures used for locomotion.

Algae were formerly classified as a main division of the large phylum **Thallophyta**, or simplest plants. **Fungi**, which lack chlorophyll, made up the other main division. Modern systems of classification are based on structural differences and body types. Most scientists today regard the Thallophytes as a subkingdom which is divided into several phyla of algae and others of fungi. (Refer to the classification of plants on page 609.) One recognizable characteristic of many algae is the colored pigmentation which gives them such predominant colors as blue-green, green, brown, golden-brown, and red. Not all phyla of algae are based on color, however.

30.3 Blue-Green Algae—Cyanophyta (sy-an-*ah*-fit-uh)

These are found in water or on very damp earth where there is much decaying organic matter. Some of them withstand temperatures as high as 185° F and are found growing in hot springs.

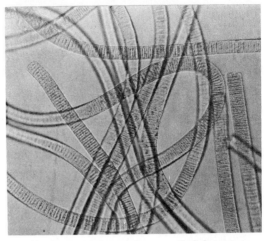

Hugh Spencer

FIGURE 30-2. *OSCILLATORIA*
Each filament is made of single cells. Lacking a definite nucleus, each cell has chromatin scattered through its center.

Blue-green algae lack a definite nucleus with a membrane, but have instead the nuclear material scattered through the center of the cell. They reproduce only by cell division or by the breaking apart of filaments.

The members of this group contain in addition to chlorophyll a blue pigment which causes their characteristic color. Some of them color the water in which they grow while others render water supplies unpalatable by giving them a fishy taste. Food is stored as glycogen.

A typical blue-green alga is *Oscillatoria* (os-sil-uh-*tor*-ee-uh). When seen under the microscope (Fig. 30-2), its delicate threadlike filaments seem to be continuously waving back and forth. These algae occur either in single strands of individual cells or in loose feltlike floating masses. They form slime or scum on mud and wet wood and stone.

30.4 The Green Algae—Chlorophyta (kloh-*rah*-fit-uh)

In the green algae the predominant pigment is chlorophyll. It is found in

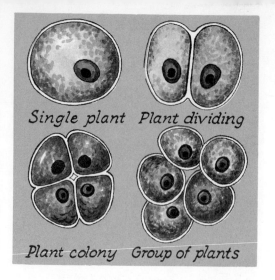

Single plant   Plant dividing

Plant colony   Group of plants

FIGURE 30-3. *SIMPLE PLANTS*

The single celled plant *Protococcus* is microscopic, but is visible as green fuzz when many plants crowd together. The cells may become dormant when conditions are unfavorable.

chloroplasts where starch is made and stored. The nucleus is well organized and the cell walls contain cellulose. Reproduction is by fission, asexual spores, or by sexual gametes.

This group contains many forms: unicellular, filamentous, colonial, and sheetlike. *Protococcus* is unicellular; *Spirogyra* is filamentous; and desmids are unicellular as well as colonial. *Ulva,* or sea lettuce, has a sheetlike form. Some of the filamentous forms grow at-

tached to stones and other objects in the water. Others float, being made light by the bubbles of gas produced by photosynthesis and respiration.

Protococcus (proh-toh-*kok*-us) is a single green cell of microscopic size. It is very abundant, showing as a green coating on the bark of trees, on old boards, walls, and walks—anywhere that moisture comes frequently and is retained for a time. A single *Protococcus* plant has a thick wall of cellulose, a nucleus, and one irregular *chloroplast*.

Like other green plants, *Protococcus* manufactures its own food, and within the limits of its tiny size, it digests, circulates, assimilates, respires, and excretes. Reproduction is by *fission* only. Sometimes the mother cell retains the daughter cells within its wall until they, too, have divided. The cells often cling together in masses and form a *colony* until they break apart, when each one becomes an independent one-celled plant.

Spirogyra (spy-roh-*jy*-ruh), also called pond scum, lives in fresh water. It has chloroplasts arranged in a spiral band, single or double (Fig. 30-4). The nucleus is held inside the spiral by protoplasmic strands which extend to the pyrenoid bodies on the chloroplasts. A gelatinous covering gives the filaments a slippery feeling.

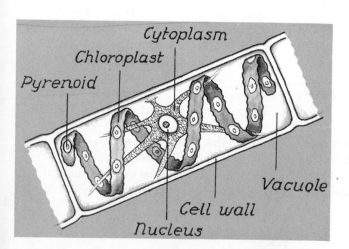

Cytoplasm

Chloroplast

Pyrenoid

Vacuole

Cell wall

Nucleus

FIGURE 30-4. *SPIROGYRA— A GREEN ALGA*

The protoplasm of spirogyra cells is spread out in strands from the central nucleus. Notice the unique chloroplast which coils around the edge of the cell. The pyrenoid bodies are associated with starch production.

440

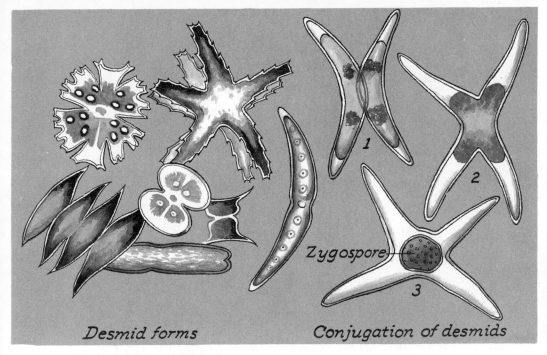

Zygospore

Desmid forms   *Conjugation of desmids*

FIGURE 30-5. *DESMIDS*

Desmids are found in a great variety of forms. Each is composed of two halves or semi-cells but they only have a single nucleus.

Most of the year this plant divides by separating the *filaments* into individual cells, but in late summer it reproduces by **conjugation**. Two strands put out projections from cells oposite each other, forming a *conjugation tube* through which the contents of one cell (the *male gamete*) pass into the other (the *female gamete*) and unite with it to form an oval mass, called a **zygote.** The zygote settles to the bottom of the pond and remains dormant. Later it starts a new filament.

Some of the most beautiful one-celled algae found in fresh-water pools or lakes are *desmids* (Fig. 30-5). They have cellulose outer coverings which show all kinds of geometrical designs. Each cell has two similar symmetrical halves, connected by an isthmus containing the nucleus. Each half has one chloroplast and divides down the middle during reproduction. Desmids also reproduce by

conjugation—two individuals come together, the walls between them disappear, and the protoplasm of the two cells flows together, forming a *zygote,* which is able to survive bad conditions and later grow into a new plant. Thus desmids have two methods of reproduction: fission and conjugation.

Many of the green algae can reproduce by **zoöspores** (*zoh*-oh-spohrs). These small green oval bodies are formed in some of the cells. They develop *flagella* and swim around much like animals. After a time they settle down against some object, withdraw their flagella, and begin to divide into **spores** which grow into new plants.

30.5 The Brown Algae—Phaeophyta (fay-*ah*-fit-uh)

This group contains microscopic plants as well as plants 150 feet long. They grow in salt water, either attached

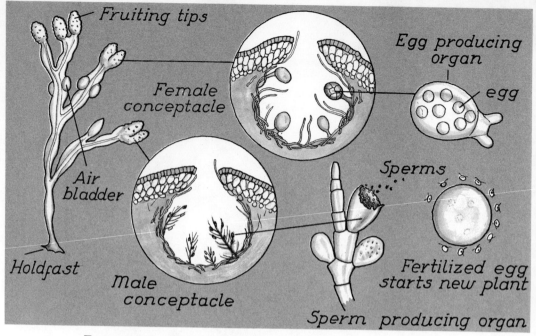

FIGURE 30-6. *LIFE CYCLE OF FUCUS—A BROWN ALGA*
The reproductive bodies of the plant are found on the fruiting tips (*left*). They are borne in male and female conceptacles (*center*). These contain sperm producing organs and egg producing organs. The ripe sperms and eggs are discharged into the ocean for fertilization (*right*).

to rocks, as in *Fucus* or rockweed, or floating, as in *Sargassum* and *Kelp*. The Sargasso Sea is an area of a quarter million square miles of floating seaweed in the Atlantic Ocean.

The larger brown algae have structures called *stipes* and *blades* which resemble the stems and leaves of higher plants. Attached forms have *holdfasts* which resemble roots. They have a conducting tissue of *phloem* for transporting food. Reserve food is stored as soluble sugars and sometimes fats. The group has a leathery texture to resist being torn by the motion of the water.

Fucus is of special interest because at the tips of its fronds eggs and sperms are produced in cavities and set free in the water. There the eggs are fertilized and a new plant started. It also has tiny gas pockets filled with carbon dioxide which help it float.

30.6 Diatoms—Chrysophyta
(kris-*ah*-fit-uh)

Diatoms (*dy*-uh-toms) are unicellular algae which are golden-brown in color due to one or two plastids in each cell. They store reserve food in the form of oils. Diatoms have varied shapes and are in two parts, like a box and cover. Their hard shells are made of glasslike *silica*. Their method of reproduction is by fission. The two parts separate, and each develops into a new box and cover which later mature and continue the dividing process. Diatoms are also able to rejuvenate themselves through cells called **auxospores** (*oks*-oh-spores). The content (*protoplast*) of two diatoms unite to form an auxospore, which then divides to form two new diatoms.

When diatoms die, their hard outer shells fall to the bottom of the sea, where they form layers of material, often of

442

great thickness. This material, which is known as *diatomaceous earth,* has various uses, including the manufacture of scouring powder, tooth paste, and bricks used for the insulation of furnaces. In temperate waters diatoms are an important food for oysters and in colder waters, for whales.

30.7 The Red Algae—Rhodophyta
(roh-*dah*-fit-uh)

These are mainly marine, brightly colored with red and other pigments, and delicate in form. Most are small. They grow attached to some solid object, sometimes in water as deep as 300 to 600 feet. They are interesting because some are a source of food (a kind of starch) and because of their peculiar structure. Each cell is attached to all the adjoining cells by connecting tubes of cellular material. In this group, too, are found the beginnings of the **alternation of generations.** *Nemalion* is a red alga which has such a life cycle. One form reproduces sexually by *gametes.* When these unite, *spores* are formed; the other form, developed from these spores, reproduces asexually to form spores of a second type. These in turn give rise to the gamete-bearing generation.

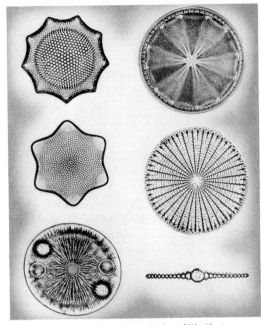

Carnegie Institution of Washington

FIGURE 30-7. *PLANT JEWELS*

There are over 5,000 different species of diatoms, both in fresh and salt water. Their beautiful designs are formed by thin perforations on the cell wall.

30.8 Economic Importance of Algae

Since algae can make their own food, they have become the source of food for whales and enormous numbers of other animals that live in the water. From the microscopic forms eaten by amebae to the floating masses of seaweed sought by

FIGURE 30-8. *IRISH MOSS*

Irish moss or *Chondrus crispus* is the name of a kind of red seaweed. It is much in demand as the basis of puddings and soups. After it is washed, bleached and dried in the sun, it is sold commercially.

Algin Corp. of America

443

the larger fish, algae are needed in enormous quantities.

Man collects brown seaweed that grows near the shore and uses it for fertilizer. Among the red algae, "Irish moss" is used to make jellies and puddings. *Laver* is made into soup by the Chinese, and *dulse* is used for food in Ireland and Scotland. Several red algae are used to make *agar-agar,* a gelatin used to culture bacteria. Marine algae are good sources of some vitamins and of iodine needed by the thyroid gland.

When algae become too numerous, they may pollute the water and make it unsafe for drinking. Some fish help to keep a balance of vegetation and in this way they help to maintain a safe water supply.

30.9 Simple and Complex Structures

Just as in the development of animal life there is a growing complexity of structure from the single-celled ameba to the two-layered hydra, so in the study of simple plant life similar changes may be noted. The tiny blue-green algae do not even differentiate specific nuclei. *Protococcus* may live either singly or in colonies. *Spirogyra* is made up of strips of cells and is able to divide by cell division or to conjugate. *Fucus,* a brown alga, is formed in sheets of many cells and has higher plantlike structures with a flat, leaflike *thallus,* rootlike *holdfasts,* and reproductive organs at the ends of stalks. Thus in the next higher group we shall find plants with stems and simple leaves.

FACTS TO REMEMBER

Botany is the study of plant life.

Algae are grouped with the *fungi* in the subkingdom *Thallophyta.* This includes several phyla of simple plants which lack roots, stems, leaves, flowers, and *vascular tissue.* Algae are independent plants which contain chlorophyll. Important phyla of algae include the *blue-green, green, brown, golden-brown* (*diatoms*), and *red* algae.

Algae may live singly or in *colonies.* All may reproduce asexually by *cell division.* Some show a beginning of sexual reproduction by conjugation and by *alternation of generations.*

Algae are of economic importance in that they pollute water and may cause disease. Algae furnish food for fish and other water life. Man also harvests algae for food, fertilizer, and for making *agar-agar.*

WORDS TO REMEMBER

agar-agar	conjugation	holdfast
algae	conjugation tube	protoplast
alternation of	diatoms	sexual reproduction
generations	filament	spore
asexual reproduction	fission	thallus
auxospore	flagella	vascular tissue
botany	fungi	zoöspore
colony	gamete	zygote
chloroplast		

PLANTS WITHOUT VASCULAR TISSUES

QUESTIONS

1. What are the distinguishing characteristics of the algae?
2. What is the basis of the modern classification of algae? Name several phyla.
3. What characteristic of the blue-green algae places them in the simplest group?
4. Describe *Protococcus*. Where would you look to find some?
5. Discuss two methods by which *Spirogyra* reproduces.
6. Define each of the following terms: zygote, zoöspore, spore, conjugation, and fertilization.
7. Describe the adaptations of *Fucus* which help to float the thallus.
8. What kinds of seaweed are used as food by man? For medicine? What other uses are made of seaweed?

COMPLETION TEST

As your teacher or classmate reads the following incomplete statements, with your book closed, write on a clean sheet of paper the word or phrase which correctly completes the statement.

1. Blue-green algae reproduce by _____.
2. Some _____ algae reproduce by alternation of generations.
3. *Protococcus* may be found as single cells or as _____.
4. The reproductive organs of _____ are at the ends of the branches.
5. _____ is a blue-green alga whose filaments are constantly waving back and forth.
6. The color of the Red Sea is due to enormous numbers of _____ algae.
7. The green coloring matter of an alga is called _____.
8. Algae and fungi belong to the main group known as _____.
9. One-celled green algae with cellulose outer coverings are _____.
10. One-celled boxlike plants classed with the golden-brown algae are known as _____.

PROJECTS

I. *Protococcus.*—1. Break off small pieces of bark from trees that appear bright green along the trunk. Bring them into the laboratory and place a small amount of the greenish material on a slide.

2. Examine under the low and high power of the microscope. Are there single cells? Are there groups of cells?

3. Draw both single cells and groups of cells if you can find them.

4. Color the chloroplasts green and shade the rest very lightly with a green crayon. Label the nucleus, chloroplasts, and cell wall.

II. *Spirogyra.*—1. Bring into the laboratory a mass of green pond scum. Place a few filaments on a glass slide and observe under the low and high power.

2. Locate the following parts: cell wall, nucleus, chloroplasts, vacuoles.

3. Draw a *single cell* and label the parts. Color the cell a light green and shade the chloroplasts a darker green.

4. If the material is living and you watch carefully, you may notice movement of the protoplasm through the chloroplasts. This is called *cyclosis*. You may also see the *pyrenoid* bodies in the chloroplasts. Add them to your drawing if you find them.

III. *Rockweed.*—1. If you live near the seashore, bring some brown rockweed, better known as *Fucus,* into the laboratory.

2. Note the flat, branching thallus, the air bladders, and reproductive structures.

3. What enables the plant to cling to the rocks? Describe the outer covering.

IV. With the use of reference books, find out how "Irish moss," laver, and dulse are prepared for use as food.

V. Explain the cause of the phenomenon of "red snow" often seen in Arctic regions.

REFERENCES

Fuller, Tippor, *College Botany.* Holt.
Gager, *General Botany.* Blakiston.
Pool, *Basic Course in Botany.* Ginn.
Ritchie, *Biology and Human Affairs.* World Book.
Smith, *Freshwater Algae of the United States.* McGraw-Hill.
Smith, Gilbert, and Others, *A Textbook of General Botany.* Macmillan.
Tiffany, *Algae, the Grass of Many Waters.* Charles C. Thomas.
Transeau, Sampson, and Tiffany, *Textbook of Botany.* Harper.

CHAPTER 31

Bacteria

31.1 Characteristics of the Fungi

The simplest plants without chlorophyll and with no true roots, stems, or leaves are included in a general group known as **fungi** (*fun*-jy). This was formerly a main division of the phylum **Thallophyta.** Modern classification systems group the fungi into at least three main phyla: the *bacteria, slime molds,* and *true fungi.* (See page 609.)

31.2 What Are Bacteria?

Bacteria are one-celled plants of the phylum **Schizomycophyta** (*skiz*-oh-my-*kah*-fit-uh) which lack chlorophyll and reproduce by fission. They are divided into three groups according to shape: (1) spherical *cocci* (*kok*-eye), (2) rod-shaped *bacilli* (buh-*sil*-eye), and (3) spiral-shaped *spirilla* (spy-*ril*-uh). The bacilli and spirilla often have *flagella,* which are projecting threads of protoplasm used for movement. Some have only one; others have many flagella.

A typical bacterial cell has a cell wall made of cellulose surrounded by a thin, slimy, gelatinous capsule. A cell membrane inside the wall controls the flow of materials into and out of the cell. Vacuoles are present in the protoplasm. Some chromatin granules clump together to form a kind of nucleus which resembles one large chromosome.

Bacteria are very small; usually less than 1/25,000 of an inch, a unit of measurement called the *micron.* They vary from .15 micron to 5 microns in length. They must be magnified at least 1,000 times to be clearly seen under a microscope. Groups of bacteria form characteristic *colonies* which vary in color, shape, and surface texture.

FIGURE 31-1. *THREE TYPES OF BACTERIA*

Bacteria are placed in three groups according to their shape: *Cocci* (*left*) are spheres; *Spirilla* (*center*) are spiral forms; *Bacilli* (*right*) are rodlike. Notice the flagella on the spirilla forms.

General Biological Supply House

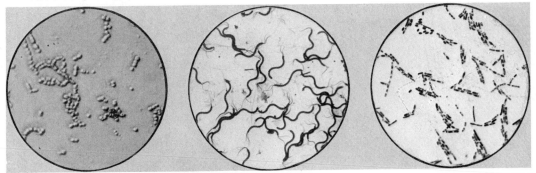

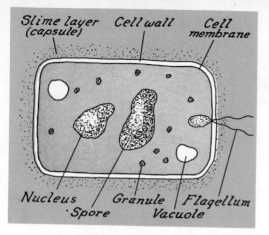

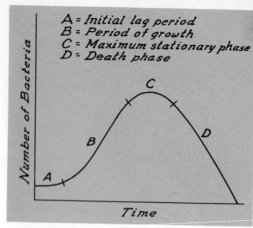

FIGURE 31-2. *STRUCTURE AND GROWTH OF BACTERIA*
The structure of a typical bacterium is shown at the left and a typical bacterial growth curve is diagramed at the right.

31.3   Conditions of Growth

Bacteria are everywhere—in the air as invisible dust, in the upper layers of soil, in water.

Like all other plants, bacteria must have all the proper conditions before they can grow and multiply. Their food is chiefly plant or animal matter, but they cannot make use of food except in the presence of warmth and moisture. Most of them require oxygen in addition, which they get from the surrounding air. Many kinds of bacteria grow best in darkness.

When bacteria begin to grow the rate is very slow, but as they adjust to their surroundings they multiply rapidly. When they reach maximum production, the growth remains steady. Lack of food and accumulation of wastes cause the growth rate to slow or to stop. This typical growth pattern is known as the *bacterial growth curve* (Fig. 31-2).

When food, air, warmth, or moisture are not sufficient, bacteria stop growing and go into a resting or dormant state. That is, they change their form, and surround themselves with a substance which forms a new thick wall and which protects the soft protoplasm from being harmed by freezing, heating, or drying. These forms are known as *spores*. When conditions are too severe, bacteria die.

Some kinds of bacteria are found in the ice and snow of glaciers and icebergs and in hailstones which have dropped from high altitudes; others are found in regions of high temperature, and their spores can resist long periods of boiling.

31.4   Life Processes

In the preparation of their food, bacteria break up organic substances absorbed through their walls; that is, they decompose these substances, causing *decay*. The bacteria use some of the material resulting from decay; some they set free in the air; and the remainder is left on the earth where it is often used by more complex plants. Bacteria cause diseases in man, his domesticated animals, and his crops. They cause food to spoil; this may result in food poisoning. Bacteria may also cause a loss of nitrogen from the soil.

Reproduction occurs in bacteria by a constriction of the cell called fission. Some scientists believe that a simple kind of sexual reproduction occurs in some bacteria.

PLANTS WITHOUT VASCULAR TISSUES

Sometimes bacteria break entirely apart, while in other cases they remain connected, forming a filament or a colony. Under favorable conditions each cell can grow to full size in half an hour and be ready to divide again. It is this ability to multiply rapidly which makes them of such great importance. A few hundred bacteria, even harmful ones, could produce little effect, but in a short time they could become millions. This helps to explain why it is so important to take immediate care of cuts and wounds and why infections spread so fast.

Under some circumstances a few kinds of bacteria have a different method of reproduction. Inside the body of a single bacterium appears a little rounded mass. It is formed by the protoplasm gathering itself into a firm sphere which contains little water and has great resistance to drying and heat. When conditions are favorable it breaks into many pieces and each is capable of forming a new individual.

31.5 How Bacteria Do Harm to Living Things

There are three ways in which bacteria may harm other organisms: (1) by their mere presence in large numbers, causing the blocking of fibro-vascular vessels in plants and of small blood vessels in animals; (2) by living on the substance of the organism itself, as in the actively parasitic forms which live in vital organs; and (3) by the effect of some of their secretions, known as *toxins*. These toxins, when present in large quantities, poison the host and even the bacteria themselves.

31.6 How Bacteria Help Us

In the process of growth, different kinds of bacteria produce substances

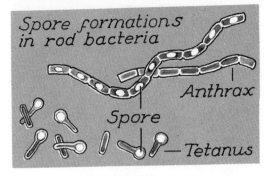

FIGURE 31-3. *SPORES*

Rod bacteria with spore formations are shown. The spores form in the center of anthrax; at one end of tetanus.

such as *enzymes* and *toxins*. Certain enzymes produce **fermentation,** a breaking-up process of which man makes use to secure certain flavors and odors and to soften hard materials. Bacteria, by making enzymes, give flavor to such foods as cheese and butter. They are also useful in making sauerkraut, vinegar, and in fermenting corn for storing. Such bacteria are classed as helpful, as are those which gather nitrogen for the plants of the bean family. Examples of other helpful bacteria are those that make it possible for man to use sponges by ridding them of the soft, slimy substance with which they are filled when alive, and those that soften the useless parts of the flax plant so that the rest of it may be separated and made into linen.

Some bacteria separate the flesh from animal skins and aid in tanning the hides; some are used in the preparation of indigo, a blue dye; others help in curing and ripening tobacco. Certain bacteria live in the intestinal tracts of cattle, sheep, and other grass-eating animals and help break some of their food materials into simpler form. Some kinds are normally found in the large intestines of man.

31.7 Soil Bacteria

The surface soil, especially if it is rich

FIGURE 31-4. *BACTERIA CAPTURE NITROGEN*

Nitrogen fixing bacteria gather in nodules on the roots of this peanut plant. These bacteria take free nitrogen from the soil air for their life processes. Their host plants may then use the nitrogen for its own process of making protein.

The most familiar kinds of bacteria are *heterotrophic,* which means they derive nourishment from complex organic compounds as found in other organisms. These include the *saprophytes,* which live on dead organic matter, and the *parasites,* which secure food from living organisms. Many bacteria live in the complete absence of air. These are called *anaerobic* (an-ay-*roh*-bic). Those which depend on air are called *aerobic.*

The soil bacteria do a most important work in breaking down parts of dead plants and animals, thus enriching the soil so that living plants can find more nourishment in it. Bacteria also help in the treatment of sewage by decomposing the organic matter and changing it to inorganic salts, water, and gases.

The roots of such <u>leguminous</u> (leh-*gyoo*-mih-nus) plants as clover, beans, peas, and peanuts form a symbiotic relationship with certain soil bacteria. These bacteria form bunches or **nodules** (*nod*-yools) on the roots in which they live. Thus protected, they gather nitrogen from the air, use what they need, and store up the rest. This surplus is used by the leguminous plants to make protein, part of which is found in the body of the plant, and part in the seeds. When the seeds are used as food, both man and animals may secure the protein which they need.

When the plants die, they leave the soil richer in nitrogen in a form that can be used by future plants. So valuable is this form of fertilizer that in some cases leguminous crops are raised and plowed under for the sake of the nitrogen in them. This is called *green manuring.*

31.8 Oxygen, Carbon, and Nitrogen Cycles

The relationship of bacteria to nonliving, inorganic substances is shown by

in organic matter, contains many kinds of bacteria. Some are *autotrophic,* which means they can make organic compounds from carbon dioxide and other inorganic substances. They are of two kinds: *chemosynthetic,* which use chemical energy, and *photosynthetic,* which use light energy. The *chemosynthetic* bacteria include (1) *sulfur bacteria* which oxidize hydrogen sulfide, (2) *iron bacteria* which oxidize iron compounds, (3) *hydrogen bacteria* which oxidize hydrogen to form water, and (4) *nitrifying bacteria* which oxidize ammonia to nitrates and nitrites. The *photosynthetic* bacteria include (1) *purple sulfur bacteria* which function much like chlorophyll-bearing plants, (2) *purple nonsulfur bacteria* which use hydrogen in light to reduce carbon dioxide, and (3) *green bacteria* which oxidize hydrogen sulfide in light to reduce carbon dioxide and thus make food.

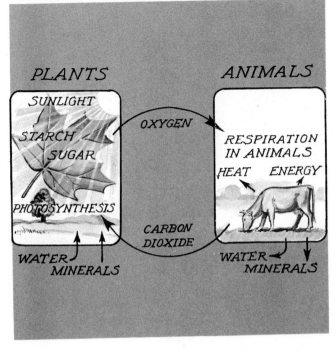

FIGURE 31-5. *THE OXYGEN CYCLE*

The oxygen cycle is the exchange of gases between plants and animals. Photosynthesis (*left*) by plants takes in carbon dioxide and gives off oxygen. The oxygen is used by both plants and animals for respiration (*right*), and the waste product of respiration is carbon dioxide.

tracing the cycles made by such elementary substances as oxygen, nitrogen, and carbon. Food is consumed to build up protoplasm. Some food also unites with oxygen and in the process of oxidation releases energy in the form of warmth or motion or both. During this process, carbon dioxide is set free.

The Oxygen Cycle.—In the cycle of oxygen, this important element is taken into the animal's body for oxidation. A waste product, carbon dioxide, is given off. When carbon dioxide is taken up by the green plant, the carbon becomes a part of the starch of the plant, while the oxygen escapes into the air ready to be used again in respiration by some organism. Oxygen can go through this series of changes an endless number of times without losing any of its properties. Thus it goes in a cycle in its relation to living things. This cycle helps maintain the constant supply of oxygen necessary to life.

The Carbon Cycle. — The carbon which is a part of food, whether starch,

sugar, fat, or protein, remains in this food until some organism uses it in nutrition. The organism then sets it free as a waste product in the form of carbon dioxide, to be later built up into starch by plant photosynthesis.

Carbon is present in large amounts in living protoplasm. It constitutes about 14% of our own bodies. The carbon that is a part of the living protoplasm remains in this relation for a variable length of time, not being released until the protoplasm dies; in this way it differs from oxygen. There is thus a carbon cycle just as there is an oxygen cycle.

The Nitrogen Cycle.—Nitrogen is another important element found in organic matter. Living things cannot use free nitrogen; it must first be changed into a complex form. Animals require very complex proteins, which are manufactured by green plants. Green plants take up nitrates (simple nitrogen compounds) and build the nitrogen into complex proteins.

Although many of the compounds

BACTERIA

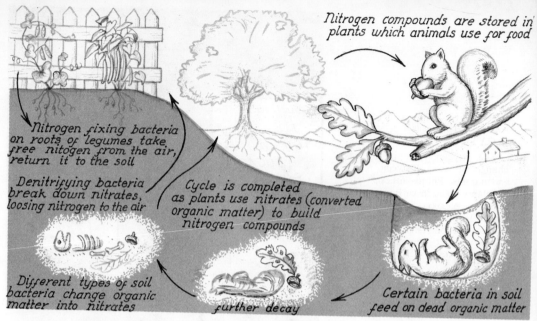

FIGURE 31-6. THE NITROGEN CYCLE

Bacteria taking part in the nitrogen cycle include: *nitrifying bacteria,* which build up nitrogen compounds; *denitrifying bacteria,* which change nitrates into gaseous form; and nitrogen-fixing bacteria.

built up by animals and plants would automatically break down after death, bacteria hasten the process. In this process of decay, the compounds are almost completely broken down, and the result is that the remaining nitrogen compound, ammonia, is so simple that green plants cannot use it. Sometimes *nitrifying bacteria* rebuild ammonia into nitrates for plant use. At other times a group of bacteria called *denitrifying bacteria* changes the nitrates into gaseous nitrogen, allowing it to escape into the air. Then the *nitrogen-fixing bacteria* rescue this gaseous nitrogen from the air and unite it with other elements suitable for green plants to use, completing the nitrogen cycle. Nitrogen-fixing bacteria thus play an important part in the lives of all the higher organisms, including that of man.

31.9 Control of Bacteria

It is possible, by governing conditions,

to secure the good effects of bacteria, and to prevent many of the bad effects. A brief definition of the commonest terms used in working with bacteria will help you to understand what you read. **Aseptic** (ay-*sep*-tik) means free from harmful bacteria, especially those that are the cause of some particular disease. Aseptic conditions are secured by fumigation and by washing with chemicals. These preparations are very important in arranging aseptic conditions for surgery in hospitals. An **antiseptic** is a substance which prevents the growth of bacteria. **Sterile** (*stehr*-il) means lacking all bacteria. This condition is secured by using heat or chemicals. Bandages must be sterile. Sterile conditions must also be present in preserving foods.

31.10 Food Preservations

Milk, one of our most important foods, is a nearly perfect food for many

452

bacteria, and they multiply very rapidly in it. By heating milk to 60° C for twenty minutes or to a higher degree for a shorter time, most of the harmful bacteria are killed. The use of ice to keep milk cold will prevent the growth of other bacteria that may get into it. The process of heating it is called **pasteurization** (Sec. 28.10). The bacteria that cause milk to sour are not harmful, but they change the taste of milk so that it is unpalatable to many persons. Ice cream should not be kept too long, or exposed to the open air, as either condition may give harmful bacteria a chance to grow in it. The more we learn about bacteria, the more use we can make of the helpful varieties and avoid the harmful.

Any device which will check the activity of bacterial growth will delay spoiling. The problem of keeping our food free from decay becomes increasingly difficult with the increase of population. The following are some of the methods used in preserving food:

Canning.—Canning is a simple plan for keeping bacteria away from food products.

The process involves, first, removing the bacteria already present in the food; and second, preventing all other bacteria from gaining access to it later. The first need is met by heating the food to a sufficiently high temperature to destroy the bacteria; the second is met by hermetically sealing the food in a can or jar while it is still hot.

Preservatives.—Preservatives are of two kinds, poisonous and non-poisonous. Non-poisonous preservatives are sugar, salt, vinegar, and spices. The relatively high degree of concentration of sugar and salt keeps bacteria from growing, since it removes moisture from their bodies. Bacteria cannot grow in

Fish and Wildlife Service

FIGURE 31-7. *CANNING TUNA*

The canning process destroys and prevents entrance of bacteria.

sugar or salt because of this lack of sufficient moisture. Condensed milk contains 30% to 40% cane sugar. Jellies are preserved from bacterial action by the large amount of sugar which they contain. Raisins, figs, and dates are preserved partly by drying and partly by the presence of sugar. These three fruits contain so much sugar that it is not necessary to add sugar while drying them.

Salt, one of the commonest and least harmful of preservatives, is used in a variety of products, of which fat pork, corned beef, hams, and fish are the most common.

Some preservatives when used in larger quantities than usual or when used over a long period of time have a poisonous effect on the body. Many of these substances are chemicals used to preserve the natural color or texture of fruits and vegetables, or traces of chemicals which have not been completely removed after use in refining or preserving.

Monkmeyer

FIGURE 31-8. *IRRADIATED POTATO*

Atomic energy is being developed for food preservation. Bottom, 16 months after exposure; top, untreated is spoiled.

Drying.—All bacteria require a considerable amount of moisture for their life processes and cannot develop in moderately dry food. Nature has used this fact in preserving the seeds of most plants. We find that the ripened seeds of grasses, wheat, corn, and many other plants are dry. In the past few years a whole new industry has grown up around this principle of drying, with dried milk as one of the best examples.

Milk is dried in four different ways: (1) A thin layer of partly condensed milk is spread on a heated drum. The dry film is scraped off and powdered. (2) A fine spray of milk is blown into a column of heated air. The water vapor passes through sieves that hold the milk powder. (3) Milk is partly condensed by boiling, then whipped and spread on a wire screen that moves through a heated chamber. The dried milk is in the form of flakes. (4) A drum in a vacuum receives the milk; the lower tem-

perature needed for drying in a vacuum causes less change in the taste of the milk than when heat is applied, as in the first three ways.

Some foods are already waterless or nearly so. They are called *dry* foods. Many fruits, such as prunes and apricots, can be preserved by drying. They retain 20% to 25% moisture, but not enough to prevent them from keeping well. These are *dried* foods.

Dehydrated foods have practically all the water removed. They contain not more than 7% water and may have as little as 3½%. Fruits, vegetables, eggs, milk, cheese, and meat can be dehydrated and still preserve 85% of the vitamins.

Fruits are ground fine while raw, but most vegetables are cooked, cooled, and pulped. The material is then put on hot metal drums which remove 96% of the water. The rising steam keeps out the air and prevents oxidation, which discolors food.

Dehydrated foods can be shipped long distances in small space. They can be carried by hikers and travelers because of their light weight and the small space they occupy. They can be packed in waterproof containers and kept for long periods of time, thus reducing the cost of storage.

Cold.—Low temperatures, as in cold storage refrigerators, or freezing may be used to preserve food. Few bacteria can grow at extremely low temperatures and so most food can be preserved for long periods of time.

Commercial freezing began with berries about 1908. The process of quick-freezing fruits and vegetables is as follows. First they are put into scalding water at about 200° F. This kills germs and molds and destroys enzymes that would act within the cells to break down

454

starch and cause the color to fade. Then they are plunged into syrup at −40° F, which produces microscopic cyrstals that lie wholly within the cells. No cell walls are broken and no nourishment or flavor is lost. Much of the freezing is done while the food lies in shallow layers on metal plates within a cabinet where the temperature is kept at −40° F to −50° F. Quick-frozen food packages must be kept at below-freezing temperatures until the foods are to be used. The vitamins are much less affected by the freezing than they are by cooking.

31.11 Forms Related to Bacteria

Under the electron microscope, some of the *viruses* (Sec. 28.16) appear to have a definite lifelike organization. Viruses have an outer case made of protein. Inside is some form of nucleic acid, either DNA or RNA. This is typical of chromatin material. But viruses can't produce enzymes to release energy or to make their own food. When a virus enters a host cell it forces the cell to produce more virus. The host cell usually dies but the new virus infects another cell. Viruses cause diseases in many plants and animals. They are causative factors in smallpox, yellow fever, poliomyelitis, and the common cold.

Rickettsiae (Sec. 28.16) are organisms similar to bacteria in that they reproduce by fission. They are like viruses in their need for living tissue in order to grow. The diseases caused by rickettsiae are carried by insects and other animals. They include typhus fever, trench fever, and Rocky Mountain spotted fever.

Bacteriophages (bak-*tee*-ree-oh-fay-jes) are substances which cause diseases among bacteria. When a bacteriophage attaches itself to a bacterial cell it forces its DNA inside. The phage and the bac-

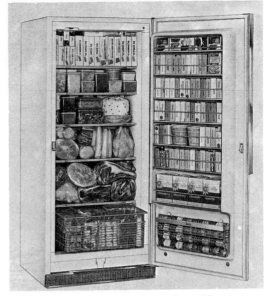

FIGURE 31-9. *FREEZER*

Most foods can be preserved without loss of vitamin content if they are quick frozen and stored at low temperatures.

terium are reproduced together. They may undergo several divisions during a *lysogenic* stage before the phage becomes active and destroys the host cell in the *lytic* stage. Bacteriophages are present in the soil and in the digestive tract of man and other animals.

FIGURE 31-10. *VIRUS*

These spheres are virus particles that cause human influenza. They are shown here magnified over 25,000 times.

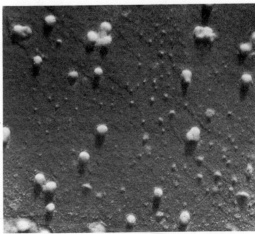

Actinomycetes are moldlike bacteria whose cells are joined end to end to form branched filaments. They produce spores at the ends of specialized branches. The antibiotic *streptomycin* belongs to this group.

31.12 Pioneers in the Study of Bacteria

The invention of the compound microscope really made the study of bacteria possible. We do not know who the actual inventor was, but the microscope was little more than a toy until it was improved by a Dutch naturalist, Leeuwenhoek, in the latter part of the seventeenth century.

In the nineteenth century, Pasteur made use of the microscope to discover the relationship of bacteria to spoiling of wine and souring of milk. Koch was able to separate bacteria so that each kind could be studied by itself. Other scientists discovered that viruses, rickettsiae, and yeasts are also microbes which cause disease. Later, substances were found which could combat these harmful organisms. Still other scientists have found new ways in which bacteria may be helpful to man.

In 1926, two Germans, von Borries and Ruska, invented the *electron microscope* (Sec. 28.14). This is a machine which shoots electrons at a speed of 100,000 miles per second. They are focused by a magnetic lens to form a magnified image of the object on a fluorescent screen. Objects are magnified from 20,000 to 100,000 diameters or more. Scientists can now study objects fifty times smaller than those it is possible to observe with an ordinary microscope. It is hoped that more viruses and bacteria that cause diseases will be detected. This will make possible more rapid advances in the study of these microorganisms.

31.13 Healthy Bodies and Bacteria

So much has been said about harmful bacteria that a word of caution is needed. Two facts should make us take a sane view of the situation: (1) for every harmful bacterium there are thousands of helpful ones; and (2) harmful ones cannot do their work, or even live, in a perfectly healthy body, for such a body is constantly preparing a substance (*antitoxin*) which neutralizes the bacterial poison (*toxin*).

FACTS TO REMEMBER

Bacteria are the simplest group of fungi. They have no roots, stems, or leaves, and exist either as single cells or in colonies. Most of them lack chlorophyll and obtain their food by living as saprophytes or parasites. The three main types of bacteria are those shaped as (1) spheres (*cocci*), (2) rods (*bacilli*), and (3) spirals (*spirilla*).

In order to grow and multiply, most bacteria require food, warmth, air, and moisture. When these conditions are present, bacteria can multiply very rapidly, but if they are lacking, some bacteria become spores and go into a stage of dormancy.

Most bacteria are helpful to man. Some bring about decay of organic matter, while others produce enzymes for *fermenting* certain foods. *Nitrifying, denitrifying,* and *nitrogen-fixing bacteria* make usable nitrogen compounds for plants.

The *oxygen, carbon,* and *nitrogen cycles* are the means by which these elements are constantly being restored in nature as useful substances for plants and animals. Bacteria perform important functions in these processes, especially in the nitrogen cycle.

To prevent *food spoilage* by bacteria, the conditions they need to survive—food, air, suitable temperature, and moisture—must be removed. *Pasteurization, canning, preservatives, drying,* and *freezing* are some of the processes used to preserve foods.

Viruses, Rickettsiae, bacteriophages, and *actinomycetes* are believed to be other forms that are related to bacteria.

WORDS TO REMEMBER

actinomycetes
aerobic
anaerobic
antiseptic
antitoxin
aseptic
bacilli
bacteria
bacteriophage
canning
carbon cycle
cocci

dehydrated foods
denitrifying bacteria
drying
fermentation
flagellum
freezing
fungi
host
leguminous plants
micron
nitrifying bacteria
nitrogen cycle

nitrogen-fixing
    bacteria
nodule
oxygen cycle
parasite
pasteurization
preservative
Rickettsiae
saprophyte
spirilla
sterile
toxin
virus

QUESTIONS

1. What is the chief characteristic that distinguishes fungi from algae?
2. Distinguish between saprophytes and parasites.
3. What are bacteria? Where are they found?
4. Name the three classes of bacteria and make a sketch of each.
5. What conditions are necessary for the growth of bacteria?
6. How do bacteria reproduce?
7. How long does it take for a bacterium to grow to full size if conditions are favorable?
8. Mention three ways in which bacteria harm living things.
9. What two kinds of substances are produced when bacteria grow?
10. Name as many foods as you can which are flavored by bacteria.
11. Explain how bacteria are helpful in these industries:
    (a) sponge manufacture   (c) the tanning of leather
    (b) the rotation of crops   (d) the preparation of flax
12. What is meant by the oxygen cycle? The carbon cycle?
13. How can nitrogen be used by a plant and returned to the soil?
14. State at least four ways in which food can be preserved. What kinds of food are preserved by each method?

COMPLETION TEST

As your teacher or classmate reads the following incomplete statements, with your book closed, write on a clean sheet of paper the word or phrase which correctly completes the statement.

1. Bacteria are found _____.
2. Harmful bacteria secrete a poison called a _____.
3. Bacteria are useful in _____ foods.
4. Bacteria are harmful in _____ foods.
5. Bacteria can live through unfavorable conditions by forming _____.
6. The _____ microscope magnifies objects that are fifty times smaller than could be seen with the compound microscope.
7. Quick freezing does not break down the _____ of the foods.
8. Foods that contain almost no water are said to be _____.
9. An example of a preservative is _____.
10. Canned goods are sealed tightly to _____.

PROJECTS

I. *Experiment to Show the Effect of Moisture on the Growth of Bacteria.*— In one series of six or more test tubes place a small amount of such dry materials as—

(a) dry beans   (d) cracker
(b) flour   (e) dry bread
(c) corn meal   (f) dry cereal

In a second series of test tubes place the same kinds and amounts of materials. Then add a little water to each. Insert sterile plugs.

Put both series of tubes in a warm place and leave for a few days. Observe and answer the following questions.

1. Which *series* showed more bacterial growth?
2. Which *foods in the series* showed more bacterial growth?
3. What is the effect of moisture on the growth of bacteria?

II. *Experiment to Show the Effect of Heat on the Growth of Bacteria.*—
1. Chop some raw beef very fine and place it in water, heating it to 130° F. Divide it into two parts. Place each in a test tube. Set one aside.
2. Boil the other for a minute and set aside for 24 hours.
3. Observe both test tubes and answer the following questions.
   a. Has putrefaction occurred in either tube? Explain your answer.
   b. What effect does a very short period of boiling have on the keeping properties of meat?
   c. How would this be of advantage where there were no good means of refrigeration?

III. *Experiment to Show the Effect of Cold on the Growth of Bacteria.*— Place some hay in water and heat to lukewarm. Allow it to steep slowly for ½ hour. Filter into two test tubes. Plug with cotton and set one in a warm place, the other in a cold place.

Pour the contents of the other test tube in a metal or some other kind of unbreakable dish. Put out of doors where it will freeze. (In warm weather place it in the freezing compartment of a mechanical refrigerator.) Let it remain there for a few hours.

Bring the dish into a warm room and leave for a few days to see if it putrefies. Observe and answer the following questions.

1. Which container shows the greater bacterial action? Can you account for this?

2. Why is food placed in a refrigerator?

IV. *Experiment to Show the Relative Effect of Prolonged Heat as a Means of Destroying Bacteria.*—Place some hay in water and steep ½ hour at 120° F. Filter it into four test tubes and boil varying lengths of time. Insert sterile plugs.

No. 1: Boil 5 minutes.

No. 2: Boil 10 minutes.

No. 3: Boil 20 minutes.

No. 4: Do not boil.

Set all the test tubes aside several days to see whether the material putrefies. Observe and answer the following questions:

1. Which test tube showed the greatest degree of putrefaction?

2. Which showed the least?

3. What is the effect of prolonged heat on the growth of bacteria?

4. How does longer boiling of meat affect its keeping qualities?

REFERENCES

Allen, *Microbes Which Help or Destroy Us.* Mosby.

Allen, *The Story of Microbes.* Swift Company.

Buchanan and Earle, *Bacteriology.* Macmillan.

Burton and Kohl, *The Electron Microscope.* Reinhold.

Cohn, *Bacteria, the Smallest of Living Organisms.* Johns Hopkins Press.

Conn, *Bacteria, Yeasts, and Molds in the Home.* Ginn.

Conn, *The Story of Germ Life.* Appleton.

DeKruif, *Microbe Hunters.* Harcourt, Brace.

Eberson, *Microbes Militant.* Ronald Press.

Ehlers and Steel, *Municipal and Rural Sanitation.* McGraw-Hill.

Epstein and Epstein, *Miracles from Microbes.* Rutgers University Press.

Greaves, *Elementary Bacteriology.* Saunders.

Park and Williams, *Who's Who Among the Microbes.* Appleton-Century.

Rahn, *Microbes of Merit.* Jacques Cattrell Press.

Seward, *Plants, What They Are and What They Do.* Macmillan.

Valery-Radot, *The Life of Pasteur.* Doubleday, Doran.

Woodhead, *Bacteria and Their Products.* Scribner.

CHAPTER 32

Molds, Yeast, and Other Fungi

32.1 Molds

Molds are many-celled plants lacking chlorophyll and with well-organized nuclei. They are larger than bacteria and reproduce asexually by spores and often by sexual gametes. Some are *parasitic,* getting food from live hosts; others are *saprophytic,* feeding on dead organic matter. The *slime molds,* **Myxomycophyta** (*mix*-oh-mye-*cah*-fit-uh), *are* in a different phylum from the *true fungi,* **Eumycophyta** (*ewe*-mye-*cah*-fit-uh).

32.2 Slime Molds—Myxomycophyta

The slime molds are jellylike substances often seen on the bark of fallen trees or leaves. Some are bright yellow, red, or orange. They move along much like the ameba and engulf particles of food. They vary in size, but each usually consists of a mass of protoplasm containing several nuclei. Reproduction is by spores produced in sporangia. Each spore has one nucleus and is enclosed within a cellulose wall. They are blown about to new locations. When a spore germinates, it produces *swarm cells* with flagella. After a time, sexual reproduction takes place. The swarm cells fuse in pairs, joining nuclei. The new cell may grow directly into a new slime mold joining others to form a protoplasmic mass, or *plasmodium.*

32.3 Bread Mold—Phycomycetes

The *true fungi,* phylum **Eumycophyta,** include the bread mold, yeasts, mushrooms, and ringworm fungi. The class **Phycomycetes** (*fy*-coh-mye-*see*-tees), or *tube fungi,* have filamentous bodies which are not divided by cross walls.

The soft, white, cottony growth found on moist bread is commonly called *bread mold.* It consists of filaments of much branched threads, **hyphae** (*hy*-fee), which grow and penetrate the bread. The whole mass of threads is called the **mycelium** (my-*see*-lee-um). There are three kinds of hyphae: (1) the **rhizoids** (*ry*-zoids), short, rootlike

Figure 32-1. *SLIME MOLD*

These are the club-shaped sporangia of the slime mold *Stemonitis.*

Courtesy Carolina Biological Supply Company

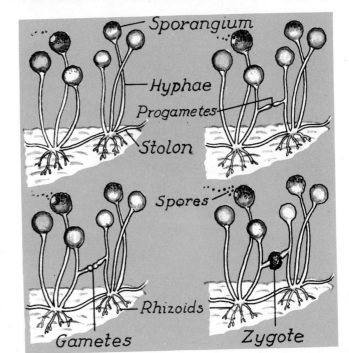

FIGURE 32-2. *BREAD MOLD*
Asexual reproduction (*top left*) is accomplished by spores, the black spots commonly found on moldy bread. Sexual reproduction occurs by conjugation when a bridge grows between two hyphae to form a *zygote*.

structures which anchor the plant and which grow downward into the bread or other food substance to absorb and digest food; (2) the **stolons** (*stoh*-lons), which grow parallel to the surface for a distance before bending downward to form more rhizoids; and (3) the upright hyphae, which are for reproduction. On the ends of these upright hyphae are round bodies called **sporangia** (spor-*an*-jee-uh), which are full of black *spores*. Each spore is capable of producing a new mold plant, if it falls into a place where it has plenty of food, the right amount of warmth and moisture.

Bread mold also reproduces by *conjugation* (Fig. 32-2). As in Spirogyra, a bridge or canal is formed between the cells of two different hyphae. Bread mold differs from Spirogyra, however, in that the contents of each cell move out onto the bridge and there unite to form a zygote with a thick wall which under favorable conditions may start a new plant.

32.4 Penicillium, a Blue Mold

The sudden rise in importance of a species of blue mold called *Penicillium notatum* came about when this member of a group of molds was discovered attacking growing colonies of bacteria. As the penicillium mold grew, it secreted a substance called **penicillin** (Sec. 28.15). When the medicinal value of penicillin became known, it was proclaimed a "miracle drug" and was grown for this use in tanks containing lactose, corn steeping liquor, and mineral salts.

An intensive search for new methods of penicillin production began. Since mold is a living substance, it needs air, food materials, and protection against organisms that destroy it. Within ten years production had increased from enough penicillin to supply 400 patients to amounts great enough for 31,000,000 patients. The story of this antibiotic illustrates just one way in which scientific knowledge of man's environment may be the means of saving many lives.

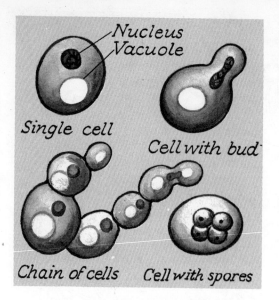

FIGURE 32-3. YEAST PLANTS

In addition to budding, yeast plants may reproduce by producing spores, which are retained within the cell wall until conditions favor growth.

32.5 Other Molds

Some molds grow on leather and cloth. Some cause many fruits to rot. Others add a desirable flavor to cheeses, as in Roquefort and Camembert cheese.

A few moldlike fungi cause disease in animals by growing in the skin, the ear, or the scalp. Others grow in the lungs, the intestinal tract, and the brain.

32.6 Yeasts—Ascomycetes

Yeast plants are included in the class **Ascomycetes** (*ass*-koh-mye-*see*-tees), or *saclike fungi.* These have a saclike reproductive body, or *ascus,* within which *ascospores* are formed. Penicillin and powdery mildews belong to this class.

The yeasts are highly specialized. They are single celled and do not develop hyphae. A yeast plant consists of an oval-shaped cell which is almost transparent. The cytoplasm contains a large vacuole and a small nucleus. Inside the cell wall is a cytoplasmic membrane which controls the transfer of materials into and out of the cell. Mitochondria contain enzymes which enable the yeast to obtain energy from sugar. Yeast plants reproduce by **budding.** A little projection bulges from the parent cell to form a bud. Later this breaks away and gives rise to a new plant. Sometimes several buds remain fastened together to form a chain. Under unfavorable conditions, a yeast cell may divide into four cells which remain within the thickened cell wall until favorable conditions return. When two such spores fuse, a sexual spore is formed.

The favorite food of yeast is a certain form of sugar which the yeast plant absorbs through its wall. This it digests by an enzyme, *zymase* (zy-mayss), which breaks the sugar up into alcohol and carbon dioxide, both of which are passed off as waste. Yeast cannot live in more than a certain amount of its own wastes. When oxygen for respiration is not present, yeast cells can get energy from the breaking up of sugar.

The action of yeast on sugar is a *fermentation* process (Sec. 31.6). It has long been used in the preparation of leavened (light) bread and in the making of beverages containing alcohol. For both processes only a definite kind of yeast is used in order to produce the effect desired. There are many kinds of wild yeasts which may interfere with the work of the cultivated yeasts used by man.

In the making of bread, yeast is mixed with moist flour, and a little sugar is added to the dough. The yeast plants grow rapidly, setting free large quantities of carbon dioxide gas. This gas makes balloonlike pockets in the sticky dough, thus making it porous and light. Alcohol is present also. When the dough is baked, both the carbon dioxide and the alcohol are driven off, and the sticky protein in the flour is coagulated. When

462

alcoholic liquors are manufactured, the gas is allowed to escape and the alcohol is retained.

The skins of fruits usually have on them many kinds of wild yeasts that live on the ground and absorb their nourishment from it when it is damp. They are blown about when dry, and so alight on fruits. When the fruit skins are broken, as happens in crushing apples and grapes, the yeasts act upon the sugar in the fruit, turning the juice to cider or wine. Yeasts also manufacture vitamins. They are an important source of vitamin B_2, riboflavin.

32.7 Mildews

It is quite probable that you have been cautioned about leaving clothes exposed to dampness for very long periods of time, because of *mildew*. But to most of you it was just a name. Little did you realize that mildew is a plant growth. Beside the black mildews on clothes there are many kinds of these fungi which appear as white, powdery substances on various plants. Recently the lilac has shown the effects of this parasite. Another form attacks potatoes. Still others are found on clover, grapevines, and rose bushes. Mildews reproduce by spores which are blown about by the wind, and spread rapidly. They are therefore very difficult to control. During damp weather the spores germinate and start new plants. Sometimes poisonous sprays are used to check their growth, but it is difficult to destroy these resistant spores completely.

32.8 Rusts and Smuts— Basidiomycetes

Rusts and smuts are parasitic fungi belonging to the class **Basidiomycetes** (ba-*sid*-ee-oh-mye-*see*-tees). The reproductive structure of this group is an

General Mills Photo

FIGURE 32-4. *YEAST ACTION*
The holes in the bread are the result of fermentation. What other product besides carbon dioxide gas does yeast give off during fermentation?

enlarged, club-shaped hypha, called a *basidium,* within which four *basidiospores* are formed. Rusts and smuts attack many wild plants and cause some of the most important diseases of such cereal grains as wheat, oats, barley, rye, corn, and other cultivated plants.

Wheat rust causes a great economic loss because it attacks the stems. It kills the cells of the wheat by using them for food. It also prevents the wheat plant from manufacturing any more food. As a result, the diseased wheat plant has small kernels and ripens early. This makes a poor wheat crop.

The fungus on the wheat bears many small *red* spores which look like rust. They grow and divide by cell division until the fungus reaches maturity. At that time *black* spores with thicker walls are produced.

The wheat rust fungus must have two hosts in order to carry out its life cycle. Wheat is one host and the *common barberry* is the other one. When the black

American Forest Products Industries, Inc. Photo

FIGURE 32-5. *RUST DISEASE*

Why has white pine blister rust caused some states to pass laws on the growing of gooseberries and currants?

spores which develop on the wheat reach the barberry, they form bright orange cluster cups which bear spores capable of attacking the stems of other wheat plants.

One method of combating this parasite is to destroy its alternate host. This the government has been doing by sending men into the country to search the woods and fields systematically and pull up all the common barberry bushes. Sometimes epidemics of wheat rust occur when there are no barberries. This may be due to spores being blown long distances by the wind, or to spores that resisted winter temperatures.

A preventive method is to plant a rust-resistant wheat which has been developed and grown in many parts of the wheat belt.

Likewise, the *white pine blister rust* has been causing the loss of much valu-

able timber land. Part of its life history is spent on wild currant and gooseberry bushes. This rust was imported from Europe on pine seedlings and first discovered in New York State. It has now spread across the continent. This, too, the federal government is seeking to destroy by sending trained men into the field to destroy the bushes and thus save the pines. Also, some white pines are developing resistance to the blister rust. This may help to check the disease.

The *apple rust* has two hosts, the apple and the red cedar. This presents a problem to man since he has use for both the apple and the cedar trees.

Other rusts with single hosts attack the leaves of roses, asparagus, hollyhocks, oranges, and blackberries.

Smuts are other parasitic fungi which frequently attack cereals such as corn, oats, barley, and wheat. Smuts produce masses of dark-colored spores in various parts of their host plants and cause some diseases. Some of the spores produced late in the season are resistant to the cold, survive the winter, and attack the young seedlings in the spring. To prevent the spread of smut, seeds are sometimes soaked in poisons of various kinds. Planting smut-resisting varieties has had good results.

32.9 Mushrooms

Some forms of fungi, like yeast and bread mold, are small and inconspicuous. Others, like puffballs and field mushrooms, are larger, and have their hyphae compact and in layers resembling tissues. In the case of bracket fungi, such as grow on trees, the outer parts become hard and woody, causing them to resemble higher plants.

A field mushroom consists of a mass of hyphae called a *mycelium*. The *vegetative part* of the mushroom is a tangled

464

mass of colorless threads. These threads penetrate the soil, wood, bark, or other material from which the mushroom takes its nourishment. Since they lack chlorophyll, they obtain food through the action of digestion enzymes on organic matter. The *reproductive part* of the mushroom consists of an expanded portion, the **cap** or **pileus** (*py*-lee-us), on the under side of which are the **gills,** which produce *spores,* and a supporting stalk called the **stipe.** In other kinds of mushrooms, the stipe expands into a bulbous body at the base, or appears to grow out of a cup. The stipe may have a ring around it. By comparing such marks one is able to distinguish the edible from the non-edible mushrooms. Edible fungi are good food, but some of the non-edible kinds are very poisonous.

32.10 Economic Importance of Fungi

A few of the fungi are helpful to man. Yeasts are used in breadmaking and in brewing; mushrooms are used for food; penicillin is used in medicine. But the vast numbers of parasitic fungi which destroy man's crops and cause diseases of his animals seem to overshadow any good the others may do. Molds, blights, mildews, rusts, and smuts annually take heavy toll of man's produce. They destroy his forests, his food crops, his fruit trees, his home, his clothing, and even himself. Unable to make their own food, they must exist either as parasites or saprophytes, gaining their existence from others and giving little or nothing in return. However, we are developing methods for their control.

32.11 Lichens. True Partnership

Lichens (*ly*-kenz) are associations of algae and fungi for mutual benefit. This relationship is called **symbiosis.** Each

FIGURE 32-6. *MUSHROOMS* poisonous

Numbering over 38,000 known species, mushrooms offer an astonishing variety of colors, sizes, and shapes.

lichen consists of an alga and a fungus. The alga, being green, manufactures food for both. The fungus, with its fine threadlike hyphae, surrounds the alga

FIGURE 32-7. *A LICHEN*

A lichen is an association of algae and fungi. In cross-section small cells of the algae can be seen enmeshed in hyphae of the fungus.

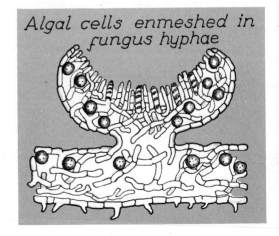

Algal cells enmeshed in fungus hyphae

465

and holds the moisture which is needed in food making. Lichens grow on the bark of trees, on rocks, and on the ground, and can live in extremes of temperature. Some grow in desert regions while others have been found within two hundred miles of the South Pole. Since lichens can grow under very difficult conditions, they often prepare the soil so that other plants may follow. They furnish food for some animals in the winter. Reindeer dig under the snow for the so-called "reindeer moss." The "rock tripe" of northern countries has been eaten by man. Lichens have also been used for tanning hides, dyeing cloth, making litmus paper, and as a fixative for perfumes.

FACTS TO REMEMBER

The *fungi* are a group of dependent Thallophytes that are unable to make their own food because they lack chlorophyll. As a result, some fungi, such as certain molds, yeasts, and mushrooms, are saprophytic; while others, such as mildews, rusts, and smuts, are parasitic. Most fungi reproduce by cell division, forming spores. Some, such as the bread mold, have a form of sexual reproduction with the union of gametes. Yeasts reproduce by budding.

Molds consist mainly of a mass of *hyphae* called a *mycelium*. Some of the hyphae (*rhizoids*) anchor the plant and absorb food; others (*stolons*) grow parallel to the surface. Erect hyphae bear the reproductive *sporangia,* which contain the spores. Most molds are destructive, but a few, like *Penicillium,* are beneficial to man.

Yeast is a one-celled fungus that reproduces by *budding*. The ability of yeast to ferment sugar, producing alcohol and carbon dioxide, makes it very useful in baking and brewing.

Rusts and *smuts* are parasitic fungi that do great damage to trees and important agricultural crops. They can be controlled by destroying the intermediate host or by developing varieties of plants that are disease-resistant.

Mushrooms form a large group of fungi, and are used for food. The vegetative part consists of the mycelium. The *cap* or *pileus, gills,* and *stipe* make up the reproductive structures. Spore producing organs are on the gills.

Lichens are a plant association of an alga and a fungus that live together for the mutual benefit of both. This type of relationship is called *symbiosis*.

WORDS TO REMEMBER

budding	mycelium	sporangia
cap	parasite	spore
gills	penicillin	stipe
hyphae	pileus	stolon
lichen	rhizoid	symbiosis
mildew	rust	zymase
	saprophyte	

QUESTIONS

1. Briefly describe a yeast plant and tell how it reproduces.
2. State two methods of reproduction in bread mold.
3. Are molds helpful or harmful? How?
4. Explain how it is possible to check wheat rust by pulling up barberry bushes.
5. What is the relationship of currants and gooseberries to the white pine blister rust?
6. What is a lichen? How are its two parts of mutual benefit?
7. How was penicillin discovered? Describe some of its uses.
8. Why are slime molds thought to be forms intermediate between plants and animals?

COMPLETION TEST

As your teacher or classmate reads the following incomplete statements, with your book closed, write on a clean sheet of paper the word or phrase which correctly completes the statement.

1. Mushrooms reproduce by _____.
2. When two organisms live together for mutual benefit, the relationship is known as _____.
3. Yeasts reproduce by _____ and _____.
4. A lichen is composed of an alga and a _____.
5. A parasite lives on its _____.
6. Two methods of reproduction in bread mold are _____ and _____.
7. Plants which live on dead organic matter are called _____.
8. The action of yeast on sugar is known as _____.

PROJECTS

I. *Study of Yeast.*—1. Dissolve a compressed yeast cake in a cup of water to which a tablespoonful of sugar has been added. Place in a fermentation tube and let stand in a warm room overnight.

2. Observe the tube. Has any gas formed above the liquid? What is the name of the gas?

3. Prepare a slide of a drop of the solution and examine it under the microscope. Make a sketch of some single cells and groups of cells.

4. Do you find any colonies? Is there any evidence of budding?

II. *Study of Bread Mold.*—1. Bring into the laboratory some pieces of bread. Moisten them slightly and let stand several days. Cover the dish to hold in the moisture and keep it in a warm place. You may find various other kinds of molds, but look particularly for the tiny black spores of the bread mold.

2. Examine the mold carefully under the microscope to see whether there are spores in the sporangia.

3. Make a sketch of a mold plant and label all the parts.

III. *Structure of a Mushroom.*—1. Bring into the laboratory a fairly large freshly picked mushroom.

2. Make a careful sketch, labeling these parts: (1) pileus, (2) rhizoids, (3) gills, (4) stipe, (5) volva (cup at base), (6) annulus (if present).

REFERENCES

Atkinson, *Studies of American Fungi.* Holt.

Christensen, *The Molds and Man.* Univ. of Minnesota Press.

Conn, *Bacteria, Yeasts and Molds in the Home.* Ginn.

Dodge, *Medical Mycology.* Mosby.

Large, *The Advance of Fungi.* Holt.

Rolfe, *The Romance of the Fungus World.* Lippincott.

Smith, *Cryptogamic Botany.* McGraw-Hill.

Sokoloff, *The Story of Penicillin.* Ziff-Davis.

Thomas, *Fieldbook of Common Mushrooms.* Putnam.

Waksman, *Microbial Antagonisms and Antibiotic Substances.* Commonwealth Fund, N.Y.

CHAPTER 33

Mosses and Liverworts

33.1 Independent Land Plants, the Bryophyta (bry-*ah*-fit-uh)

The subkingdom **Embryophyta** includes green plants which produce many-celled embryos. The reproductive organs in which they develop also have many cells. Some reproduce by an alternation of generations between sexual and asexual forms. The *Embryophyta* are divided into two main phyla: (1) **Bryophyta** lack vascular tissue and include the mosses and liverworts, and (2) **Tracheophyta** have true roots, stems, and leaves and include ferns, conifers, and flowering seed plants.

As adaptations for an independent life on land the *Bryophytes* have developed structures which (1) assure an adequate water supply, (2) protect exposed parts, (3) provide support, (4) provide for the exchange of gases, and (5) protect the reproductive cells.

33.2 Mosses—Musci

Moss plants are small and tend to grow in tight clusters. They have no true roots, stems, or leaves, since they lack vascular tissue. Rootlike structures, called **rhizoids,** anchor the plant and absorb moisture. Simple stems offer support and store food. The green structures which resemble leaves are flat and only one cell thick, except at the **midrib** which consists of long, colorless cells.

A tuft of moss consists of two kinds of plants: male plants with saucer-shaped tops, and female plants with pointed tops. At certain seasons of the year, a brown, wiry stalk bearing a **capsule** grows from the top of the female plant. It may be covered with a shaggy cap.

33.3 Life Cycle of a Moss

If a dry capsule is shaken, it sheds light, powdery spores like the "smoke" of a puffball. When these spores fall on

FIGURE 33-1. *A BRYOPHYTE*

Sphagnum moss grows in very wet places. In reproduction its sperm reaches the egg by swimming.

Hugh Spencer

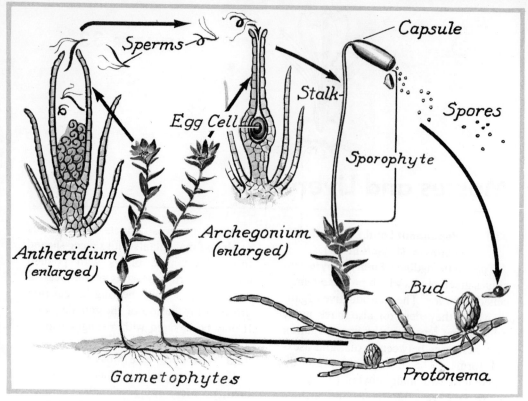

Capsule

Sperms

Stalk

Egg Cell

Spores

Sporophyte

Antheridium
(enlarged)

Archegonium
(enlarged)

Bud

Gametophytes

Protonema

FIGURE 33-2. *LIFE CYCLE OF MOSS*

Trace the moss plant from the spores to the male and female gametophytes which produce sperms in antheridia and eggs in archegonia. After fertilization the sporophyte plant grows from the tip of the female gametophyte.

moist places, each puts out a mass of fine threads called a **protonema** (proh-tuh-*nee*-muh). These threads produce buds from which the leafy moss plants grow. On some of these, sperms are formed in **antheridia** (an-ther-*id*-ee-uh) [singular, antheridium], which are the male organs; on others eggs are formed in **archegonia** (ar-keh-*goh*-nee-uh) [singular, archegonium], which are the female organs, and in some species both antheridia and archegonia are produced on a single plant.

When the sperms are ripe, they are expelled from the antheridia forcibly. If water is present, they swim about until they come in contact with an archegonium containing a ripe egg which they then fertilize, starting a new individual.

The green moss plant is thus the **gametophyte** (guh-*mee*-toh-fyte) generation, as it produces eggs and sperms. The new plant that develops from the fertilized egg is the **sporophyte** (*spoh*-roh-fyte) generation. It cannot make its own food, so it lives parasitically on the female gametophyte on which it grew, getting its nourishment from it through a pad called a *foot,* which pushes down through the bottom of the archegonium, where it begins to grow. It has for its work only the production of *spores,* asexual bodies from which the sexual plants grow. Thus there is an **alternation of generations** in mosses. The gametophyte gives rise to a small dependent sporophyte, which in turn produces a gametophyte.

470

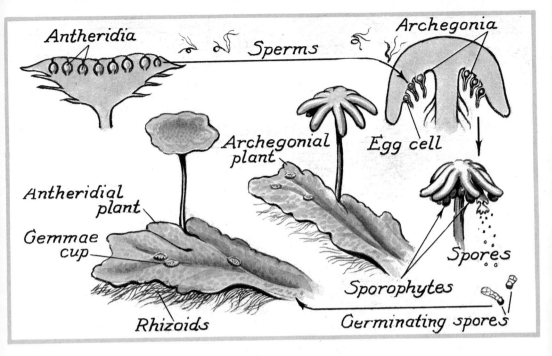

FIGURE 33-3. *LIFE CYCLE OF LIVERWORT*
Liverworts also have both gametophytes and sporophytes in their life cycle. The small sporophytes grow under the fronds of the female plant.

Some mosses bear special buds, *gemmules* (*jem*-yools). Each gemmule is capable of starting a new plant.

Habitat.—Mosses live in a variety of habitats, but thrive best in damp, shady woods, on decaying logs, and on stones wet by spray. All are dependent on water for reproduction by eggs and sperms, though some are able to exist for long periods without water by drying up and carrying on the life processes at a very slow rate. They revive quickly with moisture and resume full activity.

33.4 Economic Importance

Sphagnum (*sfag*-num) *moss* is used as packing material for plants shipped from nurseries or greenhouses, because of its ability to retain moisture for a long time before decaying. When dry it is used as litter for poultry houses. In certain areas it forms peat which may be dried and used as fuel.

Sphagnum is used by home owners and gardeners in forming a *mulch* to enrich the soil. It is also used to loosen the soil particles by planting it in areas where there is much clay and closely packed earth.

Sphagnum sometimes forms floating masses in small lakes and ponds. Mats of sphagnum moss may completely cover a small body of water and form a bog. This bog may thicken until it supports small trees and grass. This is one way in which land is built up.

Moss helps to break up rocks and loosen soil by sending its roots into the cracks and crevices. It also helps to form a ground cover.

33.5 The Liverworts

Marchantia (mahr-*kan*-shuh), a liverwort, represents a number of plants in the same phylum as the mosses. It is a ribbonlike, flat plant that grows along the surface on which it lives and to which it is attached by rhizoids. It lacks roots, stem, and leaves but it has a midrib which branches. On the surface there are tiny cups containing vegetative bodies called **gemmae** (*jem*-ee). At certain seasons Marchantia puts up two kinds of branches, one of which bears antheridia and the other archegonia. The former is like a saucer, with the openings of the antheridia scattered over its surface. It holds water which the sperms use in swimming to an archegonium. This is sexual reproduction in the liverwort. When a ripe egg is fertilized it grows into a bell-shaped *sporophyte*. This hangs down from the under side of the archegonial branch. It sheds its spores by means of threadlike bodies which twist about as they absorb water and lose it again; then the spores start a new green, *gametophyte* generation. Liverworts, like mosses, reproduce by alternation of generations, the gametophyte being the most conspicuous.

33.6 Limitations of Non-Vascular Plants

The non-vascular plants include those without definite conduction systems for fluids. They have no true roots, stems, or leaves. These plants are relatively small and numerous. The simplest are classed in the subkingdom *Thallophyta* which is subdivided into several phyla of algae and fungi. *Algae* have chlorophyll and make their own food. *Fungi* do not have chlorophyll and are usually either parasitic or saprophytic. Most of these plants are limited in size because they lack conducting systems.

Non-vascular plants which have many-celled embryos developed in female sex organs include the mosses and liverworts in the phylum *Bryophyta*. These plants are also small but have developed a method of reproduction by an alternation of generations which is a definite advance over the lower forms. They are limited in size by the lack of development of a good conducting system.

FACTS TO REMEMBER

Mosses and *liverworts* belong to the phylum Bryophyta. They have leaves, simple stems, and rootlike structures, but, like the algae and fungi, they lack vascular tissues for conducting fluids through the plant.

The Bryophytes are more advanced in their method of reproduction—*alternation of generations*. The *gametophyte* stage, which produces eggs and sperm and is the sexual generation, is the more conspicuous. It gives rise to the asexual *sporophyte* stage, which reproduces by spores and which is parasitic on the gametophyte in the mosses.

WORDS TO REMEMBER

alternation of generations	capsule	midrib
antheridia	gametophyte	protonema
archegonia	gemmae	sporophyte
	gemmule	

QUESTIONS

1. Do mosses have true stems, roots, and leaves? Explain.

2. What is meant by "alternation of generations"?
3. In mosses which is more conspicuous, the gametophyte or sporophyte?
4. Where is the sperm produced? How is it able to reach the egg?
5. Briefly describe in your own words the life cycle of Marchantia.
6. For what purposes is sphagnum moss used?
7. What is meant by a non-vascular plant?
8. Name three characteristics of the Thallophytes.
9. What characteristic puts liverworts and mosses with the Bryophytes?

COMPLETION TEST

As your teacher or classmate reads the following incomplete statements, with your book closed, write on a clean sheet of paper the word or phrase which correctly completes the statement.

1. Archegonia produce _____ cells.
2. Antheridia produce _____ cells.
3. The rootlike structures of a moss are called _____.
4. Vegetative bodies formed on the midrib of Marchantia are _____.
5. Antheridia and archegonia are produced in the _____ generation of Marchantia.
6. A fertilized egg is called a _____.
7. Alternation of generations is a method of reproduction in _____.

PROJECTS

I. *Study of Mosses.*—1. If you live in a city, you will find mosses growing in crevices of walls and copings, on trees, in cracks of sidewalks, on the brickwork near the base of houses, on old paths, and in other places.

2. Keep watch of a particular cushion of moss, noticing the change in appearance when dry, when moist, and when it has sporophytes. See how many kinds of moss you can find.

3. Bring a specimen into the laboratory and study it under the microscope. Keep a record of your observations with the dates on which you noted changes. Make sketches of the life cycle of a moss plant.

II. *Study of Liverworts.*—If you live near some wooded sections where mosses and ferns are found, you may be able to bring in some liverworts. Keep them on some of the same soil. If the soil is kept moist, the liverworts will grow and you will be able to see the gemmae and other interesting structures. Make sketches of alternation of generations in liverworts.

REFERENCES

Campbell, *General Elementary Botany.* Crowell.
Conrad, *How to Know the Mosses.* Jacques.
Dunham, *How to Know the Mosses.* Houghton Mifflin.
Grout, *Mosses with a Hand Lens.* Grout.
Smith, *Cryptogamic Botany.* Vol. II. McGraw-Hill.

UNIT **X**

The Vascular Plants

What are Vascular Tubes? These are tubes which carry water from the soil through the stems to the leaves. Other tubes carry food made in the leaves down the stem to be stored or used where it is needed. When plants developed these tubes, it was possible for them to grow larger and stronger because their supply of water and minerals was more certain. The ferns have the simplest of these conducting tubes. The trees and the plants with brightly colored flowers have these tubes arranged in groups of bundles or in rings of tubes. Have you counted the rings of growth in a tree stump? Have you ever noticed the cut ends of these tubes? The strings of celery are water tubes and food-carrying tubes.

What are the Main Groups of Plants? With the electron microscope and other methods of study, scientists are discovering new facts about plants and animals. Many scientists are giving more importance to the water tubes, or vascular systems, as a means of classifying plants and placing them into large groups. Other scientists divide the plant kingdom of higher plants on the basis of flowers. The plants with water tubes reproduce by flowers, except for the ferns and other forms related to them. As you study this unit you will have an opportunity to find the reasons for the differences of opinion.

In Unit X you will study about all of the plants with water tubes, the Tracheophyta, according to one classification. This includes the ferns, which reproduce by alternation of generations, somewhat similar to the mosses, which do not have well defined water tubes.

In Unit X you will also study about all of the plants with flowers, which some scientists have called Spermatophyta or the Flowering Plants. Both groups of scientists divide the flowering plants into the evergreens, or Gymnosperms, with unprotected seeds, and the Angiosperms, with seeds protected by seed coats.

What are the Main Parts of Plants? The main structures of the higher plants are the leaves, stems, roots, flowers, and seeds or fruit. In Unit X you will find plants that catch insects, like Venus's flytrap; plants with runners, like the strawberries; and plants that live with their roots in the air, like orchids. Some plants, like the petunia, complete their lives in one year; others, like the redwoods, live hundreds of years. Yet all of them depend upon the climate and other plants for their existence.

CHAPTER 34

Ferns and Fernlike Plants

34.1 The Vascular Plants

As green plants began to adapt themselves to free and independent living and began to grow to a larger size, some of them developed vascular tissues. The elongated cells which make up these tissues are arranged to form tubelike vessels for the conduction of liquids. Just as higher animals need a circulatory system for absorption of foods, so the higher plants need a system for absorption of foodmaking materials.

FIGURE 34-1. *ADVANCED*

The pteris fern is grouped with higher plants because it has conducting tissue.

Hugh Spencer

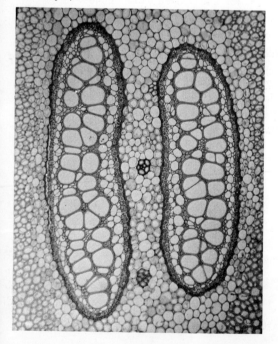

Among the simplest plants to develop vascular tissue are the ferns and fernlike plants. Their stems have conducting tubes arranged in bundles. Those *tubes which carry water from the ground up to the leaves are called* **xylem** (zy-lem). They are large, thick-walled tubes. The cells are arranged end to end to make a continuous passageway. The *tubes which carry food materials from the leaves downward are called* **phloem** (*flow*-em). They consist of large, thin-walled tubes.

The land plants which have developed vascular tissues have been placed in the large phylum **Tracheophyta** (*tray*-kee-oh-fy-tuh). This group includes club moss, horsetails, ferns, evergreens, and flowering plants.

34.2 Club Moss

The club mosses which are widely used in making Christmas wreaths and other decorations are sometimes called "ground pine." They grow along the ground in temperate regions and on tree trunks in the tropics. Their spores are borne on specialized branches in *sporangia,* the spore-bearing cases.

Selaginella, a pretty greenhouse plant, also belongs to this group. All are interesting because of their beauty and history as well as the method of reproduction by alternation of generations.

476

Hugh Spencer

FIGURE 34-2. *LIVING FOSSILS*

The only living member of its group, equisetum has a history as far back as the Carboniferous period and is still found over almost all the world. The fertile stalks (left) bear sporangia in clusters (strobili) at their tips. Sterile stalks (right) have leafy branches which perform photosynthesis.

Many of the plants in this group are known only as fossils because they are now extinct.

The spores of a club moss are used to coat pills and tablets, thus preventing them from sticking together.

34.3 Horsetail, or Equisetum

These plants have jointed stems. They represent a group of plants that was very abundant in prehistoric times but, like the dinosaurs in the reptile group, most of them have become extinct. There is only one living group.

Horsetail, or *equisetum* (eh-kwih-*see-*tum), grows in waste places either wet or dry. It is peculiar in having two types of plants each season, the first appearing early, growing rapidly from food stored up the previous season. It lacks the ability to make food for itself, having the sole function of producing spores.

These grow in sporangia at the top of the stalk,—the cluster being called a **strobilus** (*stroh*-bih-luss). The perennial stem is underground. The **fertile stalk** is made up of *nodes* and *internodes,* each node having a collar of reduced leaves around it. The stalk is hollow, and the outside is more or less ribbed. After the fertile stalk has shed its spores, it dies and is replaced by a **sterile stalk** which is green and bushy from repeated branching. This stalk performs the work of photosynthesis and stores food in the underground stem for the growth of the fertile stalk of the next season. *Scouring rush* is a form of equisetum in which one stalk performs both the functions of reproduction and of photosynthesis. It has the peculiarity of being covered with a glassy substance, a characteristic that made it valuable for scouring before the days of modern scouring powder.

FERNS AND FERNLIKE PLANTS

477

F. Hall

FIGURE 34-3. *TREE FERNS*
Ferns grow to great height in the rain
forests of the tropics, where there is a
hot climate with a heavy rainfall.

34.4 Ferns

The ferns, like the higher plants, have
true roots, stems, and leaves. For this
reason they are placed in the group
Pteropsida (ter-*op*-sih-duh), one of the
subdivisions of the Tracheophyta. This
group includes the ferns, evergreens, and
flowering plants. In order to distinguish
the ferns, they have been placed in the
class *Filicineae* (fil-iss-*sin*-ee-ee).

The ferns are more highly developed
than the club mosses. They live in rich,
moist soil and often grow to a large size.
Some grow in crevices of rocks and cliffs
where there is little soil; others grow in
fields and open woods; but most of them
live best in cool, damp, shady places.

34.5 History of the Fern

This whole group of plants is very
old. It has been estimated from some
fossil ferns that they existed 300,000,000
years ago. At one time they grew as

large as trees and were very numerous.
Their history is like that of the reptiles,
and they, too, are a declining race. They
were at their height when the earth was
younger and the climate was very wet
and very hot. The largest of their sur-
vivors are still found in the tropics.

Some tree ferns grow as tall as fifty
feet and have leaves twelve to fourteen
feet long. In the temperate zone the
stem grows just above or below the surface and sends large leaves upward and
roots downward. Most of them grow
best in moist, cool woods in a rich soil,
though some have been able to adapt to
less favorable conditions.

A study of coal beds shows that when
the earth was covered with these giant
plants, the dead ones accumulated in
masses. These turned into coal under
the influence of heat and pressure. Coal,
oil, and natural gas appear to have been
formed at the same time. Few, if any,
of these fuels are being formed at the
present time, so far as we know, and it
is necessary for us to find new kinds of
fuels before we exhaust the present
supply. Atomic power is already being
used.

Ferns, like trees and smaller flowering plants, have roots, stems, and leaves.
Unlike flowering plants, however, they
produce spores instead of seeds, and
they reproduce by the alternation of
generations like Marchantia.

34.6 Pteris

A study of *pteris* (*ter*-iss), a common
and wellknown fern, also known as
bracken and *brake,* will illustrate the
structure, the habits, and the reproduction of ferns in general (Fig. 34-5).

The stem of this fern above ground is
less complex than that of a flowering
plant. It has tissues made up of well-
defined clusters of cells which have a

478

L. W. Brownell

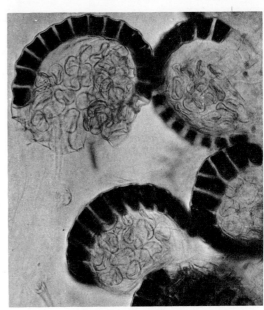

Ward's Natural Science Establishment, Inc.

FIGURE 34-4. *PTERIS FROND*

The dark edges of each pteris leaflet (*left*) are made by clusters of sporangia, the *sori*. The photograph at the right shows a group of sporangia with a thin membrane covering called the *indusium* (dark area). When the spores are mature, they are discharged from the sporangia.

constant relation to each other, a fairly constant position for each kind of fern, and the same functions as similar tissues in the flowering plants. The outside of this stem is covered by a thin epidermis. Just inside the epidermis is a tissue of thick-walled cells which provide support. Near the center of the stem are two elongated masses of tissue, slightly crescent-shaped, besides many small masses distributed somewhat evenly throughout the stem. The conductive tissue in the pteris is in definite groups, some large and some small, each made up of *xylem* and *phloem* as in flowering plants. All the space not occupied by other tissues is filled with *fundamental tissue* in which most of the vital processes of the stem are carried on.

This fern's underground stem is a **rhizome** (*ry*-zohm) often several feet long, which lives from year to year, putting up new leaves annually. Fine roots

grow from this stem. The leaves, also called **fronds,** are *pinnately compound,* that is, they have many tiny leaflets arranged along a midrib. They have the structure of a typical green leaf except that the veins are forked, a kind of venation that is characteristic of ferns. When the leaves appear above the ground in the spring, they are tightly rolled and covered with a hairy growth at the base. As they unroll they lose this covering. At certain seasons of the year lines form along the margin of the under sides of the leaves. These are made up of minute reproductive bodies, *sporangia,* each of which contains several spores capable of starting a new generation. There is great variety in the forms of the leaves of ferns and in the arrangement of the sporangia. Many ferns have the sporangia in round dots. Each is called a **sorus** (*sor*-us) and has a thin cover called the **indusium** (in-*doo*-zhum).

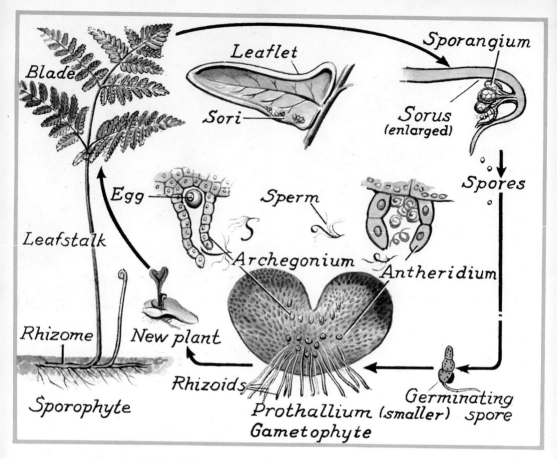

FIGURE 34-5. *FERN LIFE CYCLE*

The fern life cycle includes a sexual generation and an asexual generation. Spores (*right*) germinate to form the prothallium which is the gametophyte plant. On this plant archegonia and antheridia produce eggs and sperm. A fertilized egg grows into the sporophyte. Clusters of sporangia, sori, on the sporophyte produce spores, completing the life cycle.

34.7 Life Cycle of Pteris

The spore-bearing sporangia in the pteris are grouped together in sori. Each sporangium is made up of a lens-shaped body, and a stalk which is attached to the underside of the leaflet. The spores develop within the lens-shaped sac. A band of elastic cells extends from the stalk, part way around the edge of the sac. The rest of the sac's edge is covered by a layer of thin cells. When the spores are mature, the elastic cells exert a pull that causes the thin cells to split, opening the sporangium

and forcibly discharging the spores. Those that fall in favorable positions sprout, forming a threadlike chain of cells. This develops into a heart-shaped body, the **prothallium** (proh-*thal*-ee-um), which is notched on the upper side and has filaments, or *rhizoids,* on the underside. By these it gathers moisture and attaches itself lightly to the soil.

Among the rhizoids, near the lower margin, a group of *antheridia* develops, each one short, spherical, and containing a number of motile (active) sperms. Near the notch, on the underside, a few

480

archegonia develop, each one containing an egg cell at the base of a curved, inverted vase-shaped organ. The passage to the egg is filled with mucus and is closed at its free end by a plate of cells. When all parts are wet, this mucus swells and pushes off the plate of cells, at the same time attracting the sperm cells. One or more of these sperm cells enter the passage, and the one that gets to the egg first fertilizes it, forming a *zygote* from which a new fern plant begins to grow. This pushes its root through the bottom of the archegonium, deriving its nourishment parasitically from the prothallium, while it is putting up leaves that can make its own food. When the young fern plant is able to carry on its life independently, the prothallium dies.

Because the prothallium produces eggs and sperms, it is the *sexual* generation of the fern. The large, green, showy plant which grows from it and produces spores is the *sporophyte*. Thus the sporophyte generation gives rise to the *gametophyte,* or sexual generation, and that, in turn, to a new sporophyte. The gametophyte is so small as to escape observation, and it dies when its work is done, while a sporophyte, once established, is perennial. The fern reproduces by alternation of generations, with the sporophyte being the more conspicuous.

Eggs and sperms do not usually mature at the same time on the same prothallium, thus preventing self-fertilization. The sperm, being motile, is dependent on moisture to enable it to swim from one prothallium to another. Rain

L. W. Brownell

FIGURE 34-6. *CHRISTMAS FERN*

Ferns will grow almost anywhere in the world. They are usually found in moist, shady woods among rocks and cliffs.

and dew enable the sperms to reach prothallia with ripe archegonia.

Ferns differ from one another in the form of the leaf blade. The *sensitive fern* has leaves that are once compound; that is, the leaves are subdivided. These leaves are very responsive to the stimuli of touch and light. The *royal fern* is twice compound; that is, the subdivisions of the leaves are also subdivided. The *walking fern* is a simple leaf. When this leaf tip touches the ground a bud develops and a leaf forms. Why is it called the walking fern?

Ferns are picked in the late summer and shipped to greenhouses for packing and decorating material. Many so-called "Christmas greens" are ferns used in making wreaths for the holiday season.

FACTS TO REMEMBER

The phylum *Tracheophyta* includes plants with vascular or conducting tissues. *Club mosses* and *horsetails* belong to the simplest subdivisions of the Tracheophyta and reproduce by alternation of generations. Club mosses have small, simple leaves. The horsetails have jointed stems.

Ferns, like the evergreen trees and flowering plants, belong to the subdivision *Pteropsida,* because they all have true roots, stems, and leaves. However, ferns reproduce by alternation of generations, with the sporophyte generation being the more conspicuous.

WORDS TO REMEMBER

antheridia	prothallium	spore
archegonia	rhizoid	sterile stalk
fertile stalk	rhizome	strobilus
frond	sorus	xylem
indusium	sporangium	zygote
phloem		

QUESTIONS

1. How are ferns similar to flowering plants? How do they differ?
2. Why are ferns placed in the phylum Tracheophyta along with the evergreen trees and flowering plants?
3. Describe the life cycle of pteris.
4. What factor tends to prevent self-fertilization in ferns?
5. What characteristic of scouring rushes made them valuable in early days?
6. What characteristics of the club mosses make them useful in Christmas decorations and wreaths?
7. Describe the xylem and phloem tubes in a fern.
8. Which generation is more conspicuous in the fern, the gametophyte or sporophyte? How does this differ from a moss?

COMPLETION TEST

1. A sorus contains many _____.
2. Spore cases of ferns are known as _____.
3. When the spores grow, a heart-shaped body called the _____ is formed.
4. The antheridia and archegonia of ferns are both formed on the _____.
5. The egg cell and sperm cell unite to form the _____.
6. The rootlike structures are called _____.
7. The sexual generation of the fern is the _____ generation.
8. The leaves of ferns are called _____.
9. Fern leaves are compound because they are composed of many _____.
10. Ferns are used for _____.

PROJECTS

I. *Study of Ferns.*—1. Make a collection of ferns that grow in your locality and note the variety of branching of the leaves. Learn the names

THE VASCULAR PLANTS

of as many as you can. Make fern prints in your printing frame.

2. You may wish to make some plaster casts of fern leaves by coating each leaf with a grease, such as vaseline, and pressing it into some wet plaster of Paris. When this hardens, you can break away the uneven edges and have a print or impression of the fern leaf. Paint it green and you will have a decorative plaque to add to your collection.

II. *Fern Prothallia.*—Sow fern spores on the top of water in a tumbler. Cover, set in the shade, and look for prothallia in about a week. Place these on moist soil and perhaps you may be able to raise some ferns of your own, thus being able to watch the process of alternation of generations.

REFERENCES

Clute, Our Ferns. Stokes.
Durand, *Field Book of Common Ferns.* Putnam.
Noo, *Ferns, Fossils and Fuel.* Wilcox & Follett.
Sinnott, *Botany.* McGraw-Hill.
Smith, Overton, and Others, *Botany.* Macmillan.
Tilton, *The Fern Lover's Companion.* Little, Brown.
Transeau, Sampson, and Tiffany, *Textbook of Botany.* Harper.
Wherry, *Ferns of the Eastern States.* Science Press.

CHAPTER 35

The Root-Structure for Absorption

35.1   The Function of Roots

The roots of a plant have several important functions. First, it is upon the roots that the plant depends for its success in manufacturing food, especially starch. This is because the roots are the organs that *gather water* from the soil. Water, containing substances in solution, is the chief raw material used by the leaves in making starch. Two factors regulate the supply of water. One is the soil itself as the reservoir for moisture, and the other is the roots which gather that moisture.

A second important use of the roots is to *hold the plant* securely in place. Many plants have a system of roots larger than the parts that grow above ground. A third function of roots is to *transport the liquid* absorbed by the root hairs to the vessels that carry water and digested food. These join the vascular system of the stem and connect with the veins of the leaf. Many roots

have a fourth function, serving as *food storage* centers for the plant. Beets and carrots store food in their roots.

35.2   The Structure of Roots

The outer part of the root is covered with an *epidermis* which acts as a protective layer and keeps the root from drying. Inside this is a region called the **cortex** where most of the food is stored. The cortex surrounds the **central cylinder,** which contains vessels that carry water to the stem and digested food back to the root. Near the tip is the main growing region, the **meristem** (*mer*-ih-stem), from which the epidermis, the cortex, and the central cylinder are formed. Covering the tip of the root is a **root cap** which protects the end of the root from injury as it pushes through the soil.

The central cylinder, also known as the **stele,** consists of (1) thick-walled **xylem** in the center with a number of

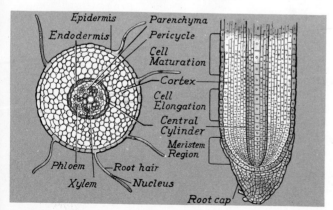

FIGURE 35-1. *DICOT ROOT*

The cross section (*left*) and longitudinal section (*right*) of this dicot root show the areas of conduction, food storage, and growth. The root cap is a protective tip.

484

arms radiating outward, (2) thin-walled **phloem** located in the angles between the arms of xylem, (3) thinner-walled unspecialized cells known as **parenchyma** (puh-*ren*-kee-muh), (4) an outer sheath called the **pericycle** (*per*-ih-sy-k'l), where the branch roots originate. A single layer of *endodermal cells* form the boundary between the central cylinder and cortex.

The xylem conducts the water and soil minerals *upward* to the stem and leaves. The phloem conducts the food made in the leaves and stem *downward* to supply the cells which need it.

In the roots of shrubs and trees, thin-walled **cambium** cells, which are able to carry on cell division, form between the xylem and phloem. This layer enables the roots to increase in diameter.

Besides the main, or **primary, root,** there are many smaller roots which divide still further into *rootlets*. The small **secondary roots** branching from the main roots start from the pericycle in the central cylinder. The root and its divisions underground may be compared, in a general way, to the stem, branches, and twigs above ground.

35.3 Root Hairs

Root hairs are found a short distance back from the tip of each rootlet of an actively growing root. They are the chief absorbing structures of the root. Each hair is a tubular projection of the protoplasm of an *epidermal* cell. Root hairs are very numerous. As the root grows, the hairs farthest from the tip die and are replaced by new ones nearer the tip. Root hairs greatly increase the absorbing surface of a rootlet. They attach themselves firmly to particles of soil from which they take almost every trace of moisture. They also serve to anchor the plant firmly in the soil.

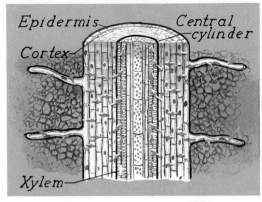

FIGURE 35-2. *ROOT AND ROOT HAIRS*

The cross section of this rootlet shows clearly that each root hair is a part of an epidermal cell. Is this portion of the root very close to the root tip?

35.4 Absorption of Water

In the higher plants, absorption of soil water containing dissolved minerals and gases takes place in the root hairs. There is a transfer of substances through the cell walls and plasma membranes which takes place by *diffusion, osmosis,* and *selective absorption.*

Diffusion is the spreading out of the molecules of gases and liquids from regions of higher concentration to those of lower concentration until the molecules are uniformly distributed. Perfume spreads from an open bottle to all parts of a room and a lump of sugar dissolves and spreads through a cup of coffee without stirring by diffusion. Molecules of water and dissolved minerals will diffuse through cell membranes into the protoplasm of cells as long as the concentration of diffusing materials is higher outside the cell than it is inside.

Cell membranes are *semipermeable;* that is, they allow substances made up of smaller molecules to pass through more readily than substances composed of larger molecules. Thus water will pass more readily into a living cell than the larger particles contained in the proto-

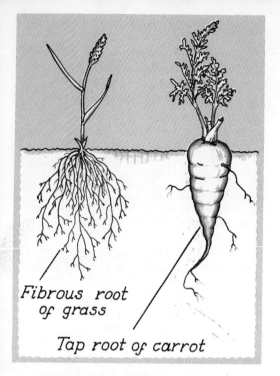

Fibrous root
of grass

Tap root of carrot

FIGURE 35-3. *ROOT TYPES*
When the primary root is larger than
its branches, it is a *tap root*. In a *fibrous
root*, the branches are equally large.

Diffusion, osmosis, and selective absorption are found in all living things.
They build up pressure within the roots
of plants and push the water and dissolved minerals up the xylem tubes of
the stems and into the veins of the leaves.
Transpiration, the evaporation of water
from the leaves, lowers the pressure so
that more water will move toward them.
The small diameter of the xylem tubes
contributes to the upward flow of water
by *capillarity,* which is caused by the
adhesion of water molecules to the walls
of the tubes. The strong *cohesion* between the water molecules helps to prevent the breaking apart of the thread of
water in the tubes. All of these processes contribute to the upward flow of
water from the roots to the leaves, known
as the **sap stream.**

35.5 Types of Roots

The two main types of roots are (1)
taproots and (2) **fibrous roots.** When
the primary root increases in diameter
much faster than the branch roots, it is
known as a *taproot.* Dandelions and
carrots have taproots. When the primary root does not become thicker than
the branch roots, it is known as a *fibrous
root.* Beans, corn, cabbage, squash, and
grasses have fibrous roots.

Either taproots or fibrous roots may
become enlarged by the storage of food.
They are then known as **fleshy roots.**
Dahlias, beets, turnips, and sweet potatoes are examples.

Adventitious roots grow from stems
or leaves, especially those that grow
freely when the cutting of a stem is put
in water or moist soil (Sec. 36.13).
Such garden plants as tomato, cucumber,
squash, and others send out adventitious
roots where their stems touch the soil,
especially at the nodes in the case of the
vines named.

plasm will move out. This diffusion of
water through a semipermeable membrane is called **osmosis.** It accounts for
the swelling of cells and organisms when
immersed in fresh water. It builds up
pressure within the cell and gives it firmness, or *turgor.* When living cells or organisms are immersed in salt water,
osmosis may take place in reverse, due
to the greater concentration of water
inside the cells. This results in the drying out of the cells, known as *plasmolysis.*

In addition to these two physical processes, living cell membranes carry on
selective absorption by complex chemical exchanges which are not well understood. In this way, substances not needed
by the living cells may be rejected while
other very similar substances which are
essential may be absorbed.

486

FIGURE 35-4. *ROOT SYSTEMS*

Corn is a good example of a plant with prop roots, which extend above the ground and give strong support (*left*). Many orchids of tropical countries (*right*) attach themselves to the bark of trees, sending roots into the air, from which they take their food and water.

Climbing roots are adventitious roots which anchor plants to walls, as poison ivy, English ivy, and other vines. These plants also have primary roots anchored in the soil.

The *prop roots* (brace roots) of corn (Fig. 35-4) grow out from the nodes which are just above the surface of the ground. These roots help to hold the plant upright.

Knees are upward projections on roots. The bald cypress tree, which grows with its roots submerged, has these projections, which extend above the surface of the water. They are so modified that the roots are enabled to secure the air they need.

Stolon roots first appear in the air on the ends of stems or runners, as in the strawberry (Sec. 36.12). After they take root in the ground, they develop like normal roots.

Aerial roots are found in orchids. They take in water from the atmosphere, such as rain and dew, and absorb other raw materials from the soil particles which collect around them. They also serve to anchor the plant.

Certain cactus plants which live in the desert have roots twenty times as long as the parts that appear above the soil. This enables them to absorb and to store up the scanty moisture. Other cacti have shallow roots. Corn also has a large number of shallow roots.

The extent and distribution of the *root system* in the soil depends partly on the kind of plant and partly on the soil, temperature, and other environmental factors.

35.6 Duration of Roots

Roots that live for only one season are called *annual roots,* examples of which are corn, peas, and beans. Those that store the food manufactured one season and use it to produce flowers and fruit the next are called *biennial roots.* Examples of these are the fleshy roots of turnips and beets. *Perennial roots* live more than two years. They do not produce flowers until the second year or later.

THE ROOT-STRUCTURE FOR ABSORPTION

FIGURE 35-5. *SUGAR BEETS*

The growing of sugar beets and the refining of beet sugar are industries of great economic importance, producing one-third of the world's sugar supply.

Photograph by the Detroit News

Woody plants (including trees and shrubs) continue to grow year after year. *Herbaceous* perennial plants have leafy parts above ground which wither away each year and grow up again the following year from the living roots in the soil.

35.7 Length of Roots

The root system of a tree growing in fertile soil is about equal to the parts which appear above the ground. An oat plant has a root system the combined length of which is about 154 feet; a wheat plant has single roots 7 feet long; and alfalfa has an enormous root system. A single root of alfalfa may extend more than 20 feet in one direction in a loose soil. Eggplant and squash send their roots down 7 feet and spread laterally from 2 to 20 feet.

35.8 Needs of Roots

Since plants are unable to move about, they are dependent upon the climate and their immediate surroundings to furnish the materials they need. There must be an adequate water supply and variety of minerals to provide the necessary plant-building materials. The soil must be loose enough to allow for the growth of the roots and yet firm enough to allow them to maintain a strong hold. Thus the plants make certain demands on the soil. If these conditions are not present, the plants cannot live there.

35.9 Economic Uses of Roots

In some plants the root is the most valuable part for food not only for man but also for his animals. Examples of this are found in many of the garden vegetables, such as turnips, parsnips, carrots, sweet potatoes, and radishes. The food stored in the sugar beet is rich in sugar, making it one of the sources of commercial sugar as well as a valuable food for stock. The roots of some uncultivated plants are edible. Cattail roots may be eaten like potatoes or ground into flour and made into puddings. Other roots furnish substances used for medicine, as rhubarb and mandrake, while the root of ginger is used in medicine and in cooking. Licorice is used in medicine and in confections. Fertilizer rich in potash is obtained from the sugar beet and food for cattle from a coarse beet known as *mangel*. A dye is produced from madder.

FACTS TO REMEMBER

The principal functions of roots are (1) the absorption of water and dissolved minerals from the surrounding soil, (2) the anchorage of plants to the soil, (3) the transportation of liquids, (4) food storage, and (5) the vegetative propagation of new plants by·adventitious roots.

The parts of a root are (1) the epidermis, (2) the *cortex,* (3) the endodermis, (4) the *central cylinder,* or *stele,* consisting of xylem, phloem, *parenchyma,* and the *pericycle,* (5) the growing region, or *meristem,* and (6) the *root cap.*

The *primary root* is the main root of a plant, and the smaller branches growing from it are the *secondary roots.*

Root hairs are small outgrowths of the epidermal cells and serve to increase the surface area of the root so as to allow for a greater absorption of water and the materials dissolved in it.

Water and dissolved substances are carried up a tree by the combined and resultant forces of (1) *root pressure* due to osmosis, (2) *diffusion,* (3) *capillarity,* (4) *cohesion,* and (5) the tension resulting from transpiration and other water loss.

Each plant forms a *root system* of a certain type of root that is suited to its environment and function.

Roots are important sources of medicines, fertilizer, and food for man and animals.

WORDS TO REMEMBER

adventitious root	fibrous root	root cap
aerial root	fleshy root	root hair
annual root	knees	root system
biennial root	meristem	sap stream
cambium	osmosis	semipermeable
capillarity	parenchyma	secondary root
central cylinder	perennial root	stele
climbing root	pericycle	stolon root
cortex	phloem	taproot
diffusion	plasmolysis	transpiration
endodermis	primary root	turgor
epidermis	prop root	xylem

QUESTIONS

1. What is a root?
2. Name four functions of a root.
3. Describe the structure of a taproot.
4. How do fibrous roots differ from a taproot?
5. In which kind of roots is the most food stored?
6. What use does man make of food stored in plant roots?

7. What roots are used in medicine?
8. Describe osmosis. What root structures are especially adapted for it?
9. Describe some of the forces which help to force sap up a tree.
10. Name and describe several different kinds of roots.

COMPLETION TEST

As your teacher or classmate reads the following incomplete statements, with your book closed, write on a clean sheet of paper the word or phrase that correctly completes the statement.

1. The outer part of the root is covered with an _____.
2. Food is stored in the _____ of the root.
3. The _____ covers the tip of the root.
4. Water rises in a root through the _____.
5. The secondary roots branch from the _____.
6. Root hairs are projections of _____ cells.
7. Roots which grow out from stems are called _____ roots.
8. _____ roots appear at the ends of runners as in the strawberry.
9. _____ roots live for only one season.
10. A root used in cooking and in medicine is _____.

PROJECTS

I. *Demonstration of Osmosis.*—1. Carefully break the shell on the large end of an egg and remove the pieces without breaking the membrane beneath. Make a hole with a large needle through the shell and membrane of the small end of the egg. With sealing wax fasten a small glass tube (open at each end) over the hole in the smaller end of the egg so that it will not leak. Set the egg with the attached tube in a tumbler half full of water. Put the apparatus away and observe it from time to time for a day or two. Does the egg rise in the tube? How far? Does the egg mix with the water in the tumbler? How much? Test the water in the glass for protein.

2. Another experiment to show osmosis requires a root, such as a carrot, parsnip, or a sweet potato. You will also need some glass tubing about eighteen inches long, a cork borer or apple corer, and some paraffin or sealing wax.

Bore a hole in the middle of the root and fit into the top of the root a one-hole rubber stopper into which you have already inserted the glass tubing about an inch. Fill the cavity with molasses or a strong sugar solution. Put the cork in place and seal it in with paraffin or sealing wax. Put the root in a glass of water and let it stand several days. Record your observations.

II. *Demonstration to Show Region through Which Liquids Rise.*—Stand cut-off roots of parsnip overnight in water tinted with red ink. In what region does the color show? Make cross sections of one and longitudinal sections of another.

III. *Structure of Roots.*—Cut a root of carrot or parsnip lengthwise and identify (1) the *epidermis;* (2) the *cortex,* the region under the epidermis; and (3) the *central cylinder.* Cut it crosswise and identify the same regions. Make drawings of both sections and label fully. In both sections look for rootlets and note the region from which they arise. Show this in your drawing.

IV. *Study of Root Hairs.*—1. Plant some bean seeds in loose soil or moistened sawdust. Keep in a warm place with plenty of sunlight. Look at the roots of the seedlings. How does the extent of roots compare with the parts above ground?

2. Examine roots grown in a moist chamber for root hairs. Compare with one grown in sawdust or soil after it has been carefully washed. How do they differ? On what part of the rootlet are the root hairs most numerous? Where are they the longest?

3. Look at a root hair under the microscope. Make a sketch of it. If possible, show its relation to the epidermal cell.

V. *Kinds of Roots.*—1. Pull weeds and examine the roots. Which have taproots? Why do they flourish better than the plants around them?

2. Cut a piece of thick sod with a sharp spade or trowel. How many grass plants are there in a square two inches on a side? What kind of roots has grass? Wash the dirt away carefully and measure the extent of the root system. Compare it with the part above the ground.

3. On how many nodes of a corn stem do prop roots grow? What is the effect of "hilling up" corn on the production of prop roots?

4. Place willow twigs in water. Watch the growth of adventitious roots, noting especially the root caps. Do duckweed and other floating plants have root caps? Account for what you find.

5. Examine a large number of roots and make a report on a table similar to the following. Do not mark your book.

Plant	Root All Under-ground	Roots Not All Under-ground	Primary Roots	Fibrous Roots	Aerial Roots
Dandelion					
Plantain					
Carrot					
Dahlia					
Corn					
Ivy					

REFERENCES

Bergen and Caldwell, *Practical Botany.* Ginn.
Conn, *Biology.* Silver, Burdett.
Cook, *College Botany.* Lippincott.
Eyster, *College Botany.* Richard R. Smith.
Holman and Robbins, *A Textbook of General Botany.* Wiley.
Mottier, *College Textbook of Botany.* Blakiston.

Quinn, *Roots, Their Place in Life and Legend.* Stokes.

Rigg, *College Botany.* Lea and Febiger.

Robbins and Rickett, *Botany.* Van Nostrand.

Sinnott, *Botany, Principles and Problems.* McGraw-Hill.

Smith, Overton, and Others, *A Textbook of General Botany.* Macmillan.

Torrey, Ray E., *General Botany for Colleges.* Century.

Transeau, *General Botany.* World Book.

Weaver, *Root Development and Field Crops.* McGraw-Hill.

Weaver and Brune, *Root Development of Vegetable Crops.* McGraw-Hill.

CHAPTER 36

The Stem—Vascular Structure

36.1 The Work of the Stem

Since the leaves make the food of the plant and the roots gather the water and other substances needed by the leaves to make their food, there has to be a pathway from root to leaf. Every plant has such a connection—its stem. The stem is the path by which the solution reaches the leaves and, in many cases, the path by which the food returns to be stored in roots. The stem contains conductive vessels to enable it to serve this function. This is our reason for calling it the plant's organ of circulation. It is more than that, however, for the stem supports the leaves holding them out toward the sun.

36.2 Two Kinds of Stems

There are two main kinds of stems as far as structure is concerned. In one kind, **monocot** (*monocotyledonous* [mon-oh-kot'l-*ee*-d'n-us], having one seed leaf), the *fibrovascular bundles* are scattered throughout the *pith* which forms the center of the stem. Such stems are always found in plants that have one **cotyledon** (seed leaf), as corn, grass, and palm. In the other kind of stem, **dicot** (*dicotyledonous* [dy-kot'l-*ee*-d'n-us], having two seed leaves), and in most gymnosperms with more than two seed leaves, the bundles are arranged in a circular zone outside of the pith and, in the early stages, have pith

FIGURE 36-1. *TREE TRUNKS*

The trunk of a tree is actually the stem of the plant. The palm tree (*left*) is a giant among the monocots, most of which have weak, pithy or hollow stems. The oak tree (*right*) has a typical woody, dicot stem.

James Sawders   Courtesy of the Davey Tree Expert Co.

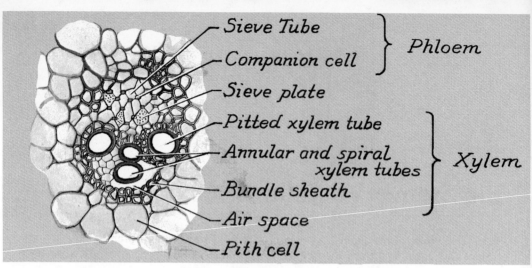

Sieve Tube ⎫
Companion cell ⎬ Phloem
Sieve plate ⎭

Pitted xylem tube ⎫
Annular and spiral ⎬ Xylem
  xylem tubes
Bundle sheath ⎭

Air space

Pith cell

FIGURE 36-2. *MONOCOT FIBROVASCULAR BUNDLE*

The small number of strong-walled xylem cells which occur in the monocot fibrovascular bundle help to explain the relatively weak structure of this type of stem. Notice the sieve plates that separate sieve tube cells from each other.

between them also. Such stems are always found in plants with two cotyledons, as the bean and all woody trees.

36.3 Fibrovascular Bundles of Monocotyledonous Plants

A vascular bundle (Fig. 36-2) in a monocotyledonous plant is made up of two kinds of tissue, called *xylem* and *phloem,* surrounded by a *bundle sheath.*

Xylem tissue includes hollow, thick-walled conducting tubes called *vessels* and *tracheids.* Vessels lack end walls and make a continuous pathway from roots to leaves. Tracheids have pits which allow some sideways movement of water. Thin-walled *fibers* and *xylem parenchyma* also give support to the stem.

Phloem tissue includes thin-walled *sieve tubes* which retain their living cytoplasm. They have perforated ends called *sieve plates* through which sugars in solution pass downward from leaves to storage regions. Also in the phloem are *companion cells, phloem parenchyma,* and *fibers* which serve as storage cells and give some support to the plant.

36.4 Fibrovascular Bundles of Dicotyledonous Plants

A fibrovascular bundle in a woody stem has *three* groups of cells; the *xylem,* on the inside, its cells thick-walled, with thin spots; the *phloem,* on the outside, thin-walled cells with sieve plates at the ends of the larger cells; and the **cambium** (*kam*-bee-um), small, brick-shaped, thin-walled cells. The cambium lies in a narrow strip between the xylem and the phloem (Fig. 36-3).

In woody stems, the cambium is the part which makes it possible for the stem to increase in diameter. This increase is brought about as follows: the brick-shaped cells on the inside edge of the cambium layer gradually change to the thick-walled xylem cells, and those on the outside of the layer turn to thin-walled phloem cells. As more and more bundles grow, the cells of the cambium layers nearly touch and become a continuous ring.

Thus it happens that a woody stem can add a layer of wood on the inside of the cambium, and a layer of phloem on

494

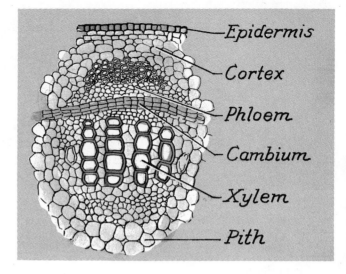

FIGURE 36-3. *DICOT FIBROVASCULAR BUNDLE*

Notice the distinctive layer of cambium cells and the number of xylem cells that are already evident in this young dicot.

the outside every year. It is easy to trace the woody rings of the inside layer which are protected and do not change. However, the bark formed from the phloem cracks and falls off in bits, making it difficult to trace the *annual rings* of the outer layer.

The vascular bundles remain separated by vertical plates of tissue called **pith rays** or *medullary rays*. The rays provide pathways for food and water at any level of the stem.

At intervals along the stem appear the **nodes**, where there are cross-connections between certain vascular bundles. At these points the vascular bundles extend into the leaf bases. These form the connections between the xylem and phloem of the stem and the veins of the leaf.

36.5 Structure of Monocotyledonous Stems

In the cornstalk, a monocotyledonous stem, the vascular bundles are scattered throughout the central pith. They have no definite position with reference to the center, except that the larger and older ones are arranged toward the center and the smaller and younger ones near the edge. The outside of the stem is covered with a hard **rind** which often con-

tains silica, a substance like glass which makes it hard and strong. The function of this rind is mainly to support the plant. In the monocot bundle there is usually no cambium. Some palms and lilies do have cambium, however.

In many grasses, the stem is hollow, and the bundles are around the edges, some of them passing off at each node into the leaf that arises from the node.

36.6 Structure of a Dicotyledonous Stem

External.—In the study of a woody

FIGURE 36-4. *MONOCOT STEM*

In addition to the few xylem cells in the scattered fibrovascular bundles, the hard rind of the monocot stem helps to support the plant. Notice the absence of the cambium.

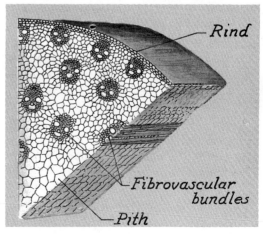

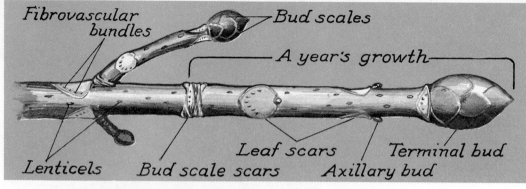

FIGURE 36-5. *YOUNG HORSE CHESTNUT STEM*

To the trained eye the details of this young stem or twig can tell a story of plant growth. The leaf scars, the terminal and axillary buds, the bud scale scars—all have a meaning and a function in the plant.

stem, let us examine twigs of birch, linden, maple, oak, poplar, or horse chestnut. You will note that on the outside is a brownish bark, some scars showing where leaves were, and some rings extending around the twig, indicating where the year's growth started (Fig. 36-5). Small markings on the smooth bark are **lenticels** (*len*-tih-sels), spots where the outer layer of the branch is broken, allowing air to enter the inner portions. Above each *leaf scar* is a bud covered with sticky scales; at the end of the branch is a large **terminal bud**.

The buds that grow above the leaves are called **axillary** (*ak*-sil-ayr-ee) **buds.** If more than one of these are found in an *axil,* the additional ones are called **accessory buds.** The strength of the terminal bud determines the stem's method of branching for if there is a good terminal bud, the main stem will continue to grow upward.

Buds which appear in other positions are called **adventitious buds.** They form on such leaves as the begonia and African violet. They often grow out as a sprout from a tree stump and from exposed parts of roots.

A bud which includes the stem tip is called a **foliage bud.** A bud which encloses the tiny parts of a flower is known as a **floral bud.** When a bud contains the parts of both leaves and flowers, such as an apple, it is called a **mixed bud.**

Very soon after the leaves have reached their full size in the spring, the buds for next season's stem and leaves are formed. Buds are protected in winter by coverings of scales which prevent them from becoming dry. A bud may contain stem and leaves only, or flowers only, or both.

Stems grow in length at the tips of the branches. New tissues are formed by cell division which takes place rapidly at the growing regions. Stems grow in diameter as a result of rapid cell division of cells in the cambium or growing layer.

Internal.—**Pith,** at the center of a stem (Fig. 36-6), is made up of large cells with thin walls. In the early stages of the plant's life, it serves as a place for the storage of food. Later it dies, and in an old stem often turns brown. Pith is smaller in an old stem than in a young one, as the woody layers crowd and compress it. Near the outside of the stem are the fibrovascular bundles. In a young stem, these lie in an incomplete ring with broad strips of pith between them.

As more fibrovascular bundles grow in a young woody stem, the rays of pith

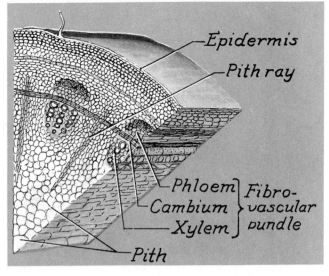

FIGURE 36-6. *DICOT STEM SECTION*

Vascular bundles are arranged around the outer part of the stem for up and down conduction while pith rays conduct materials crossways. Cambium cells between the xylem and phloem enable the stem to grow in width.

between them are gradually compressed, forming narrow radiating lines extending towards the bark. In older stems similar lines, originating in the cambium, extend towards the pith. Both of these are known as **medullary** (*med*-yoo-lair-ee) **rays** (Fig. 36-6), cells of a special kind, the functions of which are to store food and to form a connection between the outer and the inner parts of the stem.

The **bark** of an older stem and the *epidermis* of a young stem protect them from drying out, from the attacks of insects, and from the entrance of bacteria, spores, and fungi. Because of the porous structure of the bark and epidermis, they also admit air to the interior of the stem. All these parts, pith, woody portion (xylem), phloem, medullary rays, and epidermis or bark, combine to make up the stem, and at the same time each has a definite service to perform in the life of the whole plant.

36.7 Functions and Adaptations of Stems

The stem, as we have learned, is used for the support and attachment of leaves, and to provide a path for the vessels that carry water from the roots where it is gathered, to the leaves, where most of it is used. Another use of stems is for the

FIGURE 36-7. *WATER STEMS*

The stem of the water lily is adapted to its life in the water. Traversed by longitudinal air passages, it carries air to the thick, fleshy rootstock embedded in the mud.

497

FIGURE 36-8. *WOODY STEM*

By counting the annual rings in this cross section of a woody stem you can tell the age of the tree from which it came. What kind of cells compose woody tissue? What is their function?

storage of food, as in the potato. A few plants make use of stems for propagation, as in the case of the strawberry and the black raspberry.

The stem is adapted to its work (1) in being compact and sturdy, able to bear weight; (2) in branching, which usually affords a larger number of points for the attachment of leaves and a larger space in which to display them; (3) in being covered with a strong epidermis or, in woody stems, with bark which protects it from outside injury and keeps it from drying up; (4) in plants which grow in the water, in having large air spaces to carry air to the roots which lie in the mud at the bottom of the water; (5) in being provided in some cases with thorns or briers, as in the blackberry and rose, to protect it from being injured by animals.

The hard outer rind makes a monocotyledonous stem rigid, and the pith makes it light. Monocotyledonous stems are usually tall and slender and do not sustain great weight. A dicotyledonous stem is usually stouter, and its woody structure enables it to bear a heavy load of leaves and fruit.

36.8 Growth of Stems

Most woody plants grow rapidly in the spring and early summer, after which they stop increasing in size but continue to add material within the limits attained. This makes wood and enables the stems to resist being killed in the winter. Such plants are said to have a **definite annual growth,** a process illustrated by most woody trees. The advantages of definite annual growth are that: (1) it enables a tree to grow very rapidly in the spring when conditions are most favorable for growth; (2) it does not result in loss of any wood once formed.

Some plants continue to grow until the end of the season. The ends of the twigs in such plants, with the buds on them, are usually killed by the frost. The plant begins to grow next season from axillary buds below the point where it was killed. Such plants are said to have **indefinite annual growth.** Examples are red raspberry and sumac.

The plant which makes an indefinite annual growth can take advantage of favorable growing conditions whenever they occur, although it may lose some of its youngest wood if frost comes before the wood is hard enough to resist it.

In the annual growth of woody stems, a new part is added to each branch and a new layer of wood to each stem. This makes it possible to estimate how many years old a tree is for the growth of each year forms an **annual ring** (Fig. 36-8) more or less distinct according to conditions. When the conditions for growth are at their best, the cells formed are large. As conditions become less favorable, the cells become smaller and have

498

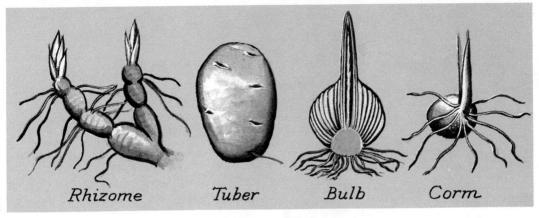

FIGURE 36-9. *UNDERGROUND STEMS*

Four kinds of underground stems are illustrated by: (*left to right*) Solomon's seal; the potato; the hyacinth; and the crocus. Notice the aerial branches on the rhizome, Solomon's seal (a member of the lily family).

thicker walls, marking distinctly the end of one season's growth from the beginning of the next. The size of the cells varies greatly in different trees, and this variation produces the different "grains" of lumber.

36.9 The Duration of Stems

The length of life of a stem depends upon the plant's method of producing seeds. An annual or herbaceous stem, like the morning-glory or corn, dies at the end of the first season, the plant having produced its seeds. Other stems, like trees, last year after year. The giant sequoia, a relative of the redwood trees in California, is more than three thousand years old, as is the cedar of Lebanon in Asia Minor.

36.10 Kinds of Stems

Plants which develop tall, woody stems capable of standing erect without support are called *trees*. Those which develop relatively short, woody, and usually freely branched stems are known as *shrubs*. Plants whose stems develop a small proportion of xylem, the stems frequently remaining relatively soft, are called *herbs* (*erbs*). Weak-stemmed

plants that attach themselves to supporting objects such as other plants and so attain an approximately upright position are known as *vines*.

You are familiar with trees such as elm, maple, pine, or hemlock. Lilacs, syringas, and hydrangeas are shrubs. Daisies, mints, burdocks, and mullein are examples of herbs. Morning-glory, ivy, and grape are vines. The morning-glory and lima bean are able to climb by twining their stems. The garden pea has tendrils which are formed by the leaves; the grape has tendrils formed by its branches. The English ivy climbs by aerial roots.

36.11 Underground Stems

An underground stem can always be distinguished from a root by the buds of new shoots or the scars of old leaves, although in some stems the leaves are reduced to mere scars, as in the potato. Underground stems usually send up aerial shoots. They often have an advantage over an *aerial stem* in being better protected. Some plants make use of the underground stem in propagating themselves.

Canada thistles, quack grass, and

FIGURE 36-10.
STRAWBERRY

The strawberry plant sends out slender runners or *stolons* during the season when the fruit is developing. These runners grow on the ground and send out roots in the soil from which new plants are produced.

Photo by Hugh Spencer

devil's-paintbrush are among the most difficult weeds to eradicate because of their branching, underground stems, each piece of which when broken off can form a new plant. In digging dandelions from lawns, care must be taken to cut deeply enough to remove the whole crown of the plant, otherwise the injured part branches and forms a weed more troublesome than the original one.

Some underground stems become thickened throughout their length and swollen with food as in the trillium and Solomon's seal. These are called **rhizomes**. Others, like the potato, become enlarged at the tip and form **tubers** (*toobers*).

When the base of the stem serves as storage for food, it is called a **corm**. It is usually covered with scalelike leaves. The gladiolus, crocus, and adder's tongue are examples. Food stored in the leaves of an underground stem, as in the onion, hyacinth, and tulip, forms a **bulb**.

36.12 Stems along the Ground

Strawberries, creeping bent grass, and others produce long stemlike branches called **runners** or **stolons** which run parallel to the ground. At intervals roots and leaves are produced. They form new plants which have the characteristics of the parent plant.

36.13 Stems as a Means of Propagation

New plants may start to grow from certain stems, from leaves, or from roots. This is called **vegetative propagation** because it does not involve the seeds of the plant. Raspberries, young grapes, boxwood, and roses often produce long upright branches which may be bent to the ground to start new plants. This is called *layering*. New shoots may spring up from underground stems; new roots may grow from trailing stems; or bulbs may store food for the next year's growth. This is a natural method of producing more plants.

When man starts a new plant from a leaf, stem, or root the process is called *artificial vegetative propagation*. Some of the common methods include cutting or slipping, layering, and the use of bulbs, runners, rhizomes, and corms.

Slipping plants is a common practice, the success of which is due to the fact that new roots, called *adventitious* roots, grow readily from the cut end of a branch of geranium, balsam, ivy, and some other plants. Two advantages make slipping popular: (1) the certainty of securing a new plant like the parent plant, (2) the short time required to produce blooms compared with that for the same kind of plant raised from the seed. Willow twigs root so readily that it is often possible to start a hedge by sticking pieces of branches into the ground when it is very wet.

36.14 Grafting

Sometimes a man wishes to grow two kinds of apples or other fruit on the same tree, or he wishes to put a more desirable fruit on a tree which is already growing, in order to have it ready to bear fruit in less time. To do this he cuts from the new fruit a small branch bearing one or more buds called a **scion** (*sy*-un) and places it on the **stock** (the tree already there). The main bud of the scion becomes the terminal shoot of the new plant. He must be careful to place the cambium layers together, since that is the only method the stem has of growing. To hold the two parts together, he uses strong binding tape. Before he puts it on, however, he puts grafting wax around the cut portions of the two pieces to prevent the action of bacteria or fungi which might cause disease. Thus one branch of his apple tree may bear Northern Spies, the original apples, and the other branch may have Cortland apples.

Grafting is used to propagate such seedless plants as seedless grapes and seedless oranges.

36.15 Budding

Apples grown from seed are called "native fruit," and are often small, sour, and undesirable as human food. In order to grow better fruit, when the tree is small, a single leaf bud is cut from an apple tree known to be good, for instance, a Baldwin. The bud is then placed in a slit in the bark of a *seedling*.

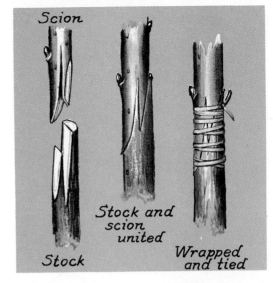

FIGURE 36-11. *SCION GRAFTING*

A twig, or scion, is cut from a tree and inserted in a cleft made in the stock, with the cambium layers placed together.

This is called **budding.** If it has been done carefully, this bud will live and unite with the stock upon which it has been budded. Then all the rest of the tree above the bud is cut off and the gardener has a tree bearing only one kind of fruit.

FIGURE 36-12. *BUDDING*

These familiar varieties of apple are propagated by budding, a kind of grafting. Other fruit trees and many ornamental plants are also grown in this way.

Ohio Agricultural Station

FIGURE 36-13. *VALUABLE DRIP*

Turpentine is made from a resinous sap obtained from the pine tree. Here the gummy resin drips into the waiting cup.

In nurseries thousands of these little seedlings a year or two old are budded to produce well-known varieties. These are then distributed to fruit growers throughout the country. The favorite apples have names to distinguish them in the market. Some of the best known are the Baldwin, Greening, Northern Spy, Delicious, Winesap, McIntosh Red, Wealthy, and Spitzenburg. Orange and other fruit trees are commonly propagated by budding.

36.16 Specialized Stems

In regions where the climate is very hot and dry most of the year, the leaf surface is greatly reduced to prevent undue evaporation. In this case the stem becomes green and performs the work of photosynthesis (Sec. 37.10), ordinarily done by leaves. The cactus illustrates this. Asparagus also has no leaves, but the stem branches in such a way as to resemble leaves.

Some stems store water for use during the dry season. In desert regions the natives cut off the tips of the stems of cacti, loosen the pulp with a stick, and squeeze out water to drink. In tropical regions, sections of certain woody vines are cut and used as a source of drinking water.

36.17 Value of Stems to Man

Man uses some stems for *food,* the white potato being one of the most familiar. The stems of asparagus, celery, and kohlrabi are valuable food. The sap from the maple tree and the juice of the sugar cane supply much of the sugar we use. Cinnamon bark is used for flavoring. Chewing gum is made from chicle from the sapodilla tree; spruce gum from spruce trees. Rubber is manufactured from the sap of rubber trees which are grown in the East Indies and South America.

Stems are also used for *clothing.* The flax plant, which furnishes the material from which linen is made, is one of the most valuable. The usefulness of flax depends upon strong fibers called *bast fibers,* which are found in the outer part of the slender stem and serve to give it stiffness. When separated from the other parts of the stem, they can be twisted, spun, and woven.

The stems, as well as the leaves, of peppermint, boneset, wormwood, catnip, foxglove, and other plants are used as *medicine.* Quinine from cinchona bark is valuable in the treatment of malaria. The bark of cherry and alder trees is used for cough remedies. Sandalwood produces a volatile oil used for colds. Camphor from the laurel tree and witch hazel from the witch hazel shrub are also used in medicine.

Stems are widely used in *industry.* All kinds of ropes and many kinds of strings

502

are made from fibers of hemp and other plants. The bark of hemlock, chestnut, quebracho, and willow are used in tanning. Logwood chips for dyes for red and black, indigo stems and leaves for blue, and gamboge for yellow have proved very useful. Resins, gums, and waxes are produced by tropical trees and are used in the making of paints and varnishes.

Trunks of trees are also stems of plants. They have so many uses that they are described separately in Chapter 40, page 547.

FACTS TO REMEMBER

The principal functions of stems are to (1) support the leaves, (2) transport liquids, (3) manufacture and store food, and (4) produce new plants vegetatively.

A *monocotyledonous,* or *herbaceous, stem* consists of *fibrovascular bundles* of xylem and phloem cells scattered throughout the central *pith.* The outside of the stem is covered with a *rind* for support.

A *dicotyledonous,* or *woody, stem* consists of fibrovascular bundles of xylem, phloem, and *cambium* cells arranged in circular zones outside the pith. *Rays* extend from the pith to the outer part of the stem for conduction of materials across the stem. The *bark* protects the stem and contains *lenticels,* which admit air to the interior of the stem.

Dicot stems *increase in diameter* by rapid growth of the cambium layer. They *increase in length* by cell division of the *terminal bud.* Other *buds* indicate where new branches, leaves, or flowers appear.

Plants with a *definite annual growth* grow only at certain times of the year, whereas plants with an *indefinite annual growth* grow whenever conditions are favorable.

Stems vary in the strength and support which they give the plant. Such stems may be *trees, shrubs, herbs,* or *vines.*

Stems are used for *vegetative propagation* by *layering, slipping, grafting,* or *budding.*

Stems are useful to man as important sources of food, clothing, medicine, and industrial raw materials.

WORDS TO REMEMBER

accessory bud	bulb	indefinite annual
adventitious bud	cambium	growth
aerial stem	corm	layering
annual ring	definite annual growth	leaf scar
artificial vegetative	dicotyledonous	lenticel
propagation	fibrovascular bundle	medullary ray
axil	floral bud	mixed bud
axillary bud	foliage bud	monocotyledonous
bark	grafting	node
bast fibers	herb	phloem
budding	herbaceous stem	pith

rhizome	sieve plate	tree
rind	sieve tube	tuber
runner	slipping	vegetative propagation
scion	stock	vine
seedling	stolon	woody stem
shrub	terminal bud	xylem

QUESTIONS

1. What is a stem? Name *two* kinds of stems.
2. State *two* uses of stems to plants.
3. Compare the fibrovascular bundles in a monocotyledonous plant with those of a dicotyledonous plant.
4. Explain how woody stems can readily increase in diameter.
5. How is it possible for plants to breathe through their stems?
6. How is a stem adapted to its work?
7. How could you distinguish a tree, a shrub, an herb?
8. Describe three methods of vegetative propagation.
9. What is definite annual growth? Indefinite annual growth? What are annual rings?
10. State at least six uses of stems to man.

COMPLETION TEST

As your teacher or classmate reads the following incomplete statements, with your book closed, write on a clean sheet of paper the word or phrase which correctly completes the statement.

1. Garden peas are able to climb by means of _____.
2. Roots which grow out from stems are called _____ roots.
3. The white potato is a _____ which forms on the stem.
4. Strawberries grow vegetatively by _____.
5. Man grafts the _____ on the stock.
6. The usefulness of flax depends upon the strength of its _____ fibers.
7. The bark of _____ is used in tanning leather.
8. The corn is an example of a _____ stem.
9. Annual rings are found in _____ stems.
10. Underground stems swollen with food are called _____.

PROJECTS

I. *To Show the Rise of Liquids through Stems.*—Place a living pea seedling in water containing eosin or red ink. If possible, use one that has been germinated in sawdust in a paper cup, make a hole in the bottom of the cup, and set it in a tumbler of water containing the eosin or red ink. After two or three hours note the presence of the stain in the stems and leaves.

Cut the stem in two and make a sketch of the cut surface. Through what part of the stem did the liquid rise? Color that part of your drawing red.

II. *The Study of Underground Stems.*—1. Draw a potato. Label the "eyes," buds. On which end are they more numerous? Label *scale,* just below bud. Note end where the potato was attached to the main plant.

2. Cut off the stem end and stand the cut surface of the potato in water colored with red ink. After two hours examine again and note what part is stained. Cut off slices till traces of color disappear. Draw to show where it is colored. Cut a thin slice and put a few drops of weak iodine on it. What happens? What does it show?

3. Cut an onion bulb vertically. Note the condensed stem on which the leaves are arranged.

III. *The Structure of a Woody Stem.*—1. Make a cross section of a limb of a tree from three to four inches in diameter. Cut it very carefully and as nearly at right angles as possible.

2. Examine it carefully and locate the following structures.

a. pith	*d.* phloem
b. medullary rays	*e.* xylem
c. cambium	*f.* bark

3. Draw the cross section and label the parts.

IV. *The Structure of a Corn Stem.*—1. Bring into the laboratory some corn stalks and cut cross sections.

2. Locate the rind, pith, and fibrovascular bundles.

3. Make a drawing of the cross section and label carefully.

REFERENCES

Bergen and Caldwell, *Practical Botany.* Ginn.

Collingwood, *Knowing Your Trees.* American Forestry Association, Washington, D. C.

Cook, *College Botany.* Lippincott.

Coulter, *Plant Life and Plant Uses.* Appleton.

Dural, Reynals, *The Fever Bark Tree—The Pageant of Quinine.* Doubleday, Doran.

Eyster, *College Botany.* Richard R. Smith.

Holman and Robbins, *A Textbook of General Botany.* Wiley.

Mottier, *College Textbook of Botany.* Blakiston.

Rigg, *College Botany.* Van Nostrand.

Robbins and Ramaley, *Plants Useful to Man.* Blakiston.

Robbins and Rickett, *Botany.* Van Nostrand.

Sargent, *Plants and Their Uses.* Holt.

Sinnott, *Botany—Principles and Problems.* McGraw-Hill.

Smith, Overton, and Others, *A Textbook of General Botany.* Macmillan.

Taylor, *Cinchona in Java—The Story of Quinine.* Greenberg.

Torrey, *General Botany for Colleges.* Century.

Transeau, *General Botany.* World Book.

Wilson, *Trees and Test Tubes—The Story of Rubber.* Holt.

CHAPTER 37

The Leaf Structure of Flowering Plants

37.1 The Flowering Plants

Vascular plants which produce flowers and seeds belong to the class **Angiospermae** (*an*-jee-oh-sperm-ee). They have well developed leaves, stems, and roots, and their seeds are enclosed in protective coats. Those vascular plants without protection for their seeds are called **Gymnospermae** (*jim*-noh-sperm-ee), and include the evergreen trees. Their seeds are produced in cones. We shall study the Gymnospermae in Chapter 40.

The flowering plants are the most highly developed of the plants. Their structures are specialized for particular functions. We shall study each of these separately: the leaf, flower, fruit and seed.

37.2 Leaf Structure

The beauty of flowers is highly enjoyable to us, but their leaves are very important. The leaf is the part of the plant which carries on many of its life processes. The food for the whole plant is manufactured in the leaves. Digestion takes place in the leaves, and there is circulation in the veins. Respiration and excretion are carried on chiefly in the leaves which have special structures to perform these functions.

The main part of a leaf is the **blade.** The stem by which it is attached to the twig is the **petiole** (*pet*-ee-ohl). This sometimes has small projections called **stipules** (*stip*-yools) at the base (Fig. 37-1). Leaves which lack petioles are called *sessile.*

The leaf of most plants contains **veins** which outline its main form, serve to keep it firm, and circulate water and food around the leaf. These are continuations of the fibrovascular bundles which run through the stem. There are two main types of arrangement of veins, called

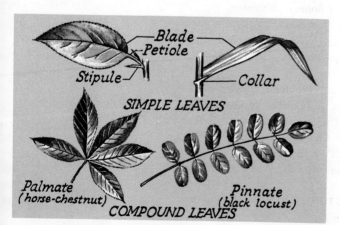

SIMPLE LEAVES

Palmate (horse-chestnut) Pinnate (black locust) COMPOUND LEAVES

Figure 37-1. *SIMPLE AND COMPOUND LEAVES*

The simple leaves at the top are (*left*) netted-veined and (*right*) parallel-veined. Compound leaves may either be *palmate*, with leaflets radiating from a central point, or *pinnate*, with leaflets arranged opposite each other on a central petiole.

506

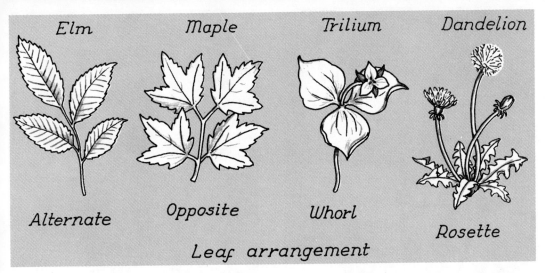

Elm   Maple   Trilium   Dandelion

Alternate   Opposite   Whorl   Rosette

Leaf arrangement

FIGURE 37-2. *LEAF ARRANGEMENTS*

Leaves are placed to take full advantage of air and sunlight. Tree leaves grow in alternate or opposite positions while leaves of plants which grow close to the ground often have a whorled or rosette arrangement.

venation (veh-*nay*-shun). In the first a few veins of about the same size run side by side straight from the base of the leaf to the tip. These are the *parallel-veined* leaves found in grasses, lilies, and most other *monocotyledonous* plants, that is, those which have only one seed leaf. In the second type, *dicotyledonous* plants, so called because they have two seed leaves, a few principal veins branch and divide, filling the spaces between them with a fine network of small veins. These are the *netted-veined* leaves found in roses, maple trees, daisies, and other dicotyledonous plants.

37.3   Simple and Compound Leaves

A leaf is said to be **simple** when the blade is all in one piece, and **compound** when it is divided into three or more leaflets. The apple, elm, oak, and maple have simple leaves; the clover, horse-chestnut, buckeye, and locust have compound leaves.

Compound leaves may be **pinnately** (pin-*ayt*-lee) **compound** when the leaflets are directly opposite each other or

alternate on the sides of a single midrib, as in the fern, the rose, and the ash; or **palmately** (*pal*-mayt-lee) **compound** when the leaflets radiate from a single common point, as in the horse chestnut, clover, and strawberry.

37.4   Leaf Arrangement

In general, leaves are arranged in three ways: (1) **alternate**—small leaves arranged spirally all along the length of a branch, the simplest example of which is found in the elm; (2) **opposite**— leaves arranged in pairs on a stem or on a branch, the pairs alternating as in the maple; and (3) **whorled**—three or more leaves at each node. In the first case the shape of the leaves is such that all the space on both sides of the twig is occupied without much overlapping; in the second, every leaf is fully exposed to the light, because the lowest pairs of leaves have the longest petioles; in the third, the space between the nodes is great enough to prevent shading those below.

A **rosette** (roh-*zet*) is formed by

THE LEAF STRUCTURE OF FLOWERING PLANTS   **507**

FIGURE 37-3. *MODIFIED LEAVES*

Fringed with sharp bristles and lined with sensitive hairs, the leaves of Venus's-flytrap (*right*) ensnare and digest insects. The spines of the cactus are modified leaves which conserve water and serve as protection to the plant.

leaves arranged spirally on a very short stem, with long petioles nearest to the ground, shorter ones alternating with them and filling the spaces. Lettuce leaves are arranged in a rosette.

Light that has passed through one leaf is of little value to a leaf below it. Some plants have finely divided leaves, as the carrot and yarrow, an adaptation which prevents any leaf from shutting off all the light from those below. Angular leaves, round leaves, and leaflets are all adaptations to use up space without overlapping. The leaves of ivy growing on a wall are so arranged as to fill all the spaces and not overlap. They form a **leaf mosaic** (moh-*zay*-ik).

Most of the grasses show adaptations (1) in having very narrow leaves, fitted to grow close together; (2) in having leaves with wavy edges if they are long, an adaptation which prevents their being torn by the wind; (3) in having a clasping base, strengthening the stem; and (4) in having a collar (Fig. 37-1) which prevents water from running down between the clasping base and stem.

Leaf Position and Movement.—Usually the position of leaves with reference to the stem is due to the fact that the light is brighter on one side of the plant than on the other. Some leaves on this account "follow the sun." Others, like the compass plant, turn only edges to direct sunlight. The clover and oxalis, which fold their leaflets at night, illustrate the "sleep movements" of plants.

Whatever the arrangement of leaves on any particular plant, the object of the arrangement is to expose the leaves most advantageously to light and air, and to prevent their shading one another.

THE VASCULAR PLANTS

37.5 Modified Leaves

Some leaves, as on the sundew, pitcher plant, and Venus's-flytrap, are adapted for catching insects for the plant's use as a nitrogenous food. In others, as clematis, the petioles are used to help the plant in climbing. In the case of the pea, leaves have become modified into *tendrils* which are used in helping the plant to climb. The tendrils of a kind of smilax and some kinds of ivy are also modified leaves. Still others have their leaves modified to thorns for protection, as in the thorny locust and barberry.

The cactus has some spines modified from leaves and others from branches. Some plants as the cabbage store food in the foliage leaves. Others as the onion use the inner leaves of the bulbs for food. Plants that live in dry regions, *xerophytes* (*zee*-roh-fytes), store water in their leaves and stems.

37.6 The Shedding of Leaves

The shedding of **deciduous** (deh-*sij*-oo-us) **leaves** (those which fall from the tree in autumn) is brought about by the growth of a layer of cells, the **abscission** (ab-*sis*-shun) **layer,** between the twig and the end of the petiole of the leaf. This seals the ends of the **vascular bundles** and loosens the leaves. Before a tree sheds its leaves, it withdraws all the food they contain and stores it in some other portion of the tree. What remains is largely the mineral matter that was not needed in the manufacture of food. This is waste, and so of no further use to the tree. The shedding of leaves thus serves two purposes—to reduce **transpiration** (*the loss of water by evaporation through the leaves*) during the period when water is not readily absorbed, and to get rid of waste.

The beautiful colors of autumn leaves are due to a combination of causes. The

A. Devaney, Inc., N.Y.

FIGURE 37-4. *AUTUMN LEAVES*

Their work at an end, leaves fall from the trees in autumn. Their bright colors are revealed when chlorophyll wanes.

normal green foliage color is due to a pigment called **chlorophyll** (*klor*-uh-fil), which is required for the normal food-making process of the plant. In addition to chlorophyll, the chloroplasts of the cell usually contain two other pigments —yellow **xanthophyll** (*zan*-thoh-fil) and yellow-orange **carotene** (*kar*-oh-teen). These are usually not visible because of the greater amount of chlorophyll. However, various weather factors in the autumn cause the green-colored material to decompose, thus unmasking the yellows and oranges. The brilliant reds are caused by other pigments, **anthocyannins** (an-thoh-*sy*-an-ins), which are formed in the cell sap when cool weather slows down other leaf functions. Copper beeches have some of this pigment all year while maples form them only in cold weather. When all the leaf cells die and the pigments decompose, the leaves become brown.

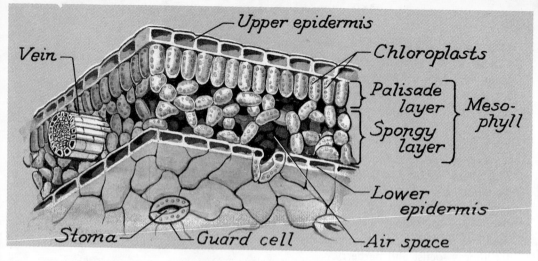

FIGURE 37-5. *INTERNAL LEAF STRUCTURE*

A leaf cut crosswise and studied under a microscope will be seen to have several layers of tissues and specialized cells. The plant respires and excretes through the stomata, usually located on the lower epidermis. The greatest number of chlorophyll bodies are contained in the palisade layer.

Some trees do not shed their leaves at one time. They form new leaves and shed old ones throughout the year. Holly, eucalyptus, orange, and live oak trees always remain green in this way.

37.7 Leaf Structure

A typical leaf is covered with a layer of thin cells called the **epidermis**. This is usually covered with **cutin** (*kyoo*-tin), a waxy substance which prevents excessive evaporation. Such plants as mullein and mint have leaves covered with hairs which are outgrowths of the epidermis. The epidermis on the under side of the leaf is thinner and has less cutin than that on the upper side. It is pierced by many openings called **stomata** (*stoh*-muh-tuh) or air pores, which allow the entrance and exit of air, water vapor, and other gases. The sugar content of the cells may affect the amount of water they take in or retain.

Between the two layers of epidermis is the **mesophyll** (*mes*-oh-fil) of the leaf, divided into two regions: (1) the **upper** or **palisade** (pal-uh-*sayd*), composed of slender, elongated cells placed side by side in an upright position, and (2) the **spongy layer** consisting of rounded cells, loosely arranged with many air spaces between them. The palisade layer cells contain the most chlorophyll pigment enclosed in small green **chloroplasts**.

37.8 How the Stomata Perform Their Function

The cutin of the epidermis prevents too rapid evaporation of water. In a leaf that extends horizontally from a plant, most of the stomata are on the under side, an adaptation which prevents their being closed by water or dust. In leaves that float on water, the stomata are on the upper surface. Plants with erect leaves have stomata distributed on both sides. In desert plants they are sunk below the level of the epidermis, or they are covered by hairs or wax, both of which tend to keep them from getting too wet or too dry.

The structure shows other adaptations. The opening is surrounded by two cells, called **guard cells**, which have the

510

property of absorbing water from the atmosphere. When these cells are full of moisture, they are plump or *turgid* (*ter*-jid); when they have only a little water, they are flabby or *flaccid* (*flak*-sid).

The turgid guard cells leave the stomata wide open and allow free passage of air into the cell, and of water and gases out of it. Flaccid guard cells, on the other hand, make the opening small, decrease the amount of air that enters, and prevent undue evaporation from the inside of the leaf. Although the stomata are very small, they are so numerous that their combined action accomplishes a great deal. A square inch of the under surface of a lilac leaf contains approximately 8250 stomata, that of white birch, 5925.

37.9   Functions of Leaves

Green leaves are chiefly concerned with two special processes: (1) *photosynthesis* or food-making and (2) *transpiration,* the loss of water from the leaves by evaporation. Leaves also carry on other life processes of the plant. These include (1) *respiration,* which takes place in all protoplasm; (2) *digestion,* changing foods to soluble form; (3) *circulation,* carrying water and food materials around; (4) *assimilation,* the growth and repair of protoplasm which is typical of all cells; (5) *excretion,* the removal of wastes; (6) *sensation,* the response of leaves in turning toward the light; and (7) *vegetative propagation,* the forming of new plants by sending out rootlike structures from the leaves.

These processes which are carried on by green leaves are of very great importance to man and other animals. Most important of all is the process of photosynthesis, since plants are the chief source of food in the world.

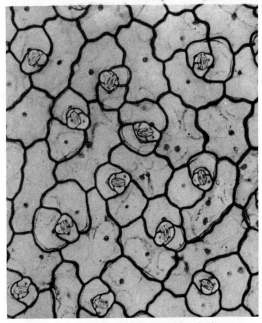

FIGURE 37-6.   *STOMATA*

The small oval openings on the lower epidermis of the leaf are controlled by two guard cells which contract and expand.

37.10   Photosynthesis, the Manufacture of Carbohydates

The word *photosynthesis* (*foh*-toh-*sin*-thuh-sis) means puttting together by light. Artificial light may be used, but sunlight is the usual source of the energy required. The raw materials are *carbon dioxide,* which plants obtain from the air, and *water,* which usually comes from the ground. The process can take place only in the presence of *chlorophyll,* the green pigment found in the chloroplasts of independent plants. The products are *carbohydrates,* such as sugar and starch. *Oxygen* is left over and released as a by-product. Thus we may define photosynthesis as *the manufacture of carbohydrates from carbon dioxide and water with the aid of chlorophyll and the energy of light.*

The mechanism of photosynthesis is quite complex. It involves a series of

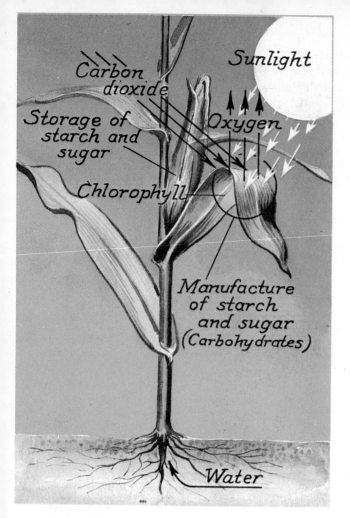

FIGURE 37-7.
PHOTOSYNTHESIS

Photosynthesis, the process of manufacturing sugar and starch from water and carbon dioxide, using energy from the sun, can be performed only by plants containing chlorophyll. The carbohydrates produced are either stored by the plant or used for growth and energy. An important by-product is oxygen, which is released into the air, and is useful to animals as well as plants.

chemical changes and energy transfers by which light energy is captured and stored up as chemical energy in the carbohydrates produced. Two distinct steps are recognized: (1) **photolysis,** which requires light, and (2) **carbon dioxide fixation,** which does not. In *photolysis,* light energy (chiefly the red and blue rays) activates the chlorophyll pigment and a series of electron transfers takes place which splits the water into hydrogen and oxygen. Gaseous oxygen is released but the active hydrogen is taken up by intermediate substances which act as hydrogen acceptors. In *carbon dioxide fixation,* this active hydrogen combines with carbon dioxide in a series of reactions which produce the carbohydrate glucose, $C_6H_{12}O_6$, and water. It is worth noting that the oxygen released in photosynthesis comes from the water in the light reaction rather than from the carbon dioxide, as was formerly supposed. Note also that water is re-formed in the dark reaction from the union of hydrogen with half of the oxygen in the carbon dioxide. The over-all reaction may be summarized by the chemical equation:

$$6\,CO_2 + 12\,H_2O \xrightarrow[\text{chlorophyll}]{\text{light energy}} C_6H_{12}O_6 + 6\,O_2 + 6\,H_2O$$

THE VASCULAR PLANTS

As glucose accumulates in the chloroplasts, much of it is carried away in solution through the conducting tissues to other parts of the plant, where it is used to supply energy for growth or stored for future needs. Some of it is turned into starch, a complex carbohydrate formed from the combination of a large number of molecules of glucose by the removal of water.

Photosynthesis takes place most rapidly in bright sunlight when the temperature is between 80° and 90° F. The limiting factor seems to be carbon dioxide since it occurs in such small quantities in the air.

37.11 Protein-Synthesis, the Manufacture of Protein

In the manufacture of carbohydrates by photosynthesis, carbon dioxide (CO_2) and water (H_2O) combine to form sugar and starch. Thus you will note that only the elements carbon (C), hydrogen (H), and oxygen (O) are needed in the manufacture of sugar and starch. This is also true in the production of fats and oils; but to form these, the elements are rearranged and combined in different proportions. In many plants of the lily family droplets of oil occur in leaf cells as storage products instead of starch.

Protein-synthesis, which is very necessary for plants, requires in addition to these same three elements, a number of other elements which usually enter with the soil water. Nitrogen (N) is needed in the largest amounts. Sulfur, phosphorus, calcium, potassium, magnesium, and iron are used in varying proportions by different kinds of plants. Soluble nitrates from the soil and sugar from the leaf combine to form *amino acids,* the substances from which proteins are made. The process by which they combine is very complicated.

Courtesy E. I. Du Pont de Nemours and Co.

FIGURE 37-8. *WITHOUT SOIL*

In *hydroponics,* minerals which normally reach the plant through soil water are supplied artificially.

One element always present in protein is nitrogen. Plants need nitrogen to manufacture proteins, with which they repair worn cells and build new ones. Most plants have to depend on the soluble nitrates and ammonium salts which enter with the soil water.

Legumes, such as clover, alfalfa, and beans, have nitrogen-fixing bacteria on their roots (Fig. 31-4). They gather nitrogen from the air and supply the plants with what they need while the roots give them moisture and shelter. This is another case of *symbiosis,* or mutual aid, among plants. Insectivorous plants secure some nitrogen by catching insects.

Plants also synthesize vitamins, hormones, organic acids, and *terpenes* which contain only carbon and hydrogen.

37.12 Transpiration

This is the process of evaporation of water from plants. Water, as vapor, escapes through the stomata. Transpiration is necessary because the roots

FIGURE 37-9. *TRANSPIRATION*

Drops of water collect on the inside of the bell jar over the plant (*right*) but not inside the one over the empty pot. How does this show that the plant loses excess water through the leaves?

water pores, at the ends of the veins. These contain cells which burst under pressure, allowing the water to exude. This process is known as **guttation** (guh-*tay*-shun), and the drops so formed are known as *guttation drops.*

Guttation drops are sometimes absorbed again by the plant and sometimes they evaporate, depending on the needs of the plant and the amount of moisture in the air. The amount of water that leaves a plant in a day by transpiration alone is very great. For example, a sunflower plant will give off a quart a day.

The rate of transpiration depends on the amount of light, relative humidity, air movement, and soil moisture. It also varies with the number of stomata per unit of leaf surface, their size and distribution, and the number, shape, and size of the leaves. When transpiration loss is too great, as on a warm, dry day, the plant cells lose their stiffness, or turgidity, and wilt.

of a plant usually take up more water than is needed for the life processes, and because this excess accumulates in spaces which communicate with the outside through the stomata. When transpiration is too rapid, the plant is deprived of needed water.

As we saw in Section 37.8, the position of the stomata on a leaf and their structure help regulate transpiration. A leaf may further check transpiration by changing its position or by rolling its edges together, as corn leaves do during a very dry period. Another device is seen in cactus plants. The leaves have a greatly reduced surface, but the stem in these plants is green and can do the work of leaves.

When the moisture in the air exceeds a certain quantity, evaporation does not take place readily. At such times too much water accumulates in the plant. To prevent damage from this condition, plants have modified stomata, called

37.13 Excretion

Plants, like animals, excrete or remove from their system substances which are harmful or no longer of use to the plant. These are not always removed promptly, but are sometimes stored where they can do no harm. An example of this is the crystals of calcium oxalate which give to sorrel, or sour grass, its sour taste.

37.14 Digestion

Plants, like animals, cannot absorb some kinds of food until they have been digested (Section 22.1). This process takes place chiefly in the leaf, but also in other organs. The digested food is carried through the vascular bundles to all parts of the plant which need it. Digestion in plants is less well understood than it is in animals. It is known that the enzyme *amylase* (also called *diastase*) is secreted by the protoplasm of the cells and digests starch. Another enzyme, *starch phosphorylase,* digests starch by adding phosphoric acid. This forms glucose phosphate which has high chemical bond energy. The enzyme *maltase* changes the double sugar, maltose, to the simple sugar glucose; *sucrase* acts similarly on sucrose. *Cellulase* changes cellulose to glucose. Enzymes known as *proteinases* prepare proteins for absorption while *lipases* act on facts.

37.15 Circulation

Circulation in plants differs from circulation in animals in not having any central organ, as a heart, for keeping the fluids in motion. **Sap** (the fluid in plants) is moved by the combined influence of root pressure created by osmosis, transpiration, and other factors. The tubes of the xylem carry water taken up by the roots from the soil to the leaves, where it is combined with carbon dioxide from the air and built up into foods. The digested foods are carried in the phloem part of the vascular bundle from the leaf to the parts of the plant which need them.

37.16 Respiration

The release of energy in living cells by respiration involves many complex reactions. Glucose is first changed into pyruvic acid by *glycolysis,* a process which requires no oxygen. The pyruvic acid undergoes a series of changes in the presence of free oxygen to form carbon dioxide and water as the final products. Throughout these changes, energy is released gradually by the action of the respiratory enzymes located in the mitochondria of the living cells.

In aerobic respiration, the cells must have oxygen to combine with food, thus releasing energy for the work

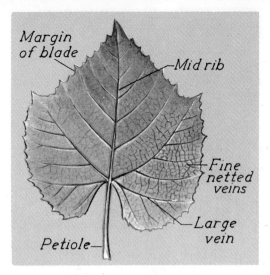

FIGURE 37-10. *LEAF BLADE*

The veins of a leaf are conducting vessels which carry soil water to the leaf, and send food and oxygen to other parts of the plant.

of the plant, and forming carbon dioxide and other wastes in the process. Air, entering through the stomata, furnishes oxygen for respiration as well as carbon dioxide for photosynthesis. Since oxygen is one of the wastes of photosynthesis, it is possible that some of it is used for respiration as soon as it is set free. Because of this, plant respiration is most easily studied in plants like mushrooms, which cannot perform photosynthesis, and in sprouting seedlings, which have not yet developed chlorophyll.

Certain vitamins are necessary for plants to use in making enzymes to help in respiration. Vitamin B_1 is needed for the enzyme which helps remove carbon dioxide. Vitamin B_2 is important in the removal of hydrogen during the oxidation of carbohydrates. Plant vitamins are being studied by scientists in their efforts to learn more about plant activities.

Anaerobic respiration is carried on without free oxygen. Rearrangement of molecular structure releases energy.

J. Horace McFarlane Company

FIGURE 37-11. *POISON IVY*

Because their tissues contain an oil very irritating to human skin, everyone should learn to recognize these shiny, green leaves arranged in groups of three.

Carbon dioxide is produced and other products such as alcohol or lactic acid found in milk. Fermentation of sugars by yeast is an example of this kind of respiration. Most higher plants respire by this method for a time if they are deprived of oxygen.

37.17 Assimilation

This is the actual use by the plant cells of such parts of the digested food as they need. By assimilation the old cells are repaired and new ones grow. As in animals, it is a building-up process which results in the growth of the plant, and which maintains it at that size when it reaches maturity.

37.18 Economic Uses of Leaves

The leaves and stalks of grasses are used as food for cattle. Man eats the leaves of lettuce, cabbage, spinach, endive, broccoli, parsley, chard, kale, and many others. The closely folded clusters of thick leaves of the onion which are formed underground are also eaten by man. Tea leaves are used for a beverage.

The leaves of wintergreen, spearmint, peppermint, sage, and thyme are used for flavoring. Menthol made from peppermint is used in medicines.

The leaves of tobacco are smoked for the temporary effect of the nicotine. The dried leaves of Indian hemp, known as marijuana (mair-uh-*wah*-nuh), contain an alkaloid that has a harmful effect on the nervous system.

In tropical countries some leaves, such as palms and grasses, are used for thatching, thus affording shelter. Sisal fibers used for binder twine are made from agave, which is native in Yucatan. Manila fiber is made from the petioles of abaca, a bananalike plant of the Philippines and Central America.

37.19 Poison Leaves

Poison ivy and *poison sumac* frequently cause painful irritation and inflammation of the skin of some people. Poison ivy may be recognized by its leaves, which are always divided into three leaflets. Its flowers, which appear late in the spring, are clusters of inconspicuous, greenish white bloom, followed by waxy white berries. Poisoning is caused by the penetration of the somewhat milky juice of the poison canals located in every part of the plant. The juice may enter the sweat glands, oil glands, hair follicles, or even the surface of the skin itself. Treatment usually consists in washing with strong soap solution or iron chloride and covering.

Poison sumac, a shrub with tall slender stems and leaves divided into seven to thirteen leaflets, arranged in pairs with a single leaflet at the end, should be avoided. The cream-colored fruits grow in loose clusters. Another species of sumac, often called "poison oak," causes skin irritations and discomfort. It is very wise to learn to recognize these and

THE VASCULAR PLANTS

other poisonous shrubs and thus avoid painful consequences.

37.20   Plants without Leaves

In plants like the cactus, the work usually done by leaves is performed by the stem. In asparagus the stem, which branches again and again, also serves as leaves, the true leaves being almost invisible scales.

Other plants which have scales instead of leaves are dodder and Indian pipe, both of which use food already prepared. The dodder is a parasite which takes nourishment from its host while the Indian pipe is a saprophyte which obtains food from humus or other organic material. Neither plant has chlorophyll, the substance that enables plants to make their own food.

FACTS TO REMEMBER

Green leaves are the chief food-making structures of the plant. They carry on other important life processes as well.

The external structure of a leaf consists of a *blade, petiole,* and *veins.* The leaf is *simple* or *compound* depending on whether the blade is all in one piece or divided into three or more leaflets. The veins may be *parallel* to each other or *netted.*

Leaves are arranged on a stem so as to obtain the maximum amount of light and air. The three principal leaf arrangements are *alternate, opposite,* and *whorled.* Some leaves have a *rosette* arrangement while others form a *leaf mosaic.*

Leaves may be modified to perform specific functions. Some serve to catch insects, some form tendrils for climbing, some form thorns and spines, and some store food.

Trees shed their leaves by forming a layer of cells, the *abscission layer,* at the ends of the vascular bundles between the twig and petiole of the leaf. This shedding reduces the loss of water by evaporation and gets rid of waste.

The internal structure of a leaf consists of the *upper epidermis* with its coating of *cutin,* the *palisade cells,* the *spongy layer,* and the *lower epidermis.* The *stomata,* which are cells located on the epidermis, control the rate of evaporation of water from the leaf, and also serve as pores for the exchange of gases.

In the process of *photosynthesis,* carbon dioxide and water are combined in the presence of chlorophyll and sunlight to form sugar and starch. *Protein-synthesis* is the manufacture of protein from the elements used in making carbohydrates, with the addition of substances such as nitrogen, sulfur, phosphorus, calcium, potassium, and others.

Transpiration is the process by which plants give off excess water through the stomata in the leaves.

In addition to the principal functions of photosynthesis and transpiration, leaves also carry on the life processes of respiration, digestion, circulation, assimilation, excretion, sensation, and vegetative propagation.

Leaves are important to man as primary sources of food, flavoring, medicine, thatching materials, and twine.

WORDS TO REMEMBER

abscission layer
alternate
amino acids
Angiospermae
blade
carbohydrate
carbon dioxide
  fixation
chlorophyll
chloroplast
compound leaf
cutin
deciduous leaves
epidermis
flaccid
glucose

glycolysis
guard cell
guttation
Gymnospermae
leaf mosaic
mesophyll
netted veins
opposite
palisade layer
palmately compound
parallel veins
petiole
photolysis
photosynthesis
pinnately compound
protein-synthesis

rosette
sap
simple leaf
spongy layer
starch
stipule
stomata
tendril
transpiration
turgid
vascular bundles
vegetative propagation
vein
venation
whorled
xerophytes

QUESTIONS

1. Name six functions carried on by leaves.
2. What is the object of various arrangements of plant leaves?
3. Mention two of the most common forms of leaf arrangement and give examples.
4. Explain what is meant by each of the following:
   - a. netted-veined leaf
   - b. parallel-veined leaf
   - c. simple leaf
   - d. compound leaf
   - e. sleep movement
   - f. leaf mosaic
   - g. rosette
   - h. tendril
   - i. thorn
   - j. guttation
5. State two reasons why trees shed their leaves.
6. Describe the structure of a leaf.
7. What two purposes are served by veins?
8. Mention at least four plants which have peculiar leaves. Describe each leaf and tell how it helps the plant.
9. Name as many uses of plant leaves as you can.
10. How do plants without leaves obtain their food?
11. Describe the process of photosynthesis.

COMPLETION TEST

As your teacher or classmate reads the following incomplete statements, with your book closed, write on a clean sheet of paper the word or phrase which correctly completes the statement.

1. The "stem" of the leaf is called the _____.
2. Small projections at the base of a leaf are called _____.

3. When the blade is all in one piece, the leaf is said to be _____.
4. The leaves of the sundew are modified for _____.
5. The act of sending off water vapor by plants is called _____.
6. The covering of the leaf is the _____.
7. Guard cells regulate the size of the _____.
8. When cells are full of moisture, they are stiff or _____.
9. The by-product of photosynthesis is _____.
10. The enzyme in plants that digests starch is _____.

PROJECTS

I. *Plant Movements.*—Place young seedlings in a window for a day. Which way do they turn? Turn the plants around and note how long it takes them to change.

Observe leaves of clover and young daisy blossoms. Do they change their positions with the sun? Do other plants do this? Does the age of the plant make any difference in its ability to change position?

Bend a grass stem and fasten it flat. After a day or two observe its position. What changes have taken place?

II. *Structure of Leaves.*—Study a section of a leaf and test every statement in this chapter about the structure of leaves.

Stand a stalk of celery in water tinted with red ink. Observe closely. Cut across it after two hours and observe the position of the vascular bundles. Trace them into the leaf.

Study a bit of epidermis with a microscope. Draw. Label stomata, epidermal cells, guard cells (2 around each stoma). Study a cross section. Label *cuticle* (outermost layer), *epidermis* (upper and under surfaces), *palisade layer* (under top epidermis), *spongy layer* (body of leaf), *vein*. Which cells contain chlorophyll? Where are the air spaces?

III. *Arrangement of Leaves.*—Pull up or cut off a large burdock plant. Measure the area covered by the lower leaves. What else grew in this area? What is its condition? Why? What plants form rosettes of leaves in the fall?

Break off leaves of burdock, plantain, dock, and rhubarb. Note the strings (fibrovascular bundles).

Make a collection of leaves to illustrate the various kinds of shape, apex, margin, and base.

What effect does wind have in helping or hindering leaves in getting light? What happens when you make a "bag" from a leaf of live-for-ever?

IV. *Experiment to Show That Light Is Necessary for Photosynthesis.*—To show that light is necessary for photosynthesis, fasten thin discs of cork to the upper and under sides of a leaf with clips, completely shutting off the light. Stand the plant in the bright light for half a day, then remove the corks from the leaf and the leaf from the plant.

Heat enough 60% alcohol to cover the leaf in a shallow glass dish. This may be done by setting the dish in hot water. Keep hot for half an hour, or until the chlorophyll is removed from the leaf. Pour off the alcohol and put drops of weak iodine on the leaf. Note that the circle covered by the cork discs shows little starch or none, as indicated by the faint blue color or by lack of color.

Make a similar test by comparing a leaf from a plant that has been in the dark twelve hours with one that has stood in the bright light for the same time, using alcohol to remove the chlorophyll and iodine as a test for the presence of starch as before.

V. *Experiment to Show the Liberation of Gas during Photosynthesis.*—To test the nature of the gas given off by green plants in growing and making food, collect a quantity of algae, Elodea, or Sagittaria and place it in a deep glass jar in the sunlight. When bubbles begin to show, place an inverted funnel over the plants. Fill a test tube with water and invert it over the upright stem of the funnel. When an inch or more of the gas has collected in the test tube, remove it carefully, and thrust a glowing splint into it. Increased brightness of the glow or bursting into flame shows that oxygen is present.

REFERENCES

Bergen and Caldwell, *Practical Botany*. Ginn.
Conn, *Biology*. Silver, Burdett.
Cook, *College Botany*. Lippincott.
Coulter, Barnes, and Cowles, *Textbook of Botany*. American Book.
Curtiss, *Nature and Development of Plants*. Holt.
Eyster, *College Botany*. Richard R. Smith Company.
Gager, *Fundamentals of Botany*. Blakiston.
Kern, *The Essentials of Plant Biology*. Harper.
Mottier, *College Textbook of Botany*. Blakiston.
Rigg, *College Botany*. Lea and Febiger.
Sargent, *Plants and Their Uses*. Holt.
Sinnott, *Botany—Principles and Problems*. McGraw-Hill.
Transeau, *General Botany*. World Book.
Wilson and Loomis, *Botany*. 3rd Ed. Holt.

CHAPTER 38

Flowers and Fruits

38.1 The Plant Advertises

Although we all enjoy the color and odor of flowers, nature has a better reason than our enjoyment for making so many gaily-colored and sweetly-scented blossoms. The flower is the plant's reproductive organ, and it is often by the bright color or sweet odor that the flowers attract insects to help perform their function of producing seeds by distributing pollen from one plant to another.

After the flower fades, the plant develops not only seeds, each containing a new plant and food for its early life in the soil, but also fruit, whose purpose is to protect the seeds for a time and finally to secure their distribution. Unless the flower develops into fruits containing seeds, it has not been of use to the plant which bore it.

38.2 Parts of a Flower

Select any typical flower for study and the identification of its parts. We shall describe the nasturtium, whose parts are common to most flowers.

Sepals (*see*-p'ls) are greenish, pointed, leaflike parts on the outside of the flower. Together they make up the **calyx** (*kay*-liks), which protects the rest of the flower while it is in the bud. When the flower is in full bloom, the calyx is on the lower side, hidden from view.

Petals are the larger parts, more showy because more brightly colored, which taken together make up the **co-rolla** (kor-*ol*-luh), above the calyx.

Stamens (*stay*-mens) are the slender organs which surround the central portion of the flower. A stamen has two parts, the **filament** or stalk, and the **anther** or box at the top, which contains the **pollen**.

The **pistil** is the central portion of the nasturtium and consists of three parts. At the top is (1) the **stigma,** below it (2) the **style,** which connects the stigma with the lowest part, (3) the **ovary.** A

FIGURE 38-1. *GERANIUM*

The wild geranium is a shade-loving woodland flower which grows best in the rich soil formed by decaying leaves.

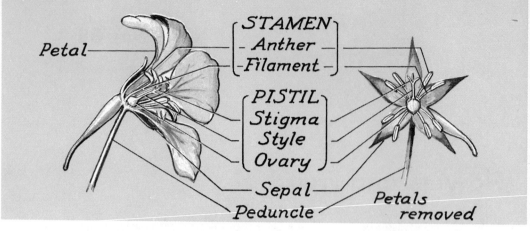

FIGURE 38-2. *NASTURTIUM FLOWER*

This drawing of a familiar garden flower shows the reproductive parts of the plant. The flower on the left with one petal and sepal removed shows the position of stamens and pistils; at right, all petals have been removed.

pistil is composed of one or more *carpels* which bear *ovules*. A simple pistil has one carpel, as in the bean or pea. A compound pistil has several carpels fused together, as in tulips and lilies.

The sepals and the petals are called **accessory parts;** the stamens and the pistil are **essential parts,** since they are necessary for the production of seeds. The nasturtium is a **perfect** flower, because it has both stamens and pistil; it

FIGURE 38-3. *VITAL ORGANS*

The pistil and the stamen are necessary for the production of seeds, and are found in every perfect flower. The pistil has three parts: stigma, style, and ovary.

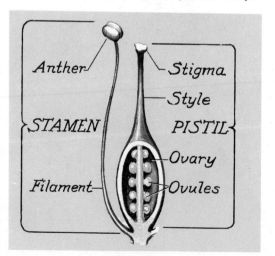

is also a **complete** flower, because it has petals and sepals as well. **Imperfect** flowers are either *staminate* (with stamens only) or *pistillate* (with pistils only). Plants which have separate staminate and pistillate flowers on the same plant are called *monoecious* plants. Those which have staminate and pistillate flowers on separate plants are called *dioecious* plants.

Besides the four principal parts (calyx, corolla, stamens and pistil) found in nasturtium flowers, other parts will be found in certain flowers. The *receptacle* (rih-*sep*-tuh-k'l), for example, is the expanded top of the stalk, or *peduncle* (peh-*dunk*-'l), on which the floral organs are placed (Fig. 38-11). It may be egg-shaped as in buttercups, or large and fleshy as in strawberries, or hollow as in the fig, where the pistils arise from its inner surface. A long hollow extension of a sepal or a petal is called a *spur,* as can be seen on the nasturtium. Violets, snapdragons, toad flax, and larkspur also have spurs. *Nectar glands,* usually found near the base of a flower, are commonly present in those flowers which are adapted to attract insects.

522

In the tulip and lily, the six parts of the same color, size, and shape make up the *perianth* (*pehr*-ee-anth), the calyx and corolla taken together. Because of the even size and regular shape of the parts of the perianth of the lily, we speak of it as a **regular** flower. The perianth is an *accessory* part of the flower, for seeds can be made without it, the stamens and the pistil being the only *essential* parts.

38.3 Functions of the Parts of a Flower

The *sepals* are adaptations that protect the inner organs in the bud while they are developing, and the *petals* are adaptations that attract insects which distribute the pollen. Sometimes one set of organs is lacking and sometimes another. Very often, sepals are colored and serve as petals.

Stamens produce **pollen,** the male reproductive grains containing sperm nuclei, which are necessary for the production of seeds.

In the *ovary,* the expanded base of the pistil, are found the **ovules** (*oh*-vyools), which contain the egg cells and become seeds if fertilized by pollen which has come to it by way of the *stigma* and the *style.*

When a flower has finished its work, namely, has secured fertilization of the egg cells in its ovules, its showy parts, if it had any, wither, and *fruit* begins to form. Usually only the ovary enters into the fruit; but in some cases, the receptacle is included.

38.4 Types of Flowers

Composite flowers is the term that is applied to flowers in which tiny individual flowers are closely crowded or grouped into a head, on a common receptacle. Such is the dandelion or the

J. Horace McFarland

FIGURE 38-4. *ASTER*

The aster is a composite flower. *Ray* flowers radiate from a central part, which is composed of *disc* flowers.

daisy, each group or head being commonly called a flower.

Two kinds of flowers are to be found in these heads, *tubular flowers,* that is, with the corolla a tube, and *strap-shaped* flowers in which the corolla is long and slender. Some composite flowers, like the dandelion, have only the strap-shaped, and others, like the thistle, only the tubular kind. Still others, like the common daisy and the sunflower, have both kinds. In the daisy, the tubular flowers, found only in the middle, are called *disc flowers.* These make up the yellow part of the group. Outside of them are the white, strap-shaped kind, known as the *ray flowers.* In sunflowers the disc flowers are brown; the ray flowers yellow.

Most flowers are borne at the tips of branches. Each flower or cluster of flowers is called an **inflorescence** (in-flor-*ess*-enss). The flower stalk is a *peduncle.* In flower clusters, the main

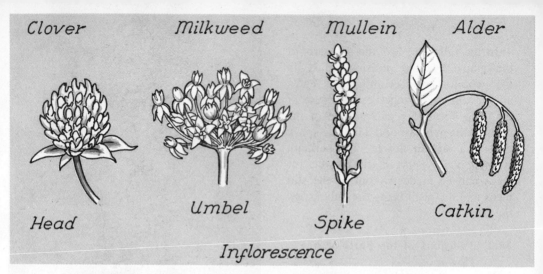

FIGURE 38-5. *TYPES OF INFLORESCENCES*

Flowers may be arranged in clusters in various ways. The separate flowers of a head and umbel branch from a central point while those of a spike and catkin grow along the length of a slender stalk.

flower stalk is the peduncle but each smaller stalk that bears a single flower

FIGURE 38-6. *POLLINATION*

A pollen grain on the stigma of a pistil produces a pollen tube containing sperm nuclei, one of which will accomplish fertilization of the egg; the other sperm nucleus unites with the polar nuclei of the egg to form the endosperm.

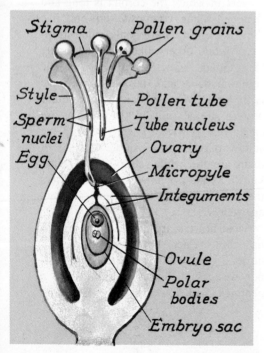

in the cluster is a *pedicel* (*peh*-dih-sel). Flower stalks grow from the axils of the leaves.

Some flowers, as willows and alders, are borne in *catkins.* Others form *spikes,* as mullein. Clover forms a *head,* and milkweed, an *umbel.* These are different types of inflorescence.

38.5   Pollination

Insects go to a plant in order to get nectar. The plant takes advantage of this by adaptations which help the insect to become covered with pollen as it leaves the flower. Other adaptations make it possible for the insect entering a flower to leave some of the pollen from the flower last visited on the stigma of the one which it is entering (Fig. 11-5).

This **pollination** (pol-ih-*nay*-shun) is only the first step in the production of a seed. Before we can understand the use of pollination, we must understand the structure of the pollen grain and the ovule.

Pollen grains vary greatly in size, structure, and markings, but all have

524

some features in common. They all have a double coat or covering, the outer side of which is thin in places. The *ovule* consists of a central mass attached to the ovary wall by a stalk and surrounded by two cellular membranes called **integuments** (in-*teg*-yoo-ments) which later form protection for the seeds. At the end opposite the point of attachment is an opening into the ovule, the **micropyle** (*my*-kroh-pyle).

When a pollen grain is caught on a sticky stigma, it soon sprouts, or germinates; that is, the inner coat pushes out through the thin places in the outer coat, producing a **pollen tube.** This contains the protoplasm of the pollen grain and three nuclei. Two of these are the **sperm nuclei** and the other is the **tube nucleus,** which governs the growth of the pollen tube until it has passed through the micropyle of the ovule and entered the **embryo sac.** When ready for fertilization, the embryo sac contains eight identical nuclei. Three of them are at the micropylar end of the embryo sac. One of these is the **egg nucleus.** The other two, and the three nuclei at the opposite end from the micropyle, do not take part in fertilization. The two remaining nuclei near the center are the **polar nuclei.**

One of the two sperm nuclei unites with the egg nucleus in the process known as **fertilization.** The other sperm nucleus unites with the two polar nuclei to form stored food, or **endosperm.** These two fusion processes are called **double fertilization** and must take place within every ovule before a seed will develop. The fertilized egg cell within the ovule at once begins to divide in the process of forming a new plant, while the ovule develops into a seed.

Cross-Pollination.—This is the term applied to the transfer of pollen from

Germanier from National Audubon Society

FIGURE 38-7. *PASSIONFLOWER*
The needle-like projections on this delicately intricate flower are the insect-attracting "nectaries."

one plant to another. It is accomplished most often by means of various insects or by the wind. Water carries pollen to some plants that live in it. Hummingbirds, snails, and bats also aid in the transfer of pollen. Pollen that is scattered by wind has two adaptations: (1) it is very abundant, for much of it will be lost; (2) it is light, so that it may be easily carried. Flowers that are wind-pollinated usually lack odor, color, and accessory parts, but they have adaptations in the stigmas, which are either plumy or feathery or broad and sticky, the better to catch and hold the pollen grains brought to them by the wind. The chief value of cross-pollination is the production of *variations.* Seeds formed as a result of cross-pollination produce

Courtesy U.S. Dept. of Agriculture

Courtesy U.S. Dept. of Agriculture

FIGURE 38-8. *STAMINATE AND PISTILLATE FLOWERS*

In the corn plant, the tassels are clusters of stamens (*left*), while the corn silks are the styles and stigmas of the pistils (*right*). The silks are attached to the young corn grains, which function as ovaries.

a larger number of variations in plants than those which grow from seeds in self-pollinated flowers.

Self-Pollination and Its Prevention.— Some flowers that never completely open, such as the violet, are adapted to insure self-pollination. Most flowers, on the other hand, have adaptations to prevent self-pollination.

One of these devices is the production of only **pistillate** flowers (bearing pistils only) on one plant and of only **staminate** flowers (with stamens only) on another plant. The willow illustrates this. A second adaptation is the maturing of the pistils and stamens at completely different times.

A third device is long stamens and a short pistil on some flowers and short stamens and a long pistil on others.

When an insect visits such a flower as the primrose, one part of its body is apt to come into contact with the stamens and another with the pistil. *Self-sterility* occurs in rye, where the pollen will not grow on the stigmas of its own flowers. Orchids are *self-poisonous,* a condition in which the pollen is poisonous to the stigma of the same flower.

Artificial Pollination. — In artificial pollination, pollen from one flower is carefully transferred by hand to the stigma of another flower of the same kind. Usually this flower has had its stamens removed before the pollen was ripe. The flower must be protected from the visits of insects after it has been pollinated artificially. Artificial pollination is practiced to develop new varieties of flowers, fruits, and vegetables.

THE VASCULAR PLANTS

Importance of Pollination. — Since pollen is necessary in the production of fruit, man takes steps to insure its transfer. When fruits are grown indoors or under glass it is necessary to hand-pollinate the flowers. To insure pollination of the apple blossoms hives of bees are placed in the orchards. Sometimes pollen is collected and shipped to greenhouses, for many pollen grains retain their viability (ability to maintain life) for a long time.

The presence of much pollen dust in the air is one of the causes of hay fever. People try to discover to which kinds of pollen they are most susceptible (allergic) so that they may avoid areas where that plant grows in abundance or receive injections which help them to overcome the allergy.

38.6   Adaptations for Pollination

The flower of the *nasturtium* offers a good example of adaptations. You will notice that (1) it has a striking color in contrast with the foliage. This enables insects to see it readily. (2) It has an odor. This enables insects that are guided largely by the sense of smell to find it. (3) It has a long nectar spur on one side of the flower. This attracts the larger insects for the food they can get. (4) The lower petals have an inner fringe which retards the crawling insects that are trying to get the nectar. (5) The upper petals project over the other parts of the flower. This keeps the rain from running down the nectar spur and prevents the pollen from becoming wet. (6) The upper petals have stripes that lead to the opening of the nectar spur. This indicates the direction that insects should travel to find the opening quickly. (7) The anthers mature at different times. This insures a supply of pollen on different days so that some of the pollen is always in condition to use, even if some has been spoiled by unfavorable weather. (8) The anthers and stigma mature at different times so that the pollen cannot get on its own stigma. Thus, in at least eight ways the nasturtium flower is adapted to the visits of insects and to the protection of its pollen and nectar.

Dandelion flowers have many adaptations. They are made up of many flowerets. The stamens are joined in a tube with the anthers opening on the inside. The anthers mature their pollen before the pistil of that floweret is ready for pollen. The pistil, with its stigmatic surfaces pressed tightly together, pushes up through the mass of pollen filling the tube and becomes covered on the *outside*. Insects crawling over the head

FIGURE 38-10. *ARBUTUS*

Trailing arbutus, a lovely creeping plant with dainty white or pink flowers, is found in eastern and central Canada and United States. Its existence is threatened in the United States by thoughtless people who are unwilling to forego the pleasure of picking it.

Oakes from National Audubon Society

drag some of these pollen grains to pistils of flowerets which are mature. When the pistil of any one floweret opens, pollen from its own anther is not likely to get on it, thus preventing self-pollination of the dandelion. These adaptations of the flowers help to make the dandelion one of the most successful of plants.

The *composite flowers,* those with tiny individual flowers grouped in a head, as a whole, show more adaptations than other flowers, so we find among them those that are of most interest to the scientist and of greatest annoyance to the farmer—dandelion, devil's-paintbrush, burdock, and thistles of all kinds. They are most successfully fought by not giving them opportunity to blossom and form fruit.

38.7 Conservation of Wild Flowers

We know the pleasure which our wild flowers give all lovers of nature. Animals and plants which do not harm us should be permitted to live. Game laws and animal preserves are helping to protect some of our rare animals that were being destroyed by man.

For many years flower protection organizations have been urging that more of the rarer wild flowers should be protected by law. You should do your part in

helping to make such legislation effective.

Because of the scarcity of tracts of wild land, particularly near cities, wild flowers will soon disappear, unless the public is educated to enjoy them without picking them. Little harm is done by picking the flowers of Trillium, because its thickened stem, deep in the ground, will put up another flower stalk the next year, if it has food enough stored away to enable it to do so. But it is difficult to pick arbutus blossoms without pulling up the long trailing stem, which then dies. Picking dogwood flowers destroys the attractiveness of this tree.

Since the seeds of the plant are developed in the flower, if you pick all the flowers, no seeds can be formed. Lovers of wild flowers are learning to enjoy their beauties where they grow.

38.8 Economic Value of Flowers

Many plants are cultivated for the pleasure their flowers give us. The vocation of florist has become a very profitable one.

Cauliflower, the buds of which are eaten, is the most familiar example of the use of flowers for food. Yucca flowers are considered a delicacy in Central America.

Cloves are the dried flower buds of a

THE VASCULAR PLANTS

tropical myrtle tree. They are dried and used as a spice and also yield an oil used in perfumes and medicine. The flower buds of the caper, a Mediterranean shrub, are pickled and used in seasoning.

A few flowers are used for medicine. Among them are dandelion, elder, mullein, and camomile.

Saffron, a yellow coloring matter, is obtained from the stigmas of the saffron crocus.

Flowers are also used in making perfumes and are grown for that purpose. However, an increasing amount of commercial perfumes are synthetic.

38.9   Nature of Fruits

To many, the word **fruit** means orange, apple, or some other common article of food. However, many fruits are not edible by man. Some are eaten by squirrels, birds, and other animals.

The fruit of a plant is the final result of the work of its flower. In its simplest form it is the ripened *ovary* and its contents, including the seed or seeds. In some cases, it involves accessory parts, especially the *receptacle*.

The development of ovules into seeds and of ovaries into fruits requires much food. Sugars, amino acids, and fatty acids are changed to insoluble foods for storage. *Auxins* (growth hormones) aid in fruit development.

38.10   Kinds of Fruits

True fruits developed directly from the ovary include the berry, stone fruit, achene (ay-*keen*), grain or kernel, nut, key, legume, and capsule. Each of these has a special meaning to a biologist because he knows the parts of the flower from which each is derived.

Fruits with soft ovary walls, as apples, peaches and berries, are **fleshy** fruits. Those with hard ovary walls are **dry**

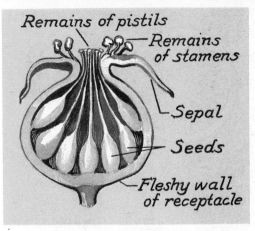

FIGURE 38-11. *FRUIT OF THE ROSE*

When rose petals drop off, a reddish bulb containing seeds remains, which attracts birds to help in seed dispersal.

fruits. Those dry fruits which open and discharge their seeds, like beans, are called **dehiscent** (dee-*hiss*-cent) fruits. Dry fruits which do not open when ripe, such as maple or mustard, are called **indehiscent** (in-dee-*hiss*-cent) fruits.

A *berry* is a fleshy fruit in which the ovary wall and inside structures have become enlarged and juicy. The seeds with hard coats of their own are embedded in the flesh. A blueberry is a true berry, as are grapes, tomatoes, and oranges.

Stone fruits or *drupes* are easily recognized by their stones or pits. In these the outer layers of the ovary wall become fleshy and edible while the inner layers become hard and form a stone which encloses the seed. Peaches, plums, apricots, and cherries are examples of this kind of fruit.

An *achene* is a small, hard, dry fruit with one seed which completely fills the fruit coat. Buckwheat, dandelions, and buttercups form achenes.

A *grain* or *kernel* has a very thin, almost transparent fruit coat fused to the seed coat. Grasses, corn, wheat, and other cereals have this kind of fruit.

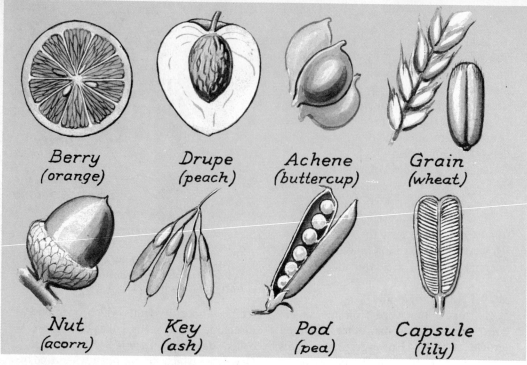

FIGURE 38-12. *KINDS OF FRUITS*

The eight true fruits illustrated show the variety of forms which they may take. While the berry and drupe are fleshy fruits, all the others are dry fruits. True fruits develop directly from the ovary.

Nuts have one seed each although the two halves sometimes appear to be separate. The shell of a true nut is the fruit coat and the softer portion the seed. Chestnuts, hazel nuts, and acorns are examples.

Key fruits like those of the maple, ash, and elm have wings to help the wind in scattering them.

Legumes (*leg*-yooms) or *pods* include beans, peas, lentils, peanuts, and the like. The pod is the ovary wall, to which the separate seeds are attached by a stalk and nourished in the parent plant. When ripe, the pod splits along the sides and the seeds fall out.

A *capsule* is a dry fruit developed from a compound ovary which cracks open when mature. The tulip, violet, and snapdragon are examples.

Accessory fruits, sometimes called **false fruits,** develop from parts other than those of the ovary. Examples are the strawberry and apple, the edible parts of which are formed from the receptacle. In the *pome* (*pohm*) the receptacle becomes fleshy and surrounds the ovary or core which contains the seeds. Apples, pears, and quinces are pomes. An *aggregate* fruit develops from a flower which has a number of pistils, as the black raspberry and strawberry.

A *multiple* fruit is formed from a cluster of flowers grouped closely together, as the pineapple, mulberry, and fig.

38.11 Functions of Fruits

The vital part of any fruit is the *seed* contained inside. The rest of the fruit is intended by the plant merely to serve the seeds. It does this in two ways. (1)

THE VASCULAR PLANTS

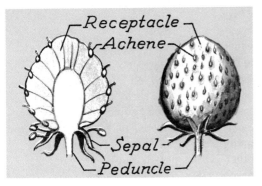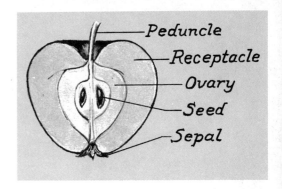

FIGURE 38-13. *FALSE FRUITS*

The apple and the strawberry are both false fruits, because the part we usually think of as fruit is actually a fleshy receptacle. The true fruit of the apple is the core; that of the strawberry, the achene.

It *protects* the seeds during their development, as in the bean, or during their period of rest or dormancy, as in the nut. In the cashew, the false fruit is soft and edible, while the true fruit furnishes the cashew nut. (2) The fruit also helps to *distribute* the seeds after they have matured.

38.12 Adaptations of Fruits and Seeds for Dispersal

In order to fulfill its function, a fruit must scatter the seeds it contains. This is necessary for three reasons: (1) the seedlings would choke one another if all were dropped near together; (2) there would be too slow growth, for the soil near the parent might be depleted, and the new plants could not grow so well as in fresher soil; and (3) there would be too great a chance of extermination if all the seeds were dropped near together, for some one unfavorable condition might kill them all.

In order to scatter seeds a plant makes use of wind, animals, and water as distributing agents, and of mechanical devices such as exploding pods. To be distributed by the *wind,* a seed or a fruit must be light. This condition is brought about in the following ways: (1) by *plumes,* known as the **pappus,** as in the case of the dandelion and thistle; (2) by *tufts of hairs* on the clematis; (3) by the *down* on a milkweed seed; and (4) by the *wings* [**samara** (*sam*-uh-ruh)] on the fruits of the maple and elm. Special devices for wind distribution are found in the tumbleweed and in tickle grass, a common garden weed. In the tumbleweed the whole plant breaks off at the level of the

FIGURE 38-14. *SEED DISPERSAL*

Seeds must be widely scattered from the parent plant to assure germination and growth for the largest number. Here we see adaptations which guarantee that some seeds of each species will have a chance to grow to maturity.

531

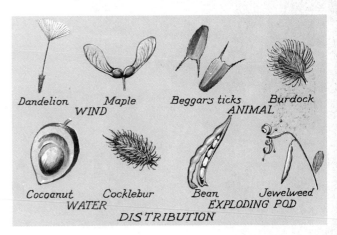

Dandelion   Maple   Beggar's ticks   Burdock
WIND   ANIMAL

Cocoanut   Cocklebur   Bean   Jewelweed
WATER   EXPLODING POD

DISTRIBUTION

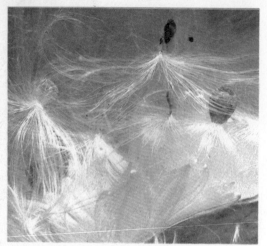

FIGURE 38-15. *MILKWEED*

The ripened seeds of the milkweed have plume-like tufts which are caught by the wind and carried far and wide.

ground, and is blown about by the wind, fruits and seeds being broken off and scattered as it rolls along the ground.

For distribution by *animals,* fruits have adaptations of two kinds: (1) they have *hooks* for attaching themselves to an animal, or (2) they are *edible.* The burdock and beggar's tick represent the first kind of adaptation, and the fleshy fruits the second. The adaptations of fleshy fruits are (1) a sour or bitter taste during development, which prevents their being eaten before the seeds are mature, and (2) edibility when ripe,

which insures their being eaten by some animal. Sometimes they are eaten without the seeds, which are likely to be dropped some distance from the plant that produced them; sometimes they are eaten with the seeds, in which case the undigested seeds are passed off with other wastes, often very far from the parent plant.

For distribution by *water,* the adaptations must insure buoyancy and the ability to withstand decay. Both are well illustrated by the coconut, and the former by the cocklebur.

To distribute seeds by forcibly expelling them, dry fruits must have elastic tissue. Take the bean, for example. The pod is elastic. When it dries, it splits and curls up, throwing the seeds out by *force.* Another elastic pod is the wild cucumber, which forces its seeds out violently. So does the pod of the jewelweed, which requires only a touch to set it off, scattering seeds abroad.

Although plants have other means of propagating themselves (see Section 36.13), the main dependence for keeping up the race in most plants, especially the wild ones, is the distribution of the seeds.

38.13 Economic Value of Fruits

In many plants, the fruit is the part of

FIGURE 38-16. *HARVEST*

The large, orange pumpkin so popular in this country is the fruit of the coarse, running pumpkin vine. A good source of Vitamin A, the pumpkin belongs to the same family as the squash.

greatest use to man. The fruit furnishes him with most of the necessities in the way of food, and supplies him with many of the luxuries as well.

In speaking of the uses of fruits to man, it must be remembered that in biology all grains are fruits and that many so-called vegetables are fruits, as, for example, the tomato, squash, and cucumber.

The most valuable and dependable source of food in the world is grass fruits found in the cereals: wheat, rice, corn, oats, rye, barley, and others. Nearly half the population of the globe depends on rice as its principal food and it is important as a supplementary food in many more parts of the world.

Not only are the cereals the most important article of food, but they are the basis of a great part of the world's work. The raising of cereals, their preparation for food, and their distribution give employment to a greater number of persons than any other industry. Besides supplying man with food directly, many cereals are used to feed the animals from which we get meat, milk, butter, cheese, and eggs.

The articles of food commonly known as fruits—apples, oranges, berries, bananas, and others—are very valuable, their chief use being to supply vitamins (Sec. 21.5), sugar, and flavor in the diet. Fruits obtained from the vegetable garden—tomatoes, cucumbers, squashes, eggplant, melons, and others—furnish a welcome variety of foodstuffs. Nuts and legumes are important sources of protein.

FACTS TO REMEMBER

The *flower* is the principal organ for reproduction in a seed plant. To carry out this function, a typical flower possesses these parts: (1) the *essential parts,* consisting of the *stamen* and *pistil,* and (2) the *accessory parts,* consisting of the *sepals* or *calyx,* the *petals* or *corolla,* and any other attached parts.

Pollination is the transfer of *pollen grains* from the *anthers* of the stamen to the *stigma* of the pistil. The pollen then sends a *pollen tube* containing three nuclei down the *style* and into the *ovary,* where it enters an *ovule. Fertilization* occurs when one of the sperm nuclei combines with the egg nucleus.

Plants may be pollinated by *cross-pollination* or by *self-pollination.* The agents of pollination are wind, water, insects, birds, animals, and man.

A *fruit* is a ripened ovary with all of its attached parts. Its function is to protect the enclosed seeds and to distribute them.

Depending on the structure of the ovary wall, fruits may be *fleshy* or *dry. Dehiscent* dry fruits discharge their seeds by bursting open when ripe; *indehiscent* dry fruits just decompose when ripe and release the seeds.

Fruits and seeds are adapted for dispersal by wind, water, animals, birds, force, and other agents.

Flowers and fruits are of great economic importance for food and other products.

WORDS TO REMEMBER

accessory fruit
accessory parts
achene
aggregate fruit
anther
berry
calyx
capsule
catkin
complete flower
composite flower
corolla
cross-pollination
dehiscent
disc flower
double fertilization
drupe
dry fruit
egg nucleus
embryo sac
endosperm
essential parts
false fruit
fertilization

filament
fleshy fruit
fruit
grain
head
indehiscent
inflorescence
integuments
kernel
key fruits
legumes
micropyle
multiple fruit
nectar glands
nut
ovary
ovule
pedicel
peduncle
perfect flower
perianth
petal
pistil
pistillate flower

pods
polar nuclei
pollen
pollen tube
pollination
pome
ray flower
receptacle
regular flower
self-pollination
sepal
sperm nuclei
spike
spur
stamen
staminate flower
stigma
stone fruit
strap-shaped flower
style
true fruit
tube nucleus
tubular flower
umbel

QUESTIONS

1. What is the function of flowers?
2. What are the essential organs of flowers? Name the parts of each organ.
3. What devices have flowers for attracting insects?
4. What devices have they for wind pollination?
5. What is an ovule? A pollen grain?
6. Define fertilization. In what does it result?
7. Explain the following terms:
   a. complete flower   c. calyx   e. receptacle
   b. perfect flower   d. corolla
8. How can you help to conserve the wild flowers?
9. What is a fruit? What purpose does it serve to the plant? How does it carry out this function?
10. Name five kinds of fruit and describe each.
11. Describe a plum, a grape, a fig, and a strawberry.
12. Why is dispersal of fruits so necessary?
13. How are fruits distributed?
14. Describe some adaptations of fruits for dispersal.

534   THE VASCULAR PLANTS

COMPLETION TEST

As your teacher or classmate reads the following incomplete statements, with your book closed, write on a clean sheet of paper the word or phrase which correctly completes the statement.

1. The sepals and petals are the _____ parts of a flower.
2. The calyx and corolla taken together form the _____.
3. The _____ produces the pollen grain.
4. Composite flowers are composed of _____ and disc flowers.
5. A flower in danger of extinction is the _____.
6. The pod of the _____ forcibly expels its seeds.
7. A flower bud eaten for food is the _____.
8. Yellow coloring matter is obtained from the _____ crocus.
9. The _____ is a fleshy fruit.
10. Insect pollinated flowers usually have bright petals and _____ glands.

PROJECTS

I. *Structure of a Flower.—*1. If possible, bring into the laboratory a nasturtium. Study it and label the following parts on your drawing.

    a. sepals (calyx)   d. stamen (filament, anther)
    b. petals (corolla)   e. pistil (stigma, style, and ovary)
    c. spur

2. Make a labeled drawing of the stamen and pistil after examining them under the microscope. Draw some pollen grains as you observe them under high power.

If you are unable to secure a nasturtium, bring any other flower into the laboratory and identify as many parts as you can.

II. *Comparative Study of Flowers.—*Study flowers and record the results, using the following table as a guide. Do not mark your book.

Flower	Corolla Regular	Corolla Irregular	Corolla Lacking	Stamens only in a Flower	Pistils only in a Flower	Flower Perfect
Geranium	X					
Castor bean						
Salvia		X				
Nasturtium						X
Pansy		X				
Etc.						

III. *Study of an Orange.—*1. Examine the stem end and note the remains of the calyx. Remove it. How many sepals had the flower? How many dots do you see? These represent the ends of the vascular bundles which supplied food to the growing fruit. Examine the opposite end for a scar showing where the pistil was attached. Scrape the skin or pinch it, and note the oil which shows as a yellow, odorous liquid.

2. Make a cross section through the middle of the orange. How many distinct parts are there? Where are the seeds? Note the oil glands in the cut skin. Draw and label the parts named above.

3. Remove the skin from a whole orange and separate the parts. How many are there? Look for a strand of conductive tissue on each one. Where does it come from? How many sections and vascular bundles are there?

IV. *Study of a Tomato.*—(Canned, unpeeled tomatoes will serve.) Examine the whole fruit for traces of parts of the flower. On which end are they found? How many sepals were there in the flower? Remove the stem and count the number of vascular bundles. Make a cross section through the middle. How many divisions are there in the tomato? Where are the seeds? Can you see the vascular bundle which entered the seed? Compare grape, another *berry*, and peach, plum, and cherry, *drupes*.

V. *Study of an Apple.*—1. Examine the whole apple. On the blossom end find the old sepals. How many are there? In the end of the stem look for vascular bundles. Draw and label. Make a cross section through the middle. Draw. Label the seeds in the papery pod (core). How many divisions has it? How many vascular bundles are there, as shown by dots near the core?

2. Make a vertical section. Label the vascular bundles you see, the stem, the fleshy wall of the receptacle, and the remains of sepals. Are the remains of sepals on the same end in the apple as in the orange?

3. See how many kinds of fruits you can find. Make a list of them.

REFERENCES

Burbank, *Partner in Nature.* Appleton.
Conn, *Biology.* Silver, Burdett.
Coulter, *Plant Life and Plant Uses.* Appleton.
Fuller, *The Plant World.* Holt.
Goldsmith, *Picture Primer of Backyard Gardening.* Houghton Mifflin.
Goldsmith, *Picture Primer of Indoor Gardening.* Houghton Mifflin.
House, *Wild Flowers.* Macmillan.
Hylander and Johnson, *Wild Flower Book.* Macmillan.
Hylander, *The World of Plant Life.* Macmillan.
Lucas, *Fruits of the Earth.* Lippincott.
Parker, *Flowers, Fruits, Seeds.* Row Peterson.
Parker, *The Garden and Its Friends.* Row Peterson.
Peattie, *The Flowering Earth.* Putnam's.
Peterson, *How To Know The Wild Fruits.* Macmillan.
Rickett, *Wild Flowers of America.* Crown.
Sinnott, *Botany, Principles and Problems.* McGraw-Hill.
Torrey, *General Botany for Colleges.* Century.
Transeau, *General Botany.* World Book.
Wilde, *A Child's Book of Flowers.* Maxton.
Zim, Martin, *Flowers: Golden Nature Guide.* Simon and Schuster.

CHAPTER 39

The Seed

39.1 The Promise of the Seed

Seeds seem dry and dead when you plant them, but if you keep them warm and moist, they sprout and grow. Each ripe seed has in its firm covering a small plant, well started. This plant is the same kind as the one from which the seed came; you can always depend on getting a pea plant from a pea seed and a tomato plant from a tomato seed. For favorable growth conditions all seeds need suitable soil, enough moisture, air, and warmth. Seeds vary in size, shape, and manner of developing. The bean seed is typical of dicotyledonous plants while the corn kernel illustrates the monocotyledonous type.

39.2 The Bean from Ovule to Seed

A young bean seed (*ovule*) consists of a mass of tissue, the **nucellus** (noo-sel-us), in one part of which, the *embryo sac,* is the *egg cell.* The ovule is covered by two coats, or *integuments.* It is attached to the ovary wall, the **placenta** (pluh-*sen*-tuh), of the fruit by a stalk, the **funiculus** (fyoo - *nik* - yoo - lus), through which it gets its nourishment. The integuments do not quite meet at one point, leaving an opening, the *micropyle,* through which the pollen tube usually enters.

As the ovule develops into a seed, several changes occur. (1) The *integuments* now become firm and hard, the outer one forming the seed coat, the **testa.** (2) The *egg cell* divides many times, forming the *embryo* which consists of the following parts: (*a*) two seed leaves, **cotyledons** (kot'l-*ee*-d'nz), (*b*) the stem tip or **plumule** (*ploo*-myool), often with leaves fairly well developed,

FIGURE 39-1. *STRUCTURE OF THE BEAN SEED*

Fertilization of the egg cell of an ovule results in the development of a complete seed. At left is the external view and at right is the internal structure. The hypocotyl develops into roots; the plumule into leaves.

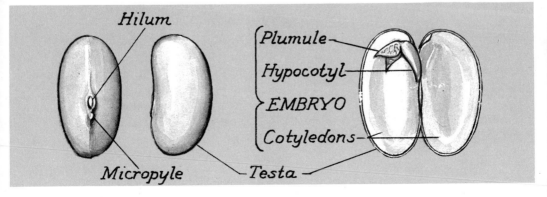

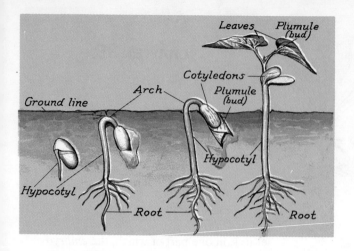

FIGURE 39-2. *GROWTH OF THE BEAN SEED*

Germination of a dicotyledonous seed is shown from the time the hypocotyl breaks through the testa (*left*) to the last stage when the cotyledons, having used up all their stored food, are much reduced in size (*right*).

(*c*) the **hypocotyl** (hy-poh-*kot*-il), the lower part of which will form the root. (3) The stalk drops off, leaving on the bean seed a scar, the **hilum** (*hy*-lum).

The bean seed has no *endosperm*. The seedling uses the food which is stored in the cotyledons.

39.3   Adaptations of the Seed

The bean seed is adapted to provide for a new bean plant in the following ways. (1) A ripe seed contains a young plant well started. (2) It can resume growth soon after being formed, or it can remain dormant for years. (3) It is surrounded by a hard testa which prevents the embryo from drying out during a long resting period. (4) It can absorb water slowly through the micropyle when covered with moist earth. This softens the testa and causes the cotyledons to swell, helping to release the entire embryo. (5) The cotyledons of the embryo supply its food till it can make its own. This insures rapid growth in the early stages, an advantage in competition with other seedlings.

39.4   Development of the Bean Embryo

The first step in the growth or **germination** of the young plant is when the root grows out through the micropyle.

It then begins to absorb water needed for further growth and soon becomes firmly embedded in the soil. This *primary root* is followed later by *secondary roots*.

The *hypocotyl* curves, forming a loop, the top of which is often called the **arch.** The hypocotyl grows rapidly, causing the arch of the loop to turn from side to side, pushing the particles of soil apart and working its way to the surface. Then the *cotyledons* are pulled up as the arch straightens.

Finally, further growth of the hypocotyl causes the cotyledons to spread apart, exposing the *plumule* to the air and light. At the same time the cotyledons begin to turn green, thus serving as leaves till the leaves of the plumule have developed. So the plumule is protected and given a chance to grow under good conditions. As soon as the food in the cotyledons has been absorbed by the young plant, they shrivel and drop off, while the stem and leaves continue to grow. The young plant is known as a **seedling** while it is dependent on the store of food in the seed for its nourishment.

In the course of a few weeks a bean plant is large enough to produce blossoms which will develop into pods containing seeds, and thus complete the *life cycle.*

THE VASCULAR PLANTS

39.5 Corn Seed

A seed of corn, commonly called a *grain* or *kernel,* is similar to a bean seed (1) in containing a young plant, the corn embryo; (2) in containing food for the use of the embryo when it first begins to grow; and (3) in having marks upon it. On one side of the kernel is a depression beneath which the embryo lies. Above the depression is a slight prominence, the *silk scar* which marks the place where the style (the so-called silk) was attached. This is most prominent in popcorn. At the base is a stalk by which the kernel is attached to the cob during its development.

Corn differs from the bean in the relative size and position of its embryo, which is at one side of the food supply. This food is called the **endosperm,** and is made up of protein and starch. Endosperm is the tissue formed after the two polar bodies in the ovule unite with one of the two sperm nuclei.

Another difference between the two is that the corn has a single modified cotyledon called the **scutellum** (skoo-*tel*-um), the part of the embryo which digests and absorbs the food stored for its use (Fig. 39-3). The cotyledon of the corn never appears above ground. The corn embryo has its leaves rolled into a tight, pointed bud, the *plumule,* an adaptation which enables it easily to pierce the earth above. *Adventitious roots* (Fig. 35-4) grow out from the stem to support the

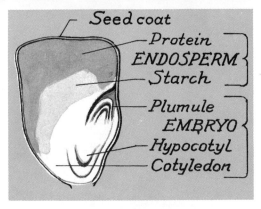

FIGURE 39-3. *CORN GRAIN*

A monocotyledonous seed, corn has a single cotyledon or scutellum, from which the plumule and hypocotyl develop.

plant. These are called *prop roots.* The true root is at the lower part of a short hypocotyl.

As the corn has but one cotyledon, it belongs to the group of plants known as *monocotyledons.* The bean, having two cotyledons, belongs to the group *dicotyledons* (Sec. 36.2).

39.6 Germination of Seeds

When a seed is fully formed and separated from the parent plant, it is considered to be *ripe.* Some seeds are able to grow or germinate within a very short time. Others remain *dormant,* a state in which the life processes are carried on very slowly. How long the seeds remain dormant may vary from a few days for a willow to nearly a year for some oaks. The length of time that a seed may keep its ability to grow is called its **viability.**

FIGURE 39-4. *GROWTH OF THE CORN SEED*

These three stages in the growth of a corn seed show an undeveloped grain, sprouting plumule and root, and a developing seedling. The endosperm contains the food supply—protein, and insoluble starch which must be changed into soluble sugar before it can be used by the plant.

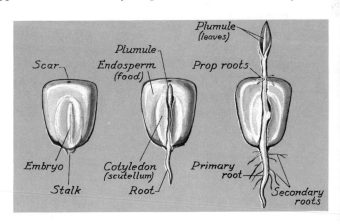

Black Star

FIGURE. 39-5. *SEEDLING*

This young radish seedling already shows many tropisms. Its plumule lifts the cotyledons into the light and air; the hypocotyl grows downward for water.

The conditions necessary for *germination* of the seed are (1) moisture, (2) suitable temperature, and (3) air or a source of oxygen. When a seed starts to grow it lives on its stored food until it is able to form and use its own root system and to make or obtain its own food supply.

39.7 Growth Response to External Stimuli. Tropisms

The tendency for a living thing to respond definitely to an external stimulus is called a **tropism** (*troh*-pizm). Although plants have no nervous system, they do respond to external *stimuli*. Regardless of the position in which the seeds are planted the hypocotyl begins to grow downward. The roots formed from this also grow downward. This response to gravity is called *geotropism* (jee-oh-*troh*-pizm). It is a *positive* tro-

pism because the roots grow *toward* gravity.

In a similar manner, the plumule begins to grow upward, away from gravity. This is a *negative* tropism. Thus plant roots are positive and plant stems negative in their response to gravity.

Plants also respond to other tropisms and usually grow toward those which are strongest at the time. The roots may need to grow toward the source of water supply. This is *hydrotropism* (hy-droh-*troh*-pizm). If this force is strong enough, the plants will respond to hydrotropism, growing toward the water, even if they have to overcome the force of gravity, geotropism, to some degree.

The tiny leaves of the seedling need sunlight to manufacture food and respond readily to its rays. Response to sunlight is called *heliotropism* (hee-lee-oh-*troh*-pizm); response to other sources of light is known as *phototropism* (foh-toh-*troh*-pizm). Sometimes the stems of seedlings grow unusually long in an effort to hold leaves up to the light.

Other tropisms are *chemotropism* (kee - moh - *troh* - pizm), response to chemicals, *thermotropism* (ther-moh-*troh*-pizm) response to temperature, *thigmotropism,* (thig-moh-*troh*-pizm), response to contact, and *rheotropism* (ree-oh-*troh*-pizm), response to water currents. With the aid of these tropisms the seedling is able to adjust itself to its surroundings, thus making the best possible use of its environment.

These responses in plants may be explained in part by the action of certain plant hormones, some of which are known as **auxins** (*oks*-ins). These are chemicals produced by the plant and which seem to affect its growth in response to various stimuli. Auxins are also used to artificially stimulate slips and twigs.

Growth-regulating substances have been made synthetically by man. They are used to produce some seedless fruits, to force pineapples into flowers, to prevent the sprouting of potatoes when in storage, and to prevent the early falling of apples and pears. Some of these synthetic substances, 2,4-D, and others, are used on grass lawns to free them of weeds such as dandelions and plantain. The chemicals do not affect cereals or grasses, but they cause the broad-leafed weeds to grow very rapidly, exhausting their supply of stored food without replacing it, and then dying.

39.8 Seeds as Food

In the bean seed, two kinds of food-stuffs are stored, namely carbohydrates and proteins. *Carbohydrate* (Sec. 21.2) is the foodstuff that includes starch and sugars. *Protein* (Sec. 21.2) is the name given to the foodstuff found in such foods as lean meat, cheese, and the white of egg, and in animal foods generally.

Beans contain more protein than any other seeds. Corn contains protein, starch, sugar, and oil. Cotton seed and peanuts contain much oil.

In the bean, both carbohydrates and proteins are stored in the cotyledons, evenly distributed. In the endosperm of a corn grain, the carbohydrates are under the scutellum, and the proteins are in a distinct layer outside the carbohydrates, covered by the flinty outside coat of the grain. (See Fig. 39-3.)

39.9 Digestion of the Food in the Seed

It may appear strange that the growing bean seedling lives upon the food stored in the cotyledons, and yet such is the case. This food, however, must be digested by means of *enzymes* before the bean embryo can use it. *Diastase* is a digestive enzyme which changes starch to sugar. The digested food can then be absorbed into the cells, and passed on into the phloem vessels, through which it is distributed to all parts of the growing plant.

39.10 Economic Importance of Seeds

The use of seeds to a plant is simply to provide for other plants of the same kind, and to insure a supply of food for the early life of each. Man, however, has learned to take advantage of this arrangement of plants, to secure food for himself and his animals. He has also found ways of enabling the plant under cultivation to store up more food than it could do in the natural state.

In thinking of the seeds used as food, we must limit the term *seed* to its biological meaning. Many articles of food, such as the cereal grains, are commonly thought of as seeds when they are really fruits. Their use as food has already been discussed (Sec. 38.13). The real seeds that are of greatest use to man as food are those of the pulse family, especially beans and peas, which alone are the source of most of the protein that is obtained from plants. The soy bean introduced from Asia is also very valuable. Mature peas and beans contain more food matter than do "green peas" and "string beans," the latter being valuable more for the bulk they furnish than for their food content.

The peanut is widely used as a food. The seeds are used in cooking. Peanut oil is also an important product. The leaves are used for forage, and many commercial products are derived from other parts of the plant. Chocolate and cocoa made from the cacao bean and coffee from the coffee bean are used more widely than ever for beverages.

J. Horace McFarland

Keystone View Co.

FIGURE 39-6. *USEFUL BEANS*

Chocolate is made by grinding the kernels of the seeds of the tropical cacao tree (*right*). Soybeans (*left*) are rich in food value. The oil is used in shortenings, and the meal is an important livestock feed.

Seeds which are used as spices include anise, celery, fennel, nutmeg, mustard, and pepper.

Besides their use as food, seeds can be used as medicine, castor oil and mustard being common remedies that are obtained from seeds. Castor oil was formerly used as a lubricant in airplanes because it is not affected by the cold of high altitudes. Two valuable products are obtained from cotton seeds: one, the oil which is used in place of lard and butter in preparing foods and also in packing foods, as sardines, and as a lubricant; the other, thread and cloth which are made from the fibers covering the outside of the seeds. The fibers are removed by a process called *ginning;* then the seeds are pressed to remove the oil. The refuse forms a valuable food for cattle, especially when mixed with other foods. The length of the fibers varies on different species of cotton, and the uses which are made of the fibers depend on their length.

Linseed oil is obtained from the seeds of the flax plant. It is used in making paint and other substances. After the oil is pressed out, a substance known as linseed cake is left. This is used as food for cattle. Tung oil, formerly obtained from China from seeds of the Tung tree, is now produced extensively in the southern part of the United States, and used in waterproofing and in making paints and varnishes.

FACTS TO REMEMBER

A *seed* consists of (1) an embryo, (2) stored food, and (3) protective seed coats.

542

The bean seed is a *dicotyledon* because it has two *cotyledons,* or seed leaves, in which the food is stored. As the bean germinates, the *hypocotyl* forms the roots and an *arch,* which pulls the cotyledons above the ground as it straightens, exposing the *plumule.*

The corn seed is a *monocotyledon* because it has only one seed leaf. In corn, food is stored in the *endosperm* and the cotyledon is modified to form a *scutellum,* which digests and absorbs the stored food. During germination, the corn seed remains in the soil.

For a seed to *germinate,* it must have (1) moisture, (2) suitable temperature, and (3) air or a source of oxygen. Until these three requirements are met, the seed remains *dormant.*

Plants respond to such stimuli as gravity, water, heat, light, and temperature by growing toward or away from them. These responses are called *tropisms.*

Seeds are valuable to man as a source of food, spices, medicines, oils, and many industrial products.

WORDS TO REMEMBER

arch	ginning	rheotropism
auxins	heliotropism	scutellum
chemotropism	hilum	seed
cotyledon	hydrotropism	seedling
dormant	hypocotyl	silk scar
egg cell	integuments	testa
embryo	micropyle	thermotropism
embryo sac	nucellus	thigmotropism
endosperm	ovule	tropism
funiculus	phototropism	viability
geotropism	placenta	
germination	plumule	

QUESTIONS

1. What is the function of a seed?
2. Name the parts of a seed and give the function of each.
3. What conditions are necessary for germination? For growth?
4. What is a seedling?
5. What adaptations have seeds that fit them to their function?
6. What kinds of foodstuffs are stored in seeds?
7. Why does a young plant (embryo) need energy?
8. What is the function of digestion to the embryo?
9. Why are circulation and respiration necessary?
10. What use does man make of the seeds of plants?
11. Describe three different tropisms.
12. What is the difference between a positive tropism and a negative tropism?

COMPLETION TEST

As your teacher or classmate reads the following incomplete statements, with your book closed, write on a clean sheet of paper the word or phrase which correctly completes the statement.

1. There are two cotyledons in the _____.
2. An ovule develops into a _____.
3. The opening through which the pollen tube enters is the _____.
4. The response of roots to water is called _____.
5. Stems show a _____ response to gravity.
6. The bean seed stores its food in the _____.
7. The corn seed stores its food in the _____.
8. The bean seed stores carbohydrates and _____.
9. In addition to these the corn seed stores _____.
10. Linseed oil is obtained from the seeds of the _____ plant.

PROJECTS

I. *Study of a Bean Seed.*—1. Soak some bean seeds overnight to soften the outer covering. Examine carefully and make a drawing to show the external view. Label the following parts.

   a. micropyle *b.* hilum *c. testa*

2. Remove the testa and separate the two halves. Note the embryo still attached to one of them. Make another sketch, showing the internal view of a bean seed. Label the

   a. hypocotyl *b.* cotyledon *c.* plumule

II. *Study of a Corn Seed.*—Soak some corn seeds overnight to soften the outer covering. Examine carefully and make a drawing showing the external view. Label the

   a. region of the embryo *c.* scutellum
   b. silk scar   *d.* stored food (endosperm)

III. *Foodstuffs in the Bean.*—The presence of different kinds of foodstuffs may be shown by applying the following chemical tests. 1. Boil beans until they are soft and then place a small portion of them in a test tube. Add water. Put in a drop of iodine. If starch is present, the mixture will turn blue. Add strong nitric acid to a second portion in a clean test tube, boil and cool. If protein is present, the mixture will be a clear yellow color which will become orange if ammonia is added. To a third portion add Fehling's solution, as a test for sugar. If the latter is present, the mixture will become dull orange when heated. Test uncooked seed for oil (1) by heating it over an alcohol lamp on a sheet of linen paper; (2) by soaking it overnight in ether. (This must not be near a flame at any time.) If oil is present, it will show on the paper as a clear spot, and in the second test the oil will appear on the surface of the ether in the test tube.

2. Test all parts of cotyledons with iodine. Is starch evenly distributed as shown by the blue color?

3. Remove small portions of the cotyledons from different regions successively and apply the nitric acid test for protein. Do you find that any one region has more protein than another?

IV. *Foodstuffs in Corn.*—1. Split kernels in different ways and apply the iodine test. Where is the starch most abundant?

2. Remove the outer layer of a corn grain and apply the nitric acid test. Test the endosperm for protein. What conclusion do you draw as to the position of protein in the seed?

3. Test all portions for sugar, including the embryo. Where do you find the most sugar? Test all parts of a corn grain for oil, using both tests suggested. In what parts is oil most abundant?

4. Repeat these experiments with castor bean, Brazil nut, etc., and record the results of each test.

V. *To Show That Seeds Contain Water.*—Weigh some squash seeds very carefully after they have been peeled. Place them in a thin dish over a hot radiator for a few hours, then weigh again. Repeat the experiment, using other fleshy seeds. What do you learn from this experiment about the use of the testa to a seed?

VI. *Germination of the Bean.*—1. Soak some of the beans for a day and then plant them in a box of moist sawdust or soil. Keep the box in a warm room. The beans should be kept moist but not wet.

2. At the end of two days remove a bean that shows signs of sprouting. Plan a series of five drawings for your notebook. In the first space, sketch the bean that you have just removed.

3. At the end of four days, remove the bean showing the greatest development. Sketch in space two.

4. Repeat this procedure at the end of seven, nine, and twelve days, sketching them in your notebook.

5. Write a description in your notebook in which you include your observations. Perhaps the following questions will help you.
(a) On which day did the hypocotyl first appear?
(b) When did it break through the ground?
(c) When did the plumule appear?
(d) When did the cotyledons turn green?
(e) Did the root increase in length as the stem grew upward?

VII. *Hydrotropism.*—Plant some seedlings in one end of a long shallow box. Keep the opposite end of the box moist. After a couple of weeks note the direction of growth of the roots.

REFERENCES

Cook, *College Botany.* Lippincott.
Fenton, *Plants that Feed Us.* John Day.
Gager, *The Plant World.* University Society.

Parker, *Flowers, Fruits, Seeds.* Row Peterson.
Parker, *Seed and Seed Travelers.* Row Peterson.
Sinnot, *Botany, Principles and Problems.* McGraw-Hill.
Smith, Overton, and Others, *A Textbook of General Botany.* Macmillan.
Transeau, *General Botany.* World Book.

CHAPTER **40**

Evergreens and Forests

40.1 The Gymnosperms

There are two main groups of vascular plants which bear seeds: (1) the **Angiosperms,** like the apple, oak, and maple, which usually protect their seeds with coats of various thickness, and (2) the **Gymnosperms,** like the pine or spruce, often called *naked-seeded* plants, because the seeds lie naked on the scale of the ripe *cone.* Unlike the Angiosperms, the Gymnosperms retain their leaves or *needles* for two or three years and shed them gradually. They also secrete *resin* (*rez*-in), which is lacking in other trees. The Gymnosperms, then, are the cone-bearing trees or **conifers** (*koh*-nih-fers), commonly called **evergreens.** They also include the *Ginkgo tree,* the only living representative of an earlier form abundant during the Mesozoic era.

40.2 The Pine Tree as a Type

The pine illustrates the plants of the evergreen group. It has all the parts of a flowering plant—stem (trunk), branches, roots, leaves, seed-producing organs, and fruit (cones).

Stem.—The trunk, the main stem, does not divide—a marked characteristic of conifers (cone-bearing trees). In a forest where trees are crowded together and there is in consequence a struggle to get light, the trunks grow tall and

straight, and most of the branches are near the top.

A cross section of a stem shows a series of rings, known as *annual rings* (Figure 36-8), by which the approximate age of the tree can be told. In the spring when all the conditions are at their best and growth is rapid, the cells of the tree are large and thin-walled, strength being sacrificed to size. In the fall or during a dry time in summer, the cells are much smaller and the walls thicker. These small cells show most plainly and form

FIGURE 40-1. *PINE TREES*

The stately evergreen has a graceful shape, unless crowded with others in a forest where only top branches can grow.

Courtesy Caterpillar Tractor Co.

547

FIGURE 40-2. *PINE CONES*

The reproductive organs of the pine are the pollen-bearing staminate cones (*top left*) and the ovule-bearing pistillate cones. They are composed of scales arranged spirally around a central axis. The shape of the cone varies with the species of pine.

Gustav Anderson from Ewing Galloway

the annual ring. During a season in which long, dry periods occur, they may make more than one ring. From the center to the bark extend *medullary* or *wood rays*. The stem increases in size by adding one or more layers annually. **Resin canals** are formed in the xylem and extend for some distances up the stem.

Branches.—The branches leave the stem almost horizontally and nearly in a circle around the trunk of the tree. In the pine they curve upward, but each kind of evergreen has its own particular curvature in its branches.

Leaves.—The leaves, called **needles,** are long, slender, and curved on one side. They grow in bundles of two, three, four, or five needles, according to

FIGURE 40-3. *POLLEN GRAIN*

The air sac in the pollen grains of staminate cones allows the grains to be blown by the wind into the pistillate cone.

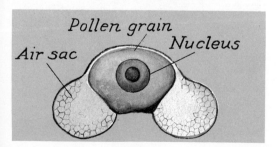

the kind of pine. The leaves remain on the tree from two to five years and then fall off, leaving the branches bare except near the ends. Each needle is a foliage leaf with chlorophyll-bearing cells, stomata for breathing, and one or two deeply imbedded veins.

Roots.—The roots vary according to the kind of pine and according to the soil, but they are always extensive. The root of a pine has an *epidermis, cortex,* and *stele (central cylinder),* and is very much like the roots of the flowering plants.

Seed-producing Organs.—Early in the spring, two kinds of organs are found on the new shoots which grow from the terminal buds. The *pollen bearers* (**staminate cones**) look like short catkins, and are borne in clusters near the base of the shoot. They consist of scales arranged spirally around the central axis. Each scale bears two *pollen sacs.* They wither soon after shedding their pollen, although they may remain on the tree for a year. The other kind of organ, the *ovule bearer* (**pistillate cone**), is short and thick, and is found at the tip of the shoot or on the side of the shoot near

548

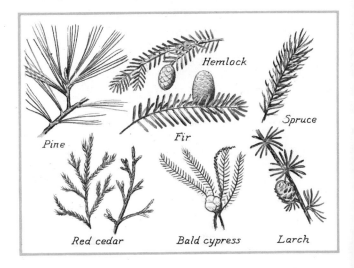

FIGURE 40-4. *EVERGREEN TIPS*

The chief variations among evergreen trees are the shape of their needles, the arrangement of the needles on the branches, and the size and shape of the cones.

Hemlock

Pine

Fir

Spruce

Red cedar

Bald cypress

Larch

the tip. It, too, is made up of scales arranged spirally around a central axis. Each scale near its base bears two ovules.

When the pollen is ripe, each grain, being provided with winglike **air sacs,** is easily blown about by the wind. Some of the pollen sifts into the ovule-bearing organ (young cone) through the spaces between the scales, which at this time are separated slightly. Then the scales close up; the cones turn downward and continue to grow for several months.

Fruit.—During the next year, the pollen grains which are shut up inside the scales grow pollen tubes and fertilize the egg cells which develop in the ovules. The *seed* consists of an embryo, endosperm with reserved food, and a seed coat.

When the cones are about two years old, the scales open and allow the seeds to drop out. Each seed of our northern pine is provided with a wing by which it is blown about, for this pine depends on the wind to scatter its seeds as well as its pollen.

Related Forms of Conifers.—Hemlocks and firs (balsams) have smaller, flatter needles than the pines, and they are not arranged in bundles. Spruce needles grow in spirals around the branches. Cedars have scalelike leaves. Larch and bald cypress trees shed their leaves in the fall, but in other respects are much like the pine.

40.3   Economic Importance

The value of the conifers can scarcely be overestimated. Most of the trees are sawed into lumber for building purposes, but some of them are used in their natural form for telegraph poles, masts of ships, and timbers of mines. Wood pulp, from which most of our paper is made, is produced from small spruce trees. The by-products of this group of trees are also of great value. From the pine come tar, pitch, turpentine, and resin, and the bark of the hemlock was formerly extensively used in tanning leather.

40.4   Tree Associations

Trees that grow without the aid of man collect in large tracts known as **forests.** When certain kinds of trees are more numerous than all the others in a given plot, they give their name to the area, although there may be several other kinds of trees in the plot. We thus have associations of trees and also of

FIGURE 40-5. *TIMBER HARVEST*

Wood is one of the most important products from the forest. After the trees are felled, they are cut into logs of proper length, and floated down river on rafts to the sawmills and processing areas.

Frank Sterrett

smaller plants, which have been able to adapt themselves well to that habitat.

Habitat.—Most evergreens grow in sandy soil in temperate or in cold climates, but a few of them occur where it is very warm, and some where it is wet and swampy. The finest evergreen forests in the world are found in the western part of North America, on the slopes facing the Pacific Ocean.

40.5 Making a Forest

When the first settlers came to eastern North America, they found forests on most of the land. They needed land for cultivation, and trees were so numerous that they were careless about cutting them. This attitude towards forests was continued by later inhabitants, so that today we find only a few old forests left. Vigorous second-growth forests are replacing them. To answer increasing needs for forest products we are improving our present tracts and replanting areas that will yield forest products for later generations. It is estimated that a country should have at least one fifth of its area in forests to provide for its needs.

40.6 Federal and State Protection of Forests

The forests of the United States now cover about 648,000,000 acres. That is

about one third of the total area. According to good authority these resources are sufficient to supply our wood needs, provided the area is properly stocked and conserved. This is being done by more and more private woodland owners, who manage 73 per cent of our commercially valuable timberland and who produce 90 per cent of our wood. The federal and state governments appropriate huge sums every year for the protection of forests and the development of parks.

National Forest Preserves.—In 1891 President Harrison set aside the Yellowstone Park Timberland Reserve, which was the first forest preserve. Since that date other presidents have set aside other regions until there are at present over one hundred and fifty national preserves with a total area over 181,000,000 acres.

40.7 Forestry

In Europe, **forestry** has been practiced for a long time; and methods of planting forests, caring for them, and cutting them are such that tracts devoted to forests are a good source of income for these countries. In the United States much progress in forestry has been made through the cooperation of government agencies and timberland owners. But many conditions have presented a lot of

THE VASCULAR PLANTS

FIGURE 40-6. *FOREST FIRE*

Forest fires in the United States ruin an average of 10,000,000 acres of forests yearly. Despite much-publicized campaigns to prevent these fires, man's carelessness is still the chief cause of the desolation.

U.S. Forest Service

problems, not all of which are yet solved. Trees are now being considered as crops, and experiments are being made with a view to obtaining the greatest possible returns from a tract in the shortest possible time. In general, only the land not suited to the raising of cultivated crops is used for growing trees, although trees, like other plants, grow best on good soil.

Some kinds of trees, those used in making paper pulp, for instance, can be used while they are still comparatively small. Quick-growing trees are often alternated with slow-growing species, the former being removed to produce income and to leave room for the others to develop properly. In general, the best way to obtain young trees for planting is to raise them in *nurseries,* starting from seed.

After a young forest is planted, it must be guarded from its enemies, the foremost of which are fire, insects, and fungi. Forest rangers keep watch from lookout points or from airplanes for fires, and also patrol the forests. Most fires come from man's carelessness with matches, cigarettes, and camp fires, but many are caused by lightning. When a fire is discovered, word is sent out, and forces of men are sent to fight it. Paths free from trees, dead branches, and

leaves afford means of access to different parts of the forest, and also act as barriers by confining the fire to a more limited region.

Different methods are employed to combat insects, one method being to scatter dust or spray from an airplane to destroy them. A knowledge of the life history of insects and their habits is needed by the ranger whose business it is to report and to help fight insects. Fungi are the hardest of all enemies to combat, since they are spread by invisible spores, gain entrance where bark is broken, and often ruin a tree before their presence is apparent. Some of the worst fungal diseases are bracket fungi, white pine blister rust, chestnut blight, and Dutch elm disease.

40.8 Lumbering

The term *lumbering* includes, primarily, cutting the trees and getting them to the sawmill. Great waste has been characteristic of unscientific lumbering. This waste assumed two forms, injuring young trees in felling mature ones, and making use only of the most valuable part of the trees felled. The latter practice not only wastes much wood that might be used in many ways, but is also a menace to neighboring forests, for it

EVERGREENS AND FORESTS

leaves dead, dry tops and limbs lying about to supply fuel for a devastating fire.

When lumbering is done scientifically, the forester either leaves a crop of younger trees to grow to maturity or reforests the cutover area with seed trees. New trees are protected from grazing animals by fencing cattle out of the woods. Protective measures are taken against insects and disease, and fire lanes are well maintained to prevent loss of valuable lumber.

40.9 The Importance of Trees

One has only to note the great number of uses for wood and lumber and the unsatisfactory results when substitutes are used, to realize how dependent we are on the forests. Forests also prevent **erosion** (wearing away) of the soil. When trees grow close together, their roots intertwine and hold the soil in place. As the leaves and dead branches drop to the ground and decay, they form a substance called **humus** (*hyoo*-mus) on top of the soil. Humus soaks up water like a sponge, and gives it out again slowly. So, when snow melts in the spring, the closeness of the trees prevents its melting as rapidly as it does in the open, and the humus takes it up, preventing the quick run-off of water which is the cause of so many disastrous floods.

Areas that have long been deforested have lost their best soil, which has washed into gullies, making cultivation impossible. Another evil connected with the loss of soil is the clogging of channels used for navigation, thus making necessary expensive dredging to keep them open. Much attention is now being given to reforesting our waste areas to

improve soil, prevent further erosion, lessen the danger from freshets, and maintain a steady supply of water.

Two kinds of trees grow in forests: the narrow-leaved, evergreen, or soft-wood trees, and the broad-leaved, deciduous, hard-wood trees. These are lumberman's terms and not those of botanists, for the basswood in the second group has softer wood than pine in the first group. The best primeval forests are now found in the southern part of the Appalachian region in the East, and in the Rocky Mountains and along the Pacific coast in the West. The oldest trees in the former forests are the pines. In the Western forests are found the largest and oldest living things, namely, the Sequoias.

Besides their association in forests, trees are grown singly and thus get a chance to develop symmetrically. In this case branches often grow almost to the ground instead of being confined to the top in their struggle for light as when closely planted. While forest trees make the finest lumber, being free from knots, those grown in open spaces where they are free to branch are more beautiful in shape.

Another use of trees is for shade, as when they are planted along city streets. Maples, elms, sycamores, oaks, lindens, tulip trees, and ash trees are most satisfactory for this purpose. Shade trees also help to regulate the temperature and humidity because of the enormous quantity of water given off from the leaves by transpiration.

Some trees have peculiarities that make them unsuited for use as shade trees. For example, poplars clog drains and water pipes with their roots, and produce sprouts from their roots long after they are cut (Sec. 39.6). Elms, soft maples, and willows also clog pipes.

Courtesy The Davey Tree Expert Co.

FIGURE 40-9. *TREE SURGERY*

Trained tree experts can treat a diseased tree by cutting out the decayed area and filling it with sectional concrete fillings.

Horse chestnuts and catalpas shed a great deal of litter, thus detracting from their usefulness as shade trees, though they are very beautiful when in full bloom.

40.10   The Care of Trees

Shade trees often need help to secure enough water and food, and pruning to improve their shape. They must also be protected from certain kinds of insects. In *pruning*, limbs should be sawed off smoothly, close to the main stem, and freshly exposed surfaces should be covered with paint. The former precaution is necessary to insure quick growth of new wood over the injured part, and the latter is necessary to prevent the entrance of the spores of fungi. Certain kinds of larvae can be kept from getting to the foliage by painting the trunk with a sticky substance that catches and holds them, or by tying bands of sticky paper

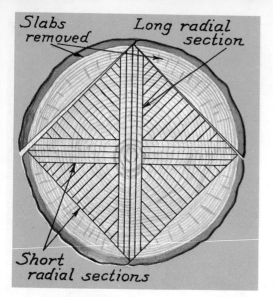

Slabs removed

Long radial section

Short radial sections

FIGURE 40-10. *QUARTER-SAWN*

When an attractive grain is desired, as in furniture and floors, lumber may be quarter-sawn. Waste is involved so this method is not used for ordinary purposes.

around the trunk below the lowest branches. The presence of birds should be encouraged, especially the permanent residents that feed upon insect eggs and larvae in the winter.

40.11 Properties of Wood

When we compare the number of articles that are made from wood with the same articles made of substitutes, we see that there are good reasons for the use of wood. Among these are its *lightness* compared with iron or steel for use in furniture, trunks, and other articles, its *pliability,* its *toughness,* its *durability,* especially when protected from dampness, the ease with which it can be shaped by tools, and its *beauty,* which depends on color and grain, and on the high polish that it can take. The grain is determined by the direction in which the logs are sawn.

Wood has remarkable resistance to crushing, twisting, and pulling apart. A piece of yellow pine one inch square and a foot long, supported at the ends, will bear a load of 720 pounds without breaking. It requires a weight of 17,300 pounds to pull it apart, and a load of 7400 pounds to crush it.

Many kinds of wood are pliable, a property which is often of much value, as in making tennis rackets. It is the closeness of the grain and the hardness of the wood which determines its use for particular purposes. For instance, where woodcuts are to be made, the grain must be very small, and the wood very hard. Holly and box are best for this. In the case of wood used for pitchfork and shovel handles, the qualities desired are toughness and smoothness. These are found in ash and hickory, and so the list might be lengthened indefinitely. Balsa wood, first introduced from the tropics, is much lighter even than cork. This property gives it value in the life preservers and rafts used in case of accidents at sea, although most of the latter are now being made of rubber. Balsa is also used for insulation.

Preservation of Wood.—There are great differences in woods as to their ability to endure in the soil or under water. Some, like cypress, cedar, and locust, contain substances such as resins, which have the ability to withstand decay. All wood lasts longer if it is **seasoned,** that is, allowed to dry out in the air before being used. Wood that is to be used in damp places, however, usually needs treatment to prevent or retard the process of decay.

As decay is caused largely by the work of bacteria or of fungi, both of which must depend upon moisture as one of their chief requirements, the thorough drying of timber is one precaution taken to insure its lasting. Another method used is *charring* portions that are to be covered by earth, and a third,

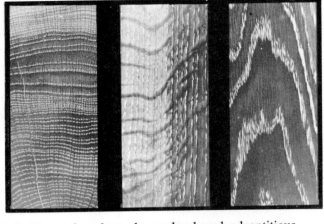

FIGURE 40-11. *WOOD CUTS SHOWING GRAIN*

These three wood cuts are all oak, cut in transverse, radial, and tangential sections, respectively. The grain in lumber is produced by the presence of annual rings and the cut-off ends of pith rays, and varies according to the method of cutting.

the most common, is the use of *chemicals*. Railroad ties, for instance, are thoroughly impregnated with a solution containing creosote and other substances. This acts as an antiseptic, preventing bacteria and fungi from growing in the wood, and prolonging the usefulness of the timber to a remarkable degree. Although treating ties in this way is costly at first, it is an economical measure on the whole, for it saves the timber and the labor of replacing ties often.

40.12 Products Made from Trees

Perhaps the most extensive use of trees is for lumber. Twenty-four per cent of our lumber in recent years was from Douglas fir and was used chiefly for construction. Southern pine and western pine supplied 22 per cent of the year's wood production. White oak is highly valued for floors and furniture. Maple is a fine-grained, hard wood much prized for ballroom floors, furniture, and other purposes. Curly maple and bird's-eye maple are valued as wood for making veneer, especially in bedroom furniture. Veneer is a superior finish obtained by laying thin sheets of the more beautiful kinds of wood over the cheaper or less attractive kinds. Curly maple has a wavy grain, and bird's-eye maple has numerous glistening points scattered through it,

thought to be undeveloped adventitious buds.

Black walnut, cherry, and mahogany are very valuable for furniture. Hickory, elm, and ash are used for handles of tools and for parts of vehicles where toughness is required. Birch, apple wood, holly, and box are sought for turned articles. Cedar, larch, and cypress are used for posts and poles, and basswood for trunks and crates on account of its toughness, lightness, and elasticity.

Some trees, besides fruit trees, furnish valuable products other than wood. Some maple trees furnish sugar and sirup. Chestnut, hickory, walnut, and other trees give us nuts year after year, as well as lumber when they are cut down. Willow trees give us a superior kind of charcoal used in medicine and in making certain kinds of gunpowder; the poplars and basswood or linden give us excelsior, so useful in packing and making cheap upholstery.

Turpentine, obtained from pine trees, is used in paint and varnish. Resin, another product of pine, has many uses. Wood alcohol, so useful as fuel, is obtained from wood wastes such as sawdust and shavings. Another valuable product, and one that is rapidly increasing in importance, is paper. Paper in various forms is gradually taking the place of many other products made from lumber. Rayon, made from wood pulp, has innumerable uses, especially for wearing apparel.

Hemlock bark which contains a large amount of tannic acid is used for tanning leather. Chestnut and oak are also used although they contain smaller amounts.

Among the many other uses of trees in our daily life may be mentioned poles for telegraph, telephone, and electric light wires, masts of ships, piles for piers, timbers for props of mines, lumber for bridge foundations, railroad ties, parts of implements and tools of daily use, vehicles, and parts of machines. Add to these the boxes, barrels, crates, trunks, pails, baskets, and other common articles which we use frequently. It is evident from this extensive list, which is far from complete, that man is seriously dependent on trees and that he could not well do without them.

One of the most valuable products of trees is rubber, which is made from *latex,* the sap of the rubber tree. The value of this product and the extent of its use are enormous. Rubbers, rainy-weather apparel, heels, erasers, bands, and wire insulation are only a few of its many uses, chief of which, in this country, is for the manufacture of automobile tires.

FACTS TO REMEMBER

The *Gymnosperms* are vascular plants with naked seeds borne on *cones.* The *conifers,* or *evergreens,* are the most numerous of this group. The stem and root structure is similar to the flowering plants, and the leaves are *needles* which make food for the plant. Most conifers shed a few needles at a time, thus remaining green.

The evergreens bear *pistillate* and *staminate* cones. The pollen formed in the staminate cones is blown by the wind to the pistillate cones, where the seeds are formed. When the ovules are fertilized they remain in the cone until they are mature, and the seeds are ripe.

Evergreens are valuable to man for lumber and other forest products. They are planted around water sheds to aid in soil conservation and are also grown as crop plants.

WORDS TO REMEMBER

air sac	forestry	pistillate cone
angiosperm	gymnosperm	pruning
annual ring	humus	resin
cone	latex	resin canal
conifer	lumbering	seasoned
erosion	medullary ray	staminate cone
evergreen	needles	wood ray
forest	nursery	

QUESTIONS

1. Name two groups of vascular plants. Give their characteristics.

2. How are evergreens like other plants? How do they differ?

3. What kind of trunk is characteristic of soft woods?

4. Describe the branches of the pine; the leaves; the roots.

5. Where is the pollen formed? How does it reach the ovule?

6. Where is the fruit formed and how is it released?

7. Name several of the evergreens. How are the needles used in distinguishing them?

8. Tell how forests are useful to man.

9. Why is reforestation necessary?

10. What is being done to conserve our forests?

11. What are the duties of a forester? A forest ranger?

12. What is forestry?

13. How does a tree which grows in a forest differ from one which grows in an open field? Why?

14. What are annual rings? How are they formed?

15. Name various wooden articles that are in everyday use.

16. Make a list of the uses to which lumber is put.

17. What other products come from the evergreen forests?

18. What regions in your own state are covered with forests?

COMPLETION TEST

As your teacher or classmate reads the following incomplete statements, with your book closed, write on a clean sheet of paper the word or phrase which correctly completes the statement.

1. _____ give a rough estimate of the age of a tree.

2. The pollen of the pine is carried by the _____.

3. _____ have scalelike leaves.

4. The bark of the _____ was formerly used in tanning leather.

5. A fungus which causes disease of forest trees is _____.

6. Rich, fertile soil found in forests is called _____.

7. An exposed cut surface of a shade tree should be covered with _____.

8. One of the most valuable products derived from trees is _____.

PROJECTS

Observation of Trees.—Most of the work in connection with conifers should be done out of doors. Each of you should learn to know by sight all the local native evergreens and those commonly planted for ornament. You should note the method of branching and the character of the trunk compared with other trees. You should observe the position of the cones on the branches and be able to give the reasons therefor. In the spring look for the male and female organs, and for leaf buds in the winter. Examine the leaf scars and the external rings which mark a year's growth, and decide how many years each tree keeps its leaves. Note the arrangement of the leaves on the branches, the annual rings in the wood and their relation to the grain of the wood, the resin on wounds, the curvature of the branches, and other features.

1. Make a list of the trees you know by sight. What are the characteristics of each? What are they used for?
2. Make a list of all other trees known to grow in your locality.

REFERENCES

Collingwood, *Knowing Your Trees*. American Forestry Association.
Curtis, *A Guide to the Trees*. Greenberg.
Curtis, *Stories In Trees*. Lyons and Carnahan.
Hough, *American Woods*. Hough, Lowville.
Keeler, *Handbook of Trees*. Houghton Mifflin.
Kieran, *An Introduction to Trees*. Hanover House.
Mills, *The Story of a Thousand-Year Pine*. Houghton Mifflin.
Moon, *The Book of Forestry*. Appleton.
Parker, *Trees*. Row Peterson.
Sargent, *Trees of North America*. Houghton Mifflin.
Yeager, *Bob Flame, Ranger*. Dodd, Mead.
Zim, Martin, *Trees: Golden Nature Guide*. Simon and Schuster.

COMPREHENSIVE TEST ON PART FOUR

I. Complete the following statements.
1. Plants without stems, roots, or leaves belong to the group of _____.
2. A plant unable to make its own food is _____.
3. Simple one-celled green plants are called _____.
4. The _____ reproduces by alternation of generations.
5. In the liverwort and moss the _____ stage is the more conspicuous.
6. Mushrooms are called _____ when they live on decaying organic matter.
7. Spirogyra reproduce by fission and _____.
8. When bacteria grow they produce enzymes or _____.
9. _____ bacteria form nodules on the roots of legumes.
10. The _____ has true roots, stems, and leaves but reproduces by spores.

II. Copy the words in column A, and opposite each write the word in column B that is most closely related.

A	B
1. leaf	circulation
2. root hair	transpiration
3. chlorophyll	pollination
4. fibrovascular bundle	germination
5. stomata	fertilization
6. flower	protection
7. pistil	photosynthesis
8. bark	absorption
9. seed	nutrition
10. ovule	reproduction

THE VASCULAR PLANTS

III. Copy the words or expressions in column A. Opposite each, write the word or expression in B that is most closely related.

A	B
1. storage place in the corn grain	chlorophyll
2. manufacture of food	medullary ray
3. liquid part of the blood	transpiration
4. passageway between pith and bark	lenticel
5. beneficial insect	spiracle
6. chemical change	cotyledon
7. pollen	endosperm
8. element	sperm cell
9. seed leaf	testa
10. opening in the bark	oxygen
	plasma
	dragon fly
	clothes moth
	digestion
	freezing of water

IV. Write your answers to the following on a separate sheet of paper:

1. Name six of the important functions common to all forms of life.

2. Describe how you can prove that one of these functions takes place in an animal or a plant.

3. Tell how your answer to 2 illustrates the scientific method.

V. Observe the following: a burning candle, a jar of germinating pea seeds, and a living frog.

1. What important process is going on all the time in these things?

2. What two substances are required to carry on this process?

3. What two substances are given off as a result of this process?

4. How can you prove that this process is going on in the candle or the seeds or the frog?

VI. List the numbers of the *Applications* below. After each number, write the letter of the *Principle* that corresponds to that *Application*.

Applications

1. Salt spilled on garden earth kills the plants in it.

2. Geranium leaves turn toward the light.

3. Germinating pea seeds turn lime water milky.

4. The roots of popular trees often stop up drain pipes.

5. All flowers must contain either pistils or stamens or both.

6. Green plants will not thrive in a cellar.

7. The temperature of the air in a bell jar containing a green plant is slightly higher than it is outside the jar.

8. Seeds do not need to be placed in the ground in any particular position to insure the downward growth of the roots.

9. Bacteria multiply by cell fission.

A. Plants absorb soil water by osmosis.

B. Sunlight is necessary to green plants.

C. Plant roots are influenced in their growth by gravity and water.

D. Oxidation goes on in all living things.

E. Life is maintained in the world through the process of reproduction.

VII. Copy the one word in each of the following groups of related words that includes all the others in the group:

1. ameba, protozoan, microorganism, bacterium, paramecium
2. bat, whale, cow, mammal, woodchuck
3. grasshopper, fly, insect, locust, ant
4. frog, animal, fish, insect, man
5. root hair, protozoan, cell, white corpuscle, neuron

VIII. Copy the number of each statement and opposite it write the word or group of words which best completes its meaning.

1. _____ forms the living parts of a cell.
2. _____ is a denser central portion that governs the actions of the cell.
3. _____ are formed by groups of similar cells.
4. _____ is the name given to animals that consist of one cell.
5. _____ is the process by which cells obtain their food and oxygen.
6. _____ is the name applied to the smallest one-celled plants.
7. _____ is the type of reproduction usually found in one-celled plants and animals.
8. _____ is the process by which lifeless food is changed until it becomes a part of the living cell.
9. _____ is the elimination of waste from a cell.
10. _____ is the individual's response to outside stimuli.

IX. Under A are listed five conclusions of experiments. Under B are listed five related statements arranged in different order. Show the relation between each conclusion and its corresponding statement under B.

A

1. Green plants give off water through their leaves.
2. Starch is changed to grape sugar during germination.
3. Root hairs absorb dissolved minerals by osmosis.
4. Green plants absorb energy from the sun when they make starch.
5. The sap of a maple tree passes down through the bark.

B

1. Most seeds contain digestible nutrients but seldom digested foods.
2. Farmers are using an increased amount of commercial fertilizers.
3. Girdling a tree kills it in a short time.
4. Showers are frequent in the Adirondack Mountains in summer.
5. Corn grows most rapidly during the hottest months.

THE VASCULAR PLANTS

Part Five

Biology Past and Future

UNIT **XI**

Life Through the Ages

The Beginnings of Life. Man has long been interested in knowing how life began on this earth. He has had a desire to find out more about his ancestors, and what life was like in ages past for both animals and men. He has searched the whole world over; from frozen wastes to tropical jungles; from ocean depths to lofty heights; from deep quarry pits to mountain tops; and has found the remains of plants and animals. He has found records in the rocks of footprints, of whole animal bodies, of implements of early man, and of paintings on the walls of caves. From all of this evidence, scientists believe that through a method not known or understood some giant molecules became possessed with the power to produce others like themselves. Life in its simplest form began. All kinds of simple water plants and animals developed, land forms appeared, and life progressed to its highest form. In Unit XI you will discover many interesting facts about these early forms.

Classification of Living Forms. Early man had to spend most of his time in obtaining food and in protecting himself. As he progressed and had more time to think about the plants and animals around him, he began to sort them and place them in groups. Man placed forms that had the same basic structure in the same large group. He placed the elephants in a different group from the cats and dogs, but he put them all in the larger group of mammals and the still larger group of vertebrates. In Unit XI you will learn how the plants and animals you have studied are classified. You will investigate some of the evidence of relationships that have enabled scientists to arrive at the classifications.

Knowing Your Ancestors. If you search your family records you may discover which members had certain colors of hair and eyes, which ones were tall or short, thin or stocky, had musical or artistic talents, or mechanical or creative abilities. By studying the laws of heredity in Unit XI you may gain some idea of your chances of inheriting these talents. You also will study how life in ages past has affected present-day life.

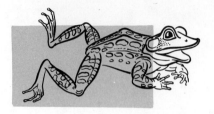

CHAPTER 41

Life Processes of Plants and Animals

41.1   Life Processes

In our study of plants and animals, we have learned many facts about the way they live, the places where they are found, and their importance to man. We have discovered for ourselves that all plants and animals carry on the same life processes but perform them in different ways.

We remember that the *life processes* (Sec. 1.6) which all plants and animals carry on are: irritability, motion, food-getting, digestion, absorption, respiration, circulation, excretion, secretion, and reproduction. These processes are vital to the existence of all living things. Different plants and animals differ in the structures with which they carry on these life processes. The diagrams in this chapter show comparisons of these body structures beginning with the simplest and proceeding to the higher forms. Study the diagrams carefully as you review the life processes in this chapter. The diagrams given here should help you to understand how different kinds of living things obtain food, digest it, and use it to build their bodies.

41.2   Irritability

You will recall that **irritability** *is the response of plants and animals to stimuli.* In Figure 41-1 you will find illustrations of the way living things respond to vari-

ous stimuli, such as light, temperature, pressure, and vibrations. The simplest organisms respond to a stimulus either by going toward it or moving away from it. In one-celled plants and animals and in those without nervous systems, this type of response is called a **tropism** (Sec. 39.7) and is inherited. That means that all euglenas react in the same manner to light. They move toward diffuse light. All amebas respond to light by moving away from it.

The leaves of some plants, like the oxalis, open in the light and fold in the dark. You will also find the leaves turning toward the light. This is *phototropism* (Sec. 39.7). Can you give other examples of simple animals or plants and their tropisms in relation to light?

Air Pressure.—Pleurococcus grows on the side of a tree away from the wind. This arrangement protects pleurococcus from too rapid evaporation of moisture. Sometimes trees are bent in the direction away from the prevailing wind. Trees also grow out of shape or become dwarfed and deformed when subjected to constant wind pressure.

Temperature.—In response to low temperatures frogs go below the freezing line. They usually bury themselves in the mud at the bottom of a pond and go into a resting, or dormant, state. They breathe through their skin during this

564

Pleurococcus grows on the side of the tree away from the wind.

Wind direction

Trees are permanently bent by constant wind in the same direction.

Wind

Euglena

Light

Ameba

Euglena moves toward the light, ameba away from it.

Oxalis opens its leaves in the light and folds them in the dark.

Plants grow toward the light.

The frog buries itself in the bottom of a pond when cold weather comes.

The ear of a crayfish is a simple organ on the antenna

The eye of a crayfish is on a stalk and movable.

The eye of a vertebrate is a complex organ, efficient under varied conditions.

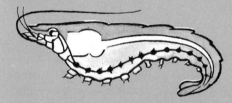

The nervous system of the crayfish is on the floor of its abdomen.

The human ear has a complicated set of apparatus for collecting vibrations.

The nervous system of vertebrates is on the dorsal surface. It has special organs highly developed to interpret the environment of the animal.

Taste is more highly developed in vertebrates than in lower animals.

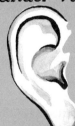

Taste bud in rabbit

FIGURE 41-1. *IRRITABILITY*

time. In response to warmer weather frogs come to the top of the water and swim to the edge of the pond.

Some animals go into a resting stage during the hottest weather in a state of *estivation*. Bears and woodchucks sleep during the winter in a state of *hibernation*. Some birds travel to a warmer climate, a habit known as *migration*. Other animals respond in their own ways to seasonal changes (page 6, Figure 1-4).

Some trees and shrubs become inactive or dormant during the colder months. Growth is usually slower during seasons of low temperature and more rapid during warmer seasons. Both plants and animals grow best in the temperature range for which they are fitted.

Nervous Systems.—Plants do not have nervous systems. They respond to their environment through tropisms and growth, as do the simplest animals.

The beginning of the nervous system in animals is found among the invertebrates. Some of the simplest nervous systems consist of scattered nerve cells that control the immediate structures, as the tentacles of a jellyfish or sea anemone, but this network of nerve cells does not provide much coordination for the animal.

A typical simple nervous system usually consists of a *ventral* chain of **ganglia** as in the crayfish. These ganglia are shown in Figure 41-1 as black dots connected by lines. The responses of this nervous system are automatic.

In higher animals, the vertebrates, the nervous system is on the *dorsal* side. There is also a larger, better developed nerve structure known as the **brain.** Compare the location of the nervous systems shown in Figure 41-1.

Some responses of higher animals are also automatic. The *reflexes* in man are automatic. An example is jumping at a sudden sound or blinking at a bright light. Other responses are *learned responses,* as habits of walking and writing. Still others require thought for each response, such as the interpretation of objects seen by the eye or heard by the ear.

From this discussion and your study of Figure 41-1 you will observe that there is a progressive development of the nervous system from the very simple like that of the earthworm (Sec. 7.6) to the well-developed system of man.

Sense Organs.—In animals with nervous systems, special sense organs are often developed. The crayfish, an invertebrate, possesses *antennae* and *antennules,* which serve as organs of touch and thus protect the animal. The *eye* is compound and attached to a movable stalk. Compare the compound eye with the simple eye of man, a vertebrate. The type of eye is a distinguishing characteristic. Be sure you know how each is constructed and how it functions.

The structure of the *ears,* which respond to sound waves, varies in animals. In the crayfish the ear is a very simple organ. In man it consists of a complicated set of apparatus for receiving vibrations. Can you recall the type of ears, if any, that are found in grasshoppers (Sec. 9-5), fish, frogs, birds, and other animals? Review the structure of the ear of man.

Likewise consider the sense of *taste* in animals and find out whether other animals have a sense of taste at all comparable to that of man. Observe your dog or cat. What kinds of food does it prefer?

Sense organs specialize in the reception of certain stimuli. Fish have a *lateral line* sense organ to respond to

FIGURE 41-2.

ADAPTATION

The woodcock, like many other birds, is especially suited to its life in the woods. The feathers are wood brown in color with black bars. This protective coloration enables the bird to blend into the surroundings and escape its enemies.

vibrations in the water. Some fish also have sensitive feelers about the mouth. You may recall that other specialized sense organs such as eyes and ears, vary with different kinds of animals. Yet all sense organs perform the life process known as *irritability*.

41.3 Motion

The ability of a living thing to move is known as **motion.** Do plants show motion? You will recall the creeping movement of slime molds (Sec. 32.3); the movement of growth of seedlings and of enormous trees; the closing of the oxalis at night; the drooping of a branch of Mimosa; and the turning of leaves toward light. The peanut flower is fertilized above ground, but the plant pulls this part of the stem and the developing seed underground. In Figure 41-3 you will note how Vallisnera coils its stem to pull its blossom under water. Diatoms and desmids, some of the tiniest aquatic plants, move about in the water. The diatoms are boxlike and free floating. Desmids change their shape. All these are plant movements and play an important part in the life of the plant.

Animals move much more rapidly and greater distances than most plants. Recall the tiniest animals which you have studied. Among the Protozoa, ameba moves by *pseudopodia;* paramecium, by *cilia;* and euglena, by *flagella*. The heliozoan moves by creeping on the tips of its projections. Rotifers move by cilia and tail.

Invertebrates have a variety of methods of locomotion. Among these are (1) creeping—the starfish with its tube feet, and the clam with its muscular foot; (2) crawling—the crayfish and earthworm; (3) walking—spiders and centipedes; (4) jumping—the grasshopper and cricket; (5) gliding—grasshoppers and katydids; (6) flying—butterflies and bees; and (7) swimming—the octopus and crab.

The structures which make possible these various methods of locomotion are very interesting. Try to name the part of the body each animal uses in moving and explain how that body part is adapted for motion. For example, the earthworm has longitudinal and circular muscles which expand and contract. It also has bristles called *setae,* which keep

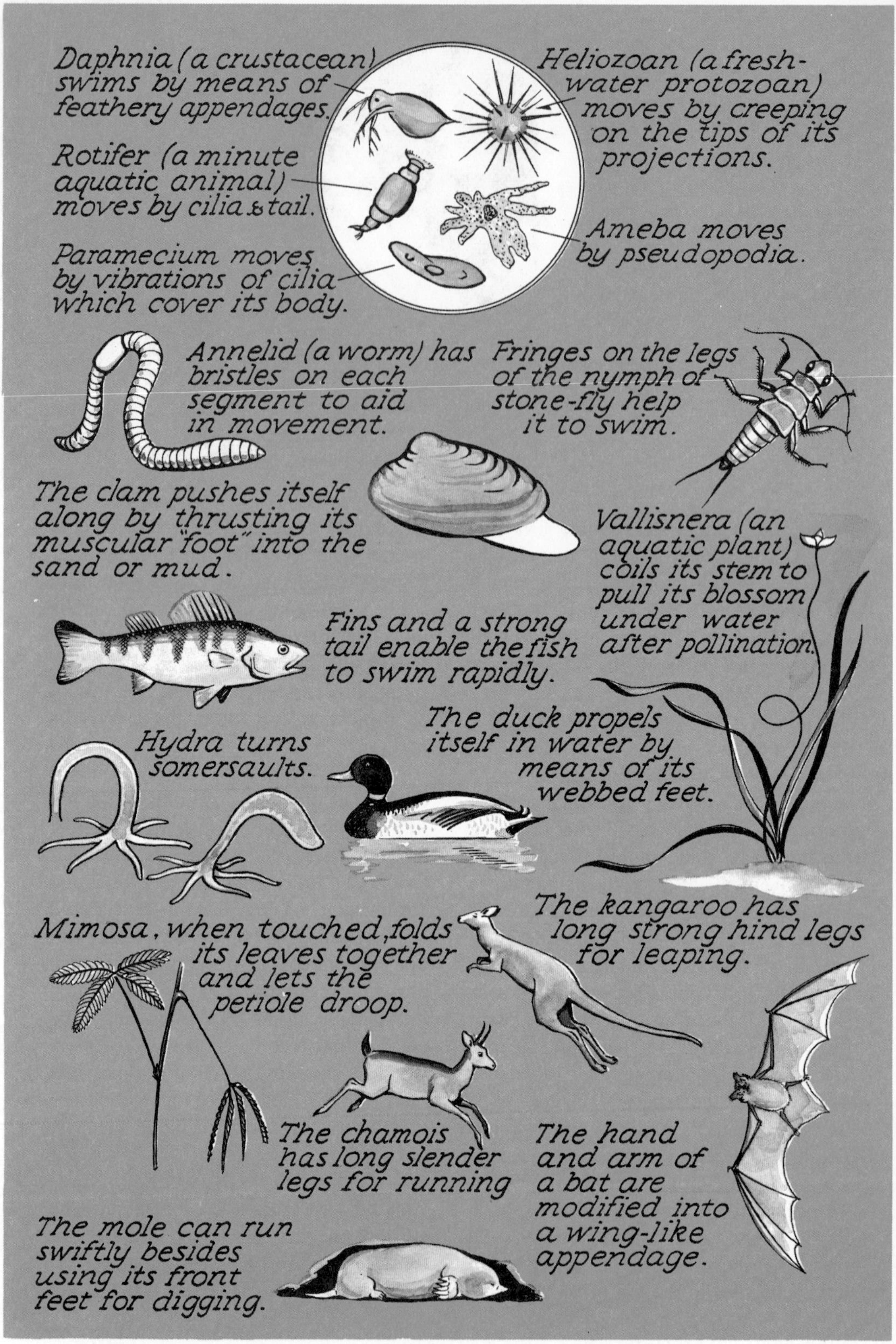

Daphnia (a crustacean) swims by means of feathery appendages.

Heliozoan (a fresh-water protozoan) moves by creeping on the tips of its projections.

Rotifer (a minute aquatic animal) moves by cilia & tail.

Ameba moves by pseudopodia.

Paramecium moves by vibrations of cilia which cover its body.

Annelid (a worm) has bristles on each segment to aid in movement.

Fringes on the legs of the nymph of stone-fly help it to swim.

The clam pushes itself along by thrusting its muscular "foot" into the sand or mud.

Vallisnera (an aquatic plant) coils its stem to pull its blossom under water after pollination.

Fins and a strong tail enable the fish to swim rapidly.

Hydra turns somersaults.

The duck propels itself in water by means of its webbed feet.

Mimosa, when touched, folds its leaves together and lets the petiole droop.

The kangaroo has long strong hind legs for leaping.

The chamois has long slender legs for running

The hand and arm of a bat are modified into a wing-like appendage.

The mole can run swiftly besides using its front feet for digging.

FIGURE 41-3. *MOTION*

the earthworm from slipping backward. You will want to explain how water insect nymphs like those of the stone-fly are able to swim.

Vertebrates also show variety in locomotion and adaptation of structures. The fins of the fish, the webbed feet of the duck, and the flippers of a whale fit these animals for swimming. The wings of bats are adaptations for flying. Special folds of skin in flying squirrels enable them to glide through the air. The hind legs of frogs and kangaroos are long for jumping. The legs of deer and chamois are slender for running. Moles have wide front feet with claws for digging. Sheep have sharp hoofs and monkeys have tails for climbing. Snakes possess muscular bodies and scales for crawling. All of them show motion but the speed of movement in these animals varies.

Motion and locomotion are important to living things. In order to make food, plants need to grow and turn toward the sunlight. Animals need to move about in search of food and to escape their enemies. Their very rapid speed enables some, like rabbits, to move quickly out of danger. Others, like the elephant, use their trunks as means of defense against their enemies and depend on locomotion for food and water. As a life process of living things, motion is essential.

41.4 Food-getting and Nutrition

Plants and animals need food to build new tissue for growth, to repair wornout tissue, and to supply energy.

You know that green plants can manufacture their own food (Sec. 35.10). They store it in their leaves, stems, and roots. Food is also stored in the fruit. The amounts of food stored in these structures varies with the kind of plant.

Cabbages store food in the leaves; celery, in the stems; and beets, in the roots.

Non-green plants, such as bacteria, are able to use this stored plant food by producing enzymes which digest it and make it into a form which can be absorbed and assimilated.

Figure 41-4 shows the wide variety of *digestive systems* to be found in animals. Ameba, with only one cell, forms *food vacuoles* where the food remains until it is digested. Hydra possesses a hollow central cavity which holds the food while digestion takes place. Study the diagram of the earthworm carefully. Note that the digestive system is shaped like a hollow tube with only a small enlargement for a crop and one for the gizzard. Then note the similarity to the digestive systems of the grasshopper and crayfish. Each has a mouth opening, an esophagus or gullet, an enlargement for a stomach, and tubelike intestines. These animals have special structures known as **glands.** The glands produce secretions which enable the animals to digest their food better.

Next study the diagram of the fish and note how its digestive system differs. Compare it with the digestive system of the frog. In each case note how the systems are adaptations of a simple tube similar to that of the earthworm.

When you have compared the fish and the frog, look at the bird. Here there is a specialized structure, the *crop,* to hold the food, and a *gizzard,* to grind it. Since the bird has no teeth, a grinding organ is necessary.

Compare the bird with a mammal. Note the *diaphragm* in the rabbit and the sheep. This is typical of all mammals. It divides the chest and abdominal cavities. Compare the digestive systems of the rabbit and sheep. Both animals have salivary glands in the mouth, an

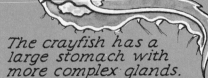

Ameba digests its food in food vacuoles.

Food is made only in the plant cells that contain chloroplasts.

The hydra takes food into its central cavity to digest it.

The earthworm has a tubular digestive system of definite parts with simple digestive glands.

The crayfish has a large stomach with more complex glands.

The locust has a large stomach, short intestine, and large glands.

The fish has a branched stomach and a curved intestine.

The frog has stomach, coiled intestine, pancreas near stomach, and cloaca.

A bird has crop, gizzard, long intestine with two branches on it.

A rabbit has salivary glands simple stomach beyond the diaphragm, pancreas, liver, and a coiled intestine with one large branch.

A sheep has salivary glands, a stomach in four divisions, pancreas, more difference in size in regions of the intestine, and one short branch.

Figure 41-4. *NUTRITION*

FIGURE 41-5. *TWO HUNGRY MAMMALS*

The giant anteater (*right*) has a slender snout much like the nozzle of a hose, and a sticky tongue, both useful for scooping up insects. The chipmunk (*left*) holds melon seeds and grinds them with sharp teeth.

esophagus, stomach, intestines, liver, and pancreas. But there is a difference in the stomachs. The sheep is a **ruminant** (*roo*-mih-n'nt), an animal which chews its *cud*. It has four divisions of its stomach to adapt it to making provision for temporary storage of food and another place for digesting it later.

When you pause to think of the habits of the ancestors of the cow and sheep, you may understand why such structures were developed. These animals fed on grass or low-growing vegetation found in open country. In places where these animals were wild and not protected by man, they easily fell prey to predatory animals like tigers and lions. To escape such risks the ancestors of animals, like cows and sheep, learned to eat fast, swallowing their food whole, and then to seek protective covering in the shade of trees. There they could lie down and chew their cuds. Over a period of time certain animals developed stomachs with four parts that better adapted them to live in their environment. Those animals were the ones that survived.

Study the diagrams again and try to explain why a rabbit and a man do not need more than one stomach. Again review the diagrams and be able to trace in your own words the development of the digestive systems of various animals from a simple tubelike structure to more complex forms.

The kind of food an animal can eat is partly dependent upon the structures he has to obtain it—the trunk of an elephant, the snout of a whale, the gnawing teeth of a beaver, the beak of a bird, the tongue of a frog, the jaws of a snake and the mouth opening of a starfish.

Each animal must obtain such food as it is able to take into its body and digest. The digested food is then *absorbed*. In animals with a circulatory system, the digested food has a means of transportation to all parts of the body. Body cells take the material needed and use it for growth and the repair of tissues in the process of *assimilation*.

Nutrition *is the means by which food is taken into the body, digested, absorbed, distributed, and assimilated.* The food needs may vary; the body structures may vary; but the process is essential to both plants and animals. Although only green plants manufacture food, all plants digest, absorb and assimilate whatever food material is present for their use.

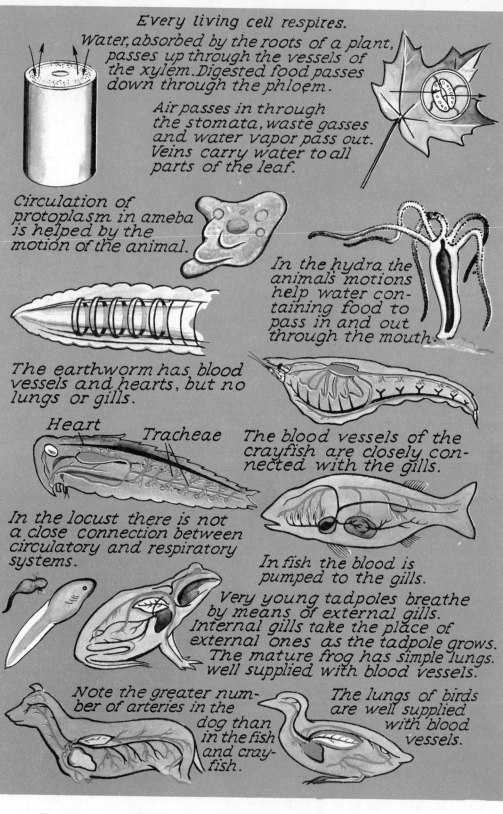

Every living cell respires.

Water, absorbed by the roots of a plant, passes up through the vessels of the xylem. Digested food passes down through the phloem.

Air passes in through the stomata, waste gasses and water vapor pass out. Veins carry water to all parts of the leaf.

Circulation of protoplasm in ameba is helped by the motion of the animal.

In the hydra the animal's motions help water containing food to pass in and out through the mouth.

The earthworm has blood vessels and hearts, but no lungs or gills.

Heart   Tracheae   The blood vessels of the crayfish are closely connected with the gills.

In the locust there is not a close connection between circulatory and respiratory systems.

In fish the blood is pumped to the gills.

Very young tadpoles breathe by means of external gills. Internal gills take the place of external ones as the tadpole grows. The mature frog has simple lungs. well supplied with blood vessels.

Note the greater number of arteries in the dog than in the fish and crayfish.

The lungs of birds are well supplied with blood vessels.

FIGURE 41-6. *RESPIRATION AND CIRCULATION*

41.5 Respiration and Circulation

The life process by which oxygen is taken into the cells and carbon dioxide is given off from the cells is known as **respiration**. In ameba this takes place at the surface of the whole animal since it possesses only one cell. In hydra and other simple organisms, respiration takes place directly in the cells. In higher forms of plant and animal life, there are breathing organs or other structures by means of which there is an exchange of oxygen and carbon dioxide.

In the higher plants, there are *stomata* on the leaf, where oxygen and carbon dioxide are exchanged according to the plant needs. There are also *lenticels* on the bark of trees, which allow the plant to breathe.

In the higher animals there is a variety of structures for breathing. Study the diagrams in Figure 41-6. The earthworm has a thin moist skin which makes it possible to take in oxygen by osmosis. Crayfish and fish possess *gills*. Insects breathe by means of *spiracles* and *tracheae*. Tadpoles breathe by gills, but adult frogs breathe by simple lungs and through the skin.

Birds and mammals have well developed respiratory systems with *lungs* well supplied with blood vessels for transporting oxygen to the cells.

From a study of these diagrams you should be able to point out the adaptations of the respiratory system. Describe the simple cell living in the water; the development of breathing structures, such as gills for water life, and lungs and skin for life on land.

As a life process, respiration is very important. Living things depend upon the intake of oxygen to burn their food to supply heat and energy. The organs of respiration, or breathing organs, are so constructed that they are closely associated with tiny blood vessels. These carry oxygen to the cells and bring back carbon dioxide to be released from the body.

Circulation *is the life process by which vital substances are distributed throughout the body and waste materials removed.* Plants absorb moisture through their *root hairs* by means of *osmosis*. The water thus taken into the plants passes up the stem through the *xylem*. Digested food passes downward through the *phloem* as shown in the diagram (Fig. 41-6). Water passes through the *veins* in the leaf. Excess moisture is excreted through the stomata of the leaves by *transpiration*.

In plants there is no pumping organ comparable to the heart of man. Osmotic pressure and other forces tend to maintain sufficient pressure to control circulation in plants.

The ameba has no special organ of circulation. The protoplasm of ameba moves as the animal moves. The movement of the tentacles of hydra aid in bringing food particles into the mouth. Such activity also brings the cells in contact with fresh water. This helps the animal to breathe and aids in circulation.

The earthworm has five small hearts which form rings around the anterior section of the intestine. It also has large dorsal and ventral arteries. Study the diagram of the earthworm. The blood of the earthworm is red, but the corpuscles have no color.

The crayfish has blood vessels closely connected with the gills. There are also several main *arteries* leading from the heart. They end in *sinuses* and do not make a *closed system*.

Compare the circulatory system of the crayfish with that of the grasshopper. Note that both of them have the *heart* and large blood vessels on the dorsal

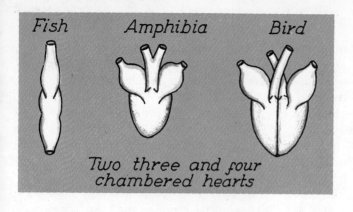

Fish   Amphibia   Bird

Two three and four chambered hearts

FIGURE 41-7. *HEART DEVELOPMENT*

Only birds and mammals have a four-chambered heart, which makes possible a constant, high body temperature, and two separate circulatory systems, the pulmonary and systemic.

side. This is a characteristic of invertebrates. Since the grasshopper has tracheal tubes leading to the cells for respiration, there is no close connection between the respiratory and circulatory systems.

Among the vertebrates there are animals which breathe by gills, the fish; those which breathe by lungs and skin, the frog; and those breathing entirely by lungs, as man. The heart is a pumping organ located on the ventral side of the body. In the fish note its relation to the gills where the blood is pumped in order to receive its supply of oxygen.

You will recall that fish have two-chambered hearts; amphibia, three-chambered hearts; reptiles, three-chambered hearts, partly or completely divided; and birds and mammals, four-chambered hearts.

These factors are important in the maintenance of a high body temperature. Only the birds and mammals are able to maintain a constant circulation of blood sufficient to keep the body temperature high.

You should be able to trace the development of the circulatory systems of animals from the simple structures in the earthworm to the more complex circulatory systems of the dog and man. Circulation as a life process is very important, since the blood distributes oxygen, food, glandular secretions, and

hormones. The blood also collects wastes for disposal in the kidneys, skin and lungs.

41.6 Excretion and Secretion

*Waste materials are eliminated from the body by the life process, **excretion**.* Plants excrete excess water through the stomata in the leaves. Mineral wastes are deposited in the leaves and other parts of the plant. When the leaves are shed, the minerals are thus deposited back in the soil. The white ashes remaining after wood is burned are the minerals that were deposited in the cells of the living tree.

Animals have as many different methods and structures for excretion as they do for some of their other life processes.

Ameba excretes liquid wastes through the *contractile vacuole*. Solid wastes are pushed out of the cell at any place. They are excreted directly through the cell membrane.

Since hydra has only one opening to the hollow body cavity, the mouth, the undigested food particles are excreted there.

The earthworm has a pair of *nephridia* (neh-*frid*-ee-uh) in each segment which aid in the elimination of liquid wastes. These nephridia consist of tiny coiled tubes. A funnel of one tubule collects the waste material of an adjacent segment and carries it to the

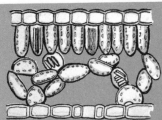

Plants store their mineral wastes in the form of crystals of various shapes.

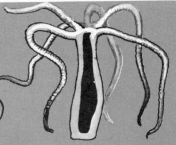

Ameba gets rid of liquid wastes by expelling them through the contractile vacuole.

The hydra uses its mouth for taking in food and expelling wastes.

The earthworm has a pair of nephridia in each segment, except the first 3. Each collects wastes from the one in front of it.

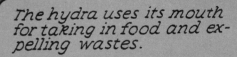

The crayfish has a pair of small organs of excretion in the anterior part of its body, the green glands.

The Malpighian tubules of the grasshopper are widely distributed throughout its body

In fish the excretory organs are paired kidneys. They are near the center of the body and have a short ureter.

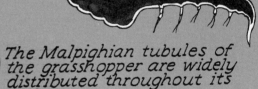

In the frog the kidneys are close to the backbone, have longer ureters, and open into a bladder connected with the cloaca.

A bird has kidneys but no bladder The ureters open into the cloaca

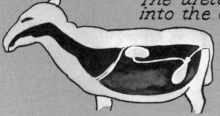

The kidneys of a mammal are compact, have long ureters and open into a bladder that is emptied through the urethra. The sheep has a typical urinary system.

FIGURE 41-8. *EXCRETION*

exterior. These are the simplest excretory structures that have any similarity to the *kidneys* of higher animals. Study the diagram in Figure 41-8. Note the funnel in one segment which is connected to the tube in the next one. Solid waste material in the earthworm and higher animals is excreted through the digestive tract.

The crayfish has a pair of *green glands* for excretion. They are located in the head region. Compare these structures with others, such as the *Malpighian tubules* of the grasshopper. These tiny tubules are structures which might be called the forerunners of the kidneys. **The wastes pass by diffusion from the cells where they are formed into the tubules of the excretory system and are thus carried to the exterior.**

The excretory systems in the vertebrates are much more similar to one another. Compare those of the fish, frog, bird, and mammal. You will note that each has a pair of kidneys composed of tiny tubules to collect wastes. The connecting tubes vary with the different animals. Note that all except the mammals have openings into the cloaca from both the intestines and ureters. You will also note other differences. Be prepared to tell how you think the excretory systems are adapted to help the particular animals perform the life function of excretion.

Secretion is the life process by which special substances such as enzymes and hormones (Sec. 26.2) *are produced and made available for use by the body.* These substances, called secretions, are required to carry on life activities. They are produced by duct-bearing and ductless glands (Fig. 26-1).

In the study of Figure 41-4 you will note the different kinds of digestive glands, such as salivary, gastric, liver

and pancreas. These are duct-bearing glands and pour their secretions into the digestive tract (Fig. 22-1). You may also wish to review the ductless glands and their secretions in Chapter 26. Plants also produce secretions but they are very few in comparison to animals.

41.7 Reproduction

The life process through which the race is maintained and life continues from generation to generation is known as **reproduction.** The life processes reviewed thus far in this chapter are essential to the life of the individual. Reproduction is essential to the life of the race.

The process of reproduction is similar in plants and animals. The simplest forms reproduce by cell division or *fission.* This is the division of a single cell to form two cells. Bacteria, Spirogyra, diatoms, ameba, paramecium, and others reproduce this way.

Study the diagrams in Figure 41-9. In addition, there are other methods of **asexual reproduction:** *spore formation,* as in yeasts, bread mold, and the malarial protozoan; *budding,* as in yeasts and sponges; *vegetative propagation,* as stolons, runners, and cuttings; and *regeneration,* as in flatworms and starfish.

Plants and animals also reproduce by the **sexual** method. In the diagram you will recognize Spirogyra in the process of *conjugation.* The protoplasm from two cells combine to form a sexual cell, the *zygospore.* Paramecia conjugate by exchanging nuclear material, a very simple form of sexual reproduction.

Some plants, like the liverworts, mosses, and ferns, which reproduce by both sexual and asexual methods, carry on this life process by alternating these two methods. This is called **alternation of generations.** The *sporophyte* (spore-bearing form) produces the spores which

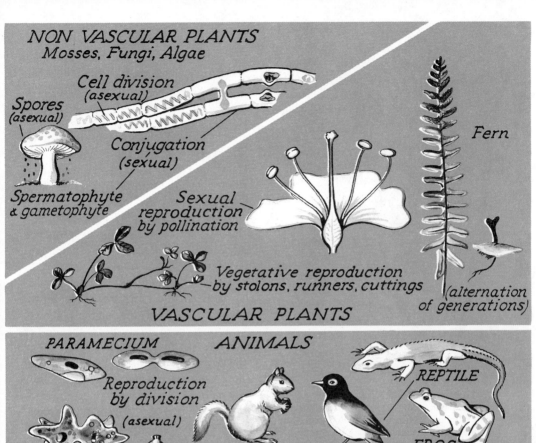

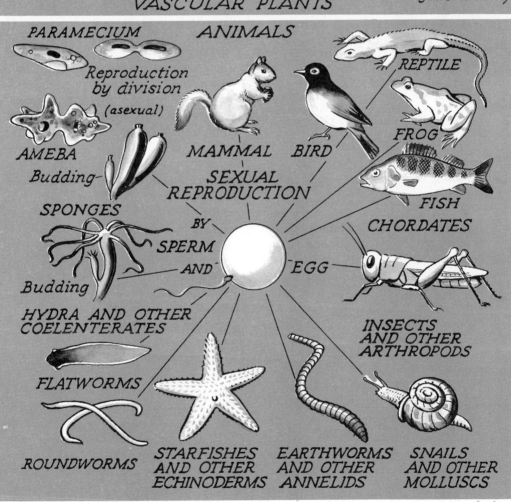

FIGURE 41-9. *REPRODUCTION*

FIGURE 41-10. *SEA HORSE
WITH YOUNG*

The male sea horse, not the female,
shelters the young in a pouch until they
are hatched. Here, several newly-hatched
babies can be seen near his head.

instead of growing into new plants similar
to themselves produce the *gametophyte,*
the form which bears the eggs and the
sperms.

In the diagram in Figure 41-9 the
frond of the fern (sporophyte generation)
is shown at the right and the heart-shaped
prothallus (gametophyte generation) is
shown near it. These represent alternation of generations in the fern. Some
animals also reproduce by this method.
Such an animal is *Obelia,* a colonial relative of the hydra.

The higher plants (Angiosperms and
Gymnosperms) and the higher animals
(Vertebrates) reproduce by the sexual
method. In the flowering plants the
sperm cells are formed in the *pollen.*
Through the process of *pollination* they
are transferred to the female part of the
plant where they are able to unite with

the egg cell and form a *seed.* The plant
structures which produce these eggs and
sperms vary widely with different plants
but the fundamental process remains the
same.

The reproductive organs of animals
also vary widely. Some animals, like
clams and fish, lay eggs in the water,
where they are fertilized by sperms which
have also been shed in the water. Other
animals, like birds, lay eggs that have
already been fertilized and are protected
by a shell. Still others, as mammals,
give birth to living young.

Study the diagrams in Figure 41-9 and
try to recall the structure of the reproductive organs of the animals shown.
You may need to turn to the earlier
chapters in this book and look at the
diagrams. You will recall that some of
these animals reproduce by *more than
one method.* Hydra reproduces by budding and also by eggs and sperms.
Paramecium reproduces by fission and
conjugation. Starfish have remarkable
powers of regeneration and reproduce
sexually. List as many different plants
and animals as you can that continue
their species by more than one method
of reproduction.

As you compare the various simpler
plants and animals, you will note that
those which have become the most
highly developed have also become
highly specialized in the reproductive
methods. This is also true of the flowering plants and of mammals including
man.

Reproduction as a life process is essential to the continuance of life to the
next generation. More young are produced than could exist on the food supply,
but this is necessary because some lose
their lives by accident and disease, not
living to maturity. In a later chapter
you will learn about the progression of

life not only from one generation to the next but from ages past to ages to come.

41.8 Importance of Life Processes

The life processes reviewed in this chapter are fundamental to the existence of life on the earth. All except reproduction are essential to the individual. Reproduction is necessary for race survival. Plants and animals possess a variety of organs and use a variety of methods to carry on these life processes. The body structures are adapted to carry on these life processes in the environment where the organisms are best fitted to live. As the environment changes, these organisms must either adapt themselves to these changes or move away. Otherwise they will not survive.

FACTS TO REMEMBER

Plants and animals carry on the same *life processes: irritability, motion, food-getting, digestion, absorption, assimilation, respiration, circulation, excretion, secretion,* and *reproduction.*

As plants and animals increase in complexity their organs and systems for carrying out their life processes become more highly developed and specialized. The structures become adapted to carry out their functions. Upon their ability to help the organism depends its survival.

WORDS TO REMEMBER

alteration of generations	ganglia	pseudopodia
antennae	gills	reflex
antennule	gizzard	regeneration
asexual reproduction	gland	reproduction
assimilation	green gland	respiration
budding	hibernation	root hair
cilia	hormone	ruminant
circulation	irritability	secretion
conjugation	kidney	seed
contractile vacuole	lateral line	setae
crop	lenticel	sexual reproduction
diaphragm	life processes	spiracle
digestion	Malpighian tubule	spore formation
dorsal	migration	sporophyte
enzyme	motion	stimuli
estivation	nephridia	stomata
excretion	nutrition	tracheae
fission	osmosis	transpiration
flagella	phloem	tropism
food vacuole	phototropism	vegetative propagation
frond	pollen	ventral
gametophyte	pollination	xylem
	prothallus	zygospore

QUESTIONS

1. Why are the life processes considered to be essential?
2. Make a list of the life processes and write a brief explanation of the meaning of each.
3. Study Figure 41-1 and name the stimuli to which the organisms are responding.
4. Compare the sense organs of the vertebrates and invertebrates shown in the diagram.
5. What is the chief difference in the location of the nervous system of the vertebrates and the invertebrates?
6. Explain how variations and adaptations of a hollow digestive tube similar to that of an earthworm, Figure 41-4, may form structures of a highly developed digestive system as in the bird.
7. Compare the circulatory systems of the vertebrates and invertebrates with regard to the location of the heart.
8. Why is it possible for birds and mammals to maintain high body temperatures?
9. Name one organism which possesses each of the following breathing organs and describe the organs: spiracles, gills, skin, lungs, stomata.
10. How does a nephridium of an earthworm resemble the internal structure of a vertebrate kidney (Figure 41-8)?
11. List as many plants and animals as you can which reproduce both sexually and asexually. Describe their reproductive methods.
12. What is meant by alternation of generations?

COMPLETION TEST

As your teacher or classmate reads the following incomplete statements, with your book closed, write on a clean sheet of paper the word or phrase that correctly completes the statement.

1. The asexual method of reproduction in hydra is _____.
2. The sexual method of reproduction in paramecium is _____.
3. The excretory organs of crayfish are called _____.
4. Malpighian tubules are found in the body of the _____.
5. The openings in the leaves for the exchange of gases and excretion of water are called _____.
6. Mammals possess a muscular _____ which separates the chest and abdominal cavities.
7. The central nervous system is located on the _____ side of vertebrates.
8. A tropism is the response of simple organisms to _____.
9. Food is made only in the plant cells that contain _____.
10. Ameba excretes liquid wastes through the _____ _____.

PROJECTS

Methods of Locomotion.—List all the methods of locomotion shown in Figure

LIFE THROUGH THE AGES

41-3. Beside each give the name of the animal and its adaptation for that method of locomotion. Make a table like this:

Method of Locomotion	Animal	Adaptation
Flying	Bats	Wings

REFERENCES

Andrews, *Nature's Ways, How Nature Takes Care of Its Own.* Crown.
Dietz, *The Story of Science.* The New Home Library.
Hegner, *Parade of the Animal Kingdom.* Macmillan.
Sedgwick and Tyler, *Short History of Science.* Macmillan.
Transeau, *General Botany.* Blakiston.

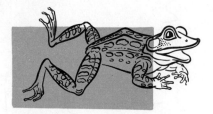

CHAPTER 42

Factors in Heredity

42.1   What Is Heredity?

Heredity refers to those characteristics which are passed on from one generation to the next. Children resemble their parents. Young plants and animals develop and grow in much the same way as their parents. They also inherit the characteristics of the species. Chickens have characteristics of a particular kind of bird, the fowl. Puppies resemble dogs. The puppies not only grow to

FIGURE 42-1. *GREGOR MENDEL*

Gregor Mendel (1822-1884) was an Austrian monk who made the first scientific study of the laws of heredity.

Brown Brothers

look like the particular breed of dog but they show individual characteristics which may differ from either parent. Traits are inherited separately and are carried by the *genes* and *chromosomes*.

42.2   The Basis of Heredity

The *germ cell* (Sec. 27.2) is the unit of heredity. This cell goes through a process of *maturation* (Sec. 27.3), in which *reduction division* takes place so that one-half of the original number of chromosomes is found in each mature sex cell. The chromosomes and genes present in each of the two cells which unite carry the hereditary factors.

There are two genes of each kind, called *alleles,* in every body cell. Every gene has two functions: (1) to duplicate itself by forming another identical gene to be passed on to the next generation, and (2) to control each step in the development of the new individual from the fertilized egg through the embryo to the adult.

42.3   Weismann and Germplasm

The body cells which nourish and support the sex cells are called **somatoplasm**. The chromosome material of the sex cells is known as **germplasm**. August Weismann, a German biologist, made a great contribution to science when he stated that the *germplasm*

582

is the factor of heredity that passes on from one generation to the next and is *continuous* throughout all generations. Like ameba, when a chromosome pair splits or separates, some of the hereditary material received from the parent is passed on to the next generation. Weismann called this the **continuity of germ-plasm.** This hereditary material seems to direct the activities of the new individuals which are produced. Scientists are now trying to learn more about how this is done by studying the chemical structure and function of the genes.

42.4 Mendel and His Garden

Gregor Mendel (Figure 42-1) was an Austrian monk who became much interested in the plants of his garden. It was not the showy flowers, but the garden peas that attracted his attention. He had tall varieties, dwarf vines, some with wrinkled peas, others with round ones. They were also varied in color, with a few green and many yellow.

The garden peas usually reproduce by self-pollination, but Mendel found that they could easily be cross-pollinated. The pollen of one plant, from which the pistil had been removed, was put on the pistil of another plant, from which the stamens had been removed. The removal of pistil and stamens was to prevent self-pollination.

Mendel began to wonder what would happen if he crossed two different pure strains. He crossed a pure yellow pea plant with a pure green one by transferring the pollen himself. When the peas ripened, he found, much to his surprise, that *all the peas were yellow,* in spite of the fact that one parent had green peas. He kept careful records, and every time the result was the same. Therefore he concluded that the yellow character must hide the green one. Thus he arrived

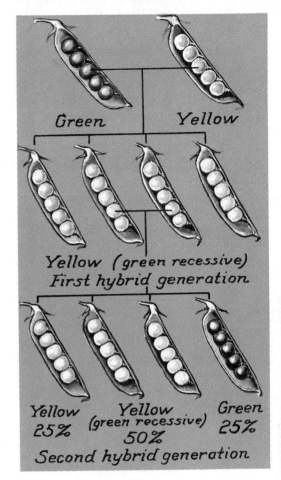

FIGURE 42-2. *MENDEL'S EXPERIMENT*

When yellow and green peas are crossed, the first hybrid, or F_1, generation will all be yellow, with green recessive. If two of these hybrids are crossed, ¼ of the second hybrid, or F_2, generation will be yellow, ¼ will be green, and ½ will be hybrid yellow.

at a conclusion which he called the **Law of Dominance.** It may be stated thus: *When two pure strain contrasting characters are crossed, the dominant character appears in the first generation.* The character which showed, he called the **dominant** character (yellow in this case). The hidden character he called **recessive** (the green one) (Fig. 42-2).

This first generation was called the **first filial** generation and designated by the symbol F_1. Since the offspring were a cross between two types, he called them **hybrids.** Mules are hybrids resulting from a cross between a horse and a donkey. Plumcots are a cross between plums and apricots. The parents of the hybrid generation are called the **parental** generation. They are represented by the symbol **P.**

Diagram A illustrates the way in which modern scientists show the result of Mendel's first cross. Since the pure strain received a yellow gene from each parent, let the letters YY stand for that pea plant. In the same manner let gg represent the green pea plant.

Filling in the squares you will see the genetic makeup of the offspring. They are all Yg; that is, *hybrid yellow,* since green is a recessive character and does not show.

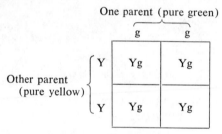

One parent (pure green)

Other parent (pure yellow)

	g	g
Y	Yg	Yg
Y	Yg	Yg

F_1 generation
100% hybrid yellow

Diagram A

Again Mendel carried on his experiments, this time crossing two of the hybrids. The offspring of those he called the **second filial** generation, designated by the symbol F_2. When two hybrid yellow peas were crossed, only three quarters of the offspring were yellow: one quarter were pure yellow, one half were hybrid yellow, and one quarter were green. Repeated experiments always showed the same proportion. Diagram B shows the cross that Mendel made.

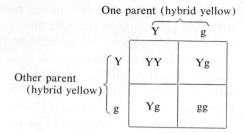

One parent (hybrid yellow)

Other parent (hybrid yellow)

	Y	g
Y	YY	Yg
g	Yg	gg

F_2 generation
¼ pure yellow
½ hybrid yellow
¼ pure green

Diagram B

When the green recessive from yellow parents (gg in Diagram B) was crossed with another pure strain green pea (gg), this always produced green peas (Diagram C).

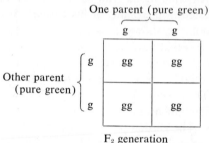

One parent (pure green)

Other parent (pure green)

	g	g
g	gg	gg
g	gg	gg

F_2 generation
100% pure green

Diagram C

When Mendel crossed the yellow hybrids with pure yellow strains, he had all yellow peas. Half were pure yellow, and half were hybrid yellow (Diagram D). He called this result an illustration

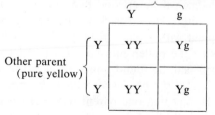

One parent (hybrid yellow)

Other parent (pure yellow)

	Y	g
Y	YY	Yg
Y	YY	Yg

F_2 generation
½ hybrid yellow
½ pure strain yellow

Diagram D

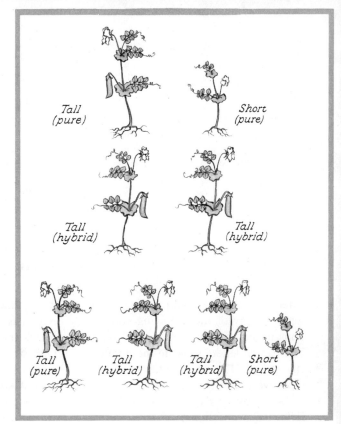

FIGURE 42-3. *GENETIC DOMINANCE*

This diagram of three genera-tions of pea plants demonstrates the Law of Dominance. Although the F₁ generation appears tall, crossbreeding produces ¼ short (pure) plants to prove that both parent plants were hybrids, and that "shortness" was recessive.

of the **Law of Segregation,** or *separation of pure characters.*

When he crossed the yellow hybrids with pure green strains, the same law operated. The pure green strains sepa-rated out (Diagram E). Thus in the law of segregation, both dominant and reces-sive characters separate from the hybrid.

One parent (hybrid yellow)

	Y	g
g	Yg	gg
g	Yg	gg

Other parent (pure green)

F₂ generation
½ hybrid yellow
½ pure strain green

Diagram E

He then used other characteristics,

crossing a plant having yellow round peas with a plant having green wrinkled peas. In the F₁ generation, peas showing both dominant characters appeared: they were all yellow round hybrids (Dia-gram F).

One parent (yellow round)

	YR	YR
gw	YR gw	YR gw
gw	YR gw	YR gw

Other parent (green wrinkled)

F₁ generation
100% hybrid yellow round

Diagram F

In the second cross for the F₂ gener-ations he found some entirely new com-binations. His results are shown in Dia-gram G. In making such a cross, the

		YR	Yw	gR	gw	
Other parent dihybrid yellow round (green, wrinkled recessive)	YR	YR YR	YR Yw	YR gR	YR gw	
	Yw	YR Yw	Yw Yw	Yw gR	Yw gw	F₂ generation (ratio per 16) YR—9 Yw—3 gR—3 gw—1
	gR	YR gR	Yw gR	gR gR	gw gR	
	gw	YR gw	Yw gw	gR gw	gw gw	

Diagram G

letters Y, R, w, g could arrange themselves in any of the following combinations in the offspring: YR, Yw, gR, gw. The capital letters indicate the dominant characters. The small letters show the recessive ones (Diagram G).

Out of every sixteen peas he had the following proportions:

> YR—yellow round—9
> Yw—yellow wrinkled—3
> gR—green round—3
> gw—green wrinkled—1

Since in the beginning he had no *yellow wrinkled* peas or *green round* peas, he concluded that each characteristic is inherited separately. This is called the **Law of Unit Characters.**

Mendel's chief contribution to science then is his Laws of Heredity. They are:

1. The Law of Dominance
2. The Law of Segregation
3. The Law of Unit Characters

42.5 Correns and His Four-O'Clocks

Although Mendel published the results of his researches, little attention was given to them at the time. A little more than thirty years afterward other scientists began to repeat his experiments and apply his laws to other plants. One of these scientists was Karl Erich Correns, who worked in Germany. He is best known for his experiments with the Japanese four-o'clocks. He grew two distinct kinds, one that produced red flowers and one that had white ones. When he crossed them, all the flowers were pink. According to Mendel's law of dominance he expected them to be red. But he repeated the cross several times, and he always obtained 100 per cent hybrid *pink* offspring in the F₁ generation. Because of this mixing or blending of color qualities, he called this occurrence **incomplete dominance** (Fig. 42-4).

When two pink hybrids were crossed, the result followed Mendel's law of segregation. He obtained one quarter red, one half pink, and one quarter white. When the red was crossed with another red, no white flowers appeared. This proved that the pure type, whether dominant or recessive, separated from the hybrid combination according to the law of segregation. Diagram H also illustrates the result of Correns' experiments.

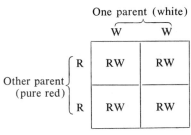

One parent (white)

W W

Other parent
(pure red)
R | RW | RW
R | RW | RW

F₁ generation
100% hybrid pink

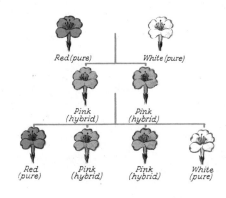

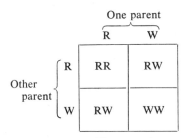

One parent

R W

Other
parent
R | RR | RW
W | RW | WW

F₂ generation
25% red
50% pink
25% white

Diagram H

Experiments since those of Correns have shown that incomplete dominance occurs in other plants and animals. The blue Andalusian fowl is one example. When a black rooster of one strain is mated with a white hen of another strain, the chickens appear speckled blue, be-

FIGURE 42-4. *INCOMPLETE DOMINANCE*

When these red and white flowers were crossed, the F₁ generation was not red as expected, but pink instead.

cause of the even distribution of the black and white feathers.

42.6 De Vries and His Primroses

While Correns was working in Germany, Hugo de Vries (duh-*vreess*), a Dutch botanist, became interested in the subject of heredity. He noticed a number of American evening primroses that had escaped from a garden. Although these flowers were self-pollinated, some of the new plants were quite unlike their parents. He even considered them different enough to be called new species. Since there was only one strain involved, he concluded that some change

FIGURE 42-5. *ALBINO*

Albinism in animals originates as a "sport" or mutant, and behaves in inheritance as a Mendelian recessive. The white spines and pink eyes of this porcupine are characteristic of albinos. Some of the pigments found in normal animals are absent.

G. E. Kirkpatrick
from National Audubon Society

FIGURE 42-6. *SELECTIVE BREEDING*

Research is being carried on by the Dept. of Agriculture to produce a superior beef cattle that can endure heat, resist insect pests, and grow rapidly. To that end, Brahman cattle from India have been crossed with Aberdeen-Angus breeds. Pictured are second generation calves, ¼ Brahman and ¾ Angus.

Courtesy United States
Dept. of Agriculture

must have occurred in the chromosomes or genes. Thus De Vries called the new forms **mutants** (*myoo*-tants), or "sports." De Vries is known for his **Theory of Mutations** (myoo-*tay*-shuns), in which he proposed that new species arise unexpectedly from existing forms.

Some mutations that have appeared are the seedless grape, the tailless dog, hornless cattle, short-legged sheep, and albino animals with white color and pink eyes. Mutations in man include albino characteristics and unusual hair patterns.

When mutations are undesirable or harmful, the young often do not live. If they do, they are not used for breeding. Those best fitted to their environment usually do survive.

42.7 Morgan and His Fruit Flies

Although new types of plants and animals were being discovered and produced experimentally, scientists were very much perplexed about the nature of the chromosomes and *genes* which cause these changes. **Gene** (*jeen*) is the name given to the individual factors which determine heredity. Thomas Morgan (page 683) began to experiment with fruit flies, since they had only eight very large chromosomes and reproduced very rapidly. He found that they developed a wide variety of characteristics when raised in different environments. Then he began a close study of the nature of the genes themselves. He found that many genes exist on a single chromosome and are normally inherited together with that chromosome. Sometimes the pattern of genes on chromosomes is disturbed, as when an individual is exposed to strong radiation. When this is the case, a decided change occurs in the heredity.

After the invention of the electron microscope, photographs of genes revealed some facts concerning their nature. Genes appear as small granules on the chromosomes and are believed to be giant molecules of *nucleoprotein* (noo-klee-oh-*proh*-tee-in), which is a compound composed of a protein molecule plus a nucleic acid molecule.

42.8 Application of Mendel's Laws

As more experiments in breeding were carried on, it was found that Mendel's laws continued to hold true. Plant and animal breeders were eager to improve their stock by the application of these laws. The chief methods are (1) selective breeding, (2) hybridization, and (3) spotting the mutants.

For a long time man has practiced **selective breeding.** He selects the most desirable varieties of animals or plants and mates them. He chooses them for traits he desires to be continued. In cattle he may wish higher percentage of butter fat, resistance to disease, or greater milk production. In dogs he may desire intelligence, speed, endurance, power, or beauty. Since not all the characteristics are found in one individual, man breeds several individuals to find the desired trait.

Hybridization (hy-brid-eye-*zay*-shun) is the crossing of two different strains. Sometimes the hybrid has desirable characters which neither of the parents possesses. Since the parent types keep sorting out in the F_2 generation by the law of segregation, man must keep careful watch over his stock.

Hybrid corn, obtained by artificial self-pollination, is widely grown in some areas.

Luther Burbank (page 678) is known for his work on plant hybridization. He crossed a plum and an apricot to produce the plumcot. A daisy from New England and one from Japan produced his Shasta daisy. He crossed the blackberry and raspberry to produce the

J. Horace McFarland Co.

FIGURE 42-7. *SPINELESS CACTUS*
Luther Burbank produced the spineless cactus, used for food in desert regions.

loganberry. Similarly he developed a spineless cactus that can be used as food for cattle near desert areas. He also developed the Burbank potato and many other fruits and flowers.

Many animal hybrids are well known. The female horse (mare) mated with the male donkey (jackass) produces the mule, which is a desirable work animal. It is sterile, however; so all mules must be produced by this method. The opposite cross, that of a male horse (stallion) with the female donkey (jenny), yields a hinny, a very inferior animal. Not all

FIGURE 42-8. *MUTANT*

Because the seedless orange is a fine fruit for eating, it has been propagated artificially since it first appeared as a mutant.

J. Horace McFarland

589

FIGURE 42-9. *IMPROVING THE SPECIES BY CROSSBREEDING*

This hybrid seed corn (*left*) is an improved type with extra large ears well filled out with even rows of kernels. Crossbreeding a purebred ram and a Navajo ewe resulted in a ram (*right*) of superior body type, which can produce more wool with a higher commercial value.

the hereditary factors have been satisfactorily explained.

Cattaloes result from mating cows with male buffaloes. They are very large and thus prized for beef. The males, however, will not breed.

Spotting the mutants means observing the offspring very carefully to detect those with traits differing from the rest. If the breeder should find just one mutant and could breed it, the animal, if it proved to be a mutant, would breed true. Thus he might be able to develop a new species. The seedless orange originated as a mutant. Since it had no seeds, in nature it would have died out. But man grafted the buds on to other orange trees and gave the world a fruit that was better and easier to eat.

When animals or plants are bred with the hybrid parent type, this is called a

back cross (Diagrams D and E). The back cross is used to determine whether a new form is a mutant. If it is a mutant, the result of further breeding will be 50 per cent pure type like the mutant and 50 per cent hybrid like the parent. Diagram I illustrates this, using the letters WW for the mutant and RW for the hybrid parent.

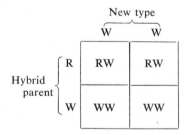

New type

		W	W
Hybrid parent	R	RW	RW
	W	WW	WW

Back cross
50% hybrid like parent
50% pure like new type

Diagram I

42.9 Improvement of Plants and Animals by Breeding

In order to improve breeds of plants and animals, scientific experts are devoting a great deal of time to experimentation. In one interesting experiment the pollen of some bearded wheat was placed on the stigma of the wheat flowers of some non-bearded wheat. When the kernels of ripe wheat in this head were sown, a plant was produced which grew a longer head and had practically no beards. This head also yielded more kernels than either of the parent heads.

The hard red winter wheat from southern Asia was crossed with a strain known as the Red Fife, by Saunders, a Canadian cereal specialist, and a hybrid form of wheat was secured which he named the Marquis. This strain has become the standard winter wheat for the United States and Canada.

The principle of unit characters in heredity works out interestingly in sheep. The tendency of sheep to collect in flocks when feeding is a dominant inherited character; but it is not true of all kinds of sheep. If the breeder wishes to get the best results, he will select the breed known as fine-wool sheep, which show this flocking instinct best. This reduces the cost of caring for sheep out on the open ranges, because one man and a dog can look after several thousand sheep if they graze in compact flocks.

Guernsey cattle furnish an interesting illustration of breeding. When the United States cattlemen sought to improve their stock, they imported registered Guernseys. Using the principles of heredity, they tried extensive experiments. Skilled men applied our modern laws of heredity, until they produced a finer animal than the native cattle in the island of Guernsey. The result is that today more registered Guernseys are shipped to South America from the United States than from Guernsey.

A small, family-size turkey has been developed for use in homes and small groups. Disease-resistant cattle are produced by crosses between native cattle and those of India.

42.10 Human Heredity

In 1883, Sir Francis Galton began a systematic study of human heredity which he called *eugenics*. By keeping careful records of family histories, scientists have traced the inheritance of more than sixty human traits. Among these are eye color, colors of the hair and skin, some kinds of blindness, and certain types of feeblemindedness.

Relatively few people have blue eyes because blue is inherited as a recessive color which shows only when brown pigment is completely absent. The large number of shades other than blue is due to varying amounts of brown coloring which mask the normal shade to a greater or less degree.

Hair color is caused by reddish and brown materials which are found in the shaft of each hair. Since a number of factors enter into the production of each color, the exact way in which these traits will be inherited is difficult to predict. However, dark hair has been shown to be dominant over the lighter shades.

Just as with hair, colors of the skin are due to many factors, each of which probably obeys Mendel's laws without reference to the others. The result is a type of inheritance in which there is the appearance of a blending of characters. Thus a mating between a full-blooded Negro and a white person would produce children who had complexions of a shade considerably lighter than that of their Negro parent, but darker than that of a white person. If the offspring of such a marriage were married to others like themselves in ancestry, their progeny, if numerous enough, would exhibit several different shades of color, but the commonest colors would be neither very dark nor particularly light.

Although several kinds of blindness are inherited, the fact that a person is blind from his earliest childhood does not mean necessarily that, if he marries, his children will be blind. His trouble may be due to an infection acquired at the time of birth and not due to a hereditary factor. The science of genetics has shown that infectious diseases are not inherited.

42.11 The Rh Factor in Blood

The discovery of another hereditary factor, the Rh factor in blood (Sec. 23.2), has helped to explain why some children died at birth or were in very poor condition without any apparent reason. The Rh factor is a dominant characteristic.

It is important in giving blood transfusions that not only the same type of blood (A, AB, B, or O) should be given to the person who needs it but also that blood with the same Rh factor be given. Where this is not the case the body of an Rh-negative person receiving the Rh-positive blood tries to set up an immunity against this substance in the same way as a body would fight against a disease.

It is this situation which occurs when a mother with Rh-negative blood is about to bear a child which has inherited Rh-positive blood from its father. The mother's body tends to counteract the effect of the Rh-positive blood entering her blood stream. This weakens the child before birth and may result in its death. Since these facts about the Rh blood factor have been made known

physicians are now able to combat this condition by taking preventive measures and giving blood transfusions before or at birth when necessary.

When two persons with Rh-positive blood or two persons with Rh-negative blood marry, they do not need to be concerned about this inherited factor. When the mother has Rh-positive blood and the father Rh-negative blood, this factor will not affect the offspring adversely. It is only when an Rh-negative woman is married to an Rh-positive man that this factor may become an important one.

42.12 The Sex Chromosomes

In man, the forty-six chromosomes (Sec. 27.7) are not all alike. Two of them appear to be quite different from the others. They are the **X** and **Y** chromosomes. Their presence or absence determine the sex of the new individuals.

The female has two X chromosomes, while the male has only one X chromosome and one Y chromosome. During the reduction division in maturation, each egg cell receives one X chromosome. In the male, one half of the sperm cells receive X chromosomes and one-half of them receive the Y chromosomes.

The sex of the new individual depends on the chance union of two X chromosomes, in which case the child would be a girl; or one X and a Y chromosome, which would be a boy. Thus, sex is determined at the time of fertilization. The unions which can occur are shown in Figure 42-10.

42.13 Variations

The causes of *variations* which appear to be due to heredity have not all been determined. A few explanations are (1) sex-linked characters, (2) crossing over, and (3) mutations.

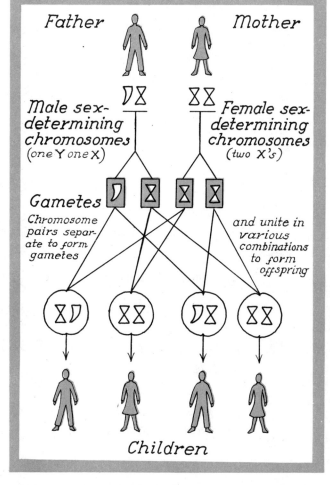

FIGURE 42-10. *SEX DETERMINATION*

Sex is determined by X and Y chromosomes. Each individual has two sex chromosomes. Females have two Xs; males have one X and one Y. During reduction division only one chromosome of a pair enters a gamete. The sex of the offspring is determined by which gametes come together at fertilization. If there is a Y chromosome present, the child will be a boy; with no Y chromosome the child will be a girl. After studying this diagram can you explain why it is the male gamete that actually determines the sex of the offspring?

Sex-linked characters are carried on the sex chromosomes. The genes are usually present in the X but missing in the Y chromosome. Color blindness, baldness, and hemophilia (the failure of blood to clot), are sex-linked and are prevalent among males. However, these traits are transmitted by the females.

Genes which normally occur on the same chromosome are said to be *linked*. Their traits are all passed on from parent to offspring in a group. Sometimes **crossing over** may occur by the entanglement of two chromosomes. They may become twisted about each other in such a way that a piece breaks off from each and becomes attached to the other. This re-sults in a rearrangement of the genes which affects the pattern of heredity.

Mutations resulting from changes in gene structure have been caused in fruit flies and in many plants by X-rays and gamma rays. A chemical known as *colchicine* may cause the doubling and tripling of chromosomes in plants, thus causing inherited variations in the cells.

Some undesirable human traits that are hereditary are deaf-mutism, extra fingers, feeblemindedness, diabetes, inherited anemia, and cleft palate. Some of these characters are dominant, others recessive. When people with the same kind of undesirable chromosomes marry, the recessive characters are apt to appear.

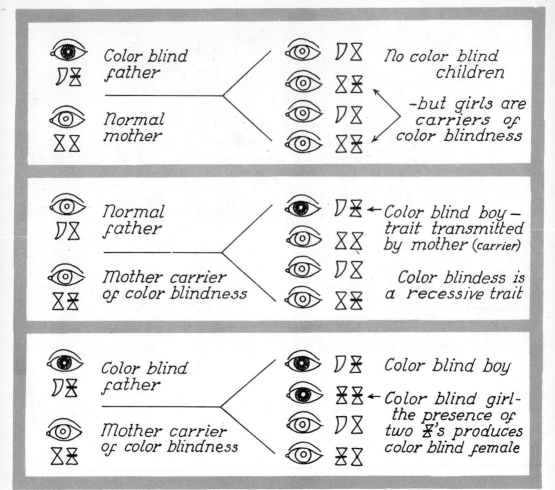

FIGURE 42-11. *INHERITANCE OF COLOR BLINDNESS IN MAN*

Color blindness, a sex-linked character, is a recessive trait transmitted by the female. The symbols in the diagram represent the X and Y chromosomes; those with the black bar carry the gene for color blindness.

Potentialities for desirable characters such as artistic and musical ability, powers of reasoning, manual skill, and verbal and mathematical skills may also be inherited. The development of these abilities is determined by the environment of the individual.

42.14 Multiple Births

The appearance of twins and other multiple births is not very common among people. There are two kinds of twins, *identical* and *fraternal*. **Identical** **twins** are produced from the same egg fertilized by one sperm cell. **Fraternal** **twins** are produced from two separate eggs fertilized by two separate sperm cells. Therefore fraternal twins are no more alike than other brothers or sisters, while identical twins closely resemble each other in physical characteristics and mental traits. Identical twins are always of the same sex. Why?

Triplets may be produced from one egg, two eggs, or three eggs. In the first case they would all be identical. If there were two eggs, there would be one pair of identical twins and one fraternal twin. They might or might not all be of the same sex. If there were three eggs, the individuals would all be fraternal twins. You can figure out for yourself the possibilities of quadruplets.

The Dionne quintuplets were all identical, that is, derived from one egg and one sperm cell. In spite of this, minor variations existed. These were *fluctuations*, in contrast to wide variations known as *mutations*.

42.15 Hereditary Factors in Evolution

Scientists have long been trying to explain the heredity of our widely varied plant and animal forms and how they changed from simple to complex. Three theories of *organic evolution* have offered explanations at the times they were presented: (1) Lamarck's Theory of Use and Disuse, (2) Darwin's Theory of Natural Selection and (3) De Vries' Theory of Mutations. Most scientists now believe that the natural selection of mutants explains many changes which they observe to be taking place.

Lamarck and His Theory of Use and Disuse.—Jean Lamarck, a French naturalist, believed that a new part of an animal or plant was produced when there was need for it. He believed that as long as this part was used it continued to develop and would be inherited. Most of Lamarck's ideas are not accepted today, since further evidence shows that acquired characteristics are not inherited.

Darwin and His Theory of Natural Selection.—It almost seems as if those plants and animals that have become successful had adopted a certain policy by which to attain success. Charles Darwin (page 678) tried to explain it by his **Theory of Natural Selection,** which

FIGURE 42-12. *TWINS*

Because identical twins develop from a single egg cell fertilized by the same sperm, they are genetically identical.

he reduced to five factors: (1) overproduction, (2) struggle for existence, (3) survival of the fittest, (4) variation, and (5) heredity.

(1) **Overproduction** means that plants and animals must produce more offspring than can survive in order to make up for the loss of some by accident or injury.

For example, the dandelion produces hundreds of seeds which are blown about by the wind. Some are lost, some fall on rocks, some in water; comparatively few fall in favorable places where they may germinate.

A housefly lays 500 eggs which require about two weeks to mature. If all the offspring lived, matured, and produced young, there would be nearly two hundred quintillion (200,000,000,000,000,000,000) flies in ten weeks. Thus they are able to compete with others and survive even though many eggs and

Photo by Hugh Spencer

FIGURE 42-13. *OVERPRODUCTION*

Thousands of seeds will be shaken from this poppy capsule, guaranteeing that the plant will be able to reproduce itself.

larvae are eaten by their enemies or otherwise destroyed.

The elephant is one of the slowest-breeding animals. It breeds first when approximately thirty years old, and during the hundred years more or less of its life, it produces only six young, but biologists estimate that within 800 years a pair of elephants would have 19,000,-000 descendants. At the end of 1600 years the offspring of these animals would be so numerous that there would

scarcely be standing room on the earth for all of them.

Although animals all have many off-spring, and plants bear thousands of seeds, careful studies of different species show that except where man disturbs the balance of nature their numbers change very slowly if at all.

(2) Since so many offspring are produced, there is a real **struggle for existence**—for food, light, oxygen, for space in which to live, and for ways to escape enemies. It is evident that most young plants and animals must die before they reach maturity. In fact, the death rate is so terrific that on the average only two out of all the young produced by an animal ever become mature.

(3) The **survival of the fittest**, then, includes those which survive the struggle for existence. If from the millions of eggs produced from a codfish, more than two lived to become adults, the species would increase and eventually occupy so much space that no other kind of life could exist in the sea. Usually, only one plant seed grows to maturity.

The plants and animals which are best fitted to their environment are those which survive. Thus out of a herd of deer, the ones which are fleetest and have the greatest endurance are most likely to escape wolves and other carnivorous animals.

With a group of seedlings beginning

FIGURE 42-14. *BATTLE*

The water snake, tormented by hunger, has come too close to the huge snapping turtle, which it has mistaken for a moss-grown rock. The survivor of this battle will have to compete again and again in the struggle for existence.

Lynwood M. Chace

596

FIGURE 42-15.
VARIATIONS

These onion plants were grown in California for seed. Since there is some variation in the plants, the best and hardiest are selected for seed production.

Los Angeles Chamber of Commerce

growth on a small area of soil at the same time, the slower-growing plants will be crowded out by those which develop quickly, if other conditions are equal. In ways such as this the unfit are eliminated, and in the long run a race is improved, because those which are weak or otherwise poorly fitted for survival are killed before they get a chance to pass their defects on to the next generation.

(4) **Variation.** Those plants and animals which survive are not necessarily alike. In fact no two plants or animals are exactly alike. The differences which make living things of the same species unlike are known as *variations.* Observe the members of your class. Note the differences in hair and eye color, in height and weight, in size of feet and hands.

If you live near a farm or are able to visit a zoo, observe the patterns of coloring in the same species of animal. Note variation in the number of petals of a daisy, or variation in the size of the petals of a sweet pea. This fact of variation extends throughout the entire range of animal and plant life.

Kinds of Variation.—Variations may be of two main types: (a) fluctuations and (b) mutations. A *fluctuation* is a slight variation which may be due to factors of the environment. Different minerals in the soil affect the growth of plants. Amounts and kinds of food limit the growth of animals. Trees grown in the forest assume a different shape than those standing alone. Others, on windy hilltops, may be stunted, and yet the heredity of all may be the same.

(5) **Heredity.** Those variations which are favorable and best enable the organism to survive in its environment continue to be inherited through many generations. Many individuals which inherit defective characteristics do not survive.

De Vries and His Theory of Mutations.—In his work on primroses which we have already studied (Sec. 42.5), De Vries developed his **Theory of Mutations.** He believed that wide variations, which he called *mutations,* could start new breeds and new forms. Those which survived and became successful would continue the race. This is a more rapid way to meet the changing environment and results in better adaptation to the environment.

FIGURE 42-16. *MUTATION CAUSED BY RADIATION*

Geneticists at the Oak Ridge National Laboratory are studying hereditary changes brought on by radiation. This picture shows the effects of such a change. The mouse on the right is a hereditary mutation, while the one on the left is a normal litter mate.

J. E. Westcott, Atomic Energy Commission

Mutations are wide variations due to heredity. Changes occur in the reproductive cells, causing different characteristics to be inherited. If the variation is desirable, the offspring survives and starts a new breed or variety. If not, the new form dies out. The seedless orange is a mutant which would not have survived, but man propagates it by grafting because he enjoys eating a fruit without seeds.

One of the first records of what we now call a *mutant* was termed a "sport." In 1791, a sheep farmer named Seth Wright discovered that one of his male sheep had a long body and short, bowed legs. He was having trouble keeping his long-legged sheep in his pasture, and it occurred to him that he might use this "sport" to reduce the length of the legs of his flock of sheep. In the spring, he found that of the lambs sired by this short-legged sheep, some were like the father and some like their mothers. Separating the short-legged lambs and continuing to breed them with short-legged lambs, he found that they produced only short-legged lambs; so in a few years, he was able to raise a flock of sheep that could not jump over fences.

We designate such a sport a *mutant,* because it is a new type and its differences are due to changes in the nature and arrangement of the genes in the chromosomes.

Students of heredity are collecting mutants of beans, tobacco, insects, and many other forms. Some changes are minute and do not attract attention. At present, we do not know how all of these changes come about. We do know that radiations can cause mutations in any cell in the body, and that gene changes in the reproductive cells may be inherited.

FACTS TO REMEMBER

The *unit of heredity* is the *germ cell,* in which the *germplasm* containing the *chromosomes* and *genes* carry the hereditary characteristics.

The *laws of heredity* as formulated by Mendel are: (1) the Law of Dominance, (2) the Law of Segregation, and (3) the Law of Unit Characters. Mendel also demonstrated how the *dominant* and *recessive* characteristics are passed on from one generation to the next and how they appear in the offspring.

LIFE THROUGH THE AGES

Some of the *variable factors in heredity* are: (1) complete or incomplete dominance, (2) the possibility of mutations, (3) the chance union of the sex chromosomes at fertilization, (4) the appearance of variations resulting from sex-linked characters, or crossing over, (5) the possible effects of radiation, and (6) multiple births.

As a result of his study of the hereditary processes, man has been able to improve his plants and animals by *selective breeding, hybridization, spotting the mutants,* making *back crosses,* and causing *mutations.*

Many scientists have attempted to explain *organic evolution* on the basis of heredity. Among the theories proposed were Lamarck's *Theory of Use and Disuse,* Darwin's *Theory of Natural Selection,* and De Vries' *Theory of Mutations.* Factors in the theory of natural selection are: 1) *overproduction,* 2) *struggle for existence,* 3) *survival of the fittest,* 4) *variation,* and 5) *heredity.*

WORDS TO REMEMBER

back cross	heredity	Rh factor
chromosome	hybrid	selective breeding
complete dominance	hybridization	sex chromosome
continuity of	identical twin	sex-linked characters
germplasm	incomplete dominance	somatoplasm
crossing over	Law of Dominance	sport
defective character	Law of Segregation	spotting the mutant
desirable character	Law of Unit	struggle for existence
dominant character	Characters	survival of the fittest
evolution	maturation	Theory of Mutations
F_1 generation	mutant	Theory of Natural
F_2 generation	mutation	Selection
fluctuations	nucleoprotein	Theory of Use and
fraternal twin	overproduction	Disuse
gene	parental generation	variations
germ cell	recessive character	X chromosome
germplasm	reduction division	Y chromosome

QUESTIONS

1. What is meant by heredity?
2. Who was Gregor Mendel?
3. For what is he noted?
4. State briefly the three laws of heredity.
5. Diagram the F_1 and F_2 generations of a cross between a pure black guinea pig and a pure white guinea pig. (Black is dominant.)
6. What is incomplete dominance? How is this shown in Japanese four-o'clocks?
7. For what is De Vries noted? What flower did he use?

8. Who is known for his hybridizing experiments with plants? What new forms did he produce?

9. What is a back cross? What is the result? By means of a diagram show a back cross, using guinea pigs. (Cross a pure type with a hybrid.)

10. Give an illustration of the use of Mendel's laws in improving plants or animals.

11. Name some probable causes of variation and explain two.

12. What is the difference between identical and fraternal twins?

13. List the five factors of natural selection and briefly tell what is meant by two of them.

14. How do you account for variation among living things?

COMPLETION TEST

As your teacher or classmate reads the following incomplete statements, with your book closed, write on a clean sheet of paper the word or phrase which correctly completes each statement.

1. A cross between two different pure types produces a _____.

2. In the F_1 generation _____% of the offspring show the dominant character.

3. When two hybrid yellow peas were crossed, _____% were _____ and _____% were _____.

4. The law of _____ states that each trait is inherited separately.

5. The Andalusian fowl is an example of _____.

6. _____ helped to explain sex-linked characters.

7. Two examples of animal hybrids are the mule and the _____.

8. The seedless orange originated as a _____.

9. One dominant trait in man is _____.

10. Man has _____ chromosomes.

11. The _____ survive the struggle for existence.

12. The differences among living things are called _____.

13. Each inherited trait is called a _____.

14. The bearer of each hereditary trait is a _____.

15. The chromosomes are reduced to one half the original number during _____.

16. The original number is restored during _____.

17. The small chromosome-bearing cells which are formed during oögenesis and which are cast away are called _____.

PROJECTS

I. *My Own Hereditary Traits.*—1. Make a list of your own physical features, such as color of hair, color of eyes, stature, and shape of head.

2. List the traits of your mother and father and note which ones you seem to possess.

3. If possible, list the traits of your grandparents. How much do you resemble these?

4. Which do you resemble more closely, your parents or grandparents? How do you account for this?

5. How much do you resemble your brothers or sisters, if any?

II. *Classroom Charts.*—Make a chart to show Mendel's laws. You may choose (a) peas, (b) Japanese four-o'clocks, (c) fruit flies, or (d) guinea pigs.

III. *Work of Luther Burbank.*—Read the life of Luther Burbank and write a composition describing several of his new plant species.

IV. *Breeding Rats or Guinea Pigs.*—1. Choose hooded and white rats or black guinea pigs and white guinea pigs. Provide an adequate balanced diet. When they have become accustomed to their surroundings in the classroom or laboratory, place them in the same cage and let them breed.

2. When the young are born, remove the male. Be sure you provide plenty of milk and give them good care. Record the results of the experiment. What color are the offspring?

3. Cross two of the hybrids and note the results. Does it show Mendel's law of segregation?

4. If there is still time during your school year, try a back cross. Mate one of the white rats or guinea pigs which appeared in the F_2 generation with a hybrid from the F_1 generation. What percentage of each appear in the offspring?

V. Copy and complete the following diagram, which will illustrate Mendel's laws with two colors and two kinds of hair in guinea pigs. Tabulate your results and compare them with those on page 586. Black curly hair is dominant over white straight hair.

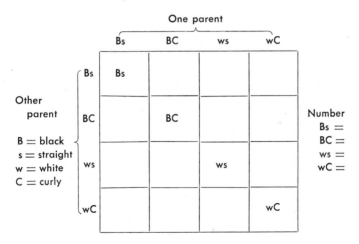

REFERENCES

Altenburg, *How We Inherit.* Holt.
Bouthilet and Byrne, *You and Your Mental Abilities.* Science Research Associates.

Burbank, *Partner in Nature*. Appleton.

Cook and Birks, *How Heredity Builds Our Lives*. American Genetic Association.

Downing, *Elementary Eugenics*. University of Chicago.

Dunn and Dobzhansky, *Heredity, Race and Society*. Penguin Books. ·

East, *Heredity and Human Affairs*. McGraw-Hill.

Goldstein, *Genetics Is Easy*. Garland Publication.

Guyer, *Being Well Born*. Bobbs-Merrill.

Howells, *Mankind So Far*. Doubleday, Doran.

Huntington, *Tomorrow's Children*. Wiley.

Jewett, *The Next Generation*. Ginn.

Leet, *Causes of Catastrophe*. McGraw-Hill.

Montagu, *Human Heredity*. Mentor Books.

Morgan, *Physical Basis of Heredity*. Lippincott.

Newman, *Multiple Human Births*. Doubleday, Doran.

Poponoe and Johnson, *Applied Eugenics*. Macmillan.

Sager and Ryan, *Cell Heredity*. Wiley.

Scheinfeld, *The New You and Heredity*. Lippincott.

Shull, *Heredity*. McGraw-Hill.

Sinnott, Dunn and Dobzhansky, *Principles of Genetics*. McGraw-Hill.

Snyder, *Biology in the Making*. McGraw-Hill.

Snyder, *The Principles of Heredity*. Heath.

Srb and Owen, *General Genetics*. Freeman.

Sutton, *Genes, Enzymes and Inherited Diseases*. Holt, Rinehart and Winston.

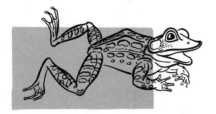

CHAPTER 43

Classification of Living Forms

43.1 What Is Classification?

The orderly arrangement or grouping of objects, usually into divisions and subdivisions, is known as **classification.** It serves as a quick and effective means of tracing identity. The army is classified into infantry, armored corps, artillery, signal corps, etc. The infantry is further classified into armies, corps, divisions, brigades, regiments, battalions, companies, platoons, sections, and squads. We have a similar way of classifying plants and animals (Sec. 9.9).

43.2 Why Is Classification of Living Things Necessary?

If you were to list all the plants and animals which you have studied this year and add to it all those with which you are familiar, you would doubtless have an odd assortment of living things. They could all be grouped, however, into large divisions and subdivisions to make an orderly arrangement. It is because man has learned to recognize such large numbers of living things that he has found it necessary to devise some system of classification. This is called **taxonomy** (taks-*on*-uh-mee).

43.3 Early Ideas of Classification

Even the primitive tribes learned to recognize some plants and animals as being useful or harmful. In Biblical times animals were referred to as "clean" or "unclean," thus requiring some method of recognition.

The first real attempt at an orderly arrangement of plants and animals was undertaken by Aristotle (384-322 B.C.). He divided animals into eight main groups, recognizing those that give birth to living young, squidlike animals, mollusks, crustaceans, insects, fishes, birds, and egg-laying animals. His works were published and used by scientists for a long time.

FIGURE 43-1. *LINNAEUS*

Carolus Linnaeus was a great botanist who established the classification system of living things based on structure.

603

As people invented better ways and means of communication and travel, they discovered new plants and animals. These did not entirely fit into Aristotle's groups. Years later the subject was intensively studied by a Swedish naturalist, Carl von Linné (1707–1778), whose Latin name is Carolus Linnaeus (lih-*nee*-us). In 1732 Linnaeus was given an opportunity to make a journey to Lapland to collect some plants. As a result of his trip he became intensely interested in working out some new method of classification which would include the new forms that he had found.

43.4 The Present Standard of Classification

Linnaeus noticed that certain plants and animals had similar characteristics. Thus he decided to base his classification on *structure* regardless of whether the plants and animals were useful or harmful to man. He grouped them into large divisions and subdivisions like the topics in an outline. Because he used the *last two* subtopics in naming them, Linnaeus' system of classification is known as **binominal nomenclature.**

43.5 Planning for Registration

Linnaeus grouped all living things into two main divisions called **kingdoms,** (1) plant and (2) animal. He thought it would be easy to distinguish them, but if you recall the euglena you will remember that scientists are still uncertain as to whether it is a plant or an animal. Linnaeus's outline looked like this:

Kingdom
Phylum
Class
Order
Family
Genus
species

He used capital letters for all except the species name. The last two names **Genus** and **species** were used to designate the animal or plant, just as two names usually are enough to identify you. The genus corresponds to your last name and species to your given name. If further identification is necessary, plants and animals are given **variety** names, just as Anna Smith may be called Anna Mary Smith to distinguish her from other Anna Smiths.

Smith, Anna Mary
Anna Mary Smith
Felis, domestica angora
domestic angora cat

Each kingdom is divided into **phyla,** which are relatively large groups possessing more or less definite characteristics. On page 611 you will notice how many representatives of different animal phyla you have already studied. Read the list of characteristics of each. Then turn to page 613 and recall the various plants you have studied. Note that the plant kingdom is divided into two *subkingdoms* which are then further divided into several phyla. Study the characteristics of each and note that the various plants are placed there because of their structures.

43.6 The Animal Kingdom

The animal kingdom is usually divided into ten major phyla (Fig. 43-2). Each phylum is distinguished by its own characteristics. Study carefully the list below and see how many you are already familiar with.

Phylum I. Protozoa.—This includes one-celled animals like the ameba, paramecium, plasmodium malariae, and many others (Sec. 6-2).

Phylum II. Porifera (Sponges).— These two-layered animals (Sec. 6.13)

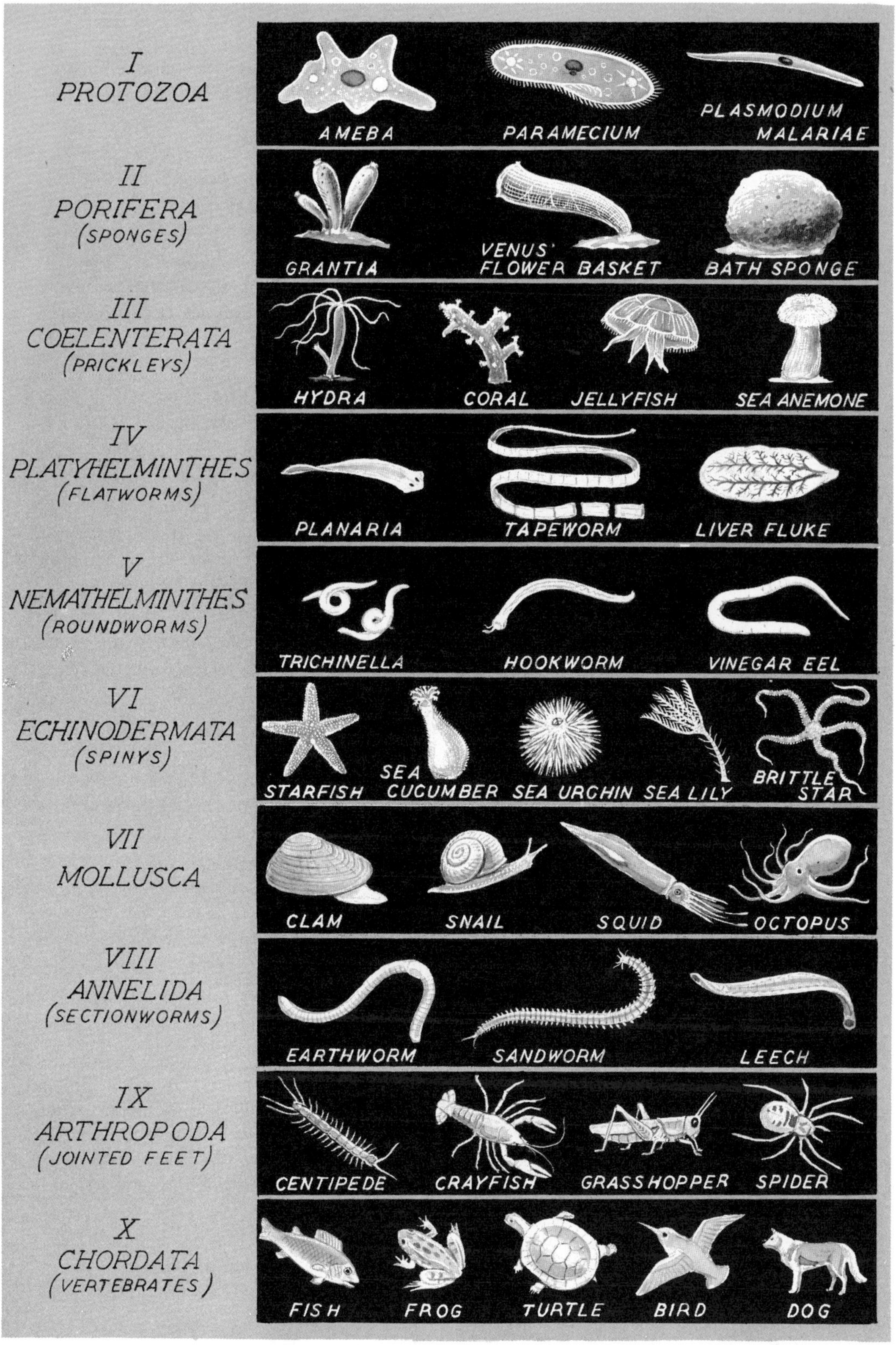

I PROTOZOA	AMEBA, PARAMECIUM, PLASMODIUM MALARIAE
II PORIFERA (SPONGES)	GRANTIA, VENUS' FLOWER BASKET, BATH SPONGE
III COELENTERATA (PRICKLEYS)	HYDRA, CORAL, JELLYFISH, SEA ANEMONE
IV PLATYHELMINTHES (FLATWORMS)	PLANARIA, TAPEWORM, LIVER FLUKE
V NEMATHELMINTHES (ROUNDWORMS)	TRICHINELLA, HOOKWORM, VINEGAR EEL
VI ECHINODERMATA (SPINYS)	STARFISH, SEA CUCUMBER, SEA URCHIN, SEA LILY, BRITTLE STAR
VII MOLLUSCA	CLAM, SNAIL, SQUID, OCTOPUS
VIII ANNELIDA (SECTIONWORMS)	EARTHWORM, SANDWORM, LEECH
IX ARTHROPODA (JOINTED FEET)	CENTIPEDE, CRAYFISH, GRASSHOPPER, SPIDER
X CHORDATA (VERTEBRATES)	FISH, FROG, TURTLE, BIRD, DOG

FIGURE 43-2. *PHYLA OF THE ANIMAL KINGDOM*

have their bodies perforated with pores. The body is supported by a skeleton of lime, silica, or spongin. Grantia, Venus's flower basket, and the bath sponge are examples.

Phylum III. Coelenterata (Prickleys). —The members of this group are also two-layered animals with the mouth surrounded by tentacles (Sec. 6.15). They are radially symmetrical. Hydra, coral, jellyfish, and sea anemone belong to this group.

Phylum IV. Platyhelminthes (Flatworms).—These are three-layered animals (Sec. 7.2), as are those of all of the phyla which follow. Their bodies are bilaterally symmetrical and much flattened. There is usually a single body cavity and they are mostly parasitic. Planaria, tapeworm, and liver fluke are examples.

Phylum V. Nemathelminthes (Roundworms).—The roundworms (Sec. 7.3) have long slender bodies and a digestive tract with two openings, the mouth and anus. Examples are trichinellas, hookworms, and vinegar eels.

Phylum VI. Echinodermata (Spinys). —These radially symmetrical animals (Sec. 7.4) with spiny skins have organs of locomotion operated by a water system. This group includes starfishes, sea cucumbers, sea urchins, sea lilies, and brittle stars.

Phylum VII. Mollusca.—The mollusks (Sec. 7.5) are unsegmented softbodied animals which are usually protected by a lime shell. Examples are clams, snails, squids, and octopi.

Phylum VIII. Annelida (Sectionworms).—These segmented worms (Sec. 7.6) are bilaterally symmetrical with a closed blood-vascular system. Examples are the earthworm, sandworm, and leech.

Phylum IX. Arthropoda (Jointed feet).—Animals with jointed append-

ages and chitinous exoskeletons belong to this group (Unit IV). It includes the centipede, crayfish, grasshopper, and spider.

Phylum X. Chordata (Vertebrates). —These animals (Unit V) possess a backbone or notochord, the forerunner of a backbone. They also have a dorsal nerve cord and gill slits sometime during the life cycle. Examples are fish, frog, turtle, bird, and dog.

43.7 Classes of Chordata

As you read through the list of animal phyla, you probably recognize the members of each group which you have already studied. Every phylum is divided into classes. There are five important classes of the Chordata (Fig. 43-3), each one identified by its own characteristics.

Class I. Pisces (Fish).—Fish (Chap. 13) breathe by gills, have two-chambered hearts, and bodies covered with scales. Examples are lamprey, shark, perch, and trout.

Class II. Amphibia.—The members of this group (Chap. 14) breathe by gills sometime during life. They have three-chambered hearts and usually undergo complete metamorphosis. Examples are frogs, toads, and salamanders.

Class III. Reptilia.—Reptiles (Chap. 15) have lungs throughout life. The three-chambered heart is partly divided in most forms. The body is usually covered with scales. Examples are turtles, lizards, snakes, and alligators.

Class IV. Aves (Birds).—Feathers, four-chambered heart, high body temperature, front limbs modified to form wings, air spaces in the bones and eggs laid with lime shells are characteristic of this group (Chap. 16). Besides wellknown birds like the crow and hawk, there are the penguin and snipe.

Class V. Mammalia. — Mammals

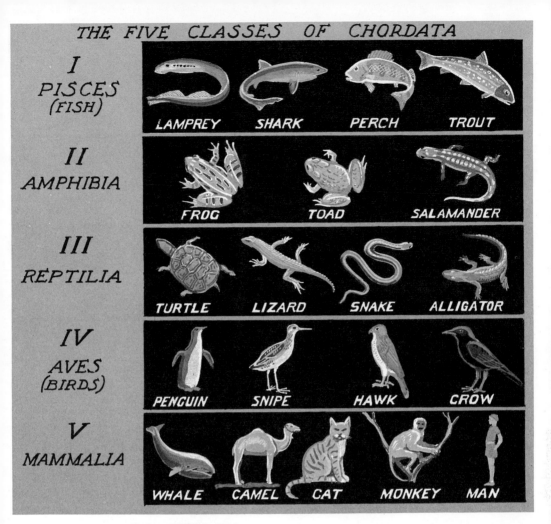

THE FIVE CLASSES OF CHORDATA

I PISCES (FISH) — LAMPREY, SHARK, PERCH, TROUT

II AMPHIBIA — FROG, TOAD, SALAMANDER

III REPTILIA — TURTLE, LIZARD, SNAKE, ALLIGATOR

IV AVES (BIRDS) — PENGUIN, SNIPE, HAWK, CROW

V MAMMALIA — WHALE, CAMEL, CAT, MONKEY, MAN

FIGURE 43-3. *CHORDATA*
  The Phylum Chordata is divided into five classes, each with its own characteristics. What features do all the Chordates have in common?

(Chap. 17) are warm-blooded. They give birth to living young and suckle their young with milk. They have hair and a diaphragm. Examples are whale, camel, cat, monkey, and man.

43.8 Introducing the Orders of Mammals

Just as every *phylum* is divided into **classes** (although only those of the Chordata are listed above), so every class is divided into **orders.** Probably you are most familiar with those of the insects and mammals (Secs. 9.9, 17.6). Note that each subdivision has its own characteristics and includes animals which resemble each other in very many ways.

Let us consider one of the orders of mammals in detail. The *Carnivora* are the flesh eaters. They have long canine teeth and claws. There are eleven **families,** eight of which are found in North America. Of these eight, five live on land and three in the water. Those living on land include the dogs, raccoons,

Lynwood M. Chace

American Museum of Natural History

FIGURE 43-4. *COUSINS*

Both the predatory wolf and man's best friend, the dog, belong in the genus *Canis,* which is a part of the larger family of *Canidae.* Can you see any family resemblances between the dog and the wolf?

bears, martens, and cats. The aquatic carnivores are the walruses and the eared and earless seals. Each family has its own characteristics in addition to the traits of all the main groups of which it is a subdivision.

43.9 Presenting the Family Canidae

The members of this family walk on their toes, possess blunt, non-retractile claws, and have a more or less elongated muzzle. It includes the wolves, foxes, dogs, and coyotes. Thus in order to distinguish the different kinds of Canidae, it is necessary to group them further into *genera* (singular, *genus*).

43.10 Final Registration—Canis familiaria

Subdivisions of a family are called *genera.* The family Canidae, then, is composed of the genus Vulpes, the foxes, and the genus Canis, the wolves.

Let us consider the genus Canis. This includes the gray or timber wolf, the coyote or prairie wolf, and the domestic dog. In order to distinguish them, each

is given a *species* name. The gray wolf then becomes Canis occidentalis, the coyote, Canis latrans, and the dog, Canis familiaris.

To give the complete classification of the dog it would be necessary to list the following:

> Kingdom—Animal
> Phylum—Chordata
> Class—Mammalia
> Order—Carnivora
> Family—Canidae
> Genus—Canis
> species—familiaris

The scientific name of the dog is Canis familiaris. But as you have concluded by now, those two names include all the information given in the complete classification.

43.11 The Plant Kingdom

In modern systems of classification, plants are grouped into two subkingdoms which are further subdivided into several phyla (Fig. 43-5). Following is a review of the principal groups of plants.

608

PHYLA OF THE
SUBKINGDOM
THALLOPHYTA

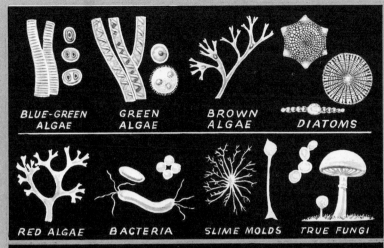

BLUE-GREEN ALGAE   GREEN ALGAE   BROWN ALGAE   DIATOMS

RED ALGAE   BACTERIA   SLIME MOLDS   TRUE FUNGI

SUBKINGDOM
EMBRYOPHYTA
PHYLUM
BRYOPHYTA

LIVERWORT   MOSS

PHYLUM
TRACHEOPHYTA

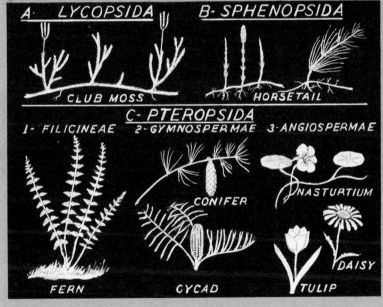

A. LYCOPSIDA   B. SPHENOPSIDA

CLUB MOSS   HORSETAIL

C. PTEROPSIDA
1- FILICINEAE   2- GYMNOSPERMAE   3- ANGIOSPERMAE

NASTURTIUM

CONIFER

FERN   CYCAD   TULIP   DAISY

FIGURE 43-5. *THE PLANT KINGDOM*

Subkingdom Thallophyta. — Simple plants without roots, stems, or leaves. Includes *algae* and *fungi,* some single-celled, some many-celled.

Phylum 1. Cyanophyta.—Blue-green algae.

Phylum 2. Chlorophyta. — Green algae.

Phylum 3. Phaeophyta.—Brown algae.

Phylum 4. Chrysophyta.—Diatoms.

Phylum 5. Rhodophyta.—Red algae.

Phylum 6. Schizomycophyta.—Bacteria.

Phylum 7. Myxomycophyta.—Slime molds.

Phylum 8. Eumycophyta. — True fungi.

Subkingdom Embryophyta. — Land plants which produce many-celled embryos in the ovary of the parent plant.

Phylum 9. Bryophyta. — Small, independent, land plants, lack vascular tissue, and reproduce by alternation of generations; mosses and liverworts.

Phylum 10. Tracheophyta. — Land plants which have vascular tissue and true roots, stems, and leaves.

Subphylum A. Lycopsida. — Club mosses.

Subphylum B. Sphenopsida.—Horsetails.

Subphylum C. Pteropsida. — Have well-developed roots, stems, and leaves. Sporophytes are larger than gametophytes. This group includes the ferns, conifers, and flowering plants.

Class 1. Filicineae.—Ferns. They reproduce by alternation of generations and do not produce seeds.

Class 2. Gymnospermae.—These are evergreens with naked seeds borne in cones. Examples are conifers and cycads.

Class 3. Angiospermae.—The highest of all plants have their seeds encased in seed coats. They bear true flowers. Tulips, daisies, and nasturtiums are familiar examples.

43.12 The Practical Value of Classification

If you know the *scientific name* of a living thing and are familiar with the system of classification, you immediately know many of the facts concerning that particular living thing. You can expect it to have characteristics like those of its relatives. This may serve as a guide in determining whether or not it can be of use to you.

Another value of classification is that the Latin names are studied and recognized by scientists in all countries. Even in this country it would be difficult to know what you meant by a Mayflower unless you should give the scientific name (Epigaea repens). *Common names* vary in different localities. The following tables provide further review:

LIFE THROUGH THE AGES

Animals Studied	having these **Characteristics**	belong to this **Phylum.**
Ameba, paramecium, euglena	One-celled animals	Protozoa (proh-tuh-*zoh*-uh)
Gonium, volvox	(colonial forms)	
Sponges	Two layers of cells, pores	Porifera (poh-*riff*-er-uh)
Hydra, jellyfish, coral	Two layers of cells, tentacles	Coelenterata (seh-len-ter-*ay*-tuh)
Tapeworm, planaria	Three layers of cells, bilaterally symmetrical, flat, ribbonlike	Platyhelminthes (plat-ee-hel-*min*-theez)
Vinegar eel, trichina, hookworm	Three layers, long, round, threadlike	Nemathelminthes (neh-muh-thel-*min*-theez)
Starfish, sea cucumber, sea urchin	Radial arrangement, spiny-skinned	Echinodermata (eh-ky-noh-*der*-mah-tuh)
Clam, snail, oyster, squid, octopus	Soft bodies, not segmented, often with a shell	Mollusca (moh-*luss*-kuh)
Earthworm, sandworm, leeches	Segmented worms, digestive tube within cylindrical body	Annelida (uh-*nel*-ih-duh)
Crayfish, lobster, crab	Jointed appendages, exoskeleton of chitin	Arthropoda (ar-*throp*-oh-duh)
	Two body regions	**Class** Crustacea (krus-*tay*-shuh)
Grasshoppers, crickets, katydids	Three body regions, six legs, spiracles	Insecta (in-*sek*-tuh)
	Straight wings	**Order** Orthoptera (or-*thop*-ter-uh)
Bugs	Half wings	Hemiptera (heh-*mip*-ter-uh)
Beetles	Sheath wings	Coleoptera (koh-lee-*op*-ter-uh)
Ants, bees, wasps, sawflies, gall flies	Membrane wings	Hymenoptera (hy-men-*op*-ter-uh)
Dragon flies	Toothed wings	Odonata (oh-duh-*nay*-tuh)
Butterflies, moths	Scale wings	Lepidoptera (lep-ih-*dop*-ter-uh)

Animals Studied	having these **Characteristics**	belong to this **Phylum.**
Flies, mosquitoes	Two wings	Diptera (*dip*-ter-uh)
Cicadas, aphids, scale insects	Similar wings	Homoptera (hoh-*mop*-ter-uh)
Spiders, daddy-long-legs, scorpions, ticks	Eight legs, no antennae, two body regions	Arachnida (uh-*rak*-nih-duh)
Centipedes	Tracheae, long bodies with many pairs of appendages	Chilopoda (ky-*lah*-poh-duh)
Millipedes		Diplopoda (dip-*lah*-poh-duh)
Dogfish, salmon, eel, perch, goldfish	Backbones, gill slits in embryo, dorsal nerve cord	Chordata (kor-*day*-tuh)
	Gills, scales, fins, air bladder, two-chambered heart	**Class** Fish (Pisces) (*pihs*-eez)
Frogs, toads, salamanders	Three-chambered heart, thin skin, breathe by gills sometime during life	Amphibia (am-*fib*-ee-uh)
Lizards, snakes, turtles, alligators, crocodiles	Lungs, scales	Reptila (rep-*til*-ee-uh)
Goldfinch, crow, bluebird, phoebe, chickadee, wren, Baltimore oriole, catbird, flicker, house sparrow, robin, swallow, owl, warblers.	Feathers, high body temperature, wings, two legs, eggs with hard shell, four-chambered heart	Birds (Aves) (*ay*-veez)
Duckbill, kangaroo, sloth, mole, whale, dog, rat, pig, elephant, bat, ape, man	Hair, mammary glands, suckle young with milk, diaphragm	Mammalia (muh-*may*-lee-uh)
Duckbill, spiny anteater	Egg-laying	**Order** Monotremata (mon-uh-*tree*-mah-tuh)
Kangaroo, opossum	Pouched mammals	Marsupialia (mahr-soo-pih-*ay*-lih-uh)
Hairy anteater, sloth, armadillo	Toothless, or simple teeth	Edentata (ee-den-*tay*-tuh)
Whale	Adapted to marine life	Cetacea (seh-*tay*-she-uh)
Beaver, rat, porcupine, rabbit, squirrel	Incisor teeth chisel-shaped, usually two above and two below	Rodentia (roh-*den*-she-uh)

Animals Studied	having these Characteristics	belong to this Phylum.
Dog, cat, civit, mink, raccoon, fox, bear, seal, lion, wolf	Long canine teeth, long, sharp claws	Carnivora (kahr-*niv*-er-uh)
Cattle, horse, deer, giraffe, pig, rhinoceros	Hoofs, teeth adapted to grinding	Ungulata (ung-yoo-*lay*-tuh)
Elephants	Trunks, tusks, broad molars	Proboscidea (proh-buh *sid*-ee-uh)
Bats	Pointed teeth, forelimbs adapted to flying	Chiroptera (ky-*rop*-ter-uh)
Lemurs, monkeys, apes, gibbons, orang-utans, chimpanzees, gorillas, man	Forelimbs with hand, fingernails and toenails	Primates (pry-*may*-teez)

Plants Studied	having these Characteristics	belong to this Phylum.
Oscillatoria	Filamentous, lack definite nucleus, reproduce by fission	SUBKINGDOM THALLOPHYTA **Phylum** Cyanophyta Blue-green algae
Protococcus	Unicellular, spherical cells, reproduce by fission	Chlorophyta Green algae
Desmids	Cells have similar, symmetrical halves, reproduce by fission and conjugation	Chlorophyta Green algae
Spirogyra	Cylindrical cells, chloroplasts in spiral bands, reproduce by fission and conjugation	Chlorophyta Green algae
Fucus	Leaflike with holdfasts, leathery, reproduce sexually by eggs and sperms	Phaeophyta Brown algae
Diatoms	Boxlike, walls contain silica, reproduce by fission, splitting lengthwise, may conjugate	Chrysophyta Diatoms
Chondrus	Mostly marine, reproduce by eggs and non-motile sperms and by asexual spores, red pigment present	Rhodophyta Red algae
Bacteria	One-celled, colonies, or filamentous; microscopic, lack definite nucleus, reproduce by fission, lack chlorophyll	Schizomycophyta Fission fungi
Slime Molds	Unicellular flagellated cells which fuse to form a creeping jelly-like, multinucleate mass of protoplasm finally transformed to asexual spores.	Myxomycophyta Slime Molds
Bread Mold	Spreading mycelium, reproduce by asexual sporangiospores and conjugation	Eumycophyta True fungi **Class** Phycomycetes

Plants Studied	having these Characteristics	belong to this Phylum.
Mildews	Spreading mycelium with short one-nucleate cells, absorb material of host, reproduce by ascospores resulting from union of sexual nuclei and asexual spores	Eumycophyta **Class** Ascomycetes Sac fungi
Yeast	Single, oval cells, reproduce by budding and ascospores	Ascomycetes Sac fungi
Blue Mold	Hyphae cylindrical. Network of mycelium forming mat on surface of substratum, anaerobic, growth at terminal cell	Ascomycetes Sac fungi
Rusts (wheat)	Alternate hosts, wheat and barberry, reproduction by fusion of non-motile sperms with female hyphae, giving rise to a succession of asexual spores	Basidiomycetes Stalk fungi
Rusts (white blister)	Alternate hosts, white pine, currant and gooseberries	Basidiomycetes Stalk fungi
Smuts (corn)	Dark-colored masses of spores, mycelium grows largely in intercellular spaces of host	Basidiomycetes Stalk fungi
Mushrooms	Mycelium strands underground, fruiting bodies develop on hypha which forms a stalk and cap	Basidiomycetes Stalk fungi
Marchantia (Liverwort)	Flat, ribbon-like rhizoids on midrib of under side, alteration of generations, gametophyte conspicuous	**SUBKINGDOM EMBRYOPHYTA** **Phylum** Bryophyta **Class** Hepaticae
Mosses	Stems, simple leaves, root-like projections, sporophyte generation lives as a parasite on the gametophyte	Musci
Horsetails (Equisetum)	Stem performs photosynthesis, special stalk produces spores	**Phylum** Tracheophyta **Subphylum** Sphenopsida
Club mosses	Special spore-forming organs, creeping plants, irregular prothallium	Lycopsida
Ferns (Pteris)	True roots, stems and leaves, alternation of generations, sporophyte conspicuous, living on gametophyte for a short time	Pteropsida **Class** Filicineae
Pine	Cone-bearing, seeds borne on naked scales with several seed leaves, usually evergreen trees with needle leaves	Gymnospermae
	Flowering plants bearing seeds in an ovary	Angiospermae
Bean	Seeds have 2 seed leaves, net-veined	**Subclass** Dicotyledons
Corn	Seeds have 1 seed leaf, parallel-veined	Monocotyledons

FACTS TO REMEMBER

Classification is the orderly grouping of plants and animals according to their structure. The purposes of classification are: (a) for convenience and (b) to show relationships. The relationships are determined by evidence from (1) vegetative structures, (2) reproductive structures, (3) comparison with fossil forms, and (4) a study of their distribution.

The *Linnean system* of classification is known as *binomial nomenclature*. The divisions are: kingdom, phylum, class, order, family, genus, and species. The genus and species names are used to designate an individual plant or animal.

WORDS TO REMEMBER

binomial	family	scientific name
nomenclature	genus	species
class	kingdom	taxonomy
classification	order	variety
common name	phylum	

QUESTIONS

1. What is meant by classification? Why is it necessary?
2. What is the name given to Linnaeus' system of classification?
3. How many names are required by each living thing? What are they?
4. Name in order the subdivisions of a kingdom.
5. Copy the following list of plants and animals. After each write the name of the phylum to which it belongs.

horse	starfish	hookworm	leech
ameba	earthworm	fern	mushroom
marchantia	green alga	bread mold	clam
bath sponge	maple tree	grasshopper	spider
crayfish	tapeworm	sea cucumber	frog

6. Name the *five* classes of the Chordata and *two* members of each.
7. List the orders of mammals and one representative of each.
8. What characteristics of the Canidae separate them from the other families of the Carnivora?
9. Write the *complete* classification of the domestic cat which belongs to the Family *Felidae,* Genus *Felis,* and species *domestica.*
10. How would you write the scientific name for the cat?
11. State briefly the modern classification of the plant kingdom.
12. State two reasons why classification is of practical value.

COMPLETION TEST

As your teacher or classmate reads the following incomplete statements, with your book closed, write on a clean sheet of paper the word or phrase which best completes each statement.

1. The science of classification of living things is called _____.
2. An early attempt at classification was made by _____.
3. _____ devised our present method of classification.
4. The modern method of classification is based on _____.
5. The two main kingdoms are called _____ and _____.
6. Ameba and _____ are in the Protozoa group because they are one-celled.
7. Both grantia and the bath sponge belong to the Porifera because _____.
8. Hydra can be distinguished from a two-layered sponge because it has _____ around its mouth.
9. The body of the earthworm is divided into _____.
10. The tapeworm is long and _____.
11. The octopus is a mollusk because it has a _____.
12. The leech belongs in the same phylum as the _____.
13. The skeleton of the grasshopper is made of _____.
14. The _____ reproduces by alternation of generations.
15. The Amphibia include frogs, toads, and _____.
16. _____ have a two-chambered heart.
17. _____ have a three-chambered heart.
18. _____ have a four-chambered heart.
19. _____ have no chlorophyll and cannot make their own food.
20. Algae and fungi are classed in the subkingdom _____.

PROJECTS

I. *Study of a Museum Collection.*—1. If your school has a small collection of preserved or mounted specimens, obtain permission to study them carefully. On notebook paper arrange a space for each of the plant and animal phyla. In the appropriate space write the name of each specimen in the collection.

Study your list carefully. Compare the members of each phylum and try to decide why they are placed there. Sometimes their external appearance is misleading.

2. If your school has a large museum, you may decide to choose one group and make a similar study of one subdivision.

II. *Classification of the Living Things Found in Your Classroom.*—List all the living things you can recognize. Using reference books, if necessary, place them in the proper phyla in your notebook. The plants may give you some difficulty if you have many cultivated varieties. However, references on cultivated forms or house plants may help.

III. *Insect Collections.*—If you are interested in insects, you may find a fascinating hobby waiting for you. Collect any and all kinds of insects and bring them into the laboratory.

Sort your specimens and arrange them in groups. Place them in the proper orders and preserve them if you wish. Find one representative of each order.

REFERENCES

Fuller and Tippo, *College Botany*. Holt.

Hegner, *College Zoology*. Macmillan.

Hegner, *Parade of the Animal Kingdom*. Macmillan.

Locy, *Biology and Its Makers*. Holt.

Smith, Gilbert, and others, *A Textbook of General Botany*. Macmillan.

Snyder, *Biology in the Making*. McGraw-Hill.

Storer, *General Zoology*. McGraw-Hill.

Transeau, Sampson, Tiffany, *Textbook of Botany*. Blakiston.

Wilson and Loomis, *Botany*. 3rd Ed. Holt.

CHAPTER 44

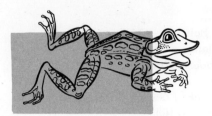

Life in Ages Past

44.1 The Birth of the Earth

No one *knows* how the earth began, but the following is the theory most generally accepted. In some way stars were formed from clouds of gas and cosmic dust that were floating in space. Forces of gravity caused them to contract into masses and rotate as they traveled their orbits in space. The pressure within increased and they became so hot that they began to radiate as stars. One of these was our sun, which continued to burn and glow within a mass of whirling cosmic dust. Some parts of this mass collided and formed planets.

We call this event the birth of the earth. At its start the earth was smaller than it is now and was probably molten for a long time. These conditions were unfavorable for the existence of life, but as time went on, the earth began to cool and to assume a more definite shape. It was able to hold an atmosphere down against its surface. Finally the earth became cool enough for some forms of living things to develop. With the proper elements available and the proper temperature reached, it is believed that some forms of simple life appeared.

In some way giant molecules acquired the ability to reproduce themselves. Certain organic compounds may have been made in the sea by solar radiation. Over a long period of time these molecules may have joined in groups to form simple organisms such as bacteria. Others such as blue-green algae acquired the ability to use the energy of the sun in photosynthesis. Flagellates appeared and probably gave rise to many other

FIGURE 44-1. *NEBULA*

Nebula is the name given to to certain hazy masses of hot gas, surrounded by stars. One of the brightest spiral nebulae is the Great Spiral in Andromeda, shown here. According to one early theory, the solar system began as a rapidly rotating nebula of hot gas.

618

one-celled organisms. These early forms of life used the necessary elements and compounds to form the substance known as *protoplasm*. Early life and all life shows itself through the medium of protoplasm.

44.2   Life on the Earth

We assume that the first living protoplasm was in the form of a single cell. Being alive, it could form other cells like itself, that is, it could *reproduce*. One cell became two cells under proper conditions of temperature and the presence of food and water.

We may assume also that for a long period of time the forms of life were one-celled only. We gain an idea of the method of reproduction by studying the paramecium or the ameba. A single one of either of these forms soon develops into thousands of individuals in a suitable growing medium.

Another step upward is shown when the animal or plant, instead of dividing and separating, divides into two cells, but remains joined. Each of these two divides into two more cells and remains joined, forming four cells. This process continues forming plants and animals of greater and greater complexity.

We are able to gain an idea of this simple multiplication of plant cells in the spirogyra (Fig. 30-3). Other higher plants, like liverworts (Fig. 33-3), mosses (Fig. 33-2), ferns (Fig. 34-5), and flowering plants (Chap. 38), show increasing complexity. A similar series of animal forms may also be found.

Life in its simplest form may have started five hundred million or a billion years ago. In any event, it was a long, long time ago. The earth may have been pulled away from the sun two billion years ago. According to these figures, the earth has been inhabited from one

National Museum

FIGURE 44-2. *TRILOBITES*

A limestone slab from the Devonian rocks of Ontario shows the now extinct crustacean that lived in the Paleozoic era.

quarter to one half of its existence.

More than half of this period was given over to one-celled forms. *Fossil* remains of animal and plant forms of the earliest times have not been found, but traces and deposits of carbon, such as graphite, indicate that life was present.

We shall never know from any fossil evidence whether the first living thing was a plant or an animal, but we may assume that it was quite unspecialized. From this elementary form there has been a development into two specialized forms that we call plants and animals. Plants and animals are alike in many ways, and unlike in a few respects.

44.3   Reckoning Time

In our legal calendar we say that this is the twentieth century A.D. Our legal calendar starts counting time from the birth of Christ. In describing events before that time, such as the life span of Aristotle, we say B.C. Of course, most of geologic time would be given as B.C., but it is so remote that it cannot be described exactly by numbers.

FIGURE 44-3. *REPTILES*

During the late Paleozoic era, the first reptiles appeared on the earth. These vertebrates were the first to break away from the water and live on land.

Geologists are agreed upon a time in the early history of life on the earth that they call the *Cambrian period*. It was a long period characterized by animals that were invertebrates. There were no birds or mammals or fishes. During this period all plants lived in the water; no trees or plants grew on land. The Cambrian had a rather mild climate; so mild that corals thrived even in the polar seas.

The Cambrian is a portion of a much

FIGURE 44-4. *HOW OLD?*

Scientists can estimate the age of a mineral sample by comparing certain naturally radioactive elements and their breakdown products. The equipment **below** is used to measure and identify these elements.

longer **geologic time** called the **Paleozoic** (early life) **era.** The next long stretch of time following the Paleozoic is the **Mesozoic** (middle life) **era.** The last portion includes the time in which we live and is called the **Cenozoic** (recent life) **era.**

You will find wide differences as you read various books that deal with geologic time. The table that we have selected is based upon the rate of change observed in radium-bearing rocks, which is a method of measuring the age of the earth. By reflecting upon these enormous spans of time, you realize that the many species of animals and plants found as fossils or living today have developed very slowly.

The total age of the earth is thought to be 1,240,000,000 to 1,710,000,000 years. The estimate of the years given in the table on page 621 is taken from Bulletin #769, United States Geological Survey. There is still a wide difference of opinion about the time in each division, and it is very difficult to find geologists who agree. The important facts are that the earth is very old, and that the period with the first record of abundant life is the Cambrian.

620

Era	Period	Significance
Archezoic		
Proterozoic 1,000,000,000 to 700,000,000 years ago		Remains of life mostly lacking. Fossil algae.
Paleozoic 470,000,000 to 350,000,000 years ago	Cambrian	Advance of invertebrates. Trilobites abundant.
	Ordovician	Chain corals, starfish, and fishlike animals appear.
	Silurian	Primitive sharks appear. Brachiopods.
	Devonian	Lungfish. Forests. First amphibians appear. Chain corals disappear.
	Carboniferous	First reptiles appear. Large amphibians. Abundant sharks. Spore-bearing plants.
	Permian	Rise of primitive reptiles.
Mesozoic 175,000,000 to 135,000,000 years ago	Triassic	Rise of dinosaurs. Connecting link between mammals and reptiles appear. Cycadlike plants.
	Jurassic	Egg-laying mammals appear. Birds appear with teeth. Great dinosaurs appear. Rich marine fauna.
	Cretaceous	Advance in mammals. Last of dinosaurs. Rise of flowering plants and modern insects.
Cenozoic 55,000,000 years ago to dawn of history	Eocene	Primitive monkey, horse, and elephant appear. Increase in number of mammals. Some of them live in tree tops. Modern flora.
	Oligocene	Extinction of early mammals. Early anthropoids.
	Miocene	Advance in anthropoids. Culmination of mammals.
	Pliocene	Man uses fire and rough tools.
	Pleistocene	Periodic glaciation. Extinction of large mammals. Neanderthal man and Cro-Magnon man.
	Recent	Domestication of animals. Written records. Dominance of man.

44.4 The Family Tree of Plants

The ancestors of early plants were quite unlike the plants themselves. Earlier forms become simpler and simpler as we go farther back. We gain some support for our line of reasoning by tracing plant remains in rocks. A plant known as horsetail or scouring rush is often found on barren ground. Fossil forms of similar plants, called **Calamites**, are found in the middle *Devonian* period of the Paleozoic era.

FIGURE 44-5. *ANCIENT FERNS*

The giant tree fern (*center*), the Calamite (*right,* with whorled leaves) and the Lepidodendron (needle-like leaves) are ancestors of modern ferns, horsetails, and club mosses.

Chicago Natural History Museum

Calamites were large plants, growing to the height of sixty feet with a diameter of a foot. The whorls of leaves of these fossil horsetails are sometimes found. They are called Annularia. The theory is that the present rush may be a descendant of the towering horsetail that lived and flourished millions of years ago, and that competition from other plants has been a factor in stunting or dwarfing the present horsetail.

Another treelike form was the Lepidodendron (scale tree). (Fig. 44-5.) These trees grew to the height of one hundred feet. They belong to a group of plants that we only find today as creeping vines in damp woods. In other words, the family tree of one of the club mosses would reach back to the tall trees of the Paleozoic age. The rank growth of such plants forms a part of the original stock that has given the modern world coal, gas, and oil.

44.5 The Family Tree of Animals

It is in the period called *Pre-Cambrian,* the longest of all the periods and the one we know the least about, that are locked the secrets of just how life began, what the earliest forms were, how

they moved, how they ate, and how they reproduced. The secrets have been lost in great part because of the destruction of fossil evidence by heat and pressure upon the rocks in which the fossils occurred.

Following the Pre-Cambrian is the Cambrian with a wealth of fossil material. As we work down through the rock layers that were deposited in these times, we find the first appearances of forms of life. It is generally considered that chain corals appeared in the *Ordovician* period, and were exterminated in the Devonian. The starfish first appeared in the Ordovician. Life made only slow progress during the entire Paleozoic era.

44.6 The Age of Fossils

The *Mesozoic era* is often called the *age of fossils.* Evidently conditions at that time were most suitable for the formation of fossils. Man has discovered large numbers of fossils formed during this era. This was the age when towering ferns and huge cycads thrived and flourished. Evergreens and redwoods appeared. Enormous reptiles (see chart, page 621) roamed the earth. The giant dinosaurs found abundant food. Some

LIFE THROUGH THE AGES

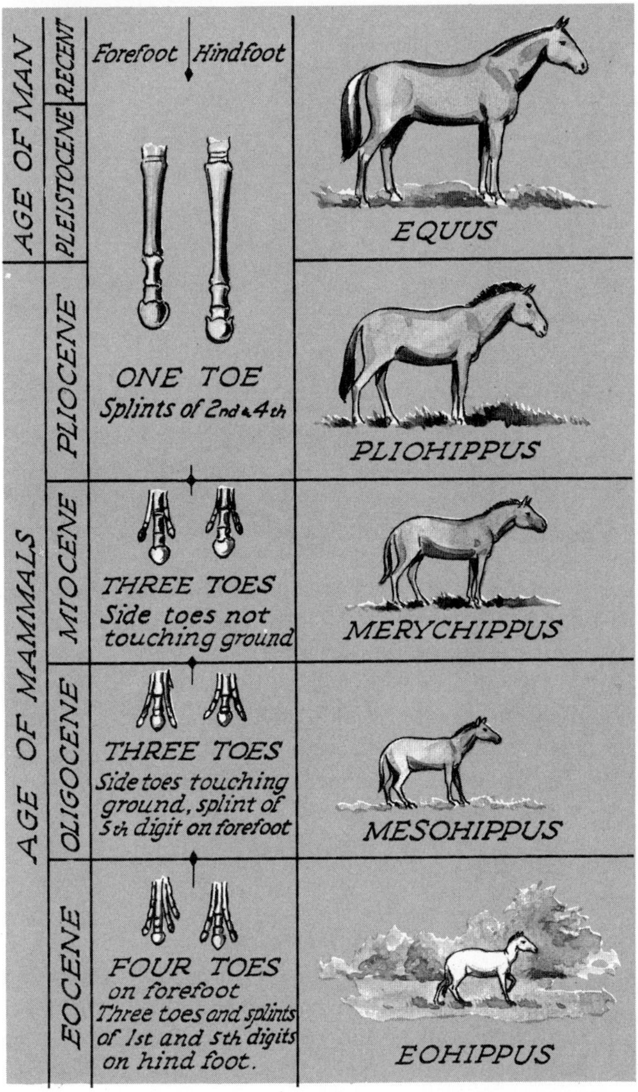

FIGURE 44-6. *HISTORY OF THE HORSE*

The horse, one of our common domestic animals, has a very long history. Although his early ancestors walked on all four toes, through the ages his bones have developed so that he now stands on only one toe. The changes in his leg and foot structure can be traced through fossil forms.

were vegetarians, or *herbivorous*. Others were meat eaters, *carnivorous*. Some could swim; some could run; others tried to fly. The study of these creatures is a fascinating one. Their story is still being revised as new evidence is discovered. Since these events occurred millions of years before the age of man, this is a real detective story based on scattered bits of evidence.

In the *Cenozoic era* many of our present-day animals had their beginning. From the larger numbers of fossils found of horselike animals, man has been able to trace the ancestry of the modern horse to a small form known as *Eohippus.*

The ancient horse had four toes and the remains of a fifth in the front foot, while the hind foot had three toes and the remains of a fourth. It also had simple teeth for eating leaves. Horses died out in North and South America but were later brought to this continent by the Spaniards. Fossils of primitive horses have been preserved in the rocks. The deer also has many stages in its de-

velopment preserved in rock, affording another example of the manner in which some present animals developed.

The domesticated horses were developed in the Old World. In the warmer regions, where food was plentiful, the largest horses developed; while in the north, where food was less abundant and conditions more severe, the Shetland pony appeared.

44.7 Where Fossils Are Found

Many fossils were formed from animals that lived in the sea. When they died, they sank to the bottom and were imbedded in the mud. When the mud was changed to **shale** (a rock formation) by long-continued pressure, the imprint of the original animal was left, especially if it was protected by a shell or other hard covering. Later uplifts of the earth's surface brought these buried shales above sea level, where eroding streams exposed them to our gaze. Thus, water-laid or **sedimentary** rocks contain most of the fossils. The same sort of process seems to be going on today.

In Siberia, *frozen* mammoths were found that are thousands of years old. The skin, hair, and internal organs were well preserved. These are fossils preserved by "nature's cold storage."

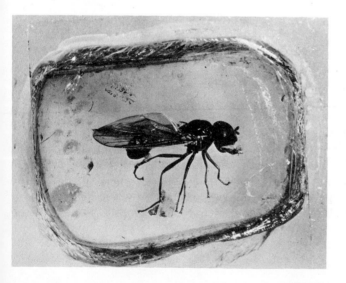

FIGURE 44-9. *PETRIFIED*

These logs, buried for thousands of years in mud and sand, have gradually been turned to stone. Minerals filled the empty cells of the decaying wood until the whole structure became solid stone. There is a famous petrified forest in northern Arizona.

Josef Muench

Other fossils are found in **amber** which, in itself, is *fossil resin*. Ants, flies, mosquitoes, and some plants are caught in the sticky resin and imbedded. The resin changes by evaporation to amber, and the forms are so faithfully preserved that the species may be determined. Most of the amber-preserved insects come from the Baltic Sea.

Near Pikes Peak in Colorado is the Florissant Valley, once a lake. The region was volcanic. During eruption, poisonous gases killed various forms of life, some of which fell into the lake. Fine ash fell upon the lake, and the insects and plant life sank to the bottom of the shallow water. The forms which fell were probably preserved by heat and poison gas, so that decay was prevented. Other eruptions followed, burying the earlier victims deeper until the weight changed the mud to shale. Uplifts revealed forms that had died more than a million years before. Some are nearly as well preserved as those of the Baltic amber.

Ancient fossil forms have also been preserved in **asphalt beds.** These beds were covered by thin soil or wind-blown dust, forming a trap. Animals walked along on the thin covering until it broke through and they were mired. Carnivorous animals were perhaps attracted by the outcries of the helpless animals, and eventually all sank in the sticky asphalt, to be preserved for thousands of years.

Some animals and plants have been preserved by a process called **petrifaction** (pet-rih-*fak*-shun), by which minerals have gradually replaced the structures of the original plant or animal (Fig. 44-9). Some of the most faithful reproductions of original forms have been produced by this method. Plants generally show better detail of their original shape and microscopic structure than animals.

44.8 Evidence of Ancestry

From the study of classification we learn that plants and animals are related and that they can be placed in different groups, each of which has similar structures. We know that these groups can be arranged in a definite order, showing increasing development from simple to complex forms. All of these forms show the relationships of plant and animal life.

*Embryology of the Chick.—***Embryology** (em-bree-*ol*-uh-jee) *is the study*

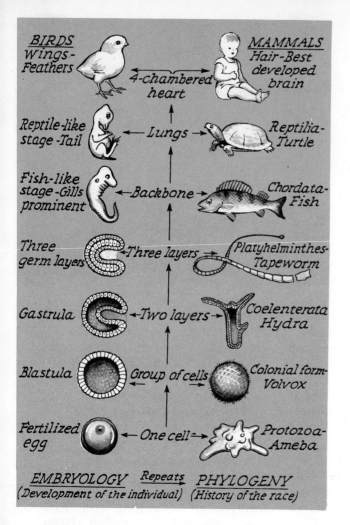

BIRDS
Wings-Feathers

MAMMALS
Hair-Best
developed
brain

4-chambered heart

Reptile-like stage -Tail

Lungs

Reptilia-Turtle

Fish-like stage -Gills prominent

Backbone

Chordata-Fish

Three germ layers

Three layers

Platyhelminthes-Tapeworm

Gastrula

Two layers

Coelenterata
Hydra

Blastula

Group of cells

Colonial form-Volvox

Fertilized egg

One cell

Protozoa-Ameba

EMBRYOLOGY *Repeats* PHYLOGENY
(Development of the individual) (History of the race)

FIGURE 44-10. *EVIDENCE OF ANCESTRY*

Each individual passes through stages in its growth and development that are similar to the changes that occurred in the development of the race. Animals still start from a single cell, the simplest form of life in history. Trace the development of the individual (*lower left*), comparing each step to the historical development of living forms (*right*).

of the development of the individual from fertilization of the egg until the individual begins an independent existence. The study of **embryos** (*em*-bree-ohs) shows the similarity of simple and complex forms in a striking manner. If you place some eggs in an incubator and break one open each day until hatching time, you will notice a very definite change taking place.

The greatest changes will be noticed in the first four days. If you observe the growth of the embryo and study them under a microscope, you will learn how each body system originates and becomes established.

The egg of the chick is typical of the eggs of other animals, except perhaps that it contains more stored food. The fertilized egg cell lies on the top of the yolk, which together with the white provides nourishment for the growing embryo. When the fertilized egg cell is incubated, it begins to divide by **cleavage**. The cells rearrange themselves to form two layers of cells, the *ectoderm* and *endoderm* (Sec. 27.5). This stage of development resembles the structure of hydra (Fig. 44-10). The third layer of cells, the *mesoderm* (Sec. 27.5), is then formed from the other two layers. The presence of three germ layers is typical

626

of the Flatworms (Platyhelminthes) and all subsequent groups.

From these three germ layers are established all the systems of organs. Gill slits are formed, but are never functional. Gills are typical structures of fish, but fish never develop any higher. Does this stage in the development of the chick suggest that birds developed from a fishlike ancestor?

Finally the chick develops scales on its legs. Such scales are typical structures of reptiles. The chick, however, also develops feathers on the rest of its body. Its forelimbs become wings instead of legs. Horny beaks take the place of teeth, and air sacs fill the long hollow bones. A chick has developed, but it has gone through stages which are very similar to the highest stages of development attained in the lower phyla. This with other embryological evidence helps to confirm the scientists' theory of the relationship of living things.

In Figure 44-10 you will see pictorial evidence of the ancestry of higher forms. You know what embryology is. **Phylogeny** (fy-*loj*-en-ee) *is the history of the development of the phyla or groups of living things.* The evidence of ancestry which you are studying in these sketches in Figure 44-10 may be summed up in the following statement: *embryology repeats phylogeny.*

Thus you would expect that the human child would go through similar stages during its embryonic development. Scientific study has proven this to be the case. You will find the study of human embryology to be a fascinating one.

There is similar evidence of ancestry among plant groups. Fertilized egg cells of higher plants pass through all the stages which are typical of the lower forms of plants.

44.9 How the Past Explains the Present

Since every individual today can trace its ancestry to some earlier form, it is interesting to note the relationships which exist among animal and plant groups and to try to explain their origin. The resemblances of living things are shown through (1) fossil evidence, (2) classification, (3) intermediate forms, (4) comparative anatomy, (5) embryology, (6) geographic distribution, (7) vestigial organs, (8) homologous structures, and (9) similarity of function.

(*1*) Forms which descended from a *common ancestor* would resemble each other more closely than those which are more distantly related. For instance, the zebra, horse, and donkey are more like each other than like cows. They all descended from a horselike form (Pliohippus). **Fossil evidence** leads to this conclusion. (*2*) In the study of **classification** you noted that dogs and wolves resemble each other more closely than they do the foxes. Therefore they are placed in the genus Canis while foxes are in the genus Vulpes. Thus those with similar structures are grouped together.

Vertebrate Relatives.—By means of embryological and other evidences scientists have also confirmed the theory of the relationship of the vertebrates. This relationship of vertebrate forms, from simple to complex, is shown in Figure 44-11.

(*3*) In spite of the careful way in which plants and animals are arranged in a progressive series, there are some forms which seem to belong to none of the groups. These are the so-called **intermediate forms.** Since scientists are not agreed as to whether *euglena* is a plant or an animal, this may be considered an example.

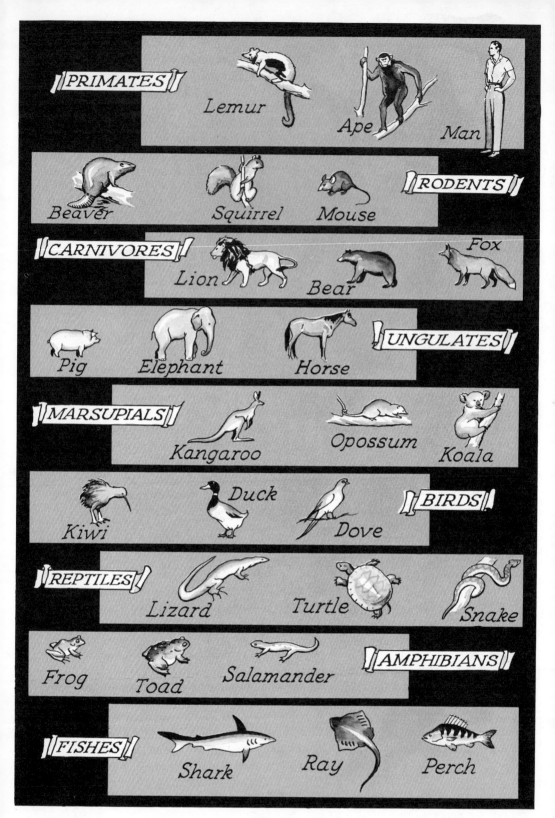

FIGURE 44-11 *THE VERTEBRATES*

Most of the intermediate forms, however, have been found as fossils. When they had given rise to other forms, most of the orignal ones then died out. The trilobites (*try*-luh-byts) (Fig. 44-12) lived back in the Paleozoic era. Their bodies were divided into three main parts instead of being bilaterally symmetrical, as were so many of their relatives. The trilobites had jointed legs like the insects, spiders, and crabs, but very thick skins. The *horseshoe crab* and the *pill bug* are among the few living relatives.

The oldest fish had cartilage skeletons instead of those made of bone, as most of our modern fish have. The living representatives are the sharks.

Perhaps you have wondered how water forms could eventually become adapted to live on land. One group of living fish, called lung fish, possess simple air sacs which they can fill with air and use for breathing when the water dries up. Note the similarity of the problem of such a fish to that of the amphibia.

The coelacanth, a fish thought to have become extinct seventy million years ago,

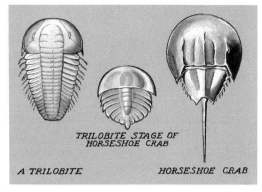

FIGURE 44-12. *TRILOBITE*

The trilobite is a marine crustacean, now known only as a fossil. We notice its relationship to present day crustaceans by its resemblance to an early stage in horseshoe crab growth.

is another intermediate form. It was believed to be extinct because it was only found in fossil form. In recent years, however, several living specimens were captured near the coast of South Africa. The coelacanth has two pairs of limb-like fins and undeveloped lungs, probably very much like those from which the legs and lungs of higher vertebrates have developed.

FIGURE 44-13. *OUT OF THE PAST*

The coelacanth is the only living member of the group of fishes which gave rise to the land vertebrates. One of the oldest types of back-boned animals known, it has an ancestry which can be traced back 325 million years. Before 1938, it had been found only as fossil remains in rocks.

Smithsonian Institution

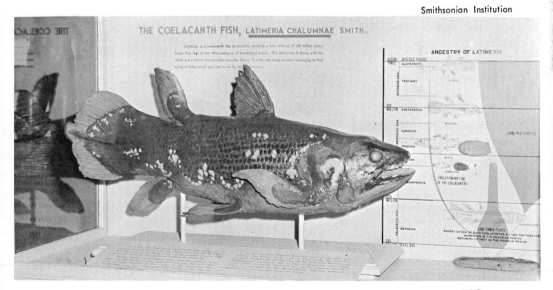

One of the best known of the intermediate forms is a reptilian bird named *Archeopteryx* (Sec. 16.1). The archeopteryx was a little smaller than a crow and had a long body. It possessed sharp, pointed teeth and a long tail with vertebrae. This bird had feathers even along the bony tail, and claws in its wings. It could live on land or in the air. How do you think these characteristics show relationship between birds and reptiles?

Among the mammals, the *duckbill,* that lays eggs but feeds its young with milk, is a form intermediate between the egg-laying reptiles and placental mammals (those giving birth to the young). Since the duckbill has hair, it is classed as a mammal, although a very primitive one (Fig. 17-6).

Many intermediate forms are still missing in this series of living things, and scientists are still hunting for their fossil remains in order to be able to write a complete story of animal and plant life.

(4) You have been making a study of **comparative anatomy** as you traced the development of the vertebrates, Chordata, from the fish to the mammal. You have found that the fish has a two-chambered heart. You found that amphibia have three-chambered hearts and that reptiles have three-chambered hearts, partly divided. You found that birds and mammals have four-chambered hearts. This is evidence of progression from simple to more complex forms. You have also compared the structure of the crayfish and grasshopper and seen that they are related.

You have been comparing the structures of plants and animals as you have traced the development of the digestive, nervous, excretory, reproductive, and other systems which are necessary to carry on the life processes. As you have studied the structures used by these plants and animals, you have seen the adaptations of the structures to their use. This comparison of different forms is known as comparative anatomy.

(5) As you have already learned, **embryology** (Sec. 44.8) is the study of the development of the young before it is hatched or born, or before the seed is produced. You will recall that the frog's egg (Fig. 14-8) begins to divide as soon as fertilization has taken place. By a series of divisions known as *cleavage,* it forms many small cells which rearrange to form distinct layers, from which the tiny tadpole develops (Fig. 14-7).

Each animal goes through a distinct series of stages. However, they seem to be very similar, and those most closely related resemble each other more closely in the embryo stages. This accounts for the presence of gill slits in the embryo bird and the thick covering of hair in the embryo whale. It shows the kind of ancestors from which they probably descended.

(6) Another problem that long confronted scientists was how to explain the presence of the kangaroo in Australia and the opossum in the United States when they were both pouch-bearing animals and thus structurally similar. This **geographic distribution** was finally explained when more of the earth's changes were noted and it was found that land bridges might have existed at some earlier date, allowing descendants from some common ancestor to become widespread.

Volcanoes, canyons, mountain ranges, deserts, and other changing conditions of the earth may limit or extend the range of a species after it has developed. Widely separated species tend to fit themselves to their immediate environments, and thus develop many noticeable variations.

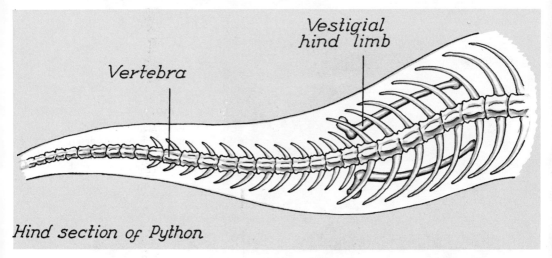

Vertebra

Vestigial hind limb

Hind section of Python

FIGURE 44-14. *EVIDENCE*
The vestigial hind limb of the python, not developed to serve any practical
purpose, shows the snake's relationship to other vertebrate forms.

(7) Another bit of evidence to show
that living things resembled each other
is the presence of **vestigial** (vess-*tij*-ee-
al) **organs.** Why does man have an
appendix? Why does the snake have the
remnants of hind limb bones and the por-
poise pelvic bones? The presence of
these and other structures in living things
brings man to the conclusion that they
descended from ancestors which needed
and used these structures.

(8) Some structures of similar origin
have developed for very different functions in different species. Such structures
are called **homologous** (hoh-*mol*-uh-
gus) **structures.** The bones in the wing
of a bird, in the flipper of a whale, the
front leg of a frog, the front leg of a
dog, and the arm of man have all developed from the shoulder region. The
origin of these bones is similar since they
are all vertebrates. However, they differ
in their functions. The bird has developed wings for flying; the whale, flippers
for swimming; and the dog, forelegs for
running. The bones in the whale's flipper are short and sturdy; those in the
arm of man are longer and the fingers
are flexible. See Fig. 17-3.

Homologous structures of similar origin but different functions show how
species have become adapted to their
surroundings. These structures also
show relationships of different forms to
each other.

(9) **Similarity of function** is shown
in the ways in which plants and animals
carry out their life processes. The blood
of the rhesus monkey shows the Rh factor in blood and made it possible to
understand this factor in man. Different
races of man have varying proportions
of the Rh blood factor. This may indicate the relationships of early man. The
secretions of ductless glands, such as
the thyroid, and digestive glands of the
stomach, in some animals are enough
like those of man to make them useful
for producing medicine. Other animals,
like rabbits and guinea pigs, are used to
test the strength of vaccines and serum
before these preparations are administered to human beings.

Development of Species.—The variety
of living things, their large numbers, and
their widespread distribution indicate
that those living in the present must have
developed some means of meeting

FIGURE 44-15. *SHIFTING SANDS*

Few plants are able to take root and grow in desert areas where the sands are continually shifted about by the wind.

John Kabel

changes in environment and competition. These methods of showing resemblances of living things help us to piece together the picture puzzle of the past, from which all present species have arisen.

44.10 Changing Environments

There are factors in your environment which you know are subject to change. That is why the topic of weather is always a current one. Perhaps you have experienced other changes, such as an earthquake, flood, fire, or possibly you have seen the results of volcanic action. Some of these changes take place slowly and others rapidly. Whenever the surface of the earth changes, the plant life and animal life are affected.

The common factors that cause a change in the environment are (1) temperature, (2) wind, (3) water, (4) volcanoes, and (5) changes produced by living things.

44.11 Inorganic Changes

(*1*) Changes in *temperature* produce freezing and thawing. During the day moisture may condense on various objects and freeze at night, causing loosening of soil and even splitting of rocks.

Accumulations of ice may form glaciers. Thawing near the edge of the glacier causes it to move, carrying some of the underlying rock with it, leaving grooves and scratches on the bed rock over which it passes.

Temperature changes may result in storms, since such changes cause air currents to rise and cause moisture to evaporate with a greater or lesser degree of rapidity.

Plants and animals can live only within certain ranges of temperature. A severe winter or a long summer drought kills many plants, with the result that the animal population which depends on a certain temperature cannot survive.

(*2*) The *wind* often causes dust storms and moves large quantities of surface soil from fertile farms, depositing it in regions where it cannot be used to advantage. In desert areas wind blows sand, forming shifting sand dunes and wearing away the softer parts of the rocks in its path. Plants in these regions have a struggle to gain and maintain a foothold strong enough to hold the soil.

(*3*) *Running water* wears away the surface of the earth very rapidly. This is called **erosion**. It results in forma-

LIFE THROUGH THE AGES

FIGURE 44-16. *PARICUTÍN*

All is devastation around the Mexican volcano, Paricutín, which erupted from a level corn-field in 1943; but in years to come a rich soil will be formed from the decay of volcanic prod-ucts, and, unless another eruption interferes, a good harvest may then be possible.

George Pickow from Three Lions, Inc.

tions such as falls, rapids, canyons, and gorges. Sometimes these are so deep that they separate and isolate plant and animal life. When floods occur, much of the life in that region is destroyed. Waves washing against the rocks and sand of the shore wear away the soil in some places and build it in others.

(*4*) The eruption of *volcanoes* causes the weaker parts of the earth to disinte-grate and builds up other places with huge quantities of dust, cinders, and lava. Since this is usually rich soil, plants will grow in it rapidly, but their existence may quickly be ended by an-other eruption.

44.12   Organic Changes

(*5*) *Living things* are not only sub-mitted to all these factors of a changing environment, but they themselves some-times play an important part. Most plant roots produce an acid in the soil. The action of acid on limestone is one of *corrosion,* or chemical action, thus wear-ing away the soil still more. The tiny shells of marine animals have built up the chalk cliffs at Dover, England. Coral reefs have resulted from the deposit of the skeletons of coral animals and red algae on the underlying rock. Plants tend to reclaim burned areas and to fill in swamps. Some gain a foothold on the edge of deserts and help to hold the soil.

44.13   Meeting the Challenge

In a changing environment plants and animals have three choices of action. They may (1) adapt themselves to meet the conditions, (2) migrate to a more suitable place, or (3) perish in the struggle for existence. The records of the rocks tell of the success and failure of plants and animals through the ages.

In the Gobi Desert in Asia have been found fossils of dinosaurs, those huge reptiles that lived in a hot, moist, swampy climate. Such skeletons have also been found in the western part of the Great Plains of the United States. This leads to the conclusion that as the climate gradually changed, the dinosaurs were unable to meet the new conditions and thus died out.

Similarly, coal formed from luxuriant growths of tropical vegetation has been found in Antarctica, in a region now covered with ice and snow. Coal has also been mined under the water along the coast of England. In this case it shows not only a change in climate but a sinking of the shoreline as well.

Marine fossils have been found in the Adirondack Mountains; coral in the

Hudson Bay region; and palms in Canada. Fossils of camels, lions, and elephants have been excavated in North America. All these migrated to a more suitable place.

This is evidence that changes have been taking place on the earth for a long time. It also indicates that those species which could not adapt themselves to the change perished in the struggle for existence. Species which are living today are descendants of those which were able to make the necessary adjustments to a changing environment.

FACTS TO REMEMBER

Scientists believe that the earth was created several billion years ago, and that after it had cooled off and acquired an atmosphere along with other favorable conditions, very primitive forms of life began to develop. A calendar of geologic time, divided into eras and periods, is used to study the history of life.

With evidence obtained from the study of (1) *fossils*, (2) *classification*, (3) *intermediate forms*, (4) *comparative anatomy*, (5) *embryology*, (6) *geographic distribution*, (7) *vestigial organs*, (8) *homologous structures*, and (9) *similarity of function*, scientists have been able to determine to a great degree how life gradually developed through the ages, and how it was modified by organic and inorganic changes in the environment.

WORDS TO REMEMBER

amber	erosion	Mesozoic era
asphalt bed	era	organic changes
Calamites	fossil	Paleozoic era
carnivorous	fossil resin	period (geologic)
Cenozoic era	geologic time	petrifaction
classification	geologist	phylogeny
cleavage	geographic	sedimentary rock
comparative anatomy	distribution	shale
corrosion	herbivorous	similarity of function
ectoderm	homologous structure	trilobite
embryo	inorganic changes	vestigial organ
embryology	intermediate form	
endoderm	mesoderm	

QUESTIONS

1. In what sense is the earth the mother of all living things?
2. How may we explain the birth of the earth?
3. Why could not the earth hold down an atmosphere when it was small?
4. What conditions existed during the Cambrian period?
5. Make a list of some of the forms of life in each period.
6. What animals ruled the earth during the Mesozoic era, becoming prominent in the Triassic period?

LIFE THROUGH THE AGES

7. What is meant by an intermediate form?

8. Briefly describe Archeopteryx. Why are scientists so much interested in it?

9. Why is the duckbill considered one of the most primitive of the mammals?

10. List at least *five* factors that cause changes in the environment.

11. What is the difference between erosion and corrosion?

12. How have living things helped to build up new land?

13. What can plants and animals do to meet the needs of a changing environment?

14. How would you explain the presence of marine fossils in the Adirondack Mountains?

15. Describe three ways in which fossils are formed.

16. Name six ways in which the resemblances of living things are shown.

17. May we expect a race of giants to appear among men?

18. Explain how it is possible to trace the ancestry of a modern form like the horse.

COMPLETION TEST

As your teacher or classmate reads the following incomplete statements, with your book closed, write on a clean sheet of paper the word or phrase which correctly completes each statement.

1. The substance of which life is made is called _____.

2. Most fossils are found in _____ rock.

3. Man became dominant in the _____ era.

4. The rate of change observed in _____ rocks is one method of measuring the age of the earth.

5. Fossil resin is called _____.

6. The process by which minerals have gradually replaced the structures of the original plant or animal is called _____.

7. The _____ of man is a vestigial organ.

8. _____ is the study of the development of the young before birth.

9. Movement of glaciers causes _____ of the earth's surface.

10. Canyons are formed by the action of _____.

11. The chalk cliffs of England were built up by _____.

PROJECTS

I. *To Show How Fossils Are Formed.*—Mix some clay (plasticine will not do) and water in a battery jar and drop into it some shells of various sizes. Pour off the excess water and put the rest of the material in a pan. When it is dry, break off a piece; note the evidences of the forms embedded in it.

II. *To Show How Imprints Are Formed.*—Mix some plaster of Paris with water and pour into a pan to form a mold. While it is quite wet, press into it the following objects:

(a) Leaf covered with petroleum jelly (to facilitate the removal of the leaf)
(b) Hand of a student
(c) Foot of a bird
(d) Other objects

III. *Early Birds.*—Write a description of Archeopteryx, the oldest known fossil bird; of Hesperonis, a swimming bird with teeth; and Ichthyornis, the "fish bird" with long jaws and slender legs.

IV. *The Horse.*—Trace the development of the modern horse from its four-toed ancestor.

V. *Factors Causing Changes in the Environment.*—Make a series of models or charts showing one of the following:

(a) volcanic action
(b) movement of glaciers
(c) a waterfall
(d) formation of mountains
(e) hot springs and geysers

VI. *History of Land Formations.*—Using references, look up the history of one of the following:

(a) Grand Canyon
(b) Niagara Falls
(c) Chalk Cliffs of Dover
(d) Bermuda Islands

VII. *Prehistoric Animals Found in the United States.*—Learn about the fossils of camels, elephants, lions, dinosaurs, and other animals found on the western plains of this country. Choose the animals that interest you most and write an interesting composition for your biology class.

VIII. *Observation of Environmental Factors.*—From your own observation describe a plant or animal which is a good example of overproduction. Describe the *struggle for existence,* and tell which ones are likely to survive and why. Do those that survive show *variation?* In what way do they show variation?

REFERENCES

American Museum of Natural History, Guide Leaflet Series:
    No. 36, *The Evolution of the Horse;* No. 70, *The Hall of Dinosaurs;*
    No. 52, *The Hall of the Age of Man;* No. 75, *How Old Is the Earth?*
Andrews, *All About Dinosaurs.* Random House.
Boyle, *Prehistoric Man.* Little, Brown.
Clark, *The True Book of Dinosaurs.* Children's Press.
Colbert, *The Dinosaur Book.* American Museum of Natural History.
Daly, *Our Mobile Earth.* Scribner.
Dickinson, *The First Book of Prehistoric Animals.* Watts.
Dreany, *A Child's Book of Mankind Through the Ages.* Maxton.
Fenton, *Life Long Ago.* Reynal and Hitchcock.
Fenton, *The World of Fossils.* Appleton-Century.
Fletcher, *Earth Science.* Heath.

Hobbs, *Earth Features and Their Meaning*. Macmillan.

James, *The Beginning of Man*. Doubleday, Doran.

Knight, *Before the Dawn of History*. McGraw-Hill.

Knowlton, *Plants of the Past*. Princeton.

Lane, *The Story of Mountains*. Doubleday.

Lankester, *Extinct Animals*. Holt.

Lee, *Stories in Stone*. Van Nostrand.

Levine and Selegman, *The Wonders of Life*. Simon and Schuster.

Loomis, *Field Book of Common Rocks and Minerals*. Putnam's.

Lucas, *Animals of the Past*. American Museum of Natural History.

Lull, *Fossils*. University Society Press.

Mather, *Old Mother Earth*. Harvard.

Newman, *The Nature of the World and of Man*. University of Chicago.

Noe, *Ferns, Fossils and Fuel*. Wilcox and Follett.

Osborn, *Men of the Old Stone Age*. Scribner.

Osborn, *The Chain of Life*. Scribner.

Pearl, *How to Know the Rocks and Minerals*. McGraw-Hill.

Pough, *All About Volcanos and Earthquakes*. Random House.

Reed and Lucas, *Animals on the March*. Harcourt, Brace.

Roberts, *In the Morning of Time*. Stokes.

Romer, *Man and the Vertebrates*. University of Chicago.

Sinnott and Dunn, *Principles of Genetics*. McGraw-Hill.

Wells, *How the Present Came from the Past*. Macmillan.

Whitnall, *A Parade of Ancient Animals*. Crowell.

UNIT **XII**

Biology for You

Your Heritage. Your heritage includes not only physical characteristics which you receive from your ancestors but also the natural resources of your environment. The minerals in the earth, the forests, the grasslands, the oil reserves, the wild and domestic animals, and the crops grown for food are some of the resources of this country. You have a rich heritage but with it you have a serious responsibility for conserving these resources and making them more productive. A broad program has been set up combining conservation practices for soil, water, forests, and wildlife. Improved industrial processes now make fuller use of raw materials and produce by-products from substances once considered only as waste.

Your Opportunities. Many problems in health are still unsolved. Scientists are using every known method in searching for the causes, prevention, and treatment of such diseases as cancer, heart disease, and some muscular disorders. They are experimenting with antibiotics. Others are studying the effects of radiation on the human body and are establishing methods for the treatment of radiation sickness as well as methods for protecting those who work with atomic-powered equipment. Biologists are trying to find more about the origin of life and the composition of the cell. With mounting birth rates in many parts of the world, the need for increased food production and distribution is increasingly acute. It is estimated that within the next forty years the population of the world will double. Many people will continue to suffer from lack of food, unless there is a great conservation of all resources and development of new plant and animal foods. Man's exploration of outer space opens up a whole new area for investigation as many new biological problems result.

Some one of these tasks may interest you enough so that you will wish to take additional training in the biological sciences and follow some career that will involve working with plants and animals or improving living conditions for people.

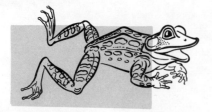

CHAPTER 45

Conservation of Our Resources

45.1 Biology and You

In the study of biology we have found that living plants and animals, including ourselves, are dependent upon each other for food, shelter, protection and space to live. Different kinds of plants and animals have become adapted to life in such climates as are found in the tropic and arctic regions. Other plants and animals live under the varied conditions of deserts and mountains.

Each kind of living thing affects every other living thing in a definite way. Animals struggle for existence among themselves, but few animals are able to compete with man's gun. This can and does

FIGURE 45-1. *BURIED TREASURE*

More and more underwater drilling is being done for petroleum, one of our most important natural resources.

Creole Petroleum Corporation

disturb the balance of nature. Man can, however, help the plants and animals by domesticating them and by producing new forms through methods of scientific breeding.

We have learned about organisms that cause disease in man as well as those that destroy his food, clothing, and property. We have learned about organisms that cause disease in animals and plants, and about those that return organic materials to the soil. Through observation and experimentation man has found ways of destroying many organisms which are harmful and protecting those which are helpful.

In our everyday living we need and use the products made from plants and animals. We need the substances on which they depend for growth. They form the basis for many of our industries. Think for a moment of the food you ate today, the clothes you are wearing, the coal, oil, or gas needed for cooking, the articles you are using, the book you are reading. Think of your home and its surroundings, your school and the playgrounds. You may wish to list the many articles made from living things. Consider carefully the large proportion of all the materials we use that are made from plants and animals. What would happen if there were no trees to furnish wood, no animals to furnish clothing, and no

640

plants to furnish food? If we burned up our total coal supply, where could we get enough oil and gasoline for our cars? Could atomic energy be used to meet all our present and future needs?

Man is also dependent on non-living things. He uses rocks, stones, and clay for building material for houses, roads, bridges, and dams. Man uses metals for machines, tools, and equipment. Plants need minerals to manufacture food. Man and animals need to eat the minerals in their food to build protoplasm and maintain health. Man has traveled long distances in search of salt for his food. Many people have suffered from disease when this and other minerals were lacking in their diet. What could man do if his mineral supply were to become exhausted?

Throughout the study of biology we have been enjoying the plants and animals. We have watched them in the laboratory. We have observed them on our field trips and many of us have had fun with them in sports. Other people have learned to enjoy plants and animals in their natural environment. Poets and naturalists have shared with us their joys and experiences in going on walks, climbing mountains, and sailing the seas. Explorers and hunters have told of strange creatures in distant lands. Sportsmen have learned about the fish of the streams, lakes, and oceans, of game birds and game animals. Travelers have sought the beauty and wonder of high waterfalls, deep canyons, and desert skies. You may have seen some of these beauties and visited some of our national parks. What an exciting experience for the person who first discovered these places! Are you not grateful that they have been left for you to enjoy? What can you do to help save it for others to enjoy?

45.2 Your Heritage

*The **natural resources** of our country include its physical capacities in addition to the materials supplied by the living things on it.* These serve as the main source of supply to meet the needs of the people. Since man first lived in this country, he has been tapping this source of supply. His numbers have been increasing. Yours is the heritage of what remains of our country's original supply. How can we make our supply last longer? How can we build up our reserves? *The wise use of our natural resources is known as **conservation.***

Natural resources are of two kinds: *renewable,* those that can be replaced,

FIGURE 45-3. *FORESTER*

Professional foresters are being trained to bring scientific methods to forest management and the lumbering industry. Here a forester prepares seedlings for reforestation work.

J. I. Case Photo

and *exhaustible,* those that cannot be replaced. The resources of our country that are renewable include forests, grass and forage lands, and animal life. Those that are exhaustible are soils and minerals, such as salt, sulphur, and potash, which may be washed or blown away. Supplies of coal, oil, and gas are also exhaustible.

45.3   Your Native Land

When the early settlers first came to America, they found a land quite different from the country as we know it today. They found large forested areas, rich soil capable of growing good crops, relatively few native people, a good climate, and an abundance of materials. They had no modern machinery, no electricity for power or light, no automobiles for transportation. But they brought the skills they had learned, their knowledge of farming, and their experience in establishing community life. Combining determination and the resources of the country, the early settlers were able to build a life here.

45.4   Man Lived on the Land

Forests yielded lumber for homes, rich soil for gardens and forage crops, gums and resins for boats, and maple sugar for food. The early settlers found an abundant supply of these products but did not use them wisely. There was much waste. Forest destruction meant the loss of homes for birds, animals, and other wild life. It meant the loss of water to land in the valleys and the washing away of the soil.

Grasslands were plowed and used for crops. Heavy rains washed the soil away and caused the grazing animals to suffer. Strong high winds blew the dust in huge clouds which traveled for miles leaving the land bare and dry. More grasslands were plowed, more herds of cattle grazed in depleted areas, and more flocks of sheep fed on the grasses of the plains.

The coming of machinery in spite of its many advantages hastened the destruction of our resources. Steamboats paddled up the rivers, railroads pushed across the country in the wake of the onrush of pioneer covered wagon expeditions. As the demands of the growing country increased, more forests disappeared; more grasslands were laid barren; more plants could not exist; and more animals had to find shelter. The large herds of buffalo decreased rapidly before man's gun. The flocks of passenger pigeons no longer darkened the skies as they flew overhead in great num-

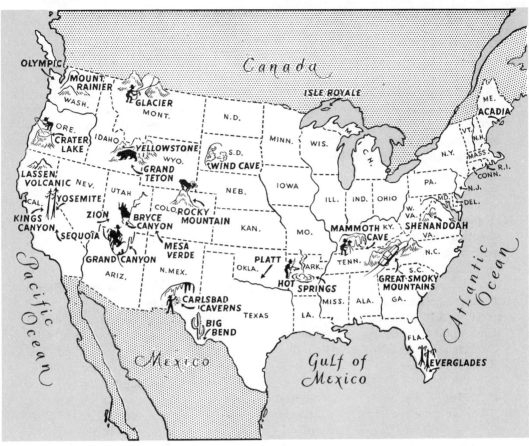

FIGURE 45-4. *NATIONAL PARKS AND MONUMENTS*
The national park system, administered by the Department of the Interior,
includes 29 parks and covers an area of almost 13,000,000 acres.

bers. Fish grew less and less numerous in the streams. Large rivers like the Mississippi, Ohio, and Red rivers grew more muddy as soil was carried away.

Some mine ore deposits gave out, oil wells dried up, and minerals were washed from the soil, lessening the usefulness of the land.

45.5 Some Action Was Needed

Americans were too busy in their land of plenty to think much about these things until 1873, when the American Association for the Advancement of Science asked Congress to have the Federal Government consider the problem.

Nearly twenty years later the Bureau of Forestry was established in the Department of Agriculture, and the first national forest reserve was set aside.

There was growing concern among thoughtful people for our resources. However, another twenty years passed before President Theodore Roosevelt took the action needed to begin a conservation program and save our natural resources. In 1908, he held a White House Conference on conservation and appointed a National Conservation Commission. This was a group of well qualified, interested citizens who were asked to study the problem of our country's vanishing soil, water, forest, and mineral supplies.

45.6 Conservation Commissions

First of all the Commission took inventories to find out what our country's resources were originally, and what was still left. An estimate was made of the rate at which our resources were being used up.

State Conservation Commissions were appointed and a North American Conservation Commission was appointed to work with Canada, Mexico, and Newfoundland on ways to protect animals that migrate, and to discuss other ways to cooperate on conservation. The interest in this conference was so great that a world conference was held later at The Hague to consider the conservation of world resources.

45.7 The Government Keeps Control

The inventory of our resources and the study of the development of our country showed that there were some lands which did not belong to private citizens but were still open to the public. It was yet possible to reserve some of these and thus prevent the kind of waste which had been taking place. The government then reserved millions of acres of national forest, watershed, phosphate deposits, and coal land.

National monuments and wildlife reserves were set aside during the next twenty years. Many of the states followed the action of the Federal Government. Some set aside forest areas. Others established game reserves, stocked streams with fish, and limited the amount taken from mineral deposits. The Soil Conservation Service of the Department of Agriculture taught people how to save their soil and use it to the best advantage. In many states the government

experts gave demonstrations of good land use and methods of flood control.

The work of conservation continues. It needs the understanding, support, and help of every person in the country. Our supplies are limited; the demand is increasing. As one of the future generation you have a right to expect that the older generation will pass on to you a country supplied with materials essential to life and security. However, you will need to understand how to take care of these supplies. You can begin now to prepare for your future responsibility.

45.8 Natural Resources That Affect Your Living

Some of the natural resources of this country are its soil, water, forests, wildlife, metals, minerals, coal, and gas. These things provide your food, clothing, and homes. The industries which produce these articles provide jobs for you. The land itself provides places for recreation and fun. Because of these factors it is important for you to know about the present supply of our natural resources.

45.9 The Soil

If you have a yard, garden, or lawn near your home or school, you have had some experience with at least one type of soil. You can observe the kinds of plants which are able to grow there. If you live on a farm that needs irrigation, one that requires drainage, or one that is rocky and steep, you are already familiar with some of the values and some of the problems of the land.

The kind and number of crops you can grow depends on the character and depth of the *soil* and the *subsoil*. It also depends on the temperature, rainfall, and the plant nutrients in the soil. If you wish to grow corn, for example, you will need a fertilizer with additional

phosphate. Cauliflower and beets will need more boron. Other plants will need large supplies of calcium or lime.

You may wish to test a small portion of your soil and find out whether it is coarse like gravel, fine as in sand, or dusty as in clay. You will look for bits of organic matter, and for animals that make their homes in the soil. You may find earthworms for fishing bait. These are helpful in enriching the soil by eating their way through it. In some places in the country you will find that gophers, ground squirrels, and woodchucks live in the soil.

Soil is produced by the breaking up of particles of rock by a great temperature change, such as in freezing and thawing. Soil is produced by the action of glaciers, winds, and waves. Chemical action also takes place in the soil, causing limestone to crumble. Some soil particles may become hard and remain firm under pressure. Others may be washed away by waves or blown about by the wind. Usually a minimum depth of 4 feet is necessary for growing crops. The depth may vary from 20 to 100 feet. The use to which the soil can be put depends upon the needs of the people.

The values of the soil are many. It forms a cover for the rocks and makes transportation and travel easier. It gives support to plant roots which grow in it. The organic matter and minerals in the soil furnish substances for plants to use in the manufacture of food. The soil affords homes for animals. Water is held in the soil.

Low-growing plants help to hold the soil in place. Forests and large plants supply organic material which aids in retaining moisture in the soil. Shrubs form hedges and thickets for small animal life. This adds richness to the soil.

The soil affects your living by supporting and nourishing the plants that supply food such as corn, wheat, fruit, nuts, and vegetables. It supports other plants that furnish clothing. These include cotton, flax, and trees that supply cellulose for rayon. The soil also supports plants that provide food for the animals on which we depend for food and clothing.

Our dependence on the soil is very great. The need for growing specific crops and the amount of each changes with our civilization. When new machines are invented, such as the farm machinery run by tractors, our need for horses and mules decreases. When new products such as nylon, orlon, dacron, and other synthetic fibers are produced, less cotton is used. When man develops a new variety of crops, such as hybrid corn, or a method of artificial breeding

FIGURE 45-6. *FERTILE FIELD*

Soil is essential to man because it supports the plants he needs for food. Many small animals make their homes in the soil. What other functions of soil can you name?

J. C. Allen and Son

for cattle, the soil needs are different. When man decides to eat more lettuce or grow a new kind of grain, both agriculture and industry are affected. For example, celery must grow on very rich land. Many people depend on raising celery as a source of income but only as long as they take care of their soil and only as long as other people continue to eat this celery, will its growth and its marketing continue to be an industry.

45.10 The Water in the Soil

You could live many days without food but only a few hours or days without water. Animals risk their lives to go into open spaces, where their enemies may be lurking, in search of watering places. Many men have perished on desert sands and barren wastes for lack of water. Man and animals are limited in the places where they can live because of water supply. Plants need water to make their own food and to supply man and animals. Plants depend upon the water in the soil to supply such needs.

An average man needs a ton of water a year in order to live. A cow needs much more than that. It has been estimated that it requires from 30,000 to 60,000 pounds of water to produce one pound of beef. A crop plant may require from 300 to 800 pounds of water for a season. The source of water for crops lies chiefly in the rainfall that collects in springs, streams, lakes, reservoirs, and deep wells.

When water is lacking, plants cannot grow. The Indians learned to irrigate the lands of Arizona and New Mexico before the early white settlers reached that section. The Mormons undertook large irrigation projects in Utah. Since then large areas in California, Arkansas, and other states have been irrigated, making it possible for plants to grow, animals to exist, and man to settle in that part of our country. When man can help to control his environment and take care of his soil, his soil can work for him. If you live in any of these sections of the country, you may be able to visit places which have not been touched by man. You will find very different kinds of plants and animals living in dry regions than living on irrigated land.

In order to insure a more dependable water supply, man has begun to build dams, such as Boulder Dam, to dig deep wells, such as artesian wells in Texas, and to construct large reservoirs, such as Ashokan Reservoir, which supplies drinking water for New York City. Man is trying to control floods and maintain

BIOLOGY FOR YOU

a constant water supply. He is encouraging people living in different sections of the country to grow the kinds of crops and animals that are best suited to the climate and food supply, without lessening the value of the soil or letting it be washed or blown away.

45.11   The Loss of Our Soil

Since colonial times soil *erosion* has been a serious problem in this country. In Virginia the early settlers cut the forests and burned over the land to clear it for raising corn and tobacco. As early as 1795, Washington gave instructions to his farm workers to grow a ground cover of grass and to put weeds and straw in the gullies to prevent further erosion. Thomas Jefferson used clover to help hold the soil. He also used a very simple method of **contour plowing,** that is, plowing around the hills instead of making furrows that would let the water rush downhill.

In the Piedmont area in Virginia and southward, much lumber was burned. Potash was extracted from ashes and sold. The fields often lost all the surface soil within a period of thirty years. Farmers living on the land had only subsoil of poor quality for growing their crops. This took twice as much fertilizer and became so expensive that many farms were abandoned. Cleared slopes became eroded and laid waste. There were fewer plant roots to hold the soil together. This situation has continued to be a very serious problem.

Each heavy rain removes much surface soil. One third of the United States has now lost from one fourth to three fourths of its surface soil. This means that minerals such as potassium, phosphorus, calcium, magnesium, sulphur, nitrogen, and organic matter are decreased in quantity. Vegetables grown

Tennessee Valley Authority

FIGURE 45-7. *FLOOD CONTROL*

The dams built on the Tennessee River by the TVA make this one of the best regulated river systems in the world. Pictured is Fort Loudoun Dam, with locks.

on such soil are of poor quality. This lessens their food value and health-giving properties.

Industrial wastes which pollute the streams and filter into the soil have a bad effect on the land and need to be controlled. Such wastes kill fish and other water life.

When the soil is dry and left exposed, it may be blown about by the wind. Sometimes it forms sand dunes, as those on the shores of Lake Michigan. At other times fine dust particles are carried long distances by high winds and deposited in undesirable places. Worthless dust or sand may cover good, productive soil and make it unfit for cultivation. It creates travel hazards and health problems.

Surface winds break many plants, blowing sand particles against the leaves. Then heavy rains beat upon plants that are exposed. The continual motion of the waves along the shore wears away

FIGURE 45-8. *SOIL EROSION*

These gullies, from 50 to 200 feet in depth, illustrate the destructive force of soil erosion. Entire farm communities are now pooling their resources in an attempt to protect their land.

Courtesy Soil Conservation Service

the rocks and in places changes the shore line.

The richness of the soil has been decreased in many places. Some of the causes have been (1) wasteful cutting of trees, (2) extensive plowing of the grassland, (3) the exposure of steep slopes, formerly covered with trees and grass, to the action of wind, waves, running water, and heavy downfalls of rain, (4) the taking of minerals from the soil by the action of water, (5) the carrying away of soil by wind, (6) poor methods of crop cultivation, (7) the overgrazing of grasslands by cattle, and (8) the destruction of wildlife by man.

45.12 The Conservation of Our Soil

The Soil Conservation Service of the United States Department of Agriculture and the Soil Conservation Districts which have been established in all 48 states as well as Alaska, Hawaii, Puerto Rico, and the Virgin Islands are cooperating and directing their efforts toward the improvement of soil and the increasing of its productivity. Each district is a local unit of government operating under state laws. The first one was organized in North Carolina in 1937. Some of the measures taken are (1) using land according to its best adaptation, (2) add-

ing organic matter to maintain or improve soil structure, (3) maintaining proper balance by the use of fertilizers, and (4) establishing needed mechanical measures to control movement of soil and water.

45.13 Characteristics of a Good Soil

A good soil (1) is loose and granular, (2) is well drained, (3) has air spaces to allow oxygen to enter and carbon dioxide to escape, (4) has abundant water supply, (5) contains sufficient minerals, and (6) must not be too acid or alkaline for a particular crop.

The **top soil** usually contains *humus* in varying amounts. **Humus** is the remains of decayed plants. Many bacteria, protozoa, and some blue-green algae are found in the soil. Earthworms crawl through it, leaving air spaces and enriching the dirt.

In order to use the land according to its best adaptations, we need to know the kind of soil, the climate, the water supply and drainage, and many other factors. Soil samples can be tested and special studies made of the land. Upon the basis of these facts recommendations may be made as to the best crops to grow, whether to plant to forests, whether to try irrigation or drainage projects, whether to build dams for flood control, or to experimentally "seed the clouds" for rain making. Through scientific experiments and careful planning, many million more acres of our land might be made productive.

45.14 Saving Our Soil

Since early Roman days man has practiced **crop rotation**, planting different ones on a particular plot each year. He has grown legumes, like clover and alfalfa, to help make nitrogen compounds available in the soil for other plants to use. Plowing under such crops is known as **green manuring**. Man is also increasing his nitrogen supply by adding sodium nitrate (saltpeter) to the soil. Much of this fertilizer has been imported from Chile.

To *keep soil fertile,* man adds manure, calcium from limestone, and phosphate from the bones of animals. The Indians taught the white settlers the value of fertilizers by using fish scraps for growing corn, a practice still in use today.

Contour farming is of great value in preventing erosion. Instead of plowing fields in straight rows parallel to the boundary of certain areas, the furrows follow the curves and general contour of the slopes. This prevents the water from running straight down the hills and washing out gullies.

FIGURE 45-9. *TOP SOIL*

The instructor is pointing out the top organic layer of soil (above his thumb), essential for plant life.

Strip cropping refers to the practice of alternating plowed land with narrow strips of grassland or close-growing crops, such as wheat and oats. Water washing from the plowed areas is absorbed in the grass plots. This prevents the formation of gullies and keeps the soil from washing down the hills.

Wind stripping is planting alternate strips of cultivated and thick crops at right angles to the prevailing wind.

Field stripping is planting alternate strips of cultivated and thick crops roughly at right angles to the main slope.

FIGURE 45-10. *FARM WITH A FUTURE*

This picture of Wisconsin farmland illustrates two methods of keeping the soil fertile: contour farming and strip cropping.

FIGURE 45-11. *EROSION CONTROL*

Agricultural experts have found that the *kudzu,* a vine imported from the Orient, helps control erosion. The roots grow rapidly and spread out, forming a tight network to hold the soil. The yearly decay of leaves helps to enrich it.

Courtesy United States
Dept. of Agriculture

Terracing is building up little ridges of soil, brick, or rock across sloping fields to slow down rainfall. This holds up the speed of runoff water, guiding it to the sides of the fields.

Drainage of excess water from wet land by ditches or by tile drains helps to bring more land under cultivation. The ditches must be kept clear from plant growth.

Irrigation is the distribution of water brought to the land by canals and ditches to help the growth of plants. This method has brought much land in dry regions under cultivation. Irrigation is used extensively in Arizona, New Mexico, California, and other states.

To stop the formation of *gullies* and prevent further erosion, water should be turned away from the top and sides of the gullies by using grass, vines, trees, and shrubs to form a cover; by building dams for catching silt; and by using flumes to lessen the cutting power of waterfalls.

The management of woodlands, according to sound forestry practices, helps to maintain good yield of forest products and promotes rapid growth. When properly cared for, the accumulation of humus on the forest floor retains moisture and helps prevent floods.

Since the basis of soil conservation is the wise use and proper management of all land, it is necessary to continue to carry on these long range conservation plans.

45.15 Value of Our Forests

Only about one fifth of the original old-growth forest areas remain. Of these, 63% are in the west and 25% in the south. The loss of our forest trees has resulted in the loss of other valuable crops which were dependent on the soil that has long since washed away. We are suffering financial loss as well from the scarcity of forest products.

Our forests are valuable for lumber, fuel, wood pulp for paper, rayon, and plastics, and for such products as gums, resins, turpentine, tannin, rubber, and maple sugar. Medicinal trees produce laxatives, as cascara, and drugs, as quinine. Trees grown on plantations produce beverages as coffee, cocoa, and tea. Trees raised in orchards produce valuable fruits and nuts. Shrubs and low-growing plants furnish berries for the support of wildlife and form a protective cover for the soil.

The crowns of trees break the force of falling rain and resist the pressure of strong winds. The roots of the trees

FIGURE 45-12. *COMMUNITY*

A forest is a community inhabited by plants and animals, all dependent on each other. Man, especially, has a high stake in the conservation of forest land.

Courtesy Canadian
Information Service

form a network in the soil on which the humus collects and holds moisture. Forests help to keep the temperature more even. Strips of forest growth serve as windbreaks. Forest range is used for grazing. In some forests deer, elk, and moose feed on tender shoots of young trees. Bears roam the woods for berries and other vegetation.

A forest is a home for many living things. It is a community where trees, shrubs, flowering plants, and fungi may live together with birds, bats, monkeys, and insects. When man destroys a forest, he has done more than just cut a few trees for lumber. The total community has been affected to some degree.

45.16 Destruction of Our Forests

Forests have been destroyed by (1) poor lumbering, (2) forest fires, (3) insect enemies, (4) diseases, and (5) animals. Woodsmen used to cut the trees for lumber and then burn over the land. This not only cleared the brush but destroyed the humus, which is rich in minerals and organic matter needed for plant growth.

Forest fires may burn as crown, surface, or ground fires. The fire may be of one type or a combination of any of them. About one fourth of the fires are caused by the carelessness of (1) hunters, (2) smokers, (3) campers, (4) fishermen, (5) vacationists, and (6) men burning brush. Another one fourth are caused by burning debris. The other half of the fires are caused by such factors as (1) lightning, (2) railroads, (3) lumbermen, and (4) unknown causes.

Insects destroy forest trees, causing tremendous loss of valuable produce. Bark beetles, gypsy and brown-tailed moths, tamarack sawflies, spruce bud worms, white pine weevils, locust borers, and others cause much damage. *Fungi,* such as the white pine blister rust and chestnut blight, have caused some kinds of trees to become nearly extinct. *Rodents* such as beavers, mice, and rabbits, have caused a serious loss of forests.

This destruction of our forests has been taking place for a long time and has been growing more serious as the population has increased and civilization has advanced. Unless this destruction is prevented and protective measures are taken now, the forests of our country will disappear and their value as a resource will be gone forever.

FIGURE 45-13. *TREE X-RAYS*

Research in forestry has been steady and profitable. One innovation has been the use of x-rays to examine the inside of a log before sawing, in order to get the highest grade material from it.

American Forest Products
Industries, Inc.

45.17 Saving Our Forests

Land has been set aside in national forests to preserve one third of the timber supply. More than 160 national park areas, including 21,000,000 acres, have been set aside for the protection of forests and wildlife and for preserving spectacular natural wonders such as the Grand Canyon of the Colorado River in Arizona, the geysers and hot springs of Yellowstone National Park in Wyoming, the Carlsbad Caverns of New Mexico, and the Natural Bridge of Virginia.

The U.S. Forest Service, working through nine regions in the United States and one in Alaska, protects the forests by (1) planned cutting of timber, (2) reforestation, (3) forest fire protection by its foresters and forest rangers, (4) detection and prevention of the spread of diseases with the aid of specially trained scientists, (5) the development of new methods of forestry at experiment stations, (6) training men and women to help in this work, and (7) teaching students in our schools and the people who own land or visit parks about the need for conservation and the ways they can help. When many people understand and care about saving their forests and protecting their incomes, it may be possible to prevent further loss of valuable property.

45.18 Value of Our Wildlife

The animals that supply our food, such as fish, shellfish, game and domestic animals, are finding less food for themselves. Animals that supply our clothing, such as furbearing animals, those supplying skins for leather, and animals useful for other products such as glue, fertilizer, ivory, and medicine, are decreasing in numbers. Man has used these animals as a source of income for his industry, has hunted them for pleasure, and has done very little to protect them. They are valued at millions of dollars, and man has become dependent upon many of them for his living.

45.19 Destruction of Our Wildlife

Buffalo herds once roamed the fields from New York to Georgia and from Mexico to Canada. Elks were numerous from the east to the Rocky Mountains. Moose lived in the eastern forests. Deer were everywhere. Game birds and waterfowl were plentiful. Passenger pigeons traveled from the Wisconsin woods to Kentucky. The early settlers hunted wild turkeys, ducks, and geese. Squabs were a common delicacy. Sable and beaver were killed for their fur. Food and fur were so abundant that little thought was given to conservation.

But when the forest trees were cut, destroying homes of wild animals, when soil was washed away, carrying with it their source of food supply and when enormous numbers were killed by man's guns, it was impossible for the animals to maintain their numbers or even survive. The passenger pigeon and heath hen became extinct. Buffalo became scarce and were only saved from extinction by special protection given to the small remaining herd.

Excessive fishing, pollution of streams by sewage from cities and industrial wastes, the building of barriers such as huge dams and irrigation ditches, and the illegal use of gill nets have depleted our supply of fish.

As new machinery has been invented, huge steamboats have been built for ocean travel, and larger and more powerful guns have come into use. Methods of hunting, fishing, and trapping have become more efficient. It is now possible to catch more fish, trap more animals, and shoot more wild game in shorter periods of time. Our wildlife is in real danger of extinction.

The chief causes of decrease of our wild animals are (1) destruction of their habitats by forest fires and cultivation, (2) decrease of their food supply, (3) market hunting, (4) *pollution* of their water supply, (5) increase of natural enemies when man disturbs the balance of nature, and (6) the carelessness of man. It is very important that every person, boy or girl, man or woman, should aid in the conservation efforts and help to protect our wildlife.

45.20 Saving Our Wildlife

The United States Fish and Wildlife Service studies food habits, determines economic value, and studies diseases and habits of wildlife. With the help of this organization it has been possible to

National Film Board Photo

FIGURE 45-14. *FISHING INDUSTRY*

Fishing is an important industry in this country, and all states have laws which forbid excessive fishing. The demand for fish increases every year.

establish some control measures. These include (1) passing laws regulating open and closed seasons for hunting and fishing, (2) establishing wildlife refuges, (3) making treaties with other countries to protect migratory birds and animals, such as the Federal Migratory Bird Treaty Act (Sec. 16.9), (4) making regulations about the size or age of the animal caught, the number to be taken, and the time of day for hunting, (5) restocking of streams with fish or land with animals, (6) encouraging fur and game farming, (7) growing shrubs for ground cover and for food supply, and (8) cooperating with such other services as the Soil Conservation and Forest Service.

State Conservation Departments have been established and state game preserves set aside. After all of the native deer in Vermont had been exterminated by 1870, it was decided to restock the

Courtesy Massachusetts Institute of Technology

FIGURE 45-15. *SOLAR HOUSE*
As the earth's resources dwindle, new sources of power must be found to replace them. This house is heated by solar energy. The glass roof is part of a 640 square foot solar collector.

land. Thirty Virginia white-tailed deer were introduced in 1875, and a closed season maintained for twenty-two years. Now there are several thousand deer in Vermont. Hunting is enjoyed there as a sport. Many people count on the killing of deer to supplement their food supply.

The nutria, a rodent valuable for its fur, was imported into Louisiana for fur farming. Only six pairs were introduced since they multiply rapidly. Several years later some of the animals escaped and a hurricane helped many others to float over their fences into the marshes.

Because of lack of natural enemies, the nutria has become a pest. These animals have burrowed into irrigation canal levees, causing rice field washouts. Their numbers have increased so quickly that they are driving out the muskrats, another valuable fur animal, by using up their food supplies. Again man is faced with problems because he has upset the balance of nature.

It is very important to study the con-

ditions carefully and not to disturb the balance of nature more than is necessary in order to prevent animals from becoming pests, as was also the case of the English sparrow and starling.

The National Audubon Society has helped to arouse public appreciation of the beauty and economic value of birds. It establishes sanctuaries and trains teachers and youth leaders to protect birds (Sec. 16.9). Other organizations are helping to teach people the urgent need of protecting our wildlife. You can assist in this work by knowing which animals are helpful and which are the most destructive. You can also follow the laws and regulations made to help protect the future wildlife for your enjoyment and source of income.

45.21 Conservation of Other Resources

The need of saving our coal and oil supply, our petroleum and natural gas, our minerals and metals is as great as the need for conservation of many of our other resources. We do not have time to study all of these in as great detail as we could wish, but you may want to select one of these resources for a special study. This will be of particular importance if you live in a region where these substances are mined or quarried, or where there is an industry which makes products derived from them.

45.22 Your Responsibility

You can begin your conservation efforts now, at home, at school, and in your community. Some of the ways you can help are these: (1) learn all you can about the soil, water, forests, wildlife, and resources that need to be saved and protected, (2) know the laws and regulations made by your community, county, state, and national government,

FIGURE 45-16. *FIELD TRIP*
Students who leave the class-room for a field trip have an opportunity to learn about the soil, forests, wildlife, water, and other resources which it will one day be their responsibility to protect.

Philip Gendreau

(3) follow these laws and encourage others to do so, (4) undertake some conservation project.

You will have dozens of ideas of how to help in these important projects. A few suggestions for you to consider are these: (1) help to keep your yard and the local parks clean, (2) find out what measures can be taken to make the grounds or lawns more beautiful, (3) encourage the birds to come around your home, using a feeding station or bird bath, (4) use humane methods when catching fish or trapping animals,

(5) learn about the health of animals by studying the needs of your pets, (6) plant trees in areas which are being reforested, (7) test the soil of your garden and try different fertilizers for the best plant growth, (8) prevent fires by extreme care of matches, camp fires, and firearms, (9) help preserve natural beauty by not destroying property, (10) report evidence of unusual insect or disease outbreaks, (11) be a leader in the conservation effort. Conservation is your responsibility. Conservation is for your future.

FACTS TO REMEMBER

Conservation of our *natural resources* is an ever-present problem to our modern civilization. Individuals and governments must take wise steps to insure the preservation of our soil, water, forests, wildlife, and minerals.

To prevent the erosion and wasting of *soil,* man uses such practices as crop rotation, contour plowing, strip cropping, wind stripping, field stripping, terracing, drainage, and irrigation.

Water is conserved by building dams and reservoirs and by digging wells. Trees and grass are planted near watershed areas to prevent the water from running off, which not only serves as a flood control but also prevents valuable top soil from being washed or blown away.

It is necessary to conserve our *forests* for their products, for their beauty, as a home for wildlife, to prevent soil erosion, and to control floods. Fires, insects, fungi, rodents, and unwise cutting have greatly depleted our timber resources. Such steps as planned cutting, reforestation, forest fire prevention, new methods of forestry, and educating the public on the value of our forests are helping to preserve this vital resource.

Much of our *wildlife* has been destroyed by thoughtless killing and destruction of their forest homes. Establishing game laws, setting up refuges and sanctuaries, restocking streams and forests, and making treaties with other countries are a few of the ways that wildlife has been protected.

It is the responsibility of each and every citizen to be keenly aware of the necessity of conserving our natural resources, to know and respect the laws pertaining to conservation measures, and to cooperate with government and private organizations in maintaining these laws and promoting new ones. Our country is only as rich as its natural resources, and its future depends on wise use and preservation of these resources.

WORDS TO REMEMBER

closed season	humus	restocking
conservation	irrigation	sanctuary
contour plowing	natural resource	soil
crop rotation	open season	strip cropping
drainage	pollution	subsoil
erosion	reforestation	terracing
exhaustible natural	refuge	top soil
resource	renewable natural	wildlife
field stripping	resource	wind stripping
green manuring		

QUESTIONS

1. What is meant by conservation? Why is it your responsibility?
2. Explain the term "natural resources." Which are renewable? Which are exhaustible?
3. How are you dependent on the living things studied in biology?
4. Discuss the factors which have led to the present urgent need for conservation.
5. Describe the work of the National and State Conservation Commissions.
6. How is soil produced? Why does it wash away?
7. Name and describe as many ways as you can for saving the soil.
8. Give three examples of soil erosion which you have observed.
9. Explain the value of water in the soil.
10. How do plants help to protect the soil?
11. State four characteristics of a good soil.
12. What is meant by the statement, "A forest is a community for living things"?

13. State some of the ways the United States Forest Service helps protect the forests.

14. Explain at least five causes of the destruction of our wildlife.

15. Describe at least five control measures now being taken to protect our wildlife.

16. In what ways can you begin now to aid in the conservation effort?

COMPLETION TEST

As your teacher or classmate reads the following incomplete statements, with your book closed, write on a clean sheet of paper the word or phrase which correctly completes the statement.

1. When land is too dry for growing crops, man uses the method of _____ to make it productive.

2. When land is too wet for growing crops, man uses the method of _____.

3. The practice of alternating plowed land with narrow strips of grassland is known as _____.

4. The method of plowing furrows that follow the curves of the slopes is called _____.

5. High winds blow fertile topsoil long distances and cause _____ storms.

6. The wearing away of the soil is called _____.

7. Organic matter and minerals are added to the soil by man in the form of _____.

8. An animal saved from extinction by man is _____.

9. Two birds which have become extinct through the carelessness of man are _____ and _____.

10. Everyone can help with conservation by _____ our wildlife and _____ the regulations of the parks and recreation areas.

PROJECTS

I. Collecting Samples of Soil.—Select several different kinds of places to collect samples of soil. At each place cut a block of soil 4–6 inches square and 4–6 inches deep. Carefully lift this block of soil and place it in a can, box, or other container. Keep each sample separate.

When you are ready to study your soil, empty the contents of one of the containers onto a flat surface. Remove the plants and shake the roots. Make separate piles of each kind of plant or animal materials. You may find worms, snails, insects, and many other forms of life.

Let the soil dry a little. Sift it through a series of sieves of different sizes. Put the soil which passes through each sieve in a separate pile.

If you wish to save your samples and compare them with soil taken from other places, put each pile you have sifted into a separate glass jar and label. Indicate on each label the place from which the soil was taken and the things you have found in it. Repeat this method for each soil sample you have collected.

Compare the different kinds of soil and try to explain how they might have been formed.

II. *Comparing Different Kinds of Soil.*

a. Size of Particles.—Place a small amount of soil in a quart bottle or jar and shake vigorously. Let it stand until the water above the soil appears quite clear. Measure the depth of each layer of soil such as the layers of sand, gravel, loam, and clay. Make a table to record the depth of each of these layers.

b. Holding Water in the Soil.—Put equal quantities of soil samples in separate cans with perforated bottoms. Place each can over a glass jar. Pour equal quantities of water into the top of each can and let it drain into the glass jar.

(1) Measure the amount of water which runs through the soil.
(2) Note the length of time it takes for the water to run through the different kinds of soil.
(3) Which kind of soil retained the most water?
(4) Was water left standing on the surface of the soil?
(5) Which soil acts much like a sponge?
(6) Which soil had the most sediment washed away?

III. *Showing the Effect of Contour Plowing on Erosion.*—Fill a large, flat box with fine soil. Divide the soil area into two sections. On one section make small ridges across the slope. On the second section make ridges up and down the slope.

Using a watering can with a sprinkle top or any perforated can for a rain-maker, pour water on each section. What happens to the water on both sections? Which section has gullies start to form first? What is the value of growing plant crops in contour lines?

IV. *Signs of Wildlife.*—When you are walking in the park, or woods, or hiking along a road, look for tracks, feathers, shells of nuts, chewed cones, nests, bits of hair, bones, holes in the ground, runways and signs of browsing. What do these signs tell you of animal life around you?

V. Visit a florist, greenhouse, or nursery and try to find the answers to some of the following questions.

a. What kinds of plants are best suited to grow in the gardens, lawns, and yards or houses in your locality?

b. What are the most common kinds of soil in your surrounding country?

c. What fertilizers and plant nutrients need to be added to the soil to make most of the plants grow better?

d. What house plants are best fitted to grow in the kind of place where you live?

VI. Select five plants which you find growing in the greenhouse, or potted plants found in a florist shop. Find out the best conditions for their growth, such as (1) the amount of water, (2) the kind of soil, (3) the amount of light, and (4) the best temperature.

VII. Write to the Soil Conservation Service in your state and find out what services are available to you. It may be possible to have the soil of your land scientifically tested and suggestions made for its care and improvement.

If your soil has already been tested, plan with your teacher ways in which you and your group may carry out one or more soil improvement measures.

VIII. Visit an agricultural experiment station, a forest ranger station or a flood-control project. Find out why each has been located in that particular place. Describe the chief work being done there.

IX. Find out why the people came to settle in your community. How did they use the land, the forests, and the streams? What industries have been developed as a result of their efforts? How has this become a resource to you, a liability to you, and a responsibility for you?

X. Find out what conservation programs are being given on the radio or television and make a careful report on a series that your teacher helps you to select.

XI. Help to arrange a window display in a store or a cabinet display in your school to feature such special topics as Conservation of Forests, Fire Prevention Week, Forest and Farm Products, Reforestation, and Garden Club activities.

REFERENCES

Bodsworth, *Last of the Curlews.* Dodd, Mead.
Bromfield, *Malabar Farm.* Harper.
Bromfield, *Out of the Earth.* Harper.
Bromfield, *Pleasant Valley.* Harper.
Burgess, *Soil Erosion Control.* Turner E. Smith.
Chase, *Rich Land, Poor Land, A Study of Waste in the Natural Resources of America.* McGraw-Hill.
Conservation Education in American Schools—29th Yearbook, American Association of School Administrators.
Conservation Excursions, Bulletin 13. U. S. Office of Education.
Curtis, *Conservation in America.* Lyons and Carnahan.
Elliott, *Conservation.* Smith.
Fanning, *Our Oil Resources.* McGraw-Hill.
Faulkner, *Plowman's Folly.* University of Oklahoma Press.
Furnas, *Man, Bread and Destiny.* Garden City.
Gabrielson, *Wildlife Conservation.* Macmillan.
Gabrielson, *Wildlife Refuges.* Macmillan.
Gustafson, *Conservation in the United States.* Comstock.
Lord, *To Hold This Soil.* U. S. Department of Agriculture. Misc. Pub. 1943.
Lord, *Behold This Land.* Houghton Mifflin.
Osborn, *Our Plundered Planet.* Little, Brown.
Pearson and Haynes, *The World's Hunger.* Cornell University Press.

Person, *Little Waters, Their Uses and Relation to the Land*. U. S. Government Printing Office.

Petersen, *Forward to the Land*. University of Oklahoma Press.

Pinchot, *Breaking New Ground*. Harcourt, Brace.

Sears, *Deserts on the March*. University of Oklahoma Press.

Soil Defense in the Piedmont. United States Department of Agriculture.

Soil: The Nation's Heritage. United States Department of Agriculture.

Top Soil, Its Preservation and Ten Billion Little Dams. Soil Conservation Service.

Vogt, *Road to Survival*. William Sloan Associates.

Walker and Foster, *This Is Our Soil*. Rev. Ed. Interstate Printers and Publishers.

Weaver, *Conservation Handbook*. Interstate Printers and Publishers. (National Association of Biology Teachers.)

CHAPTER 46

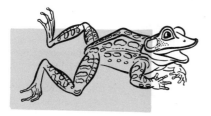

Biological Progress

46.1 The Search for Knowledge

Ever since early man first began to use tools and weapons, learned to use fire, and developed speech and writing so that he could leave records, there has been an ever-increasing search for knowledge. Man, possessed with this *intellectual curiosity,* strives to understand and better his environment, just as the small boy takes his toys apart to see how they are made, or the youth puts new gadgets on the family car. It is this intense interest in the world about him that has led many a man to risk his life in the search for knowledge and the quest for truth.

46.2 Steps in Biological Progress

The *cell theory* (Sec. 4.4), formulated as a result of the work of Schleiden, Schwann, and other biologists, marked a very important stage in the development of biology as a science. This theory states (1) that the cell is the unit of structure and function in the body, (2) that all living things are composed of cells, and (3) that these cells have come from previously existing cells.

The *theories of organic evolution* (Sec. 42.15) helped to explain the diversities and similarities of large numbers of living things and their relationship to the past. These theories are (1) natural selection, and (2) mutations. Man is

trying to improve his plants and animals by applying these principles.

The *discovery of microorganisms* led to the conquest of many diseases. Koch's postulates (Sec. 28.11) outlined the procedure for studying them. Koch, Jenner, Pasteur, Lister, and von Behring made important contributions about the nature and control of diseases. The invention of the electron microscope made it possible to observe viruses and very

FIGURE 46-1. *DECOMPRESSION CHAMBER*

The effect on guinea pigs of atmospheric conditions at an altitude of 18,000 feet has been studied with this equipment.

Science Service

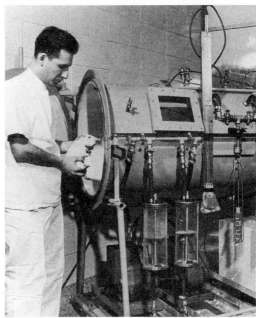

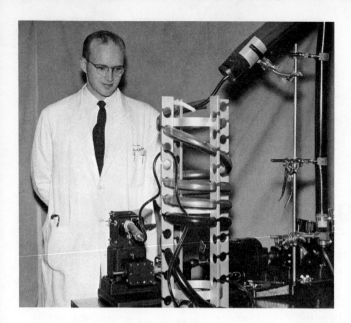

Figure 46-2.
OXYGENATOR

The complicated apparatus is a bubble oxygenator recently developed by this surgeon at the University of Minnesota to oxygenate the blood of a patient during open heart surgery. Oxygen is mixed into the blood in the tube at right. The blood is then debubbled, filtered, and passed through the narrow plastic tubing at the left to the patient.

University of Minnesota News Service

small microorganisms, and the recent use of radioactive materials has increased our knowledge of them.

The *principles of heredity* (Chap. 42) were stated as Mendel's laws of (1) unit characters, (2) dominance, and (3) segregation. They were applied by Burbank in hybridization and De Vries in propagating mutants. These were important steps in the improvement of crop plants and domestic animals used for food supply.

Man is still trying to improve his environment and add to his joy of living. His knowledge of *genetics* (the science of heredity) is helping to make life better for everyone.

46.3 Contributions of Some Biologists

While some biologists were working on the problems that led to the major steps in biological progress, other scientists were undertaking to solve problems which have since proved to be valuable intermediate steps toward that progress.

Alexis Carrell, a French surgeon and biologist, succeeded in growing living tissues, except brain tissue, outside of the body. This made it possible to transplant glandular tissue from one person to another. As a result of his work other scientists have helped to devise machines such as the artificial kidney, the mechanical heart, and the heart-lung machine. Growth of tissues outside of the body has also made possible the production of the *Salk vaccine* for poliomyelitis. This vaccine is made from cultures of kidney tissue from healthy monkeys. These are grown in nutrients and inoculated with the three kinds of polio virus. Later the virus is destroyed; the vaccine is prepared from the dead virus and is tested for producing immunity to the disease.

Elie Metchnikoff, a Russian zoologist and bacteriologist, discovered that some of the white blood cells which he called *phagocytes* (Sec. 23.2) were able to surround and digest foreign materials in the body. He formulated the *phagocyte theory*—the body is protected by the phagocytes which destroy harmful disease germs. This discovery was a step toward solving the problems of immunity.

Ivan Pavlov, a Russian physiologist,

BIOLOGY FOR YOU

was experimenting with digestion in dogs when he noted a relationship between the dog's response to food and to other distractions. He explained how *reflexes* are conditioned in the process of learning (Sec. 25.18). This was an important step that has led to the study of nervous differences in human beings and is leading toward better mental health and the treatment of the mentally ill.

Edward Trudeau, an American doctor, suffering from tuberculosis in the days when such cases were almost hopeless, decided to abandon the usual procedures and to spend the rest of his life enjoying his favorite activities outdoors in the Adirondack mountains of New York. He discovered that rest, fresh air, and nourishing food rich in protein were restoring his health. This method of treatment became a very important step in the prevention and treatment of tuberculosis.

A vaccine known as *BCG,* Bacillus Calmette-Guerin, named for the two scientists who developed it, is being used for immunization in underdeveloped areas of the world where the general health of the population is very poor. BCG is an additional aid to the prevention of tuberculosis. It does not replace other preventive health measures.

More recent research has resulted in drug therapy for tuberculosis. The three drugs most commonly used are isoniazid, streptomycin, and PAS. None of these kill all the bacteria in a patient but they stop the multiplication of bacteria. New drugs are continually being tested for their effectiveness.

Edmund Wilson, an American zoologist, studied the structure of cells. He became particularly interested in the number and structure of the chromosomes and the characteristics of the cells that varied with each kind of living

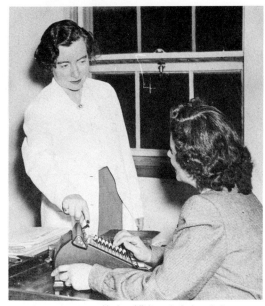

FIGURE 46-3. *THE ROAD BACK*

A patient recovering from tuberculosis learns an occupation to guarantee financial independence after hospitalization.

thing. His findings were important steps that led to the study of genetics by Galton. Research workers are still trying to solve the mystery of the gene.

46.4 Some Recent and Important Discoveries

Scientists are constantly carrying on *research* in many different fields hoping to make a major contribution that will advance mankind's knowledge. Photosynthesis, the gene and its place in heredity, vitamins and hormones, effects of radiation on living things, prevention and treatment of disease, and many other subjects are now being investigated.

The Mystery of Photosynthesis.—For centuries man has marveled at the strange power of green plants to make sugar from carbon dioxide and water, and chemists have long tried to duplicate this process. In 1953 Dr. Lemieux from Canada and Dr. Huber from Switzerland succeeded in producing a fraction

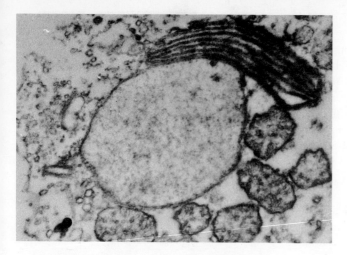

FIGURE 46-4. *CELL STRUCTURE*

This electron micrograph shows part of a cell magnified 50,000 diameters. The large circular object is the cell nucleus; the striped band at the right is the chloroplast which contains chlorophyll; and the smaller bodies are mitochondria, in which the chemical reactions of respiration occur.

Courtesy J. J. Wolken,
University of Pittsburgh

of an ounce of sucrose. This was an important discovery because it may lead to a better understanding of other plant activities that are concerned with photosynthesis. Other scientists are using radioactive atoms to determine how compounds are made in the living leaf. Radioactive phosphorus has aided in the discovery of how the first sugars are formed, and seems to be an important chemical of the photosynthetic process. It may help the chloroplasts to carry on photosynthesis. Many scientists are making an intensive study of these processes by which the green leaf captures energy and makes food. Their work may lead to "artificial photosynthesis" that will help to increase man's food supply.

The Mystery of the Cell and the Gene.—For a long time scientists have studied the structure and function of *cells,* the basic units of life. Chemists have determined what elements are in protoplasm and have learned the kinds of substances needed for the cell to grow and to repair itself, but they are still trying to find out just what it is that gives life to the protoplasm. If scientists could put these same elements together and make the same kind of substance in a test tube, they might be able to re-create life.

Biologists believe that the *gene* is located in the light and dark bands of the chromosomes, and that each gene can be associated with hereditary traits. The gene can duplicate itself, control the rate

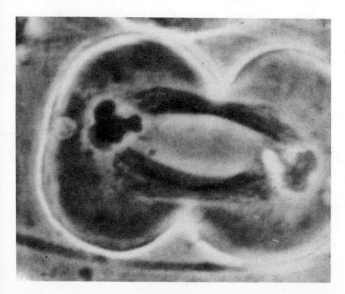

FIGURE 46-5. *TWO FROM ONE*

How does this cell divide into two identical copies of itself? By what chemical method are genes and chromosomes duplicated? How do they control the activities of the cell? These problems are a great challenge to the biologist.

Science Service

664

FIGURE 46-6. *MUSCLE RESEARCH*

Dr. Albert Szent-Gyorgyi, (*right*) renowned biochemist and winner of many awards including the Nobel Prize in medicine (1937), has made significant contributions in the field of muscle research.

Photo by Edwin Gray, Falmouth

of growth of the cell, and determine the kind of molecule to be made. Experiments have shown that a gene is made of *deoxyribonucleic acid,* or *DNA.* Dr. Maurice Wilkins in London worked out the structure of DNA by X-ray diffraction studies and Drs. James Watson and Francis Crick constructed a model of the DNA molecule. The three men shared the Nobel prize in 1962 for this work. DNA consists of two long spiral strands of atoms containing repeating units of a sugar (deoxyribose), phosphate, and four kinds of nitrogenous bases (adenine, cytosine, guanine, and thymine). These bases are joined in pairs to form frequent cross connections between the intertwined strands. The two strands are able to split between pairs of bases and the spirals break apart. Each half then rebuilds an exact duplicate of the other. In this way, the gene duplicates itself. Anything which upsets this pattern, such as a chemical bond that breaks, or a disturbance caused by radiation, may result in a new chemical pattern and a variation in heredity.

The gene sends messages to the cytoplasm of the cell through a chemical messenger known as *ribonucleic acid,* or

RNA. This directs the rebuilding of new proteins characteristic of the organism. Biologists are trying to decipher the code by which the arrangements of bases on the RNA molecules carry the hereditary messages to the cell. If they can learn to control this process, it may be possible to correct gene defects and thus to improve the heredity of man.

46.5 Improvement of Plants and Animals

Work has only begun on the chemical hormones in plants. The use of *colchicine* in doubling the number of chromosomes has many possibilities in developing new flowers. Fertile hybrids have been produced by crosses between plants that ordinarily give sterile hybrids. Seedless tomatoes and watermelons have been developed by spraying the flowers with a certain chemical. Unusual kinds of plant growth have been observed after application of *gibberellic acid.*

Animals likewise can be crossed to establish desired characteristics. Hybrid colors are used in sex determination of day-old chicks. Cattle are widely being vaccinated against anthrax and other diseases. Tuberculin testing is becoming universal. Many cattle are now being tested for evidence of brucellosis, also known as Bang's disease, and undulant fever. Dogs are vaccinated against rabies. Thus knowledge of science is being applied to the improvement of animals.

46.6 Other Problems Still Unsolved

The electron microscope has greatly facilitated the study of cell functions and of microorganisms such as the virus. The virus that causes the mosaic disease of tobacco has been found to be a protein. The giant-sized molecules, when put into a leaf of tobacco, cause a disease of the plant as the virus increases in quantity.

Among problems now under investigation are the following:

a. The cause of cancer.

b. The development of vaccines and sera for many diseases.

c. The knowledge of how antitoxins are produced.

d. The effects of light, food, and muscular exercise on immunity.

e. The control of more insect pests and parasites.

f. The exploration of more of the earth's surface and the study of the fossils and existing fauna and flora.

g. space travel and its effects on living things.

FACTS TO REMEMBER

Man is continually searching for knowledge in an attempt to improve both himself and his environment. Some of the steps in *biological progress* have been the formulation of the *cell theory* and the *theories of organic evolution,* the discovery of *microorganisms* and the statement of the *principles of heredity.* Many biologists have made contributions which have become *intermediate steps* in biological progress. Biologists are continuing their *research* on a wide variety of problems, with each step leading to further progress.

WORDS TO REMEMBER

antitoxin	flora	phagocyte theory
BCG	fossil	photosynthesis
cancer	gene	principles of heredity
cell	genetics	research
cell theory	gibberellic acid	RNA
colchicine	immunity	Salk vaccine
conditioned reflex	intellectual curiosity	serum
DNA	microorganism	theories of organic
eugenics	parasite	evolution
fauna	phagocyte	vaccine

QUESTIONS

1. What do you think is meant by "intellectual curiosity"?

2. State the three parts of the cell theory and explain each.

3. Why is the cell theory considered such an important step in biological progress?

4. Explain how the factors in natural selection could produce a strong herd of deer.

5. How could the mutation theory account for a white elephant?

6. How can a knowledge of genetics be of help to man?

7. Name some scientists whose discoveries proved to be intermediate steps in biological progress. Describe one such discovery.

8. Why is man trying to learn more about photosynthesis?

9. Describe some improvements in plants or animals which have been produced by man.

10. Of what importance is the study of the tobacco mosaic disease?

11. State five problems which have not yet been solved.

COMPLETION TEST

As your teacher or classmate reads each of the following incomplete statements, with your book closed, write on a clean sheet of paper the word or phrase which correctly completes each statement.

1. Living tissues were first successfully grown outside of the body by _____.

2. White blood cells that destroy disease germs are known as _____.

3. Conditioned reflexes were studied by _____.

4. An important preventive measure and treatment for tuberculosis was discovered by _____.

5. Edmund Wilson is known for his work on _____.

6. Radioactive _____ is used to trace compounds in the living leaf.

7. Hereditary traits are carried by _____.

8. BCG is being used as a treatment for _____.

9. A chemical which affects the number of plant chromosomes is _____.

10. Seedless _____ have been developed by spraying with a certain chemical.

PROJECTS

Finding Facts.—Read the current issues of the magazines on nature study, health, physical culture, and biology. Search diligently and carefully for articles announcing new discoveries. Take notes or cut out clippings for your notebook. Be sure to write the date on each one.

CHAPTER 47

Vocations in Biology

47.1 What Is a Vocation?

Your **vocation** is your chosen life work, whether it is a profession or any other occupation. This work should interest you very strongly and it should be of such nature that you enjoy working at it.

Some of you will choose a career in biology or a related field. Others who do not make biology their vocation, will find that the study of living things can add much to your own lives. You will understand and enjoy the world around you. You will become more observant and apply scientific attitudes and methods to your problems. You will be able to improve your health and home and to find fascinating hobbies.

47.2 Vocations That Depend on Biology

Many students of biology find lifelong interests in it and choose some phase of it for their life work. At the present time there is great need for biologists trained in physiology and chemistry who can contribute their knowledge to industry and research.

Pharmaceutical companies are required to meet definite standards in their preparation of vitamins, enzymes, and hormones; the *dairy* industry needs to control the growth of bacteria in the manufacture of cheese and in the protection of our milk supply; and the *public health department* must keep a constant check on the food and water supply. *Lumber companies* are eager to find new uses for their by-products and to increase their methods of production, while the *food canning* companies demand experts who can test their products and maintain high standards. Agriculture requires a thorough knowledge of

FIGURE 47-1. *EXPLORERS*

Disease is slowly and surely being conquered by modern scientific research. Technicians like these might well have started their careers with a course in biology.

668

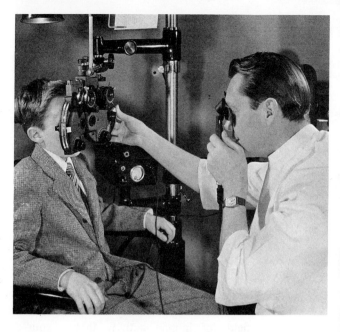

FIGURE 47-2. *OPTOMETRIST*

Optometry, the scientific measurement of the eye to detect disease or defect, is one of the professions related to biology. Here, the retinoscope is being used to test the young patient's eyesight.

Ewing Galloway

biology to produce improved crops and livestock. There are also many different kinds of *professions*. The added emphasis on health calls for more doctors and nurses, supervisors of health centers and play activities, and teachers of biology and first aid. The dentist, the oculist, and the landscape architect all receive their preliminary training in the field of biology. Some scientists spend their full time studying the basic problems of life. These are research biologists and biochemists.

47.3 Choosing Your Life Work

The choice of a lifetime career should be based upon a thorough investigation of the requirements and opportunities of the various professions and vocations, as well as on personal preference. If you are unfitted for your occupation,

you will not be interested in your job and will not do it well. *Aptitude tests* are given in many fields of study to determine a person's adaptability to a certain profession. As fast as such tests are perfected, we should take advantage of them; for different persons have different abilities, and each should choose a vocation he is well suited for.

If you plan to enter the biological field, you should select the branch that has the strongest interest for you, and learn all that you can about it in regard to (*a*) advantages, (*b*) disadvantages, (*c*) essential qualifications as to personality and ability, (*d*) qualifications as to health, (*e*) training necessary, and (*f*) rewards.

A group of teachers prepared this list of vocations dependent on a knowledge of biology:

Physician	Optometrist	Sanitary	Landscape
Nurse	Dietitian	Engineer	Architect
Dentist	Teacher	Veterinarian	Tree Surgeon
Oral Hygienist	Bacteriologist	Entomologist	Forester
Pharmacist	Laboratory	Farmer	Phytopathologist
Oculist	Assistant	Nurseryman	Biochemist

FIGURE 47-3. *NATURE STUDY*

These boys on an outdoor expedition are learning to improve their powers of observation. Experiences like this are often the beginning of a lifelong interest in nature.

Courtesy The Loomis School

47.4 Biological Hobbies

Even if you do not enter any of the various fields of human activity that depend on some phase of biology, this study may furnish recreation to many of you. If during this year of study, the text gave too brief a story of some animal or plant that interested you, you can begin your recreation in biology by learning more about it.

You must explore the library to learn how much is already known; if this source of information fails to tell you all that you wish to know, you must observe the plant or animal you are interested in by yourself. What does it do in the summer, winter, spring, and autumn? What devices does it possess that are especially helpful in its peculiar form of life? What enemies must it escape?

Nearly every high school student enjoys taking a walk. The distance may not be great, but the pleasure and benefit derived from the exercise, the companionship, and the interesting things found along the way may remain among your most happy memories.

Have you ever noticed that some people seem to see more things than others, and have more interesting stories to relate? Those who are keen and alert can delve far into the secrets of nature. From such walks you, too, may find your source of fun for a lifetime. The next time you go out for a hike or a stroll through the park, try some of the following suggestions:

a. Observe the *weather,* the atmosphere, temperature, humidity, clouds, and wind. Are you a good weather prophet?

b. Notice the *trees.* How many can you name? Have they been harmed by weather conditions or insect pests? Notice the difference in shape of a tree growing alone in the open and one of the same kind growing in the woods.

c. Observe the *birds.* Can you recognize any by their songs? Can you locate any nests or glimpse a mother feeding her young? In what respects do airplanes resemble the structures of birds?

d. Look for *flowers.* How many different kinds do you recognize? Do the same kinds of flowers live in the fields, the woods, and the swamps?

e. Collect a few *insects.* Do you remember how to classify them? How does a beetle differ from a butterfly?

f. Be alert for small *animals.* Who will be the first to see a squirrel, a rabbit, a woodchuck, or a snake?

FIGURE 47-4. *RACCOONS*

Animal photography can be very rewarding, but it requires a high degree of patience and persistence, as well as knowledge of photographic technique.

Jack Dermid

No matter whether you go on a hike, ride horseback, or travel by car, train, or bus, you can always find interesting things in your surroundings. If you choose one of the fields of nature for your hobby, you will be assured of fun for your lifetime.

47.5 Photography

Taking pictures is an ideal hobby. Taking biological pictures is especially fascinating. Pictures of flowers, birds, and other animals are among the most attractive that you can get. Sometimes you can set a trap so that the animal takes its own picture, when the camera has been put in proper position. This is done by baiting a trap which sets off the flash bulb and at the same time trips the shutter of the camera. Sometimes, with patience, you can get a charming picture of a squirrel, a rabbit, or of a bird at a feed box.

Night photography is especially difficult. You must wait long, weary hours at some spot where you think the game will appear. You must rely on your own ingenuity to make the mechanical arrangements which accomplish this, but the results are exciting and well worth the trouble.

47.6 Aerial Medicine

Now that rockets and other craft are being developed to leave the earth's atmosphere, penetrate outer space, and return to earth, the problem of human space flight arises. Experts in aerial and space medicine are considering the health dangers that will confront man as he travels through space.

It is atmospheric pressure which enables our bodies to absorb oxygen. It is also atmospheric pressure which prevents the body fluids from evaporating. Beyond the limits of our atmosphere, then, we need some kind of protection from these dangers. Pressurized space cabins and pressurized space suits have been developed. As storage space for oxygen will be limited, very long trips will be impossible without an artificial atmosphere that can renew itself. Experiments are now being done on biological methods of renewing the air such as using algae to absorb carbon dioxide and give off oxygen.

Weightlessness is another problem that the space traveler will face. Unless engineers can build a space ship that eliminates weightlessness, man must learn how to function under this new condition. Other important factors to

FIGURE 47-5. *VISITOR IN SPACE*

The young Air Force major who went up 19 miles above the earth to collect data on the problems of space flight is a doctor and a specialist in space biology. Survival for these pioneers in space depends on their specialized knowledge.

Wide World

be considered in space medicine are the effects of solar radiation outside the filter of the earth's atmosphere, the hazards of cosmic radiation and the extremes of temperature that will be encountered.

Aerial medicine is but one of the many applications of biology to our present and future lives. Man's continuing exploration of the unknown brings countless problems for the biologist to investigate.

FACTS TO REMEMBER

The study of biology can lead to many interesting *vocations*. In determining a vocation in the field of biology, a person should first pick the area in which he is most interested and learn all about it. He should then take an *aptitude test* to see if his talents are suited to this area. Finally, he should consider all the advantages and disadvantages of working in this field, the essential qualifications, the length of training he will require, and the rewards.

From the study of biology a person might also choose to undertake a particular biological *hobby* such as collecting specimens, starting a garden, or studying an animal. Not only will this develop a greater knowledge and understanding of the plants and animals in our environment, it will also give many hours of pleasure and recreation.

WORDS TO REMEMBER

aerial medicine	hobby	pharmacist
aptitude test	landscape architect	phytopathologist
bacteriologist	nurseryman	sanitary engineer
dietitian	oculist	tree surgeon
entomologist	optometrist	veterinarian
forester	oral hygienist	vocation

672

QUESTIONS

1. What is a vocation?
2. Make a list of at least ten vocations which depend on biology.
3. What is a *hobby*? List your hobbies and tell why you enjoy them.
4. In what fields of biology do you expect to learn of new discoveries in the near future?

COMPLETION TEST

As your teacher or classmate reads the following incomplete statements, with your book closed, write on a clean sheet of paper the word or phrase which correctly completes the statement.

1. A person trained in the care of the sick is a _____.
2. The man who cares for the trees along a city street is called a tree _____.
3. A person who repairs teeth is a _____.
4. A person who learns how to clean teeth and teach people about their care is an _____.
5. The _____ raises food for the nation.
6. A _____ prepares the menus for the students in a college dormitory.
7. A man who specializes in the care and treatment of the eye is an _____.
8. A person who cares for the health of people is a _____.
9. A person who cares for the health of animals is a _____.
10. A _____ specializes in the study of bacteria.

PROJECTS

I. *My Vocation.*—1. If you have already chosen your lifework, write a brief description of the kind of career you hope to have. Then list all the ways in which you think your knowledge of biology may be helpful to you.

2. If you have not chosen your vocation, find out all you can about one of those dealing with biology and list all the reasons why you would or would not like to follow it as a career.

II. *My Hobby.*—If you have been making collections or have a hobby along the lines of nature study, bring some of your work to class and arrange with your teacher to work on it as a part of your project.

III. *Hiking for Fun.*—Take a hike through a park or the countryside, following some of the suggestions found in the text. Write a complete report of your trip. If you take pictures, here are some suggestions.

a. Different kinds of trees.
b. Birds (if you can get close enough).
c. Wild animals of the vicinity.
d. Domestic animals and their young.
e. Typical habitats.

IV. *Famous Biologists.*—You will find many fascinating books about the lives of famous men of science who have devoted their lives to biology. Write a careful report of some of their contributions.

V. Find out all you can about the physical effects of space travel on the human body.

REFERENCES

Asterod and Vorderwinkler, *Color Guide To Tropical Fish.* Sterling.
Barr, *Flying Men and Medicine.* Funk and Wagnalls.
Brown, *How to Make a Home Nature Museum.* Little, Brown.
Brown, *The Amateur Naturalist's Handbook.* Little, Brown.
Butcher, *Seeing America's Wildlife in Our National Refuges.* Devin-Adair.
Freeman and Freeman, *Fun with Chemistry.* Random House.
Fitzpatrick and Stiles, *The Biology of Flight.* Macmillan.
Geogan, *Nature I Loved.* Coward-McCann.
Greenberg and Raskin, *Home-Made Zoo.* David McKay.
Hass, *Men and Sharks.* Doubleday.
Jaeger, *Nature Crafts.* Macmillan.
Kieran, *Footnotes on Nature.* Doubleday.
Kuder and Paulson, *Discovering Your Real Interests.* Science Research Associates.
Pollock, *Careers In Science.* Dutton.
Pray, *Taxidermy.* Macmillan.
Ray and Washburn, *Are You Fit to Be a Pilot?* Funk and Wagnalls.
Renner and Bauer, *The Air We Live In.* Macmillan.
Tannenbill, *All About the Weather.* Random House.
Teale, *Byways to Adventure.* Dodd, Mead.
Todd, *The Tropical Fish Book.* Arco.
Zim, *Man in the Air.* Harcourt, Brace.

COMPREHENSIVE TEST ON PART FIVE

I. Complete the following statements by writing in the space provided the word or phrase which best completes them.

1. Taxonomy refers to a system of _____.
2. Linnaeus' system is called _____ _____.
3. His system is based on _____.
4. The two main divisions are called _____.
5. The two parts of the scientific name are made up of the _____ name and _____ name.
6. The rate of change observed in radium-bearing rocks is one method of measuring the _____.
7. Most fossils are found in _____ rocks.
8. Fossils of _____ have been found preserved in amber.
9. The process by which minerals replace the structures of the original plant or animal is called _____.

10. The study of the development of the young before it is hatched or born is called _____.

II. *a.* List five kinds of evidence to show the relationship of living things.

1. _____.   3. _____.
2. _____.   4. _____.
5. _____.

b. Explain the similarity of the stages in the development of a chick embryo to the degree of development of the animal in each of the phyla of the animal kingdom.

III. In the parenthesis at the right of each expression in Column B write the number of the expression in Column A which is most closely related.

Column A	Column B
1. euglena	fish and frogs ( )
2. Archeopteryx	reptiles and mammals ( )
3. lung fish	reptiles and birds ( )
4. duckbill	simplest vertebrates and
5. fish with cartilaginous	modern fish ( )
skeletons	between plant and animal ( )

IV. List five common factors which cause changes in the environment. After each factor give one example.

V. Name and give examples of five factors in Darwin's *Theory of Natural Selection.*

VI. Define each of the following:
1. variation
2. mutant
3. fluctuation
4. hybrid
5. gamete
6. chromosome
7. gene
8. maturation
9. polar body
10. spermatogenesis

VII. Describe the contribution to biology of each of the following men.
1. Mendel
2. Correns
3. De Vries
4. Burbank

VIII. *a.* Show by diagrams the result of a cross between a hooded rat and a white rat. (Hooded rats are dominant.)
b. Show the result obtained by crossing a hybrid with a recessive.

IX. Explain what is meant by:
1. recessive character
2. crossing-over
3. sex-linked character
4. fraternal twins
5. identical twins
6. unit character
7. F_1 generation
8. back cross
9. law of segregation
10. law of dominance

X. For what purpose are the following used?

1. BCG
2. Salk vaccine
3. colchicine
4. ribonucleic acid

XI. *a.* What is a vocation?

b. What vocation do you think you will choose?

c. List at least five vocations that depend on biology.

d. Name five living biologists and briefly explain what problem each is working on.

e. List five biological hobbies.

f. Describe at least three kinds of living things which might be observed on a hike.

Biographies

Louis John Rudolph Agassiz (1807–1873)

Louis John Rudolph Agassiz (*ag*-uh-see) was born at Motier, Switzerland, and died at Cambridge, Massachusetts. He introduced the laboratory method in zoology to students in America and trained many who later became prominent in biology. His motto, "Study nature, not books," has been taken as a slogan by thousands of students all over the world. He was the founder of the summer laboratory method of study now so common, establishing the first such laboratory, on Penikese Island off the coast of Massachusetts.

Agassiz was professor of zoology and geology at Harvard University and curator of the University museum that now bears his name. His scientific contributions cover a wide range of subjects in zoology and geology. He identified more than 1500 species of fossil fish and published a five-volume work on that subject. His study and writings on glaciers opened new lines of thought about prehistoric conditions and early life.

John James Audubon (1785–1851)

John James Audubon, of French and Spanish ancestry, was a self-trained naturalist. Although he was born on this side of the Atlantic, as a young man he spent a few years in France. There he gave as much time as he could to music, drawing, and natural history during a period when he was in training for the navy.

After his return to America about 1800, he became a wandering naturalist, ever seeking for new birds to study. As he went from place to place, he would often pay for his lodgings or a new pair of shoes by making a portrait of his host or of the shoemaker.

His most famous work consists of one thousand and sixty-five natural-sized paintings of American birds, the publication of which alone took ten years and cost $100,000. The next time you visit a large library, ask to be shown Audubon's *Birds,* the most noted book on American birds.

Charles Edwin Bessey (1845–1915)

Charles Edwin Bessey was born in Milton, Ohio, and died at Lincoln, Nebraska.

He graduated in 1869 at the Michigan Agricultural College, and in February, 1870, he took up his duties as professor of botany at the Iowa State College, at Ames, Iowa. In addition to botany, he taught zoology and entomology for the larger portion of the fifteen years that he remained at that institution. He assumed the professorship of botany at the University of Nebraska in November, 1884, a position held by him until his death.

His greatest contributions to botany are the introduction of the laboratory method in teaching the science, and a new method of classifying plants which had profound influence upon students and future investigators.

Luther Burbank
(1849–1926)

LUTHER BURBANK was born in Lancaster, Massachusetts, where he attended the local academy for several winters. He became interested in plants and started a nursery. By selecting and raising the most promising young plants, one or two out of hundreds, he greatly improved their quality.

Burbank conducted the Burbank Experimental Farms at Santa Rosa, California, where as many as 6000 experiments were often under observation at one time. He aimed to improve plants for commercial use and to create more beautiful flowers. By cross-pollination and selection Burbank produced the thornless cactus, the stoneless prune, the plumcot, and the famous Burbank potato. He also produced the Shasta daisy, with very large flowers, and corn that grows eighteen feet tall.

Frank M. Chapman
(1864–1945)

FRANK M. CHAPMAN was born in Englewood, New Jersey. During World War I, he was Director of the Bureau of Public Relations for the American Red Cross, but his life interest was in ornithology. His success in this field of zoology brought him medals and the presidency of several organizations. Dr. Chapman wrote many books on birds. Among his best-known are *A Handbook of Birds of Eastern North America, Bird Life, Bird Studies with a Camera,* and *The Economic Value of Birds to the State.* He was the founder and editor of *Bird Lore.* His whole life was devoted to efforts to make more people appreciate the economic and esthetic value of birds.

John Henry Comstock
(1849–1931)

JOHN HENRY COMSTOCK was born in Janesville, Wisconsin. He graduated from Cornell University in 1874 and did graduate work at Yale and in Leipzig. His great interest was the study of insects. He was an authority on many phases of insect science.

He aided many young men who showed an interest in insect study to graduate from college. His enthusiasm has passed on to hundreds of young men who are now aiding the world in its war on insect pests. He tried to make the study of insects as popular as the study of birds and flowers. In writing his book *How to Know the Butterflies,* he was assisted by his wife, Anna Botsford Comstock, who has written many books of her own. The best-known book of the Comstocks is *A Manual for the Study of Insects.*

Professor Comstock held the first professorship of entomology to be established in America.

Charles Robert Darwin
(1809–1882)

CHARLES ROBERT DARWIN, born in Shrewsbury, England, made many original observations on animals and plants and conducted numerous experiments with them. But he was not satisfied simply to discover new facts; he wished to find some way to explain how all the many forms of life came to live where they do and to have the size and habits that they do. Darwin believed that there was a natural struggle continuously going on in nature between the weak and the strong, and that those animals which could survive under the worst conditions were the ones to win the competition.

Darwin formulated a number of explanations. The best known of his theories is that of the origin of species by natural selection. The main idea emphasized by Darwin in this theory is that life has gradually unfolded, or evolved (hence evolution), having progressed from the simpler types like sponges and hydra to the more complex with division of labor and differentiated organs.

Jean Henri Fabre
(1823–1915)

JEAN HENRI FABRE (*fah*-br) was born in southern France. He was a teacher in the school of Avignon and a professor of physics at the college of Ajaccio. His greatest work was the writing of ten volumes on insects. He also wrote on physics, history, astronomy, and botany. *The Social Life of Insects, The Life of the Spider,* and *The Life of the Fly* are some of his writings that have been translated into English. He was a careful observer and wrote in a way to interest the reader. He wrote to be understood and sometimes sacrificed accuracy for clarity. His greatest admirers came from the world of literature rather than from the world of science. His writings are still popular.

Alexander Fleming
(1881–1955)

SIR ALEXANDER FLEMING discovered penicillin in 1929. For this work and that of Sir Howard Florey the Nobel Prize in Medicine was shared in 1945. Dr. Fleming was born in Scotland, studied at the University of London, received honors in medicine, and became a professor of bacteriology. After the discovery of penicillin, he continued his research in the field of immunology and of human blood.

Penicillin was discovered by accident while Fleming was doing some research on influenza. He had left some culture plates of special disease germs exposed to the air. In a short time mold spots developed and formed a ring around them that had no bacteria. This seemed to indicate that the mold (*Penicillium notatum*) killed the bacteria in the immediate vicinity. After more experiments Fleming found that the mold grew best in cheese. He then began to try to discover how to purify the drug from the mold.

It was not until 1939 that much attention was given to further research on penicillin. During that year Sir Howard Florey and his associates took up Dr. Fleming's work and succeeded in growing mold cultures in sugar solution and keeping them in incubators. When penicillin was produced it was extracted.

Penicillin has produced amazing results in bone infection, blood poisoning, pneumonia, gas gangrene, and other infections.

Howard Walter Florey
(1898–   )

SIR HOWARD FLOREY was born in Australia and educated at Oxford, where he became a teacher of pathology. He continued with the work undertaken by Dr. Fleming following his accidental discovery of penicillin in 1929, and developed methods of extracting the antibiotic from the mold.

In 1944 Dr. Florey and Dr. Fleming were knighted for their work on penicillin. Florey's method of extraction of the antibiotic was so slow that shortages of this drug were in effect for several years. When the synthetic form later became available it resulted in saving many lives. Its greatest effectiveness has been in the treatment of wounds and certain types of infection.

Louis Agassiz Fuertes
(1874–1927)

LOUIS AGASSIZ FUERTES (*fur*-tez) was born in Ithaca, New York. His main interest all through his high school and college life was birds. He learned to imitate their calls and in this way could bring them to him for intimate study. Later, he studied drawing and painting so that he could portray them in color. He traveled over many countries to learn of the other birds of the world.

Fuertes illustrated numerous books. Among them are Coues' *Key to North American Birds,* Eaton's *Birds of New York,* Burgess's *Bird Book for Children,* and Burgess's *Animal Book for Children.* In his later years, he had more calls for his talents than time would allow him to answer. He ranks among the finest of the bird artists.

Joseph Goldberger
(1874–1929)

JOSEPH GOLDBERGER was born in Austria-Hungary. When he was six years old, he came to the United States with his parents. In 1895 he graduated from the Medical College of New York University. Shortly after this date, he entered the United States Public Health Service, where he remained all his life.

Dr. Goldberger's greatest contribution to science and to humanity was the discovery of the cause, cure, and prevention of pellagra.

Pellagra is caused by the lack of fresh proteins in the diet. We can cure this malady by adding milk and meat to the patient's diet, and we can prevent it by seeing that these foods are eaten regularly.

The persistence of this great benefactor to mankind in searching for the cause of this mysterious malady, and the numerous experiments which he tried on himself to prove that pellagra was not a germ disease, should serve to inspire any student who aims to be of service to his generation. The splendid assistance which Dr. Goldberger's wife gave him, sharing dangerous experiments, will make her name almost as well known as her husband's.

Asa Gray
(1810–1888)

ASA GRAY, born in Paris, New York, was a man of whom American botanists are justly proud. He was a poor boy, but he had a great interest in plants, the will to work, and ambition. As a man, he first earned his living by practicing medicine. On long rides to see his patients, he collected plants and studied them, and after a time gave up his profession and devoted himself wholeheartedly to study of botany. In those days botany was taught only as a division of natural history, even in colleges,

for the importance of the subject was not recognized. Through Gray's work and enthusiasm, botany was very soon established as a separate science. He is widely known for his *Manual of Botany,* which contains keys that help students in the identification of plants. Besides writing books and teaching at Harvard University for nearly twenty years, Gray founded the University's Botanical Garden at Cambridge, Massachusetts.

William Harvey
(1578–1657)

WILLIAM HARVEY, born at Folkstone, England, began his studies at a period when science was not in good standing. The study of the structure of the human body was just being undertaken anew after a period of nearly twelve hundred years of neglect.

Harvey was an industrious student, and the result of many years of painstaking dissections was his great book: *An Anatomical Disquisition on the Movement of the Heart and Blood in Animals.* He was the first to describe the blood as moving in a circuit in the body and to state that the beating of the heart supplies the propelling force. From his brilliant dissections, man learned the difference between a vein and an artery and learned how to stop bleeding.

Accurate knowledge about secretions, respiration, and the distribution of food in the body began to increase as soon as the exact course of the blood was known. This is why Harvey's discoveries are of such importance.

Robert Hooke
(1635–1703)

ROBERT HOOKE was born on the Isle of Wight, which lies off the southern coast of England. He was an outstanding mathematical and mechanical genius, and became a physicist. As an assistant to the famous chemist, Robert Boyle, Hooke experimented with pumps, diving bells, and many other mechanical devices.

In 1662, Hooke was appointed Curator of the Royal Society of London, the purpose of which was to separate truth from superstition. The Society later became the clearing house for scientific ideas and theories. Although he had the responsibility for reporting the results of several experiments at every meeting of the Royal Society, Hooke still found time to grind lenses and make them into microscopes.

Robert Hooke published his record of observations in a book, *Micrographia,* which he dedicated to the Royal Society. His greatest contribution in the field of biology was the discovery and naming of the "cell," from his observation of cells in cork. He also reported quite accurate observations on the life history of the mosquito.

Leland O. Howard
(1857–1950)

L. O. HOWARD was born at Rockford, Illinois. After graduating from college, he became assistant entomologist in the Department of Agriculture, at Washington. He remained in this position until 1894, when he was made chief of the Bureau of Entomology. He resigned from the Bureau in 1927.

Mosquitoes—How They Live, The Insect Book, The Housefly, and numerous government publications are included among Dr. Howard's writings. For both the Century and the Standard dictionaries, he has prepared definitions in entomology. He showed the relationship of the housefly to the spread of disease, especially typhoid fever and malaria; and from Europe he brought parasites of the brown-tail moth, introducing them into Massachusetts, and also imported many parasites of the European corn borer.

Dr. Howard devoted his main energies for many years to applying the technical discoveries in entomology to human welfare.

Thomas Henry Huxley
(1825–1895)

THOMAS HENRY HUXLEY was one of the greatest of the English scientists and was the father of the modern method of biological study. Up to 1850, information about plants and animals was passed on only by lectures. Huxley found that the science of his day contained many errors which were due to lack of first-hand information on the part of the writers. He corrected many of these errors by personal study of plants and animals, and devoted years to developing methods of laboratory study. His directions for studying the crayfish were probably the first laboratory outlines used by students of biology.

David Starr Jordan
(1851–1931)

DAVID STARR JORDAN was born in Gainesville, New York. He took his master's degree at Cornell in 1872, his medical degree at Indiana Medical College in 1875, and his doctor's degree at Butler University in 1878. The honorary degree of doctor of laws was conferred upon him by four of the leading American universities.

In addition to teaching biology for many years, he wrote numerous technical and popular books on various phases of biology. From 1885 to 1913 he was president first of Indiana University and then of Leland Stanford University, but during all this time he continued his scientific studies and became one of the most eminent authorities on fishes in the United States.

Dr. Jordan's life and attainments are striking examples of what can be accomplished by one's own efforts and individuality.

Robert Koch
(1843–1910)

ROBERT KOCH (*kokh*), born at Klausthal, Germany, attained great renown when, in 1882, he discovered the germ which causes tuberculosis. In the next year he announced that he had found the germ of Asiatic cholera. He advanced medical science by making other important discoveries. For some time before his death, he was the director of the Institute for Infectious Diseases, in Berlin.

In all of his investigations he applied strictly scientific methods, some of which have become a regular part of the procedure used in studying a germ disease. Before one can be certain that the cause of a germ disease has been discovered, four steps must be taken: first, a microscopic organism of a particular type must be found in abundance in the blood or tissues of the sick animal; second, a pure culture must be made of the suspected organism; third, this pure culture, when introduced into the body of a similar animal, must produce the same disease; and, fourth, there must then be found in the blood or tissues of the diseased animal large numbers of this introduced organism.

Jesse Lazear
(1866–1900)

JESSE LAZEAR (luh-*zeer*), with Walter Reed, James Carroll, and Aristides Agramonte, in 1900 was appointed to study sanitary conditions in Cuba. This group of scientists gave special attention to yellow fever, which was prevalent. There was some evidence connecting the mosquito known as *Aëdes aegypti* with this scourge.

The mosquitoes were allowed to suck the blood of a yellow fever patient and were then placed on susceptible persons. James Carroll was the first volunteer to become infected. He recovered, but died seven years later from complications following the attack of yellow fever. Dr. Lazear also became infected, and died on September 25, 1900. Twelve soldiers who volunteered were also infected by mosquitoes.

The following facts were established by the commission: (1) yellow fever is acquired only through the bite of the female *Aëdes aegypti;* (2) the mosquito to become infected must bite a yellow fever patient during the first three to five days of the disease; and (3) at least twelve days must elapse, after the mosquito has obtained blood from a yellow fever patient, before it can infect another person.

Anton van Leeuwenhoek
(1632–1723)

ANTON VAN LEEUWENHOEK (*lay*-venhook), a well-to-do Hollander, born at Delft, devoted himself entirely to science.

His first publication on microscopic objects appeared when he was forty-one years old. He became fascinated with the making of crude microscopes and possessed no less than 247 complete microscopes with many additional lenses. In 1686, he observed the minute circulation of the blood and demonstrated the capillary connection between veins and arteries. He discovered, also, three forms of bacteria and the very tiny living animals in water, which are now known to us as Protozoa.

As you watch the demonstration of capillary circulation in the web of the foot of the frog, you should have before you Leeuwenhoek's enthusiastic description of the circulation in the lung of the frog. The first sentence runs as follows: "A sight presented itself more delightful than any mine eyes had ever beheld: for here I discovered more than fifty circulations of the blood in different places, while the animal lay quiet in the water and I could bring it before my microscope to my wish."

Sir Joseph Lister
(1827–1912)

SIR JOSEPH LISTER was born at Upton, Essex, England. His great achievement was the recognition of the relation between the cause of fermentation which Pasteur's discoveries revealed and the cause of decomposition in wounds. In 1867 he published his famous article, "On a New Method of Treating Compound Fractures,

Abscesses, etc. with Observations on the Condition of Suppuration," in the English medical journal, *Lancet*. Lister reasoned that if fermentation and putrefaction were due to living organisms, then suppuration (the formation of pus) had a similar cause. This focusing of attention on living organisms carrying on their physiological processes and the discovery that carbolic acid prevents this activity laid the foundation for antiseptic surgery. Every hospital in the entire world employs the principles which this famous Englishman first applied. It is impossible to calculate the number of lives that have been saved and the suffering that has been prevented through the introduction of scrupulous cleanliness into surgical operations.

Marcello Malpighi
(1628–1694)

MARCELLO MALPIGHI gave to Italian scientific men a challenge of excellence that it has been difficult to surpass. This modest, quiet man was born near Bologna of peasant parents. He became a doctor of medicine and was immediately made a teacher in the University of Bologna. He was soon promoted to the University of Pisa.

Malpighi was active in research for forty years, during which time he made important discoveries. He actually saw blood flow through capillaries in the lung of the frog. The pigment layer in the skin is known today as the Malpighian layer. But his fame really lies in the marvelous dissections and drawings that he made. His description of the structure of the silkworm is one of the scientific classics and reveals great skill, for at that time hardly any animal had been carefully described.

His anatomy of plants is one of his best works; in it he foresaw the cell theory that was announced more than two hundred years later.

Gregor Johann Mendel
(1822–1884)

GREGOR JOHANN MENDEL was born of peasant parents at Heizendorf, a German colony in Austrian Silesia. He graduated from the University of Zurich where he had an opportunity to study under a great botanist, Karl Wilhelm von Nägeli; so it is not strange that he knew how to work with plants.

After his college education was finished, he entered the priesthood. He spent his leisure time experimenting with plants in his garden. His experiments, which continued for many years, were so carefully made that they could be repeated and proven by others. The result was a great discovery revealing the manner in which the traits of parent pea plants are transmitted to their offspring. When the same method of study was applied to other plants and to animals, it was found that Mendel had discovered how traits in all living things are transmitted from parents to their offspring.

Thomas Hunt Morgan
(1866–1945)

THOMAS HUNT MORGAN was born in Lexington, Kentucky, and for many years devoted his energies to teaching and research in biology. He attended the University of Kentucky and Johns Hopkins University and received many honorary degrees and other honors from scientific societies. In addition to these distinctions, Dr. Morgan was given the Nobel Prize in 1933 for his theory of the gene and its bearing on health. He was the first American biologist to receive this reward.

For about twenty-five years before his death, Dr. Morgan devoted his research to the study of heredity and made a very thoroughgoing investigation of the fruit fly, *Drosophila melanogaster*. This small fly is very common and can easily be collected and studied as it feeds on various fruits. It is important to recognize that this small insect has been the means of contributing to a scientific analysis of heredity and that Dr. Morgan and his scientific associates did much to advance our knowledge in this difficult field of research.

Henry Fairfield Osborn
(1857–1935)

HENRY FAIRFIELD OSBORN was born at Fairfield, Connecticut. After receiving his undergraduate and graduate training at Princeton, he became a teacher of the natural sciences. The field of paleontology (the study of fossils) had an early fascination for him, and his research turned chiefly to the discovery of fossil mammals. Every visitor to the American Museum of Natural History, in New York City, has an opportunity to see some of the famous fossils of extinct horses. But Dr. Osborn was not content merely to make discoveries; he attempted to offer an explanation of them in his books, *Men of the Old Stone Age* and *The Origin and Evolution of Life*. He wrote more than five hundred technical scientific papers.

Even before he became the president of the Museum of Natural History, numerous gold medals had been awarded him, and honorary degrees had been conferred upon him by American and European universities.

Louis Pasteur
(1822–1895)

LOUIS PASTEUR was born at Dôle, in eastern France. He was trained as a chemist and made a notable contribution to that field of knowledge before he began to study germs. Soon after the invention of the microscope, germs were found in water and the theory of spontaneous generation of life aroused new interest. Pasteur showed that there is no spontaneous origin of life.

Pasteur attained his greatest success in his study of microscopic organisms. His first success was in the study of fermentation of beer and wines. This was followed by his investigation of the silkworm plague. He then began the study of the prevention of disease, making a repeated series of pure cultures which rendered the germ less poisonous. This weakened germ he injected into animals to protect them from disease. He first tried this experiment with fowl cholera; then with splenic fever. After many years of experimentation, he was successful in preventing hydrophobia in a human being who had been bitten by a mad dog.

The Pasteur Institute was established in Paris in 1888. More than thirty similar institutes have since been established in different parts of the world. Pasteur's discoveries were directly beneficial to human welfare, making it possible to prevent the spread of infectious disease.

Jonas Salk
(1914–   )

DR. JONAS SALK developed anti-polio vaccine in 1953 while he was a research professor of bacteriology and director of the Virus Research Laboratory at the University of Pittsburgh. He is also known for his earlier work with long-lasting influenza vaccines which he helped to develop for commercial use.

Dr. Salk studied medicine and specialized in bacteriology. With the aid of fellowships and funds provided for research he became interested in public health and the prevention of epidemics. While continuing his work on influenza, he began a study of the polio virus. He found three strains in the United States, types I, II, and III, and began to develop a vaccine that would immunize against all three types. He used kidney tissues from monkeys in his work. After much experimentation, he tested his vaccine on his wife, his three children, and himself.

When these tests and those on 600 other persons proved favorable, Dr. Salk made available the results of his work for mass testing of over one million school children in 1954. Support was given to this project of mass injections by The National Foundation for Infantile Paralysis. During the years following the tests, the incidence of polio decreased. More children are receiving the vaccine each year in an effort to prevent this dread disease with its crippling effect.

Matthias Jakob Schleiden
(1804–1881)
Theodor Schwann
(1810–1882)

MATTHIAS JAKOB SCHLEIDEN (*shly*-den) and THEODOR SCHWANN (*shvon*) were two friends who worked on the minute structure of plants and animals. They were the first to set forth the theory that all living organisms are made up of cells.

Schleiden was educated to become a lawyer. Students will be interested in reading an account of his life and seeing how he became a famous scientist. He worked principally on plant cells. Schwann was trained under the famous teacher of physiology, Johannes Müller. Schwann made a special study of animal cells.

William Thompson Sedgwick
(1855–1921)

WILLIAM THOMPSON SEDGWICK, born at West Hartford, Connecticut, a member of the Department of Biology and Public Health at the Massachusetts Institute of Technology for thirty-eight years, devoted his training and energy largely to making cities healthful. He was one of the foremost American biologists to investigate milk, water, sewage, and epidemics of typhoid fever, and showed how to apply the results of these technical studies to human welfare.

Sedgwick was one of the first to study the bacteria of the air, and his *Principles of Sanitary Science and Public Health* (1902) was an important contribution to public health education. He devoted his life to teaching biology and sanitary science and to training biologists and public health workers, and rendered a great service to the world by making life safer than it had been before his time.

Theobald Smith
(1859–1934)

THEOBALD SMITH, born at Albany, New York, was a technical scientist bent on discovering how disease germs live, and he was an acknowledged authority in his field. For his "original research and observation on the diseases of animals and men," he received the Copley Medal from the English Royal Society.

His best-known discoveries are as follows: 1. He discovered that the protozoan parasite in the blood of cattle which causes Texas cattle fever is also found in ticks. It is carried from one cow to another by the infected ticks. This discovery led to similar discoveries in malaria, sleeping sickness, and other protozoan diseases. 2. His scholarly researches in human tuberculosis have been of great value to mankind. 3. Present standards of meat inspection are based upon his investigations in the diseases of cattle and other food animals. 4. He was a pioneer in the manufacture and extensive public use of antitoxin.

Charles Wardell Stiles
(1867–1941)

CHARLES WARDELL STILES was born at Spring Valley, New York. He was appointed zoologist in the Bureau of Animal Industry of the United States Department of Agriculture in 1891, and became zoologist in the United States Public Health Service and assistant surgeon general in 1902. Dr. Stiles was awarded honorary degrees by several American universities and was a member of international commissions.

The symptoms of hookworm disease were clearly described by the early Egyptians, and for centuries the disease was recognized by anemia, its most marked symptom. In the United States, a few years ago, it existed to an alarming degree. Dr. Stiles estimated from his researches that more than 2,000,000 people were infected with hookworm in the area east of the Mississippi from the Potomac River to the Gulf of Mexico. In the eastern hemisphere two distinct parasitic worms are the cause of the disease; in America a third species is found.

Dr. Stiles made important discoveries about the cause and prevention of the hookworm, and his services to human betterment in this field alone entitle him to be ranked as one of America's great benefactors.

Selman Waksman
(1888–   )

SELMAN WAKSMAN discovered the antibiotics streptomycin and neomycin while making an intensive study of soil. These fungi were found to destroy some organisms which live in animal bodies without producing serious ill-effects on the animal bodies.

Dr. Waksman was born in Russia where he received his early education. He came to the United States as a young man and entered Rutgers University. During this time he began extensive work on soil microbiology, trying to find out more about the organisms that live in the soil.

After thirty-nine years of teaching and research in this and related fields, Waksman began to search for antibiotics that would destroy the germs in man. He found that streptomycin would attack some of the bacteria that penicillin had failed to destroy. Streptomycin has been of help in arresting the progress of tuberculosis, typhoid fever, brucellosis, tularemia, infections of the urinary tract, and others. Neomycin has been used to treat other types of infection. In 1952, Dr. Waksman received the Nobel Prize for his discovery of streptomycin.

Glossary

A

Abdomen (*ab*-duh-m'n): the third region of an insect's body; the region between the chest and the pelvis in man.

Abscission (ab-*sis*-shun) **layer:** the layer of cells between a twig and the petiole of a leaf; the point where the leaf breaks off from the twig.

Absorption: the process of taking in water and dissolved substances through the walls of cells.

Accessory buds: more than the normal number (one) in the axil of a leaf. Accessory parts of a flower are the sepals and petals.

Accessory foods: those foods, such as minerals, water, and vitamins, which do not supply the body with heat and energy; they are necessary, nevertheless, for the growth and repair of tissue and also to regulate certain body functions.

Acetylcholine (uh-set-il-*koh*-leen): a chemical that transmits impulses from the end of a neuron to the muscles, causing them to relax.

Achene (uh-*keen*): a dry, indehiscent fruit, as in buttercup, dandelion, and clematis.

Acquired immunity: that which results from having had a disease, or from having taken preventive measures such as a vaccination.

Acromegaly (ak-ruh-*meg*-uh-lee): abnormal enlargement of the bones of the head, hands, and feet caused by over-secretion of the somotropic hormone from the anterior lobe of the pituitary gland.

ACTH: a hormone secreted by the pituitary gland which stimulates the secretion of hormones by the adrenal cortex.

Adaptation: change in, or peculiarities of, organisms which make them fit for their environment; fitness.

Adenoids (*ad*-in-oids): large masses of lymph tissue which grow in the cavity behind the nose.

Adolescence: the period of growth after childhood until maturity.

Adrenal (ad-*ree*-n'l) **glands:** a pair of ductless glands located above the kidneys.

Adrenaline (ad-*ren*-uh-lin): a chemical from the adrenal gland that causes muscles to contract; epinephrine.

Adulterate: to add a cheap or inferior substance to a good one; to cheapen, weaken, or reduce.

Adventitious (ad-ven-*tish*-us): appearing at unusual places, as roots on a slip.

Aerobic (ayr-*oh*-bik) **bacteria:** organisms that require free oxygen to exist.

Afferent (*af*-er-ent) **fibers:** those which convey impulses to the brain or spinal cord.

Agar agar (*ay*-gahr *ay*-gahr): a gelatinous substance obtained from seaweed and used as a food medium in the study of bacteria.

Agglutinin (uh-*gloo*-tih-nin): any organic substance which causes red blood cells or bacteria to clump together.

Aggressive coloration: a color which conceals an organism as it lies in wait for prey.

Air bladder: a structure in most species of fish which assists the fish in remaining level in the water.

Alcohol: a narcotic poison; the intoxicating element in whisky, beer, wine, etc.

Algae (*al*-jee): simple, aquatic plants with no true stems, roots, or leaves. They contain chlorophyll.

Alimentary (al-ih-*men*-tuh-ree) **canal:** the digestive tube or tract.

Alkaline (*al*-kuh-lyn) **substance:** one which neutralizes an acid.

Allergy (*al*-er-jee): an abnormal reaction of the body to certain substances, such as drugs, foods, or pollen.

Alternation of generations: a form of reproduction in lower plants in which the gametophyte generation alternates with the sporophyte generation.

Altricial (al-*trish*-ul) **birds:** those that are helpless when hatched, as robins, sparrows, etc.

Alveoli (al-*vee*-oh-ly): the pouchlike sacs of the lungs.

Amber: a yellowish resin found as fossil material in alluvial soils.

Amino (uh-*mee*-noh) **acid:** organic acid containing the amino (NH_2) radical, from which proteins are built.

Amitosis (ay-my-*toh*-sis): direct cell division in which there is a simple cleavage of the nucleus without change in its structure followed by a division of the cytoplasm.

Amphibians (am-*fib*-ee-anz): vertebrate animals that spend the first part of their lives in water and may or may not spend the rest of their lives in water; as frogs, toads, and salamanders.

Amylase (*am*-ill-ase): a digestive enzyme that changes starch and glycogen to soluble sugars.

Anabolism (uh-*nab*-uh-lizm): the body process by which food material is built up into protoplasm.

Anaerobic (an-ayr-*oh*-bik) **bacteria:** organisms that do not require free oxygen to exist.

Anaesthetic (an-us-*thet*-ik): a substance that causes loss of sensation.

Anaphase (*an*-uh-fayz): the stage in mitosis when one of each pair of chromosomes is pulled to the opposite end of the cell.

Anatomy (uh-*nat*-uh-mee): a study of the parts of the body.

Androgen (*an*-druh-jen): any substance capable of producing male characteristics, such as a male sex hormone.

Anemia (uh-*nee*-mee-uh): a lack of the proper amount of red blood corpuscles, hemoglobin, or both.

Angiosperm (*an*-jee-oh-sperm): a plant which bears its seeds in a case, as the flowering plants.

Annelida (uh-*nehl*-ih-duh): a phylum of worms composed of rings or segments, as earthworm and sandworm.

Annual ring: the concentric growths of light and dark cells formed in a woody stem during a year.

Antenna (an-*ten*-uh): a jointed sensory organ on the heads of insects, crabs, etc.

Antennules (an-*ten*-yools): small antennae or similar appendages such as are found in crayfish.

Anterior: nearer the head (zoölogy); facing outward from the axis (botany).

Anther (*an*-ther): the pollen-bearing part of a stamen.

Antheridium (an-ther-*id*-ee-um): the male sexual organ in non-flowering plants.

Anthropologist (an-thruh-*pol*-uh-jist): one who studies the development of a racial relationship and culture of mankind.

Antibiotic (an-tih-by-*ot*-ik): organic compound made by living things and effective in stopping the growth of certain germs; penicillin is an antibiotic.

Antibodies: substances in the blood or body fluids that fight disease.

Antigen (*an*-tih-jen): any substance which when introduced into an animal's body stimulates the production of antibodies.

Antihistamine (an-tee-*his*-tuh-meen): one of a family of drugs which act to neutralize symptoms of the common cold, hay fever, etc.

Antiseptic (an-tih-*sep*-tik): a substance which prevents the growth of bacteria or other organisms.

Antitoxin (an-tih-*tok*-sin): a substance formed in the blood by certain diseases and which confers immunity from further attacks for a greater or lesser period.

Anus (*ay*-nus): the posterior opening of the alimentary canal.

Anvil: one of the three bones of the middle ear for transmitting sound vibrations from the eardrum to the inner ear.

Aorta (ay-*or*-tuh): the largest artery in the body, the one which leaves the left ventricle.

Appendage (uh-*pen*-dij): a part which is attached to the body as a limb.

Aquarium: a tank for keeping water plants and animals alive.

Aqueous (*ay*-kwee-us) **humor:** the transparent liquid between the cornea and the lens of the eye.

Arachnida (uh-*rak*-nih-duh): a class of arthropods which includes spiders, scorpions, mites, etc.

Archegonium (ar-keh-*goh*-nee-um): the egg-producing organ of the mosses, ferns, and pines.

Archeologist (ar-kee-*ol*-uh-jist): one who studies past human life and activities as shown by relics of ancient people.

Archeopteryx (ar-kee-*op*-tehr-iks): a fossil reptilian bird.

Arteriosclerosis (ahr-teer-ee-*oh*-skler-oh-sis): hardening of the arteries.

Artery: a blood vessel that carries blood away from the heart.

Arthropoda (ar-*throp*-oh-duh): a phylum of invertebrate animals having jointed legs; as insects, crayfish, and spiders.

Articulation (ar-tik-yoo-*lay*-shun): the joining or place of meeting of two bones.

Artificial respiration: that produced by mechanical means in an attempt to revive drowned persons or those suffocated by gas.

Ascorbic (us-*skor*-bik) **acid:** vitamin C, occurring in citrus fruits and tomatoes which prevents scurvy and keeps capillaries in good condition.

Aseptic (ay-*sep*-tik): sterile; not liable to putrefaction by exclusion of micro-örganisms.

Asexual: without sex; reproduction by other means than by fertilization of egg by sperm.

Assimilation (uh-sim-uh-*lay*-shun): the process of changing digested food or stored materials into protoplasm.

Associative neuron: a nerve in the brain or spinal cord that transmits impulses from one nerve to another.

Aster: a star-shaped figure found chiefly in cells dividing by mitosis.

Astigmatism (uh-*stig*-muh-tizm): a defect in the curvature of the lens of the eye which causes indistinct vision.

Atabrin (*at*-uh-brin): one of the synthetic drugs used in place of quinine to combat malaria.

Atoll (*at*-ol): a coral island consisting of a belt of coral reef surrounding a central lagoon.

Auditory canal: the tube leading from the visible part of the outer ear to the eardrum.

Auditory nerve: the nerve that carries the sound stimuli to the brain.

Aureomycin (aw-ree-oh-*my*-sin): an antibiotic produced by a mold which is effective against diseases spread by lice and ticks, such as Rocky Mountain spotted fever, typhus, "virus" pneumonia, and parrot fever.

Auricles (*aw*-rih-k'ls): the upper chambers of a vertebrate heart.

Autonomic (aw-tuh-*nom*-ik) **nervous system,** or **sympathetic nervous system:** ventral chain of ganglia which help to control the action of the involuntary muscles.

Auxin (*awk*-sin): plant hormone.

Axil: the angle between the stem and the leaf.

Axillary (*ak*-sil-ayr-ee) **buds:** those which arise in the angle between the stem and the leaf.

Axon (*ak*-son): the principal elongated branch of a nerve cell which forms the central core of the nerve fiber.

B

Bacillus (buh-*sil*-us): a rod-shaped bacterium.

Back cross: the cross between a hybrid and its pure type parent.

Bacteria (bak-*tihr*-ee-uh): the smallest and simplest plants without chlorophyll.

Bacteriology (bak-tihr-ee-*ol*-uh-jee): the study of the one-celled plants known as bacteria.

Bacteriophage (bak-*tee*-ree-oh-fayj): a virus-like substance which can cause disease in bacteria.

Balanced diet: one in which there are the correct amounts of carbohydrates, proteins, fats, mineral salts, and vitamins.

Ball-and-socket joint: one in which the enlarged end of one bone fits into a depression in another, allowing free motion.

Basal metabolism (muh-*tab*-uh-liz'm): the rate at which the body is releasing energy to support all the life processes and to maintain proper functions.

Bast: tough fibers in the inner bark of trees and other plants; part of the phloem.

Behavior: the response of an organism to the factors in its environment.

Beriberi (*behr*-ee-*behr*-ee): a disease of the nerves due to the lack of vitamin B.

Berry: a fleshy fruit with enlarged, juicy ovary wall.

Biennial (by-*en*-ih-ul): a plant which grows and stores food the first year and bears fruit the second year.

Bilateral symmetry: structures arranged in a similar pattern on each side of a central line.

Bile: the fluid secreted by the liver.

Bile duct: the tube that carries bile from the gall bladder or the liver to the small intestine.

Binomial nomenclature: the system of naming plants and animals with two names, the genus and the species.

Biology: the study of living things.

Bisexual: one organism having both sexes.

Bivalve: a mollusk having two valves or shells, as a clam or oyster.

Bladder: the muscular sac in which urine collects; or any thin sac holding a fluid.

Blade: the expanded portion of a leaf.

Blastula (*blas*-tyoo-luh): the hollow-sphere stage in the development of animal embryos.

Blood: the fluid tissue of the body.

Blood bank: A storage place for blood and blood plasma for use in transfusions.

Blood heat: the normal body temperature of 98.6° F.

Blood pressure: the force with which the blood pushes against the walls of the arteries with every heartbeat.

Blood transfusion: to give one person the whole blood or plasma from another person.

Blood type: one of several groups into which blood may be divided.

Botany: the study of the structure, function, description, and classification of plants.

Brain: the compact anterior portion of the nervous system; in vertebrates, the part inclosed in the skull.

Breathing: the mechanical process of getting air into and out of the body.

Bronchus (*bron*-kus), pl. **bronchi:** one of the two large subdivisions of the trachea.

Bryophyta (bry-*off*-ih-tuh): the phylum of plants that includes liverworts and mosses.

Bubonic (byoo-*bon*-ik) **plague:** a malignant infectious disease caused by bacteria transmitted to man from rats and other rodents by the bites of fleas.

Bud: an undeveloped branch or flower; an outgrowth on sponge, hydra, and yeast.

Budding: a form of grafting; the insertion of a bud of one tree under the bark of another. Also a method of reproduction in yeast, hydra, and some other simple organisms.

Bulb: a cluster of thickened leaf-bases attached to a reduced stem, and surrounding a bud, as in onion, hyacinth, etc.

C

Caecum (*see*-k'm): a blind pouch growing out of the intestine; may secrete digestive fluids, as in the grasshopper.

Calorie (*kal*-er-ee): a unit used to measure the amount of energy produced by foods; the amount of heat required to raise 1,000 cc. of water one degree Centigrade.

Calorimeter (kal-oh-*rim*-eh-ter): an apparatus for measuring quantities of heat.

Calyx (*kay*-liks): the outermost row of leaves or parts of a flower, usually green.

Cambium (*kam*-bee-um): the active, growing cells between the xylem and the phloem in the fibrovascular bundles of dicotyledonous plants.

Canine (*kay*-nyn) **teeth:** the large tearing teeth of mammals.

Capillaries (kap-'l-*air*-ees): the microscopic blood vessels which occupy the spaces between the ends of arteries and the beginnings of veins.

Carapace (*kair*-uh-payss): the shell-like dorsal covering of crustaceans and turtles.

Carbohydrate (kahr-boh-*hy*-drayt): the class of foodstuffs made of carbon, hydrogen, and oxygen, the hydrogen and oxygen being in the same proportion as in water.

Carbon dioxide: a gas formed as a waste product of oxidation in both plants and animals.

Cardiac (*kahr*-dee-ak): pertaining to the heart or upper end of the stomach.

Cardiac valve: a muscular ring where the esophagus joins the stomach; prevents food from passing back into the esophagus.

Carnivora (kahr-*niv*-er-uh): an order of flesh-eating mammals.

Carnivorous (kahr-*niv*-er-us): flesh-eating.

Carotene (*kar*-oh-teen): an orange pigment found in certain chloroplasts; also, the substance from which vitamin A is produced.

Carpus (*kahr*-pus): the wrist; the bones in the wrist.

Carrier: a person, or animal, immune to certain germ diseases, but capable of infecting others with germs which he carries on his body.

Cartilage (*kahr*-tih-lij): the elastic animal tissue forming parts of organs or bones.

Casein (*kay*-see-in): the kind of protein found in the curd of milk.

Catabolism or **katabolism** (kuh-*tab*-uh-lizm): the process by which protoplasm is broken down into less complex substances.

Catkin: a deciduous, scaly spike of unisexual, apetalous flowers; as in the pussy-willow.

Caucasian (kaw-*kay*-zhun): in man, the chief races of Europe, North Africa, and southwestern Asia.

Caudal (*kawd*-'l): pertaining to the tail.

Cell: the unit of structure and function of living things. A mass of protoplasm inclosing a nucleus, and usually inclosed by a cell wall.

Cell body: the part of a neuron in which the nucleus and cytoplasm are found and which regulates all the activities of the neuron.

Cell differentiation: specialization of cells for different kinds of work.

Cell membrane: a semipermeable membranous surface surrounding a cell.

Cell specialization: the modification of a part of a particular cell to carry on a certain function.

Cell wall: the outer, non-living wall around plant cells.

Cellulose (*sel*-yuh-lohs): an organic substance usually found in the walls of plant cells.

Central cylinder: the core of a root, where the conducting tissue is located.

Central nervous system: the brain and spinal cord.

Centrosome (*sen*-truh-sohm): a minute protoplasmic body usually found in the cytoplasm which takes an active part in mitosis.

Cephalothorax (sef-uh-loh-*thor*-aks): the fused head and thorax of certain arthropods, as crustaceans and spiders.

Cerebellum (ser-uh-*bel*-um): the part of the brain behind the cerebrum in man, and overlying the midbrain.

Cerebral (*seh*-ruh-brul) **hemispheres:** the two lobes that make up the cerebrum.

Cerebrum (*seh*-ruh-brum): the front part of the brain; in man, the center of thought and memory.

Cervical (*serv*-ih-k'l): pertaining to the neck.

Cetacea (seh-*tay*-she-uh): an order of aquatic mammals with fishlike bodies and forelimbs modified into flippers as dolphins and whales.

Character: a trait or structure passed on from parent to offspring. Characters may be *dominant* or *recessive*.

Chela (*kee*-luh): the large pincer of a crayfish or lobster.

Chelipeds (*kee*-lih-peds): the pair of legs of a crustacean that bear the chelae or pincerlike claws.

Chiroptera (ky-*rop*-ter-uh): the "hand-winged" mammals, as bats.

Chitin (*ky*-tin): the substance which forms the outer covering of the bodies of some animals, as insects.

Chloromycetin (kloh-roh-my-*see*-tin): an antibiotic drug produced from a mold and used in the treatment of typhus and typhoid fever.

Chlorophyll (*klor*-uh-fil): the green coloring matter characteristic of plants which is necessary for photosynthesis.

Chloroplast (*klor*-uh-plast): the granules in the protoplasm of a plant cell which contain chlorophyll.

Choroid (*koh*-roid) **coat:** the membrane which forms the second, inner coat of the eyeball.

Chromatin (*kroh*-muh-tin): the substance in the cell nucleus that forms into chromosomes.

Chromosomes (*kroh*-muh-sohm): structures which appear in the cell nucleus during mitosis. They bear the hereditary factors.

Chrysalis (*krih*-s'l-iss): the quiescent stage in the development of a moth or butterfly; the pupa inclosed in a thin, smooth case.

Ciliary (*sil*-ee-ay-ree) **muscles:** the muscles which keep the lens of the eye in focus.

Cilium (*sil*-ee-um): a tiny hairlike projection of cytoplasm attached to some portion of the surface of a cell.

Circulation: the movement of blood through the body of an animal or the movement of sap in a plant.

Class: a group of individuals with similar characteristics comprising a subdivision of a phylum.

Classification: the orderly arrangement or grouping of objects.

Clavicle (*klav*-ih-k'l): the collar bone, so named from its shape.

Cleavage (*kleev*-ij): early stages of cell division in a fertilized egg.

Climatic region: a geographic division which includes several life zones.

Cloaca (kloh-*ay*-kuh): the lower end of the digestive tract which receives also wastes from the kidneys and the reproductive products in some vertebrates, as frogs and birds; the central cavity of a sponge.

Closed circulatory system: one in which the arteries and veins are connected by capillaries.

Coccus (*kok*-us): a spherical bacterium.

Coccyx (*kok*-siks): the bone below the sacrum composed of four fused vertebrae.

Cochlea (*kok*-lee-uh): a spiral-shaped passage of the internal ear in mammals.

Cocoon (kuh-*koon*): the hairy or silken covering of the pupa of some insects; the egg case of spiders and earthworms.

Coelom (*see*-lom): the body cavity; the part of the body in which the organs lie.

Colchicine (*kol*-chih-seen): a plant extract which when applied to other plants causes changes in chromosome number.

Coleoptera (koh-lee-*op*-ter-uh): an order of insects having hard wing covers over the flying or true wings; the beetles.

Collar cells: specialized cells in sponges for capturing food and circulating water.

Commensalism (kuh-*menss*-uh-lizm): a relationship of two organisms living together in which one receives more benefit than the other.

Communicable diseases: those which can be passed by one person or animal to another.

Complemental air: the air which remains in the lungs and does not pass in or out during normal breathing.

Complete flower: one which contains all the parts, i.e., calyx, corolla, stamens, and pistil.

Complete metamorphosis (met-uh-*mor*-fuh-siss): the life cycle of certain insects consisting of egg, larva, pupa, and adult.

Compound eyes: an eye made up of many separate facets or parts, as in insects and crayfish.

Compound leaf: one in which the blade is divided into leaflets.

Conditioned reflex: a response to a stimulus other than the original one.

Cone: a nerve ending in the retina of the eye that is sensitive to bright light and color; also a reproductive organ of conifers.

Conjugation (kon-joo-*gay*-sh'n) : the temporary union of two similar cells for the purpose of exchanging nuclear protoplasm; as in paramecium.

Conservation: the preservation, development, and wise utilization of our natural resources.

Constrictor: in snakes, one that kills its prey by crushing.

Contact poison: an insecticide which kills by coming in contact with the body of an insect.

Contractile vacuole (kun-*trak*-t'l *vak-yoo-ohl*) : a cell organ found in many Protozoa, which appears and disappears regularly for the excretion of wastes.

Corm: a solid, underground stem for storage of food, as in jack-in-the-pulpit.

Cornea (*kor*-nee-uh) : a horny, transparent membrane that forms the front of the eye.

Corolla (kor-*ol*-luh) : the petals of a flower taken together.

Corpuscle (*kor*-pus-'l) : the floating cells in the blood, red and white.

Corrosion: the wearing away of a substance by chemical action.

Cortex: the fleshy portion of a root surrounding the central cylinder and covered by epidermis; the outer region of the brain and kidney.

Cortin (*kor*-tin) : a hormone secreted by the cortex of the adrenal glands.

Cortisone (*kor*-tih-sohn) : a hormone in the adrenal gland produced by the action of ACTH.

Cotyledon (kot'l-*ee*-d'n) : the seed leaf of a plant. Monocotyledonous plants have only one, dicotyledonous plants have two.

Cranial (*kray*-nee-'l) **nerves:** nerves which enter and leave the brain.

Cranium (*kray*-nee-um) : the skull which incloses the brain.

Cretinism (*kree*-tin-izm) : a condition in children resulting from marked thyroid deficiency.

Cro-Magnon (kroh-*man*-yon) **man:** an early race of man whose remains were found in France; regarded as belonging to the same species (*Homo sapiens*) as modern man.

Crop: a structure in the alimentary canal of certain animals where food is stored after it has been swallowed.

Cross-fertilization: the union of the nuclei of the egg of one individual and the sperm of another.

Cross-over: to pass over from one homologous chromosome to another in an interchange of chromatin material.

Cross-pollination: the receiving of pollen from one plant by the pistil of another.

Crustacea (krus-*tay*-shuh) : a class of arthropoda covered with a hard exoskeleton made of lime, as crayfish.

Culture: a controlled growth of cells, such as bacteria, fungi, or protozoa, usually in a prepared nutrient medium. A pure culture contains only one kind of organism.

Cuticle (*kyoo*-tih-k'l) : the outer layer, or epidermis, of the skin.

Cutin (*kyoo*-tin) : the transparent waxy covering of leaves.

Cycle: a series that repeats itself, as life cycle.

Cyst (*sist*) : a membranous sac or vesicle; a cell containing reproductive bodies in the lower non-flowering plants.

Cytoplasm (*sy*-toh-plazm) : the form of protoplasm which makes up the main part of a cell. It incloses the nucleus, and is inclosed by the cell wall or cell membrane.

D

Daughter cell: the newly formed cell resulting from cell division.

Deciduous (deh-*sij*-oo-us) **leaves:** those which fall from the tree in autumn.

Decomposition: the act of separating into constituent parts; decay or rotting.

Deficiency disease: a disease caused by a lack of vitamins, minerals, or other necessary elements in the diet.

Dehiscent (dee-*hiss*-cent): a term applied to fruits that open; a pod, capsule, etc.

Dehydrate: to remove water.

Demonstration: an orderly sequence of events, repeated by some one who wishes to explain or illustrate certain facts to learners. In a demonstration, the facts are already known.

Dendrite (*den*-dryt): a branching process of a neuron.

Denitrifying bacteria: those which change soil nitrates into gaseous nitrogen, allowing it to escape into the air.

Dentine (*den*-teen): the inner bony portion of a tooth.

Dermis (*der*-mis): the part of the skin lying beneath the epidermis.

Diaphragm (*dy*-uh-fram): the sheet of muscle which separates the chest cavity from the abdomen in a mammal.

Diastase (*dy*-uh-stayss): the enzyme of ferment in plants which converts starch to maltose.

Diatom (*dy*-uh-tohm): a species of microscopic algae.

Dicotyledon (dy-kot'l-*ee*-d'n): a plant which bears seeds having two cotyledons, as the bean.

Diffusion: the movement of molecules from areas of greater concentration to areas of lesser concentration.

Digestion: the process of preparing foods for absorption by breaking them down and making them soluble.

Digestive gland: any gland that secretes a fluid used in the process of digestion, as the liver, pancreas, and gastric glands.

Diploid (*dip*-loid) **number:** the number of chromosomes in a germ cell before reduction division.

Diptera: an order of insects which have only two wings, as fly and mosquito.

Direct cell division: see *amitosis*.

Disc flowers: the flowers of the central portion of composite flowers like the daisy or sunflower.

Disease: any condition which interferes with the normal function of the body of an organism.

Division of labor: specialization of cells to perform a specific function.

Domesticate: to bring under the control of man; to tame, as with wild animals.

Dominant characters: those which mask the characters of the other parent and appear in the hybrid.

Dormancy: the state of quiescence characteristic of seeds before germination.

Dorsal: pertaining to the back.

Drone: the male of bees and ants.

Drug: special preparations used to relieve pain or to increase or slow down activity of certain cells.

Drupe: a fruit that contains a stone or pit.

Dry fruits: not fleshy, as nuts, cereals, pods, etc.

Duct: any tube or canal by which a fluid or other substance is conveyed from a gland.

Ductless glands: those which pour their secretions directly into the blood by osmosis; as thymus and adrenal glands.

Duodenum (doo-oh-*dee*-num): the part of the small intestine nearest the stomach.

E

Echinoderm (eh-*ky*-noh-derm): an invertebrate animal with radial symmetry and possessing spines, as starfish and sea urchins.

Ecology (eh-*kol*-uh-jee): the study of the relationship between living things and their environment.

Economic insects: those insects that are either beneficial or harmful to man.

Ectoderm (*ek*-toh-derm): the outer layer of cells of animals, especially of the embryo.

Ectoplasm (*ek*-toh-plazm): the outside layer of unicellular organisms which have no cell wall.

Edentata (ee-den-*tay*-tuh): a group of mammals which have no teeth.

Efferent (*ef*-er-ent) **fibers:** the fibers that carry impulses away from the brain; the motor fibers.

Egg: the female germ cell in sexual reproduction; the ovum.

Element: a basic substance which cannot be further simplified by chemical means because it is made of only one kind of atom.

Elimination: the removal of wastes from the body.

Embryo (*em*-bree-oh): an organism in its early stages of development.

Embryology (em-bree-*ol*-uh-jee): the study of the early development of organisms.

Embryo sac: the tissue in a plant ovule which contains the egg cell and the two polar bodies.

Enamel (eh-*nam*-'l): the hard outer covering of the upper part of the teeth.

Encystment (en-*sist*-ment): the act of being inclosed in a resistant covering; forming a cyst.

Endocrine (*en*-doh-kryne) **gland:** ductless gland, that is, a gland which has no duct or tube leading to another part of the body.

Endoderm (*en*-doh-derm): the inner layer of cells in the embryo or a simple animal.

Endoplasm (*en*-doh-plazm): the inner or central portion of the cytoplasm of a cell.

Endoskeleton (en-doh-*skel*-uh-tun): a skeleton within the body, as in man, frog, fish.

Endosperm (*en*-doh-sperm): the food that is stored near the embryo of a plant, as in a grain of corn. It is principally starch.

Energy: the ability to perform work.

Entomologist (en-tuh-*mol*-uh-jist): a person who studies insects.

Entomology (en-tuh-*mol*-uh-jee): the study of insects.

Environment: the surroundings of an organism, such as air, water, temperature, other life, etc.

Enzyme (*en*-zym): a substance secreted by certain organisms and body cells and inducing chemical changes, as digestion or fermentation.

Epidemic: a disease that is widespread, affecting many people or many plants or animals at the same time.

Epidermis (ep-ih-*der*-mis): the covering of the skin; the outer layer.

Epiglottis (ep-ih-*glot*-iss): the lid which closes the opening into the trachea when anything is swallowed.

Epithelium (ep-ih-*thee*-lee-um): the outer layer of a mucous membrane; epidermis of some animals.

Era: a major division of geologic time.

Erepsin (ee-*rep*-sin): an enzyme secreted by the intestinal glands; changes peptids to amino acids.

Erosion: the slow wearing away or disintegration of a substance, especially soil, by the continued action of the natural elements, as wind or water.

Esophagus (uh-*sof*-uh-gus): the tube through which the food passes from the pharynx to the stomach; the gullet.

Essential parts (of a flower): the stamens and pistils, both of which are necessary in forming a seed.

Estivate: pass the summer in inactivity.

Estrogen (*es*-troh-jen): a female hormone secreted by the ovaries.

Eugenics (yoo-*gen*-iks): the study of heredity in its relation to the improvement of offspring.

Eustachian (yoo-*stay*-kee-un) **tubes:** the tubes which connect the middle ear with the throat.

Evergreens: plants which retain their leaves for several years; the cone-bearing trees, in general.

Evolution: development; the succession of changes by which an organism passes from a simple to a complex condition.

Excretion: the process of removing waste products from the protoplasm.

Exoskeleton (eks-oh-*skel*-uh-tun): the outer, crustaceous or horny covering of animals, as in crayfish, lobsters, and insects.

Experiment: a test under controlled conditions for the purpose of discovering new facts, truths, or relations. In a real experiment, the result is not known beforehand. As a verb: to test under controlled conditions, etc.

Expiration: the process of emptying the lungs of air in breathing.

Extensors (ek-*sten*-sers): the muscles which straighten or extend an appendage at the joint.

External parasite: one that lives on the outside of an organism, as a louse.

Eyespot: a small spot of color in lower organisms thought to be sensitive to light.

F

F₁ (first filial) generation: the first generation of offspring from a genetic cross.

F₂ (second filial) generation: the offspring of the F_1 generation.

Facet (*fass*-it): the lens of one eye in a compound eye.

Fainting: a condition caused by an insufficient supply of blood to the brain.

False fruits: accessory fruits which develop from flower parts other than the ovary, as the apple and strawberry.

Family: in classification, a group made up of several genera of organisms.

Fangs: the organs through which spiders, snakes, and other animals inject poison or venom into their prey or enemies.

Farsightedness: a condition in which a person cannot see near objects clearly because the eyeball is too short from front to back or the lens is too flat.

Fatigue (fuh-*teeg*): the effect of exertion or other stimulation of cells or organs.

Fats: one of the common classes of nutrients, containing much carbon and hydrogen and little oxygen.

Fauna (*fawn*-uh): animals of a given life zone.

Feathers: the characteristic covering of birds.

Feces (*fee*-seez): indigestible material in the alimentary canal; excrement.

Femur (*fee*-mer): the upper bone of the lower limb in vertebrates; the large portion of the leg of a grasshopper.

Fermentation: chemical decomposition of an organic compound induced by living organisms or by chemical agents as in the souring of milk.

Fertilization: the union of the sperm nucleus with the egg nucleus in forming a new individual or organism.

Fertilizer: a substance added to the soil to promote plant growth.

Fever: the elevation of the body heat above 98.6° F.

Fibrinogen (fy-*brin*-oh-jen): the substance in the blood which induces clotting by the production of fibers when exposed to air.

Fibrin threads: the netlike material which forms a blood clot; formed by the action of prothrombin on fibrinogen.

Fibrous roots: those composed of many slender fibers, as in grass.

Fibrovascular (fy-broh-*vass*-kyoo-luh) **bundles:** the conductive system of plants. A fibrovascular bundle consists of xylem cells which communicate by means of perforations in the sides of their thick walls, and phloem cells which are thin-walled and perforated at the ends. Other cells, nonconductive, are found in or near the bundle.

Fibula (*fib*-yoo-luh): the smaller of the two bones in the lower leg.

Filament: the slender stalk of a stamen; any thread-like projection.

Fin: a locomotor organ characteristic of fishes and used for locomotion, balancing, and steering.

Fission (*fish*-un): cell division by a process of splitting or pinching in two.

Flaccid (*flak*-sid): a soft or relaxed condition of a cell due usually to shortage of water.

Flagellum (fluh-*jel*-um): a whiplike cytoplasmic projection, used chiefly as a swimming organ.

Flatworms: a group of unsegmented worms, many of which are parasitic, as liver fluke and tapeworm.

Fleshy fruits: those that have the seeds surrounded by an edible, juicy layer, as pome (apple), drupe (plum).

Fleshy roots: roots that have become enlarged for the storage of food, as beets and turnips.

Flexors (*fleks*-ers): the muscles which cause an appendage to bend or flex at the joint, and hence work in opposition to the extensors.

Flora (*flor*-uh): plants of a given life zone.

Flower: the organ of a plant which produces fruit containing seeds; or one of the essential parts of such an organ, as staminate flowers of corn, pistillate flowers of willow.

Fluctuation: a variation in hereditary development which is not inherited.

Food: a substance that furnishes material for the growth or repair of an organism, or that yields energy for it.

Food vacuole: a space in the cytoplasm found in many protozoa, which acts as a stomach for the digestion of food.

Foot: in mollusks, a muscular organ for locomotion.

Forestry: the study and practice of producing successive crops of trees from a given tract.

Fossils: the stonelike remains of plants and animals no longer living on the earth.

Frond: the leaf of a fern.

Fruit: the ripened ovary and its contents. In some fruits traces of other parts of the flower may be seen adhering to them.

Fry: young fishes just able to take care of themselves.

Fumigant: a gaseous insecticide or other chemical used to kill animal pests.

Function: the normal action of any organ or set of organs; use.

Fungus (*fung*-gus): a plant which lacks chlorophyll. Fungi are dependent on other organisms for food.

G

Gall bladder: the sac in which bile is stored temporarily.

Gamete (*gam*-eet): a sexual reproductive cell.

Gametophyte (guh-*mee*-toh-fyte): the plant which produces the gametes in plants that have alternation of generations.

Gamma globulin (*glob*-yoo-lin): a plasma protein in blood that carries antibodies.

Ganglion (*gang*-lee-un): a collection of nerve cells.

Gas: one of the forms in which matter exists, as oxygen, hydrogen.

Gastral cavity: the central body cavity in Porifera and Coelenterata.

Gastric (*gass*-trik): pertaining to the stomach, as gastric glands.

Gastric mill: the front part of the stomach in the crayfish, used for crushing and grinding food.

Gastrula (*gas*-troo-luh): the two-layered stage in the development of an egg into an embryo.

Gemma (*jem*-uh): a budlike vegetative body of liverworts, providing asexual reproduction.

Gemmule (*jem*-yool): one of the buds of mosses; one of the reproductive spores of algae; a special type of reproductive bud in sponges.

Gene (*jeen*): a factor on a chromosome which carries hereditary characteristics.

Generation: the individuals existing at one time or period. Applied both to plants and animals.

Genus (*jee*-nus): a group of organisms including one or more species. Used in classifying plants and animals.

Geologic time: the method of dating the earth by eras and periods.

Geologist: one who studies the earth's crust and its history.

Germ: a microorganism; the rudimentary vital element; an embryo.

Germinal (*jer*-min-al) **layer:** the innermost layer of the skin; it is constantly undergoing cell division.

Germination: the beginning of growth of a seed or pollen. The term is commonly used to describe the growth of a plant from a seed. It more properly describes the growth of the embryo within the seed.

Gill arch: the bony structure that supports the gill of a fish.

Gill bailer: a structure in certain crustaceans for circulating water through the gill chamber.

Gill filaments: the thread-like projections, each containing a blood vessel, that make up the gills of a fish.

Gill rakers: projections on the gill arches of some fishes to assist in gathering food.

Gill scoop: see *gill bailer*.

Gills: thin, finely divided organs of aquatic vertebrates, used to gather oxygen; also present in crayfish.

Gill slits: openings in the neck through which water, taken into the mouth, passes out over the gills, as in fishes.

Girdle: the bones which attach vertebrate limbs to the axial skeleton (the anterior is called the *pectoral* and the posterior the *pelvic* girdle); to encircle with a deep cut or by removing the bark, as to girdle a tree.

Gizzard: the muscular chamber where food is ground. A characteristic organ of birds.

Gland: an organ which produces a substance for use in the body, or for removal from it; examples, salivary gland, kidney. It may have ducts or be ductless.

Glomerulus (gloh-*mer*-yoo-lus): tiny rounded bodies in the cortex of a kidney containing a knot of blood vessels.

Glottis (*glot*-iss): the opening into the trachea.

Glucose (*gloo*-kohss): the form of sugar found in fruits; the product of the digestion of starch.

Glycogen (*gly*-kuh-j'n): animal starch, stored in the liver.

Goiter: an enlarged condition of the thyroid gland resulting from a deficiency of iodine.

Gonad (*goh*-nad): a reproductive organ, either male or female.

Gonadotropic (guh-nad-oh-*troh*-pik) **hormone:** a hormone secreted by the anterior lobe of the pituitary which influences the development and secretions of the reproductive organs.

Grafting: the process of inserting a small piece (twig) of one plant (the scion) into a slit in a larger one (the stock) and protecting it till the parts grow together.

Grain: one of the cereals, or cereals in general; a kernel of corn; the markings on wood due to annual rings and medullary (wood) rays.

Gray matter: the nerve tissue which contains the nerve cells in the brain and spinal cord and lacks a medullary sheath.

Green glands: excretory organs of a crayfish, found in the head region.

Green manuring: the process of plowing under a crop of some leguminous plant, as clover, for the sake of the nitrogen which has been gathered by bacteria living on its roots.

Guard cells: cells around the stomata which regulate the passage of gases into and out of the leaf.

Gullet (*gul*-it): the tube that extends from the back of the mouth to the stomach; the esophagus.

Guttation (guh-*tay*-shun): the loss of excess water through the ends of veins at the margin of a leaf.

Gymnosperm (*jim*-noh-sperm): a plant that does not bear its seeds in a protective case.

H

Habit: a tendency towards an action or condition which, by repetition, has become spontaneous.

Habitat: the region where any organism or group of organisms is usually found; the place where it lives.

Hammer: one of the three bones of the middle ear.

Haploid (*hap*-loid) **number:** the number of chromosomes in a germ cell after reduction division.

Hapten: a substance obtained from red blood cells that helps prevent the destruction of red cells by the Rh factor.

Head: the division of the body which contains the brain; a collection of small flowers; the collection of grains which make up the fruit of cereals.

Health: the condition resulting from the normal performance of all the life functions.

Heidelberg (*hy*-d'l-burg) **man:** an early race of man whose fossil remains were found in Germany.

Hemiptera (heh-*mip*-ter-uh): an order of insects which have the anterior part of their wings hard and the posterior part membranous.

Hemoglobin (hee-moh-gloh-bin): the red coloring matter in the red blood corpuscles; unites easily with oxygen.

Hemophilia (hee-moh-*fil*-ee-uh): hereditary tendency to profuse bleeding even from slight wounds.

Hemorrhage (*hem*-er-ij): the discharge of blood from a ruptured blood vessel.

Herbaceous stem: a soft, non-woody stem.

Herbivorous (er-*biv*-er-us): animals which feed upon grass and other plants.

Heredity: the passing on to offspring of the genetic characteristics of parents or other ancestors.

Hibernation: the condition induced by severe cold in the case of some animals; a deathlike torpor and rigidity brought about by extreme cold.

Hilum (*hy*-lum): the scar on a seed showing where it was attached to the fruit.

Hinge joint: one which admits only of back-and-forth motion, as the elbow.

Hobby: a favorite subject or activity which occupies much attention.

Homologous (hoh-*mol*-uh-gus) **structures:** structures in animals that have similar origin but different functions.

Homoptera (hoh-*mop*-ter-uh): a group of insects having their wings of the same texture throughout, in contrast to the Hemiptera.

Homo sapiens (*hoh*-moh *say*-pee-enz): the scientific name of modern man.

Honey: the partly digested food of bees. They suck up nectar, which is retained in the crop till partially digested, after which it is pumped up and stored in cells of wax.

Hookworm: a small parasitic, unsegmented, round worm found in the intestine of man, sheep, and other animals.

Hormones (*hor*-mohns): substances secreted by endocrine glands directly into the blood in one part of the body which are carried by the circulation and incite action in another part of the body; chemical messengers.

Host: the larger organism on or in which a smaller, dependent one (parasite) lives.

Human: pertaining to mankind.

Humerus (*hyoo*-mer-us): the larger bone of the upper arm.

Humus (*hyoo*-mus): the substances in the soil formed by the decay of organic matter; vegetable mold.

Hyaline (*hy*-uh-lin) **cartilage:** cartilage that never changes to bone and found in such places as the nose, ears, and between the vertebrae.

Hybrid: the offspring of parents of two different species or varieties. The mule is a hybrid.

Hybridization (hy-brid-eye-*zay*-shun): the crossing of two different strains to get a new variety.

Hydra (*hy*-druh): a two-layered aquatic animal; a polyp.

Hydrogen: one of the two elements that composes water; the lightest known substance.

Hygiene: the study of health, especially as to maintaining health by observing proper conditions.

Hyperthyroidism: overactivity of the thyroid gland.

Hymenoptera (hy-men-*op*-ter-uh): an order of insects (including bees and wasps) which have membranous wings.

Hyphae (*hy*-fee): the single strands or threads which make up the body of a fungus.

Hypocotyl (hy-poh-*kot*-il): the part of a developing plant embryo from which the primary root is formed.

Hypogastric plexus (hy-poh-*gass*-trik *plek*-sus): a sympathetic nerve mass located in front of the sacrum and supplying the organs of the abdomen.

Hypopharynx (hy-poh-*fair*-ingks): the tonguelike organ of a grasshopper.

Hypothyroidism: underactivity of the thyroid gland.

I

Immovable joint: one that does not allow movement between the bones, as in the bones of the skull; also called a *suture* (which see).

Immunity: the condition which protects a person from an infectious disease.

Incisor (in-*sy*-zer): a cutting tooth. In gnawing animals the incisors have chisel edges.

Incomplete dominance: the failure of one character to dominate another in the off-spring resulting from a cross of these characters.

Incomplete metamorphosis (met-uh-*mor*-fuh-siss): the life cycle of certain insects consisting of the egg, several nymph stages, and the adult.

Indefinite annual growth: the forming of new wood throughout the whole growing season, as in sumac.

Indehiscent (in-dee-*hiss*-cent) **fruits:** those that do not open, as nut, grain of corn, akene.

Independent living: the ability of a plant or animal to survive in its environment by securing its own food.

Indirect cell division: see *mitosis.*

Indusium (in-*doo*-zhum): an outgrowth of a fern leaf which covers the sorus in many species.

Inflorescence (in-flor-*ess*-enss): the arrangement of the flower or cluster of flowers on the peduncle.

Inheritance: characters transmitted from previous generations.

Inner ear: the part of the ear that receives sound stimuli and sends the resulting impulses to the brain over the auditory nerve; also contains the semicircular canals associated with balance.

Inoculation: the introduction of a virus, as of smallpox, into the system through the skin to produce immunity.

Inorganic matter: that which has not been formed by living (organic) processes.

Insect: a group of small animals having three distinctly marked-off body regions.

Insecticide: that which kills insects.

Insectivora (in-sek-*tiv*-er-uh): an order of insect-eating vertebrates, including moles and shrews.

Inspiration: the act of taking air into the lungs.

Instinct: an inherited reflex.

Insulin (*in*-soo-lin): a hormone secreted by the islet cells of the pancreas which regulates blood sugar.

Integument (in-*teg*-yoo-ment): an outer covering or envelope, as the skin.

Internal parasite: one that lives on the inside of an organism, as the tachina-fly larva.

Intestinal glands: digestive glands in the small intestine that secrete intestinal fluid.

Intestine: that portion of the alimentary canal in vertebrates between the stomach and the anus. There are two divisions or sections, the small intestine and the large intestine.

Invertebrates (in-*ver*-tuh-brayts): all animals which lack a vertebral column, as worms, insects, mollusks.

Involuntary muscles: those which are not under the control of the will, as the muscles of the intestine.

Iris (*eye*-riss): the colored portion of the eye.

Irritability: the property of reacting to stimuli; a life function.

Islands of Langerhans (*lahng*-er-hahns): groups of glandular cells in the pancreas which secrete the hormone insulin.

Isotope (*eye*-suh-tohp): any of two or more forms of the same element which differ only in the number of neutrons their atoms contain.

J

Java man: an early race of man whose fossil remains were found in Java.

Jellyfish: a soft, jellylike animal related to hydra.

Joint: the place where two bones meet; an articulation.

K

Katabolism or **catabolism** (kuh-*tab*-uh-lizm): the process by which protoplasm is broken down into less complex substances.

Keel: the projection on the breastbone of birds for the attachment of muscles for moving the wings.

Kidney: an organ which filters waste products from the blood, chiefly urea and water.

Kingdom: one of the two main divisions used in the classification of living things, as plant and animal kingdoms.

L

Labium (*lay*-bee-um): the lower "lip" of a grasshopper's mouth.

Labrum (*lay*-brum): the upper "lip" of a grasshopper's mouth.

Lactase: an enzyme secreted by the intestinal glands for changing lactose to glucose.

Lacteals (*lak*-tee-als): the vessels which carry the absorbed fats from the intestine to the vein which receives it.

Lactic acid: a chemical formed when glucose is broken down in the muscles to produce heat and energy. Build-up of lactic acid causes muscle fatigue.

Larva (*lahr*-vuh): the eating and growing stage in the complete metamorphosis of some insects, as moths and butterflies.

Larynx (*lair*-inks): the portion of the trachea which contains the vocal cords; the voice box; "Adam's apple."

Lateral line: a series of glandlike sacs along both sides of the body of some fishes which detect changes in pressure and current movement.

Law of Dominance: when two contrasting characters are crossed, the dominant character appears in the first generation.

Law of Segregation: when two hybrids are crossed, both dominant and recessive characters appear in the F_2 generation.

Law of Unit Characters: each characteristic in a cross is inherited separately, hence the resulting characteristics in a cross come from the individual genes.

Layering: the covering of the nodes of a stem with dirt to induce it to produce roots; a means of propagating such plants as grape vines.

Leaf mosaic (moh-*zay*-ik): the arrangement of leaves to cover all spaces, as ivy on a wall.

Legumes (*leg*-yooms): plants which have pods for fruits; the seeds of such plants, as peas, beans, etc.

Lens of the eye: a transparent body of biconvex form which brings light rays to a focus on the retina.

Lenticel (*len*-tih-sel): an opening in bark for the admission of air.

Lepidoptera (lep-ih-*dop*-ter-uh): the order of insects characterized by scaly wings, as moths and butterflies.

Lichen (*ly*-ken): a plant composed of an alga and a fungus.

Life cycle: the stages of development, maturity, reproduction, and decline through which every organism passes.

Life processes: the various physical processes upon which the continuance of life depends; the vital processes, as digestion, respiration, etc.

Life span: the length of life of living things between the beginning of life and death.

Life zone: an area which serves as a common range for the homes of certain plants and animals.

Ligament (*lig*-uh-m'nt): a band of tissue which binds one bone to another.

Lipase: a digestive enzyme that changes fats to fatty acids and glycerol.

Lipoid (*lip*-oid): a fatty substance, found in abundance in cells of the nervous system, which is dissolved by anesthetics and narcotics.

Liver: the largest organ of the body, a gland which secretes bile, stores glycogen, and performs other functions.

Loam: a form of soil containing much humus (which see).

Locomotion: moving from one place to another.

Lumbar: pertaining to the lower part of the back.

Lung: one of a pair of respiratory organs in man and other air-breathing vertebrates.

Lung books: the respiratory organs in spiders.

Lymph (*limf*): the circulatory fluid resembling plasma which fills intercellular spaces. The watery substance in a blister is lymph.

Lymphatic (lim-*fat*-ik) **circulation:** the movement of lymph through lymph nodes and lymphatic ducts.

Lymph nodes: the small, irregular spaces between cells in which lymph collects to bathe the cells.

M

Macronucleus (mak-ruh-*noo*-klee-us): the large nucleus found in paramecium and certain other Protozoa.

Maggot (*mag*-ut): the legless larva of a fly.

Malaria: a disease caused by parasitic protozoans which develop in the body of the Anopheles mosquito and are transmitted to the blood of man by the mosquito's bite.

Males: individuals of the sex which produce sperms.

Maltase: an enzyme secreted by the intestinal glands for changing maltose to glucose.

Mammary (*mam*-er-ee) **glands:** the milk-secreting glands which are characteristic of mammals.

Mandible (*man*-duh-b'l): the cutting part of the mouths of crustaceans.

Marrow: the soft tissue in the center of certain bones.

Marsupials (mahr-*soop*-ee-uls): an order of mammals having a pouch in which the young are carried, as opossum, kangaroo.

Maturation (mat-cher-*ay*-shun): maturing of the germ cells during which process reduction division takes place.

Maturity: adult life.

Maxilla (mak-*sil*-uh): one of the mouth parts of crustaceans.

Maxilliped (mak-*sil*-ih-ped): an appendage near the mouth of a crustacean which assists in getting food.

Medulla (meh-*duhl*-uh): the inner part of certain organs, such as the kidney and adrenal gland; sometimes the short form for *medulla oblongata* (which see).

Medulla oblongata (meh-*duhl*-uh oblong-*gay*-tuh): the posterior or lower part of the brain, connecting it with the spinal cord.

Medullary (*med*-yoo-lair-ee) **rays:** thin bundles of wood cells extending from the pith to or toward the cambium and from the cambium to or toward the center; wood rays.

Medullary sheath: the thick, fatty, protective sheath that covers all nerve fibers which connect the brain and spinal cord with all parts of the body; also called *white matter*.

Medusa (meh-*doo*-suh): a jellyfish.

Meiosis (my-*oh*-sis): a type of cell division in which there is a reduction of chromosomes to the haploid number during maturation; reduction division.

Membrane: a thin, sheetlike structure, connecting other structures or serving to cover or line some part of an organ.

Menadione (men-uh-*dy*-ohn): vitamin K, which helps in the clotting of blood.

Meristem (*mer*-ih-stem): the actively growing tissue found in the tips of roots and stems.

Mesentery (*mes*-en-ter-ee): a fold of tissue which suspends the intestine from the dorsal wall of the abdomen.

Mesoderm (*mes*-oh-derm): the middle germ layer formed during embryonic development.

Mesoglea (mes-oh-*glee*-uh): the middle, non-cellular layer of hydra.

Mesophyll (*mes*-oh-fil): the middle portion of a leaf, consisting of irregular, loosely packed cells.

Mesothorax (mes-uh-*thor*-aks): the middle section of the thorax of an insect. It has one pair of wings and the second pair of legs on it.

Metabolism (muh-*tab*-uh-liz'm): the process by which non-living food is made up into living material; and the process by which protoplasm is broken down into less complex substances.

Metacarpals (meh-tuh-*kahr*-p'ls): the bones of the hand.

Metamorphosis (met-uh-*mor*-fuh-siss): the passing of an organism through several very marked changes of form, as do the butterfly and frog.

Metaphase (*met*-uh-fayz): the stage in mitosis when the chromosomes line up in pairs along the equator of the cell.

Metatarsals (meh-tuh-*tahr*-s'ls): the bones of the feet.

Metathorax (met-uh-*thor*-aks): the third division of an insect's thorax. It bears the last pair of legs and the second pair of wings, if there is a second pair.

Microbe (*my*-krohb): a microscopic organism; a bacterium.

Microbiology (my-kroh-by-*ol*-uh-jee): a branch of biology dealing with micro-organisms, especially bacteria, fungi, yeasts, Protozoa, and algae.

Micronucleus (my-kruh-*noo*-klee-us): a small nucleus located near the macro-nucleus as in Protozoa.

Microorganism: any organism so small that a microscope is required to see it.

Micropyle (*my*-kroh-pyle): the opening in the testa of an ovule through which the pollen tube enters.

Midbrain: the central region of the brain through which all nerve-pathways to and from the brain pass.

Middle ear: that part of the ear which contains the hammer, anvil, and stirrup and the opening of the Eustachian tube as well.

Midrib: the main vein or rib of a leaf.

Migration: the act of changing a dwelling place from one locality to another, as birds and salmon do.

Mildew: a fungus which causes decay and disease.

Milt: the sperms of a fish.

Mimicry (*mim*-ih-kree): resemblances of organisms in form or color to other objects, for protection.

Mineral: inorganic substance such as salt or metals.

Mitosis (my-*toh*-sis): indirect cell division: a series of changes to insure equal division of the chromatin.

Mixed diet: one that contains a large variety of foods.

Mixed joint: one which allows only a limited movement, as those of the spinal column.

Mixture: a combination of several ingredients in which each retains its own individuality.

Molars: the grinding teeth of mammals.

Molecule (*mol*-uh-kyool): the smallest part of a substance that can exist without losing its identity.

Mollusks: a group of animals having soft bodies, usually covered by one or two shells.

Molt: to cast off, as skin in snakes, feathers in birds, skin in larvae.

Monocotyledon (mon-oh-kot'l-*ee*-d'n): a plant which has only one cotyledon in its seeds, as corn.

Monotremata (mon-uh-*tree*-mah-tuh): an order of egg-laying mammals such as the duckbill.

Mosaic (moh-*zay*-ik) **vision:** the image formed by the compound eye of an insect, each facet producing a part which fits in with others to make a complete picture.

Motion: in biology, the ability of living things to change their position without using an outside force.

Motor fibers: nerve fibers which convey impulses from the brain to the muscles, producing motion.

Movable joints: those capable of motion; opposed to sutures, which are immovable joints.

Mucous (*myoo*-kuss) **membrane:** the lining of the alimentary canal and respiratory tract.

Mucus (*myoo*-kuss): a slimy substance secreted by certain cells of the mucous membrane.

Muscle: an organ made up of contractile fibers, the function of which is to produce motion.

Mushroom: a kind of fleshy fungus, particularly the edible field mushroom with pink gills.

Mutant (*myoo*-tant): any organism showing a mutation; also called a *sport*.

Mutation (myoo-*tay*-shun): a sudden variation due to genetic change which is then inherited.

Mycelium (my-*see*-lee-um): the (hyphal) threads which make up the body of a fungus.

Myxedema (mik-seh-*dee*-muh): skin condition in adults resulting from serious thyroid deficiency.

N

Narcotic (nahr-*kot*-ik): a substance which dissolves lipoid, thus dulling the senses, and in sufficient quantity producing insensibility.

Natural immunity: an immunity which is natural to the individual, though one has neither had the disease nor been immunized by treatment.

Natural selection: the survival of those organisms which are best adapted to live under certain conditions, and the perishing of those less well adapted.

Neanderthal (nee-*an*-der-tahl) **man:** an early race of man whose fossil remains were found in Germany.

Nearsightedness: a condition in which a person cannot see distant objects clearly because the eyeball is too long from front to back or the lens is too curved.

Nectar: the sweet fluid secreted by nectar glands in a flower; the substance from which bees make honey.

Nemathelminthes (*neh*-muh-thel-*min*-theez): a phylum of roundworms, with unsegmented bodies, often parasitic, as the trichina.

Nematocyst (neh-*mat*-uh-sist): minute stinging organs found especially on the tentacles of the hydra and used to paralyze tiny animals with poison.

Nephridia (neh-*frid*-ee-uh): the tiny, coiled, excretory tubules found in each segment of the earthworm; the earliest forerunners of the kidneys.

Nerve fibers: the separate fibers of which a nerve is made up; the elongated processes of neurons (nerve cells).

Nerve impulse: the reaction to a stimulus that is carried along a nerve pathway.

Nervous system: the system by means of which an animal becomes aware of its surroundings, and by which it can direct itself to adjust to them; the coordinating system.

Net-veined leaf: one in which the veins branch again and again, forming a network.

Neurofibrils (noo-roh-*fy*-brils): strands of protoplasm in paramecium which regulate the cilia.

Neuron (*noo*-ron): a nerve cell with its processes.

Neurosis: a disorder affecting the function but not the structure of the nervous system.

Niacin: a substance found in foods, which forms a component part of vitamin B complex and is used in the prevention of pellagra.

Night blindness: the inability of the eyes to adapt themselves to dim light; caused by a deficiency of vitamin A.

Nitrifying bacteria: bacteria in the soil which convert simple nitrates into the more complex nitrates that green plants can use for protein synthesis.

Nitrogen: an element which naturally occurs in the form of gas. Besides constituting about four-fifths of the air, it is found in many organic substances, as protein.

Nitrogen-fixing bacteria: those bacteria which live in the nodules on the roots of legumes and convert the gaseous nitrogen in the air into nitrates which the green plants can use.

Node: the point from which leaves and branches arise on a dicotyledonous stem, and from which leaves arise on a monocotyledonous stem.

Nodules (*nod*-yools): clumps of nitrogen-fixing bacteria on the roots of leguminous plants.

Notochord (*noh*-tuh-kord): an unsegmented rod of cartilage in the back of the embryos of vertebrates around which the spinal column develops, eventually replacing it.

Nourishment: that which sustains or promotes growth in any way.

Nucellus (noo-*sel*-us): the tissue which fills the space not occupied by the embryo sac in an ovule.

Nuclear membrane: the membrane surrounding the nucleus.

Nucleolus (noo-*klee*-oh-lus): a denser staining body within the nucleus.

Nucleoprotein (noo-klee-oh-*proh*-tee-in): any protein composed of a protein plus a nucleic acid molecule; genes and viruses are believed to be nucleoproteins.

Nucleus (*noo*-klee-us): the specialized body in the protoplasm, part of which transmits heritable traits to offspring.

Nurses: in social insects, those who care for the young after they are hatched.

Nut: a dry, indehiscent fruit with a hard pericarp, as walnut, hazel nut.

Nutrients (*noo*-tree-ents): foods, such as starch, sugars, proteins, edible fats, and mineral matter, which contain the necessary elements for keeping the body in repair and making it grow; food compounds.

Nutrition (noo-*trish*-un): the process by which growth is promoted and repairs made in living organisms.

Nymph (*nimf*): an immature form of an insect, as grasshopper, which has incomplete metamorphosis.

O

Ocellus (oh-*sel*-us): tiny simple eye, as of many invertebrates.

Oculist (*ok*-yoo-list): one skilled in treating diseases of the eye.

Odonata (oh-duh-*nay*-tuh): an order of insects including dragon flies and damsel flies.

Oil: a liquid substance of organic origin, containing carbon, hydrogen, and oxygen, insoluble in water. A food substance (edible fat).

Olfactory (ohl-*fak*-tuh-ree) **lobes:** the brain region in many vertebrates that receives the smell impulses.

Olfactory (ohl-*fak*-tuh-ree) **nerve:** the nerve which connects the organ of smell with the brain.

Omnivorous (om-*niv*-er-us): animals which feed on both plant and animal substances.

Oögonium (oh-uh-*gon*-ee-um): female reproductive organ within which oöspores are developed in some algae and fungi.

Open circulatory system: one in which the blood does not flow continuously through blood vessels, as in the crayfish and other arthropods.

Operculum (oh-*per*-kyoo-lum): the gill cover in fishes.

Optic lobes: the brain region that receives the sight impulses.

Optic nerve: the nerve which conducts impulses from the retina to the brain.

Optometrist (op-*tom*-uh-trist): one who measures the powers of vision and fits glasses.

Oral groove: a deep depression along one side of paramecium through which food enters the body.

Order: in classification, a group of organisms made up of several similar families.

Organ: any part of a plant or animal which performs some definite function.

Organic substance: any substance containing carbon made by plants or animals.

Organism: a plant or an animal.

Ornithology (or-nih-*thol*-uh-jee): the study of birds.

Orthoptera (or-*thop*-ter-uh): a group of insects whose outer wings meet in a straight line in the middle of the back. It includes grasshoppers and crickets.

Osculum (*oss*-kyoo-lum): the opening into the central cavity of the sponge.

Osmosis (oz-*moh*-sis): the passing of soluble substances and water through a semi-permeable membrane, the greater movement of soluble substance being from a region of high concentration to a region of low concentration. However, the water always flows from the more dilute to the more concentrated solution faster than the soluble substances move in the opposite direction.

Ostia: the slits in the heart of insects through which the blood enters.

Outer ear: the part of the ear which consists of the visible portions, the auditory canal, and the tympanic membrane.

Ovary: the organ in female animals and in plants which produces ova or eggs.

Overproduction: the production by plants and animals of more offspring than can survive so as to insure survival of the species.

Oviduct (*oh*-vih-dukt): the tube through which the eggs leave the body.

Ovipositor (oh-vih-*poz*-ih-ter): the organ in insects by which eggs are thrust into a hard substance, as earth or wood.

Ovule (*oh*-vyool): the body, in plants, which contains the egg cell. In case the egg cell is fertilized, the ovule develops into a seed or a fruit, as a grain of corn.

Ovum: the reproductive cell or egg produced by the female.

Oxidation: the chemical union of oxygen with another substance.

Oxygen: a gas, one of the elements. It is very abundant in nature, existing in the air as O_2 and is in combination with carbon and hydrogen in all organic compounds.

Oxyhemoglobin: the compound formed when the hemoglobin in the red blood cells combines with oxygen.

P

Palate (*pal*-it): the roof of the mouth.

Palisade (pal-uh-*sayd*) **cells:** a row of cells longer than wide lying just beneath the epidermis of leaves.

Palmately (*pal*-mayt-lee) **compound leaves:** those in which the leaflets, five or more in number, arise from the top of the petiole.

Palp: one of the sensory, jointed mouth parts of crayfish, insects, etc.

Pancreas (*pan*-kree-us): a gland which secretes a liquid containing enzymes used in the intestinal digestion of food.

Pancreatic duct: the tube that carries digestive enzymes from the pancreas to the small intestine.

Pantothenic (pan-tuh-*then*-ik) **acid:** a substance closely associated with riboflavin in vitamin B_2.

Papilla (puh-*pil*-uh): a small projection, as from the surface of the tongue or on skin.

Pappus: the tuft of down on the fruits of certain plants, as thistle, dandelion, for distribution by wind.

Parallel venation (veh-*nay*-shun): the characteristic venation of monocotyledonous plants in which a number of veins of about the same size run side by side from base to apex of the leaf.

Parasite (*pair*-uh-syte): a small, dependent organism which gets its food directly from a larger one, the host, without any benefit to the latter.

Parathormone (pair-uh-*thor*-mohn): hormone secreted by the parathyroid glands.

Parathyroid (pair-uh-*thy*-roid): two pairs of ductless glands located posterior to the thyroid gland in the neck.

Parenchyma (puh-*ren*-kee-muh): thin-walled unspecialized cells in the central cylinder of roots.

Parotid (puh-*rot*-id): the salivary gland below the ear.

Parthenogenesis (parh-then-oh-*jen*-eh-sis): the development of an unfertilized egg.

Pasteurization (pass-ter-ih-*zay*-shun): the process of killing most of the harmful bacteria in milk by heating it for twenty minutes at 60° C. and cooling it quickly.

Patella (puh-*tel*-luh): the flat oval bone in front of the knee joint.

Pectoral (*pek*-tor-ul) **girdle:** the bones which support the anterior limbs of vertebrates and attach them to the trunk.

Peduncle (peh-*dunk*-'l): the axis or stem to which the several flowers of an inflorescence are attached, as in lily of the valley.

Peking (*pee*-king) **man:** an early race of man whose fossil remains were found in China.

Pellagra (peh-*lay*-gruh): a deficiency disease caused by the lack of niacin.

Pellicle (*pel*-ih-k'l): a thin skin, film, or layer.

Pelvic girdle: the bones to which the posterior limbs of vertebrates are attached.

Pelvis: the broad, curved bones which support the organs of the abdomen; the hollow area near the center of the kidney.

Penicillin (pen-ih-*sil*-in): an antibiotic from the penicillium mold which is used against infections.

Pepsin: the ferment in the gastric juice which acts on protein.

Peptid: the substance resulting from the breakdown of peptones and proteoses by the enzyme trypsin from the pancreas.

Peptone: a substance resulting from the digestion of protein by pepsin.

Perennial: a plant which lives year after year, as a tree.

Perfect flower: one which has both stamens and pistil, the essential organs.

Perianth (*pehr*-ee-anth): the sepals and petals of a flower taken together when they are similar in shape and color, as in a lily.

Pericycle (*per*-ih-sy-k'l): the tissue in the central cylinder of a root from which the branch roots arise.

Period: a subdivision of time in a geologic era.

Peripheral (peh-*rif*-er-al) **nervous system:** a system composed of nerves going from the spinal cord to all parts of the body.

Peristalsis (pehr-ih-*stahl*-sis): the wavelike motion in the intestine caused by the alternate contraction and relaxation of its muscles.

Pernicious (per-*nish*-us) **anemia:** a disease in which the red blood cells are destroyed.

Perspiration: sweat.

Petal: one of the colored parts which make up the corolla of a flower.

Petiole (*pet*-ee-ohl): the part of a leaf by which it is attached to the stem; the leaf stalk.

Petrifaction (pet-rih-*fak*-shun): the process of changing into stone, a method of fossil formation.

Phagocytes (*fag*-uh-syts): the white corpuscles of the blood which act as scavengers.

Phalanges (fuh-*lan*-jeez): the bones of the fingers and toes.

Pharynx (*fair*-ingks): the cavity back of the mouth common to the respiratory and digestive systems.

Phloem (*flow*-em): the outer part of a fibrovascular bundle in a dicotyledonous plant.

Photosynthesis (foh-toh-*sin*-thuh-siss): the process of making starch, peculiar to green plants.

Phylogeny (fy-*loj*-en-ee): the history of the development of groups or phyla of living things.

Phylum (*fy*-lum): a large division of the plant or animal kingdom.

Physiology (fiz-ee-*ol*-uh-jee): the study of the life processes of organisms.

Pigment: a substance that imparts color.

Pileus (*py*-lee-us): the cap or expanded portion of a mushroom.

Pineal body: a small vestigial organ located in the upper part of the head.

Pinnately (pin-*ayt*-lee) **compound:** having leaflets arranged on both sides of the petiole, as in compound leaves.

Pistil: the central part of a flower consisting of a stigma, style, and ovary (which see).

Pith: the soft, spongy tissue in the center of a woody stem; the substance between the vascular bundles in a monocotyledonous stem.

Pituitary (pih-*tyoo*-ih-ter-ee): a ductless gland on the floor of the brain.

Placenta (pluh-*sen*-tuh): the tissue to which seeds are attached in the ovary of a plant, and to which embryos are attached in the uterus of mammals.

Plasma (*plaz*-muh): the liquid portion of the blood of vertebrates.

Plasma membrane: thin membrane on the outside of the cell through which osmosis takes place.

Plasma proteins: protein substances found in blood plasma, such as serum albumin, gamma globulin, fibrinogen, and thrombin.

Plastron: the ventral part of the shell of a turtle.

Platelet (*playt*-let) : one of the small bodies in the blood which is necessary to the process of clotting.

Plexus (*plek*-sus) : an interlacement of nerves forming a nerve mass.

Plumage (*ploom*-ij) : all the feathers of a bird.

Plumule (*ploo*-myool) : the first bud of an embryo plant.

Pod: the seed case of certain plants, as peas; a form of dry, dehiscent fruit.

Poison: any substance which acts in a harmful manner when taken into the system of an organism.

Polar body: a small cell formed during the maturation of the egg.

Pollen: the fine, powdery substance formed in the stamens of flowers. Each grain contains the male germ cells for fertilizing the egg cell in an ovule.

Pollen tube: the tube that grows from the pollen grain on a stigma, down the style, and to the ovule in the ovary.

Pollination (pol-ih-*nay*-shun) : the act of receiving pollen on the stigma of a pistil.

Polyp (*pol*-ip) : a many-armed aquatic animal of the radiate-type, as a hydra, sea-anemone, or coral.

Pome (*pohm*) : a fruit having thick, fleshy walls which inclose the papery pod containing the seeds, as apple, pear, quince.

Portal circulation: the movement of blood from the digestive organs to the liver.

Posterior part: the hinder portion of an organism.

Precocial (preh-*koh*-shul) : birds which are able to run about soon after hatching.

Premolars: grinding teeth in mammals.

Preservative: a substance added to food to prevent its "spoiling," as sugar in fruit, salt on meat.

Preserve: a place in which plants or animals, or both, may not be molested.

Primary root: the first and usually the main root of a plant; the tap root.

Primates (pry-*may*-teez) : the highest order of mammals, which includes monkeys, apes, and man.

Proboscidia (proh-buh-*sid*-ee-uh) : a group of animals characterized by a proboscis.

Proboscis (proh-*boss*-iss) : an elongated appendage for gathering food. In insects, a coiled tube; in elephants, a prehensile nose and upper lip.

Prophase (*proh*-fayz) : the stage in mitosis when the chromatin granules form into spiremes.

Propolis (*prop*-oh-liss) : bee-glue.

Protective coloration: coloration which resembles that of the environment, as that of toad, frog, grasshopper, tree frog.

Protective resemblance: the resemblance of a harmless organism to a harmful or distasteful one, as viceroy butterfly to monarch.

Protein (*proh*-tee-in) : the compound of oxygen, hydrogen, carbon, and nitrogen, and traces of other elements of which protoplasm is made; a nutrient.

Proteoses: a substance resulting from the digestion of protein by pepsin.

Prothallium (proh-*thal*-ee-um) : the first thallus formed by germination of asexually produced spores in the fern group's life cycle.

Prothorax (proh-*thor*-aks) : the first of the three regions of an insect's thorax.

Prothrombin: a protein substance formed during the clotting of blood that acts on the fibrinogen and changes it to fibrin threads.

Protonema (pro-tuh-*nee*-muh) : a filament in mosses formed by the germination of an asexual spore which produces a sexual plant.

Protoplasm (*proh*-tuh-plazm) : the living substance composing the cells of plants and animals.

Protozoa (proh-tuh-*zoh*-uh) : one-celled animals.

Pseudopodium (soo-doh-*poh*-dee-um): a projection of protoplasm used by Protozoa for locomotion.

Psychosis (sy-*koh*-siss): a serious mental disturbance.

Ptomaine (*toh*-mayn): a substance produced by the decomposition of animal matter, poisonous if eaten.

Ptyalin (*ty*-uh-lin): the enzyme in saliva which changes starch to sugar.

Pulmonary artery: the vessel that carries de-oxygenated blood from the heart to the lungs.

Pulmonary circulation: the movement of blood between the heart and lungs.

Pulmonary vein: the vessel that carries oxygenated blood from the lungs to the heart.

Pulp: the central portion of a tooth; contains the nerves and blood vessels.

Pulse: the beating of the arteries near the surface, as at the wrist.

Pupa (*pyoo*-puh): the quiescent, inactive stage in the development of an insect between larva and adult.

Pupil of the eye: the round opening in the iris which admits light into the eye.

Pyloric (py-*loh*-rik) **valve:** the opening between the stomach and the intestine.

Pyrenoid (*py*-reh-noyd): a tiny body in chloroplasts for the storage of starch.

Pyridoxine (py-rih-*dok*-zeen): part of the B complex, known as vitamin B_6, which helps oxidize the food.

Q

Quarantine: the enforced isolation of persons, animals, or plants infected with contagious diseases or of places harboring disease germs.

Queen bee: the mother of a community of bees; the only reproductive female in the community.

R

Race: in man, a subdivision of a main group within the human species.

Radial symmetry: structures arranged in a similar pattern radiating from a central point.

Radioactive elements: elements which give off rays by the disintegration of their atoms.

Radius (*ray*-dee-us): the bone of the forearm on the same side as the thumb.

Range: in biology, the definite area of distribution to which each plant or animal is limited.

Raphe (*ray*-fee): the band running lengthwise around the outside of a bean seed.

Ray flowers: the outer flowers of certain composite flowers, for example, common daisy, with white ray flowers, sunflower, with yellow ones.

Realm: in biology, a large area made up of a group of neighboring regions separated by barriers.

Receptacle (rih-*sep*-tuh-k'l): the expanded end of a modified branch on which the floral parts are arranged.

Recessive characters: those which do not appear in a hybrid, because of the dominance of other characters.

Reclamation (rek-luh-*may*-shun): the act of bringing wild or arid land to use in raising crops; supplying water for irrigation.

Rectum (*rek*-tum): the terminal portion of the alimentary canal.

Red corpuscles (*kor*-pus-'ls): the cells in the blood that carry oxygen.

Red rust: a parasitic fungus which has two hosts, wheat and barberry, during its life history; called also black rust from its mature stage on wheat.

Reduction division: reduction by half, of the chromosome number during the process of maturation.

Reflex (*ree*-fleks) **action:** that which takes place in voluntary muscles without the intervention of the brain, the impulse going first along a sensory nerve to the spinal cord and being switched to the motor nerves, causing movement. One of the simplest types of response.

Reflex arc: the path over which a reflex act travels.

Reforestation: the act of replanting areas with trees, or setting out trees on new areas.

Regeneration: the act of restoring a lost part by growing a new one, as the tentacle of a hydra, or the end of an earthworm.

Regular flower: one which has all its petals, also its sepals, of the same size and shape, as rose, buttercup. Pansies, violets, and salvia have *irregular* flowers.

Rejuvenation: the renewal of vitality.

Renal circulation: the movement of blood from the body organs through the kidneys.

Rennin (*ren*-in): an enzyme that curdles milk and is found in gastric juice.

Repellent: a substance which makes a thing distasteful.

Reproduction: the process by which life continues from one generation to the next.

Reptilia (rep-*til*-ee-uh): the class of vertebrates containing lizards, snakes, turtles, alligators, and crocodiles.

Reservoir: in euglena, a cell organ for receiving food from the gullet.

Residual air: the part of the complemental air which is never removed from the lungs in any one breath.

Respiration: the function of living cells which consists of taking in oxygen for oxidation and giving off carbon dioxide.

Resting stage: the stage between cell divisions.

Retina (*ret*-ih-nuh): the inmost layer of the coat of the eyeball which receives the stimuli of light rays and conducts them to the brain through the optic nerve.

Rh factor: a substance present in the red blood cells of most but not all persons; those who have it are said to be Rh positive, those who do not have it are Rh negative.

Rhizoid (*ry*-zoid): rootlike filament in ferns, mosses, and liverworts that act as absorptive organs.

Rhizome (*ry*-zohm): a thickened, underground stem used for food storage, as in Solomon's-seal and Pteris, or for propagation, as in quack grass and Canada thistle.

Riboflavin (ry-boh-*flay*-vin): substance found in foods, a component part of the B complex which prevents disorders of the eye, often called B$_2$.

Ribs: the bones protecting the chest and attached to the spine.

Rickets: a disease of the bones caused by lack of vitamin D.

Rickettsia (rik-*et*-see-uh): a type of minute disease-producing agent that may be intermediate between bacteria and viruses, causing typhus fever and others.

Rind: the hard outer covering of a monocot stem.

Rod: a nerve ending in the retina of the eye that is sensitive to dim light.

Rodentia (roh-*den*-she-uh): a group of animals having chisel-edged incisor teeth for gnawing, as squirrel, rat.

Root cap: the loose protective cells covering the end of a rootlet.

Root hairs: elongated projections of epidermal cells of roots for absorption.

Root pressure: the osmotic force which causes sap to rise in stems.

Rosette (roh-*zet*): the spiral arrangement of leaves on a very short axis, as shepherd's-purse or bull thistle in early spring.

Royal couple: the reproductive king and queen of a termite colony who produce the offspring.

Ruminant (*roo*-mih-n'nt): an animal which chews its cud, as cow. The food is swallowed with very little chewing. Later it is returned to the mouth partially digested and is thoroughly chewed.

Rust: a form of plant disease caused by certain fungi; especially red rust (black rust) of wheat.

S

Sacrum (*say*-krum): that part of the spinal column directly connected with and forming part of the pelvis.

Saliva (suh-*ly*-vuh): the natural moisture in the mouth secreted by the salivary glands, a digestive juice.

Salivary (*sal*-ih-vehr-ee) **glands:** glands which secrete saliva.

Samara (*sam*-uh-ruh): an indehiscent winged fruit, as in maple, elm, and ash.

Sanctuary: a place of refuge from violence, particularly designated localities where birds or other animals may not be molested.

Sanitation: the devising and applying of measures for preserving and promoting health, especially public health.

Sap: the watery solution which circulates in plants.

Saprophyte (sap-roh-fyte): the group of fungi which live on dead organic matter.

Scapula (skap-yoo-luh): one of the shoulder blades.

Scavenger: an animal that feeds on dead or decaying matter.

Schick test: a test to determine whether a person is immune to diphtheria.

Scientific method: a step-wise procedure used by scientists in solving problems.

Scion (sy-un): the small branch inserted into the large plant (stock) in grafting.

Sclerotic (skleh-rot-ik) **coat:** the tough outer coat of the eyeball.

Scurvy: a deficiency disease caused by lack of vitamin C.

Scute (skoot): one of the large scales on the abdomen of a snake.

Scutellum (skoo-tel-um): the shield-shaped cotyledon lying under the embryo in corn and other grains.

Seasonal biology: the study of living things at the time of year when their habits can be observed in their natural environment.

Secondary root: a branch root; develops from the pericycle in the central cylinder.

Secretin (seh-kree-tin): an intestinal hormone capable of stimulating the pancreas to secrete.

Secretion: a substance formed in the cell and discharged, such as an enzyme or a hormone.

Sedimentary rock: that formed by materials deposited from a state of suspension in water.

Seedling: a young plant during the period when it is dependent on food stored in the seed.

Segment: one of the ringlike divisions of the abdomen of insects and earthworms.

Self-pollination: the act of getting pollen on the pistil of any flower from its own stamens.

Semicircular canals: structures in the inner ear which aid in maintaining balance.

Semipermeable (sem-ee-per-mee-uh-b'l): allows only certain substances to pass.

Sensation: the consciousness (awareness) of a stimulus received through a sense organ.

Sensory nerves: those which convey impulses to the brain, producing sensation.

Sepals (see-p'ls): the outermost leaflike parts of a flower; part of the calyx.

Serum albumin (al-byoo-min): a plasma protein in blood.

Sex-linked characters: those traits carried on the chromosomes which determine the sex of the offspring.

Sexual reproduction: that in which the new individual arises from the union of an egg and a sperm.

Sieve (siv) **cells:** large cells with perforated ends which are a part of the phloem of a fibrovascular bundle.

Silk glands: the organs in a silkworm larva in which the material for making the cocoon is manufactured.

Simple eye: a single organ of sight found in insects, resembling one of the numerous parts of the compound eyes.

Simple leaf: one in which the blade is all in one piece.

Sinus (sy-nus): a hollow or cavity in a bone; an irregular, widened space in a blood vessel or among the cells of a tissue.

Siphon (sy-fun): one of the openings in the mantle of a clam through which water flows in or out.

Siphonaptera (sy-foh-nap-ter-uh): an order of insects which have sucking mouths, as fleas.

Skeleton: the firm part of an animal's body to which the muscles are attached.

Skin: the outer covering of an animal's body.

Skull: the bones forming the skeleton of the head.

Slaves: in an ant colony, those ants captured in a battle.

Smooth muscle: involuntary muscle, lacks cross-striations.

Social insects: those that live in large groups, or colonies, and are dependent on each other, such as bees, ants, and termites.

Soil: the finely divided particles of rock, humus, etc., which make up the outer layers of the earth not covered by water.

Solar plexus: the largest sympathetic plexus, located behind the stomach and in front of the aorta.

Soldier: among certain social insects, the member of the colony who does the fighting.

Solitary: single, alone; especially a flower which grows at the end of its own stalk.

Somatic (soh-*mat*-ik) **cell:** a body cell.

Sorus (*sor*-us): a natural group of spores or sporangia, on the surface of the leaves of the host plant.

Spawn: to deposit eggs or roe for reproduction; as fishes.

Special senses: seeing, hearing, smelling, tasting, feeling.

Species (*spee*-sheez): a group composed of individuals having similar characteristics; a subdivision of a genus.

Sperm: the male reproductive cell.

Spermary (*spur*-muh-ree): the organ which produces sperms; the testis.

Spicule (spik-*yool*): a small, hard, pointed body found in sponges.

Spike: a flower cluster with numerous sessile flowers arranged closely on an elongated common axis, as in plantain.

Spinal column: the backbone.

Spinal cord: the main nerve cord in the vertebrates; located dorsally running from the medulla of the brain down the back.

Spinal nerves: those arising from the spinal cord, a pair between each two vertebrae.

Spindle fiber: fiber of a spindle formed in mitosis of plant cells.

Spinneret: tubelike appendage for producing fine silken threads from the secretion of glands such as those of the female spider.

Spiracle (*spy*-ruh-k'l): an opening for air in the body of an insect or whale.

Spirillum (spy-*ril*-um): a spiral form of bacterium.

Spleen: a glandlike, ductless organ in the upper part of the abdominal cavity of vertebrates which functions as a blood filter and aids in the removal of worn out red blood corpuscles.

Spongin: soft fibers comprising the skeleton of certain types of sponges.

Sporangium (spor-*an*-jee-um): the case in which spores are produced.

Spore: an asexual reproductive body common to fungi, mosses, and other plants.

Sporophyte (*spoh*-roh-fyte): the generation which produces asexual spores in plants that reproduce by alternation of generations.

Sprain: the injury resulting from a violent twisting or tearing of the ligaments or muscles.

Spur: a short, stiff, sharp spine, as on a rooster's leg; a projection from a sepal or petal.

Stamen (*stay*-men): the organ in a flower which produces pollen.

Starch: a substance composed of carbon, hydrogen, and oxygen in which hydrogen and oxygen occur in the same proportion as in water; a carbohydrate.

Statocyst (*stat*-oh-sist): an organ for balance found in many animals.

Stele: the central cylinder or core of a plant root where the conducting tissues are located.

Sterile (*stehr*-il): free from bacteria of every kind.

Sternum: the breastbone.

Stigma: the part of a pistil which receives the pollen.

Stimulant: any agent that excites to organic action.

Stimulus: that which causes a reaction in nerve, muscle, or vegetable tissue, as light, sound, electricity, warmth, etc.

Sting: an organ of offense or defense in animals, as bees, wasps, etc.; hollow hairs of plants filled with acrid liquid secreted by the plant, as nettle.

Stipe: a stem or stalk, commonly of mushrooms.

Stipule (*stip*-yool): one of the two leaf-like growths at the base of the petioles of certain leaves, as clover, strawberry.

Stirrup: one of the three bones of the middle ear.

Stock: the large stem on to which a smaller one (scion) is grafted; in man, a main division or group of the human species, or *race* (which see).

Stolon (*stoh*-lon): a threadlike, leafless branch which has a vegetative bud on the end, as in strawberry plants.

Stoma (*stoh*-muh): one of the very small openings in the epidermis of a leaf through which water vapor passes out and air in.

Stomach: the sac or enlarged portion of the digestive tract in which digestion is carried on.

Stomach poison: an insecticide which kills when it has been eaten.

Strain: the injury resulting from stretching the ligaments or muscles.

Strap-shaped flower: one in which the narrow petals are united and turned in the same direction, as in dandelion.

Streptomycin (strep-toh-*my*-sin): an antibiotic that combats infections that resist penicillin and sulpha drugs.

Striated (*stry*-ayt-ed) **muscle:** voluntary muscle; has cross-striations.

Strobilus (*stroh*-bih-luss): a conelike structure in club mosses, bearing sporangia; in conifers, the cone; and in seed plants, the pistillate inflorescence of the hop.

Style: the slender portion of a pistil connecting the stigma and the ovary.

Subcutaneous (sub-kyoo-*tay*-nee-us) **arteries:** vessels that carry blood to the skin.

Sublingual (sub-*ling*-wul): one of a pair of salivary glands which are located under the tongue.

Submaxillary (sub-*mak*-sih-lehr-ee): one of a pair of salivary glands in the angle of the lower jaw.

Sucrase: an enzyme secreted by the intestinal glands for changing sucrose to glucose.

Suffocate: to kill by excluding air from the lungs or by substituting some other substance for air, as smoke.

Sugar: a carbohydrate of sweetish taste, soluble in water. (See *starch*.)

Surface layer: the outermost layer of the epidermis of skin; it consists of dead cells which are constantly being shed.

Suture (*soo*-cher): the joining of two bones by mutually serrated edges, forming an immovable articulation, as in the bones of the skull.

Swarming: the departure from the hive of a queen bee and most of the workers to start a new hive.

Sweat gland: an organ in the skin mainly to help regulate body heat but also secretes some fluid wastes.

Swimmerets: small appendages on the abdomen of a crayfish, useful in swimming.

Symbiosis (sim-bee-*oh*-sis): the close relationship of two kinds of organisms which results in mutual benefit.

Synapse (*sin*-aps): the place where the dendrites of two neurons join.

Syrinx (*sihr*-inks): the voice box of birds.

System: a group of organs which work together to perform a life function, as digestive system, circulatory system, respiratory system.

Systemic circulation: the movement of blood through all parts of the body except the lungs.

T

Tactile (*tak*-t'l): pertaining to the organs, or the sense of touch.

Tadpole: the larval stage of frogs and toads.

Talon: a claw, especially of a bird of prey.

Taproot: the main root of a plant; often used for food storage.

Tarsus (*tahr*-sus): the ankle; the scaly part of a bird's leg; the terminal segment of an insect's foot.

Tartar: the accumulated food deposits between the teeth.

Taste buds: nerve endings in the papillae of the tongue that are sensitive to the four fundamental tastes of sweet, sour, bitter, and salt.

Taxonomy (taks-*on*-uh-mee): the science that deals with the classification and naming of organisms.

Telophase (*tel*-uh-fayz): the stage in mitosis when the daughter cells are formed.

Telson: the last abdominal segment of the crayfish.

Tendon: the connective tissue ending of a muscle which attaches it to other structures.

Tendril: an organ of certain plants which clasps a support, enabling it to climb.

Tentacle (*ten*-tuh-k'l): a jointed flexible appendage on the head of insects and other invertebrates, used for touch, grasping, or motion; a feeler.

Terminal bud: one which appears at the end of a branch or stem.

Termitary: the home of a termite colony.

Terrarium (teh-*rair*-ee-um): an artificial place for keeping live land plants and animals.

Testa: the hard outer covering of a seed.

Testis: an organ in a male animal where sperms are produced.

Testosterone (tess-*toss*-ter-ohn): a male sex hormone used in the treatment of acromegaly, a condition due to the oversecretion of the pituitary gland.

Tetany (*tet*-uh-nee): a state of muscular contraction.

Thiamin (*thy*-uh-min): vitamin B_1, a complex compound whose absence from the diet results in beriberi.

Thoracic (thor-*ass*-ik) **cavity:** the second part of an insect's body; in mammals, the cavity above the diaphragm; the chest cavity.

Thrombin: an enzyme which aids in the clotting of blood.

Thymus: a ductless gland located in the neck region of many vertebrates.

Thyroid gland: a large ductless gland on the outside of the trachea below the larynx.

Thyroxin (thy-*roks*-in): the hormone secreted by the thyroid gland.

Tibia (*tib*-ee-uh): the shin bone in man; the fourth division of an insect's leg.

Tidal air: the air which passes in and out of the lungs in normal breathing.

Tissue: a collection of similar cells that perform the same function.

Tonsil: one of two masses of lymph tissue lying in the throat back of the tongue.

Toxin (*tok*-sin): a poisonous substance given off by disease-producing bacteria.

Toxoid (*tok*-soyd): a poisonous bacterial extract that has been treated to be non-poisonous, used in vaccines to stimulate the formation of antibodies.

Trachea (*tray*-kee-uh): the air passage leading from the pharynx to the lungs; an air tube in insects.

Transpiration: the evaporation of water through the stomata of leaves.

Trichina (trih-*ky*-nuh): a small round worm sometimes found in pork, living as a parasite, and the cause of trichinosis in man.

Trichocysts (*trik*-oh-sists): minute, dart-like organs of offense and defense found in paramecium.

Trilobite (*try*-luh-byt): any of numerous extinct arthropods that lived in a geologic era.

Trochanter (troh-*kan*-ter): the second joint of an insect's leg.

Tropism (*troh*-pizm): movement of a living thing in response to an external stimulus.

True bugs: those insects that belong to the order Hemiptera.

Trunk: the stem of a tree; the main part of the body of a vertebrate to which the appendages are attached.

Trypsin: a digestive enzyme, found in pancreatic juice and acting on protein substances.

Tube feet: special muscular structures used by starfish and other echinoderms for locomotion and grasping.

Tuber (*too*-ber): a short, thick underground stem used for storage, as potato.

Tundra: the treeless plains of the Arctic.

Turgid (*ter*-jid): distended with air or liquid; swollen.

Tympanic (tim-*pan*-ik) **membrane:** the thin partition which separates the middle ear from the outer, commonly known as the eardrum.

U

Ulna (*ul*-nuh): the long bone in the forearm that forms the elbow.

Umbel: a flower-cluster in which a number of pedicels of the same length spring from the same point, thus radiating like the stays of an umbrella.

Ungulata (ung-yoo-*lay*-tuh): a group of mammals characterized by hoofs as cows, horses, and elephants.

Unit character: a characteristic that is inherited as a whole.

Univalve: a mollusk shell consisting of one piece as a snail.

Urea (yoo-*ree*-uh): the nitrogenous waste of animals which is passed off in the urine.

Ureter (yoo-*ree*-ter): a tube, one of two, leading from the kidneys to the bladder and carrying off the waste from the kidneys.

Urethra (yoo-*ree*-thruh): the canal which, in most mammals, carries off the urine from the bladder.

Urine: the liquid wastes excreted by the kidneys.

Urinogenitals (yoo-ree-noh-*jen*-uh-t'ls): the organs common to the urinary and the reproductive systems, or the combination of these systems.

Uropod (*yoo*-roh-pod): the modified swimmeret on either side of the last segment of a crayfish. These, together with the telson (the modified last segment), make up an appendage useful in swimming backwards.

Uterus (*yoo*-ter-us): in female animals, an organ for containing the young during development.

V

Vaccination: inoculation with the virus of cowpox as a preventive of smallpox. The term is loosely used to denote inoculation for other diseases.

Vaccine (vak-*seen*): the virus of cowpox prepared for or introduced by vaccination; now commonly applies to any substance that produces an active immunity by inoculation.

Vacuole (*vak*-yoo-ohl): a space in the cytoplasm of a cell usually filled with a clear liquid secreted by the cell, or by food in the process of digestion.

Valve: one or more folds in the lining tissue of a blood vessel or other organ to prevent or check the flow of a liquid in the opposite direction; one of the parts of the shell, as of a mollusk.

Variation: deviation from the normal type in structure or function.

Vascular (same as fibrovascular) **bundles:** elongated cells which communicate with one another, forming tubelike vessels for the transportation of liquids in plants.

Vegetative propagation: reproduction by any organ of a plant except the flower.

Vein: one of the vessels which conduct blood towards the heart; one of the ribs of an insect's wing; one of the larger supporting and conducting vessels in a leaf.

Vena cava (*vee*-nuh *kay*-vuh): large vein entering the heart.

Venom: the poison secreted by the glands of snakes or other animals.

Ventilation: the control of the supply, circulation, temperature, and humidity of the air in a room.

Ventral: pertaining to or located on the abdominal side of the body.

Ventricle (*ven*-trih-k'l): any cavity of a hollow organ, especially one of the lower chambers of the heart.

Vermiform (*ver*-mih-form) **appendix:** a slender tubular pouch of the large intestine at its juncture with the small intestine.

Vertebrae (*ver*-tuh-bree): the bones in the spinal column of vertebrates.

Vertebrates (*ver*-tuh-brayts): the group of animals which have backbones.

Vestigial (vess-*tij*-ee-al): pertaining to a structure which is no longer developed or functional, as the appendix in man.

Viability: having life or the ability to live, as a seed.

Villi (*vil*-eye): the minute projections which cover the lining of the small intestine; an organ of absorption.

Virus (*vy*-rus): the element or principle that is the agent or medium for communicating infection.

Viscera (*viss*-er-uh): the organs of the abdominal cavity.

Visual purple: a chemical secreted by the rods in the retina of the eye to aid in seeing in dim light.

Vital energy: all of the processes going on in an organism that enable it to carry on its activities.

Vitamin: certain substances in foods which are necessary for the proper functioning of the vital processes.

Vitreous (*vit*-ree-us) **humor:** the liquid which fills the posterior chamber of the eyeball.

Vocation: a chosen life work or profession.

Voluntary act: one that is done with conscious thought.

Voluntary muscles: those under the control of the will, as in the hand.

Volvox: a colonial organism in which certain cells are set apart for reproduction.

W

Warm-blooded: having a constant temperature, as man.

Warning coloration: marks or colors which make an insect or other animal conspicuous to its enemies.

Wart: a small tumor on the skin, usually hard, formed by enlargement of the papillae and thickening of the epidermis which covers them.

Wax: in bees, a secretion with which they cap the cells of the hive.

Weed: a plant that grows where it is not wanted.

White corpuscles (*kor*-pus-'ls): colorless cells in the blood, mainly for fighting infection.

White matter: see *medullary sheath.*

Whole blood: blood from which nothing has been removed, consisting of plasma, corpuscles, platelets, and all other substances normally dissolved in it.

Workers: underdeveloped females in a community of bees which perform all the work of the hive except reproduction.

Worm: a group of animals having flat or cylindrical bodies which in some cases are composed of segments.

Wriggler: the larva of mosquitoes.

X

X chromosome: a chromosome that helps to determine the sex of the offspring. Females have two X chromosomes, while males have one.

Xerophthalmia (zee-rof-*thal*-mee-uh): a dry and thickened condition of the conjunctiva leading to a lusterless condition of the eyeball, due to serious deficiency of vitamin A.

Xylem (*zy*-lem): the thick-walled cells in a fibrovascular bundle.

Y

Y chromosome: a chromosome that helps to determine the sex of the offspring, found only in males.

Yeast: a unicellular fungus which causes fermentation.

Yolk: the yellow portion of an egg; the food material used by the embryo.

Z

Zone: a certain area, such as a life zone.

Zoology (zoh-*ol*-uh-jee): the branch of biology that treats of animals.

Zoospore (*zoh*-uh-spohr): an asexual swimming spore produced by some of the green algae.

Zygospore (*zy*-goh-spohr): a spore formed by the union of two similar gametes.

Zygote (*zy*-goht): the product of the fusion of two dissimilar gametes.

Zymase (*zy*-mayss): an enzyme found in yeast.

Index

Index

Page numbers in *italics* refer to illustrations.

720

Buds
  axillary, 496
  hydra, 83, 578
  mosses, 470, 471
  sponge, 80
  underground stems, 500
  woody stem, 496
  yeast, 462
Bulb, 500
Bullfrog, *191,* 198, 201
Bullhead, 182, 186
Bundle sheath, 494
Burbank, Luther, 589, 662, 678
Burdock, 528
Bushman, South African, 273
Butterfish, 184
Butterflies, 134-144
  characteristics of, 137
  coloration and mimicry, 137
  enemies of, 143-144
  monarch, 134-138
  viceroy, *137*
  wing, *38*
Buttons, 255

C

Cacti, *39, 508, 589*
Caecum, 125
Calamites, 621-622
Calcium, 308
Calcium phosphate, 291
Calories, 312
Calorimeter, 313
Calyx, 521, 523
Cambium, 485, 494
Cambrian period, 620, 622
Cancer, 60, 401-402, 429
Canidae, 608
Canine teeth, 245, 323
Canning, 453
Caper, 529
Capillaries
  frog, 194
  man, 328, 340, *342,* 343
Capillarity, 486
Capsule, 469, 530, 596
Carapace, 105, 108, 207
Carbohydrates, 307, 326, 329,
    511-513, 541
Carbon cycle, 451
Carbon dioxide
  in human body, 335, 352
  in photosynthesis, 511-513
  as a waste product, 10

Cardiac muscles, 293, *294*
Cardiac plexus, 366
Cardiac valve, 325
Cardinal, 229, *229*
Cardinal veins, of fish, 181
Carnivora, 239, 245
  families, 607
Carotene, 309, 509
Carotid artery, of frog, 194
Carpel, 522
Carpus, 291
Carrell, Alexis, 662
Carriers of disease, 409
Cartilage, 291, 292, *292*
Casein, 326
Cashew, 531
Cat, 51, *244*
Caterpillar, 134, *142,* 167
Catfish, 184, 186
Cattle, 249, 588, 591, 665-666
Caucasian stock, 273, 274
Caudal fin, 178, *178*
Cauliflower, 528
Caviar, 186
Cell
  animal, 11, *52,* 53, 54
  and assimilation, 342, 355
  colonies, 88, 97
  defined, 7
  differentiation, 54, 97
  discovery of, 50-51
  division, 60-61, *61, 62*
  function, 60
  growth, 62-63
  man, 51
  membrane, 11, 52-53
  mystery of, 664-665
  oxidation in, 355
  plant, 11, *52,* 53, 54
  reproduction, 60-61, *61, 62*
  specialized, *54-55,* 97
  structure of, *52,* 52-53
  theory, 52, 661
  unit of heredity, 582
  See also names of special-
    ized cells
Cellulase, 515
Cellulose, 11, 53
Cement glands, 110
Cementum, 323
Cenozoic era, 620, 621, 623
Centipedes, 104, 114-115
Central cylinder, 484
Central nervous system, 195,
    363, *363*

Centrosome, 53, 61, 62
Cephalothorax, 105
Cereals, 533
Cerebellum, 196, 217, 363-364
Cerebral hemisphere, 195
Cerebrum, 195, 217, 363-364
Cervical vertebrae, 290, *290*
Cetacea, 250
Chalk Cliffs, *79*
Chambered nautilus, 95, *95*
Chameleon, 208, 210
Chance, law of, 393-394
Chapman, Frank M., 228
Chapped hands, 283
Chara, 108
Character, 583
Chela, 106
Cheliped, 106, 107
Chemotropism, 540
Chest, 288
Chewing, 324
Chickadee, 225, *225*
Chicken, 220
  embryology of, 625-627
Chiggers, 113
Chilopoda, 104, 114, 115
Chimney swift, *217*
Chimpanzee, 251, 271
Chipmunk, 11, *570*
Chiroptera, 243-245
Chitin, 104, 447
Chloromycetin, 408
Chlorophyll
  in photosynthesis, 512
  in plant cells, 53
Chlorophyta, 439-440, 609
Chloroplasts
  euglena, 76
  algae, 439-440
  in leaf, 509, 510
  in plant cells, 53, *664*
Cholera, 421
Chordata, 70, 177
  classes of, 606-607
Choroid coat, 369
Chromatin, 53, 61, 62
Chromatophores, 186
Chromosomes
  chance distribution, 393-394
  of dividing cell, 61, 62, 391
  frog, 197
  fruit fly, *389*
  and heredity, 53, 390-391,
    582, 588
  X and Y, 592

Crayfish pearls, 109
Cretinism, 382
Cricket, *120* 120-121, 128, 129
Crocodile, 207, 210
Crocus, *499*
Cro-Magnon man, 266, 268-269
Crop
  bee, 150
  bird, 216, 569
  earthworm, 96
  grasshopper, 124
Crop rotation, 649
Crossing over, 593
Cross-pollination, 325
Crow, 226, *226*
Crown, of tooth, 323
Crustacea, 104, *106*
  characteristics, 105
  economic value, 110-111
Cud, 248
Culex mosquito, 164
Cuticle
  human skin, 280
  roundworm, 90
Cutin, 510
Cuttlefish, 95
Cuts, 343
Cyanophyta, 439, 609
Cypress tree, *37, 43*
Cyst
  euglena, 77
  tapeworm, 89
Cytoplasm
  ameba, 71
  cell, 52, 53

D

DDT, 169
Daisy, 507, 523
Dandelion, 523, 527-528, 529
Darwin, Charles, *396,* 595, 678
Daughter cell, 62, 391
Davenport, Charles B., 395
Deadleaf butterfly, 137
Death Valley National Park, 27
Decay, 448
Deer, 19, 241, *241*
Dehiscent fruits, 529
Dehydrated foods, 454
Deltoid muscle, 296
Dendrites, 54, 336

Denitrifying bacteria, 452
Dentine, 323
Deoxyribonucleic acid (DNA), 53, 455, 665
Dermis, 280, 281
Desert, *27, 632*
  adaptation for life in, 39, *39, 272*
Desmids, 441, *441*
Devil's-paintbrush, 528
Devonian period, 622
DeVries, Hugo, 587, 597, 662
Diabetes, 384, 400
Diaphragm, *350*
  man, 288, 325
  mammals, 238, 569
Diastase, 515, 541
Diatoms, 442, *443*
Dick test, 410
Dicotyledons
  seed, *538*
  stem, structure of, 493, 494-499, *495, 497*
Diet, balanced, 313-314
Diffusion, 9, 53, 485
Digestion
  a life process, 7, 9
  nature of, 321
  in plants, 514-515
  process of, 326-327
Digestive system, 56, *570*
  animal, 569-571
  bird, *216,* 569
  clam, 92, *93,* 97-98
  crayfish, *107,* 108, 569
  earthworm, *95,* 96, 97, 569
  fish, 180-181, *182*
  flatworm, 89
  frog, *192,* 192-193
  grasshopper, *124,* 124-125, 569
  human, 321-329, *322*
  roundworm, 90
  starfish, 92
Digitalis, 516
Dihydrostreptomycin, 408
Dinosaurs, 623, 633
Dioecious plant, 522
Dionne quintuplets, 595
Diphtheria, 408, 409, 410
Diploid number, 391
Diplopoda, 104, 114, 115
Diptera, 163
Direct cell division, 60-61
Disc flowers, 523

Disease
  and alcohol, 426
  carrier, *164*
  causes of, 403, 408-409, 455
  communicable, 409
  defined, 400
  dietary, 402
  treatment with drugs and molds, 407
  germ theory of, 404
  glandular, 402
  inherited, 400
  kinds of, 400
  occupational, 400-401
  organic, 402
  prevention, 403, 410
  spread of, 409, 419-420
  use of animals in study of, 251
  See also specific diseases by name
Disinfectant, 409
Division of labor, 73
Dog, *608*
Dogfish, 184
Dogwood, 528
Domestication, 271
Dominance, incomplete, *587*
Dominance, Law of, 583, 662
Dominant character, 583
Donkey, 589
Dormancy, 539
Dorsal aorta, 181, 194
Drainage, 650
Dried foods, 454
Drone, 147, 148-149
Drugs, 12
  defined, 422
  and diseases, 407
  habit-forming, 422-423
  problem to man, 421-422
Drupe, 529, *530*
Dry fruits, 529, *530,* 532
Drying foods, 454
Duck, 185
Duckbill (Platypus), 630, *242*
Duct glands, 193
Ductless glands, 193, 380, 576
  See also Endocrine system
Duodenum, 327
Dyes, 12

E

Eagle, 216, 218, 219

Ear
  animals, 182, 566
  care of, 373
  man, *372,* 372-373
Earth
  birth of, 618-619
  life on, 619
Earthworms, *36,* 109, 114, 334
  economic value, 96
  life processes, 569, 573, 574
  locomotion of, 567, 569
  nerve center of, 362, 566
Echinoderms, 91-92, *92,* 606
Ecology, 19, 31
Economic insects, 158
Ectoderm, 82, 392
Ectoplasm, 71, 73
Edentata, 247-248
Edwards, Jonathan, family of,
    396
Eel, 184, 186
Efferent nerves, 366
Egg
  algae, 442
  bird, 220-221
  crayfish, 109
  fern, *480,* 481
  fish, 182
  flowering plants, *524,* 525
  frogs, 196-197, *197*
  grasshopper, 126
  human, 390-391
  hydra, 82
  invertebrate, 78
  mosses, *470,* 470-472
Egret, *223*
Ehrlich, Paul, 407
Elder, 519
Elephant, *40, 250,* 596
Elimination, 357
Embryo
  bean, *537,* 537-538
  human, stages in forma-
    tion, 392-393, *393*
  sac, 525, 537
Embryology, 625-626, 630
Embryophyta, 469, 610
Emerson, Haven, 426
Enamel, 323
Encystment, 73
Enders, John, 412
Endocrine system, 380-385,
    381
Endoderm, 392, 485
Endoplasm, 71, 73

Endoplasmic reticulum, 53
Endoskeleton, 104, 177, 288
Endosperm, 525, 539
English sparrow, 218, 226-
    227, *227*
Entomology, 170
Environment
  adaptation of living things
    to, 6
  and control of insects, 167-
    168
  factors causing change in,
    632-633
  favorable to man, 273, 275
  See also Adaptation
Enzymes
  defined, 324
  in digestion, 72, 326, 327,
    380
  of plants, 449, 515
Eohippus, 623
Epidemics, 420
Epidermis
  human skin, 280, *281*
  leaf, 510
  root, 484
  stem, 497
Epiglottis, 349
Epinephrine, 384
Epithelial cells, 55
Equisetum, 477, *477*
Eras, 620-621
Erepsin, 327
Erosion
  environment changed by,
    632-633, 647
  control of, *552, 648*
Eskimo, 273
Esophagus
  bird, 216
  earthworm, *95,* 96
  fish, 180, *182*
  frog, *192,* 193
  human, 321-325, *322*
Essential parts, of flower, 522
Estivation, 192, 566
Estrogen, 385
Ethiopian stock, 273
Eugenics, 394-395, 591
Euglena, *76,* 76-77, 367, 564,
    567
Eumycophyta, 460, 610
Eustachian tube, 325, 372
Euthenics, 395
Evergreen trees, 547-549

Evolution
  hereditary factors in, 595
Excretion, 7, 10, 357, 514, 574
Excretory system
  ameba, 72
  crayfish, *107,* 108-109
  earthworm, *95,* 96
  euglena, 76-77
  fish, 181, *182*
  frog, *192,* 196-197
  grasshopper, *124,* 126, 576
  human, *355,* 355-356
  hydra, 82
  paramecium, 74-75
  vertebrates, 576
Exercise, 297, *297,* 344, 416
Existence, struggle for, 595,
    596
Exoskeleton, 92, 104, 109,
    126
  clams, 92
  crayfish, 109
  grasshopper, 126
Experimentation, scientific
    method, 14-15
Expiration, 350
Extensors, 296
Eyes
  bird, 216
  care of, 371
  crayfish, 107
  fish, 182
  grasshopper, 122, 126
  human, *369, 370,* 369-371
  snake, 209
Eyespot
  euglena, 76
  flatworm, 89
  starfish, 92

F

Fabre, Jean Henri, 119-121,
    120, 679
Facet
  crayfish, 107
  grasshopper, 122
Facts to remember, 16, 31-32,
    44, 56, 63, 84, 98-99,
    115, 130, 144, 155, 170,
    188, 201, 211, 233, 255,
    276-277, 285, 299-300,
    317, 328, 344-345, 357,
    375, 385-386, 397, 413,
    429-430, 444, 456, 466,

Facts to remember (*cont.*)
472, 481-482, 589, 503,
517, 533, 542, 556, 579,
598-599, 615, 634, 655-
656, 666, 672
Fainting, 344
False fruit, 530, *531*
Family
human, inheritance in, *393,*
394-397
plant and animal, 604-608
Fangs, 209
Farsightedness, 371
Fat cells, 55
Fats
in diet, 307-308
digestion of, 326-327
Fauna, 25
Feathers, 215
Feces, 329, 357
Federal Food, Drug, and Cos-
metic Act, 316-317, 424
Federal Migratory Bird Treaty
Act of *1918,* 223-224
Femur, 291
Fermentation, 449, 462, 516
Fern
history of, 478
life cycle, 480-481, 578
Fertile stalk, 477, *477*
Fertilization
flowering plants, 525
frogs eggs, 196-197
life cycle, 391
mosses, 470
See also Reproduction
Fertilizers, 649
Fever, 338
Fibers, muscle cell, 294
Fibers, plant stem, 494
Fibrin film, 336
Fibrin threads, 338
Fibrinogen, 336, 337
Fibrous roots, 486
Fibrovascular bundles, 493,
494, *494, 495*
Fibula, 291
Fiddler crab, 110
Field stripping, 649
Fig, 530
Filament, 521
Filicineae, 478, 610
Fingerlings, *187*
Fingerprints, 284, *285*
Fins, 178, 179

Firs, 549
First filial generation, 583
Fish, 104, 108, *176*
artificial propagation, 187
body structure, *178,* 178-
179, 182
care of young, 183-184
characteristics, 177-178, 606
circulatory system, 181, 574
digestive system, 180-181,
569
divisions, 178
enemies of, 184-185, 186
excretion, 181
as food, 186
fossil, *624*
hatcheries, 187-188
ladders, 187, *187*
locomotion, 179
migration, 184
nervous system, 182, 362
oil, 186
protection of, 186-187
reproduction, 182-183, 578
respiration, 179-180, 573
sense organs, 566-567
Fish and Wildlife Service,
253, 653
Fishing industry, *653*
Fission, 73, 576
bacteria, 448
euglena, 76, 77
paramecium, 75
Flagellates, 153
Flagellum
bacteria, 447
euglena, 76, 567
sponges, 79
sperm, 391
Flat foot, 299
Flatworm, 88-89
digestive system, 97
Flax, 11
Fleas, 166
Fleming, Alexander, 407, 413,
679
Flesh-eating mammals, *244,*
245
Fleshy fruits, 529
Fleshy roots, 486
Flexors, 296
Floating ribs, 290
Flora, 25
Floral bud, 496
Florey, Howard W., 679

Flowers
economic value of, 528-529
parts and functions of, 521-
523, *522*
pollination, 524-528
types of, 523-524
Fluctuations, 595
Fluorine, 308
Fly, 121
and disease, 163, 165-166,
166, 409
fossil, *624*
parasitic, 143, 167
Flying animals, *38*
Flying mammals, *243,* 243-245
Food
absorption of, 327-329
accessory, 307
adulteration, 316-317
from animals, 12
classes of, 307
defined, 306
digestion, 7, 9, 326-327
elements, 307
groups, basic four, *314,* 314-
315
habits, 315-316
laws, 316-317
from plants, 11, 12
preservation, 452-453
Food vacuole, 569
ameba, 72
paramecium, 74
Food-getting
adaptations for, 35, 36, 38
animals, 569-571
life process, 7, 9
Food-making in plants, 511-
512
Foot
adaptations, 219, *219*
clam, 92
man, 299, *299*
Forestry, 7, 550-551
Forests, *41, 550, 549, 642*
destruction of, 551, 651
insect damage to, 551
making, 550
national preserves, 550
protection, federal and state,
550
saving, 652
value of, 650-651
Formalin, 316
Fort Loudoun Dam, *647*

Plant louse, 151, 163
Plants
    adaptation, 9, 35-39, 569, 571
    airborne, 38
    and animals, 11, 41-42
    assimilation, 10
    in changing environment, 633
    circulation, 9, 573-574
    classification, 608-610
    communities, 43
    digestion, absorption in, 9
    diseases caused by, 403
    excretion, 10, 574
    family tree of, 621-622
    growth without soil, *513*
    harmful, 13-14
    improvement of, 665-666
    life processes, 7-10, 564-579
    movement, 8, 367, 567-568
    non-vascular, 438-472, *439*
    nutrition, 571
    organs, 56
    parasites, 463
    reproduction, 10, 576, 578
    respiration, 10, 573
    response to stimuli, 8, 564
    secretion, 574
    study of, 6
    systems, 56
    tissues, 55-56
    uses of, 11-12
    vascular, 474-556
    See also. Flowers; Leaves; Roots; Stems; Trees; *names of individual plants*
Plasma, 195
    composition of, 334-336
    source, 336
Plasma membrane, 52
Plasmodium, 460
Plasmolysis, 486
Plastids, 53
Plastron, 207, *207*
Platelets, 54, 334, 336
Platyhelminthes, 88, 606
Platypus, 241, 242, *242*
Pleural membrane, 350
Plexus, 366
Pliohippus, 627
Plumage, 217
Plumule, 537
Pneumonia, 408, 409
Pod, 530

Poison, 422
    and control of insects, 168
Poison glands, 111
Poison ivy, *516*
Poison sumac, 516
Polar bodies, *390, 391*
Polar nuclei, 525
Poliomyelitis, 409, 410, *410, 662*
Pollen, 521
    and allergy diseases, 354
    staminate cone, *548, 549*
    structure of grain, 524-525, *548*
Pollen basket, 150, *151*
Pollen tube, 525
Pollination
    adaptations for, 527
    artificial, 526, 527
    by bee, *150*
    cross-, *524, 525*
    importance of, 527
    self-, 526
Polyp, 81, 84
Pome, 530
Pond lily, 7
Poppy, 596
Porcupine, *241*
Pores, sponge, 79
Porifera, 70, 88, 604
Portal circulation, 341
Portal vein, 328
Posture, 297-298, *298*
Potassium, 308
Potato, *499*
Potato beetle, 159-161
Pouched mammals, 241, 242
Praying mantis, 128, *128, 129*
Pre-Cambrian period, 622
Precocial bird, *220, 221*
Prehistoric man, 266
Premolars, 323, *323*
Preservatives, 452-453
Pressure
    in air habitat, 25
    in water habitat, 23
    in space, 671
Pressure points, 343, *343*
Primary root, 485, 538
Primates, 250-251
    characteristics, 271-272
    terms used for, 271
Primordial germ cell, 390
Primroses
    experiment with, 587-588

Problems in biological progress, 666
Proboscidea, 250
Proboscis, 134
Projects
    Principles of Biology: 17-18, 33-34, 45-46, 57-59, 64-65
    Biology of Animal Life: 86-87, 99-100, 116-118, 131-133, 145-146, 156-157, 171-172, 189-190, 203-204, 212, 234-235, 257-258
    Biology of Man: 278-279, 286-287, 301-302, 318-320, 331-332, 346-348, 359, 377, 387, 398, 414, 431-432
    Biology of Plant Life: 445-446, 458-459, 467-468, 473, 482-483, 490-491, 504-505, 519-520, 535-536, 544-545, 557
    Biology Past and Future: 580, 600-601, 616, 635-636, 657-659, 667-668, 673-674
Prolactin, 381
Prop roots, 487, *487, 539*
Propagation, stem, 500
Prophase, 61
Propolis, 149
Protection
    adaptations for, 236-241
Protective coloration
    birds, 217
    butterflies, 137
    grasshopper, 121
Protective covering
    animals, 280
    man, *282*
Protective resemblance
    butterflies and moths, 137, *137*
    grasshopper, 129
Protein
    in bean and corn seeds, 541
    digestion and absorption of, 326-328
    function of, 307
    manufacture of, 513
Proteinases, 515
Protein-synthesis, 513
Proteoses, 326

Proterozoic era, 621
Prothallium, 480, *480*
Prothorax, grasshopper, 123
Prothrombin, 312, 337, 338
Protococcus, 440, 444
Protonema, 470, *470*
Protoplasm, 619
  ameba, 71
  assimilation, 355
  defined and function, 7, 51
  discovery of, 51
  differences in, 51-52
  mystery of, 664
  nature and composition, 52
  paramecium, 73
Protozoa, 70-71, 604
  colonial, 77
  diseases caused by, 403, 409
  economic importance, 78
  motion, 567
  parasitic, 78
  See also Ameba *and* Para-
    mecium
Pruning, 553
Pseudopodia, 71, *71,* 76, 567
Psychosis, 418
Pteris, 476, *476,* 478
  life cycle, 480
Pteropsida, 478, 610
Ptomaine, 408
Ptyalin, 324, 326, 515
Public health, 419, 421
Pulmonary circulation, 340
Pulp, tooth, 323
Pulse, 339
Pupa, 134-136, *135*
Pupil, eye, 369
Pure food laws, 316-317, 324
Pyloric caeca, 180
Pyloric valve, 325
Pylorus, 180, 193
Pyrenoids, 76, *440*
Pyridoxine, 311
Pyruvic acid, 515
Python, 209

Q

Quadruplets, 595
Quarantine, 419-420
  insect control by, 169
Queen
  ant, 150, 151
  bee, 147-148
  termite, 153, 154

Questions
  Principles of Biology: 16-
    17, 32, 44, 57, 63
  Biology of Animal Life: 85,
    99, 115-116, 131, 144-
    145, 155-156, 171, 188-
    189, 202, 211, 233-234,
    256
  Biology of Man: 277-278,
    286, 300-301, 318, 330,
    345-346, 358, 376, 386,
    398, 414, 430
  Biology of Plant Life: 445,
    457, 467, 472-473, 482,
    489-490, 504, 518, 534,
    543, 556-557
  Biology Past and Future:
    580, 599-600, 615, 634-
    635, 656-657, 666-667,
    673
Quinine, 405
Quintuplets, 595

R

Rabbit, 247, 569, 571
Rabies, 409, 666
Raccoon, 111, 185, *244*
Races of man, 273, 275
Racial mixing, 273
Radial symmetry, 92
Radiation
  atomic, 344
  solar, *654,* 672
Radioactive atoms, 406
  uses of, 407, *407*
Radioisotopes, 406, *407*
Radium, 406
Radius, 290
Range of living things, 27
Rat, 246, *247*
Rattlesnake, 209, 403
Ray, 186
Ray flowers, 523
Realm, 29
Receptacle, flower, 522, 529
Recessive character, 583-585,
    593-594
Rectum
  bird, 216
  grasshopper, 125
  man, 325
Red corpuscles, 54, 195, *334,*
    334-335
Red Cross, 421

Red fox, *9, 36*
Red spider, 113
Reduction division, *390, 391,*
    582
Reed, Walter, 405
References
  Principles of Biology: 18,
    34, 47, 59, 65
  Biology of Animal Life: 87,
    100-101, 118, 133, 146,
    157, 172-173, 190, 205,
    212, 236, 258-259
  Biology of Man: 279, 287,
    302, 320, 333, 348, 359,
    378, 388, 399, 415, 431-
    432
  Biology of Plant Life: 446,
    459, 468, 473, 483, 491-
    492, 505, 520, 536, 545-
    546, 558
  Biology Past and Future:
    581, 601-602, 617, 636-
    637, 659-660, 668, 674
Reflex
  action, *364,* 373
  conditioned, 373-374
Regeneration, 576
  crayfish, 109
  hydra, 83
  planarian worm, 89
  sponges, 80
  starfish, 92
Reindeer, 11, 13
Rejuvenation, paramecium, 76
Relapsing fever, 166
Remora fish, 42, *42*
Renal artery, 342
Renal circulation, 342
Rennin, 326
Repellent, 169
Reproduction
  cell, 60
  defined, 10-11
  asexual and sexual, 576-578
  a life process, 7, 576, 578
Reproductive systems
  ameba, *72, 73*
  euglena, 76, 77
  fish, 182-183
  frog, 196-197
  grasshopper, 126
  hydra, 82
  mammals, 238
  man, 288
  paramecium, 75-76